Feminist Perspectives in Music Therapy

Edited by

Susan Hadley

Feminist Perspectives in Music Therapy

ISBN: 1-891278-38-X
13 Digit ISBN: 978-1891278-38-X

Distributed throughout the world by:

Barcelona Publishers
4 White Brook Road
Gilsum NH 03448
Tel: 603-357-0236 Fax: 603-357-2073
Website: www.barcelonapublishers.com
SAN 298-6299

Cover design:
© 2006 Frank McShane

In recognition of my maternal lineage:
Mum, Gonny and Great Great Granny Greenfield

ACKNOWLEDGEMENTS

There are many people whom I would like to thank sincerely:

The contributors, for the time and effort they put into writing their chapters. This was a long and difficult process and I thank them for their perseverance and their willingness to be vulnerable. I feel honored to have worked with this group of truly wonderful women, many with whom I have gained a very close bond of friendship.

Kenneth Bruscia, not only for immediately seeing the value of this book, but also for his ongoing support and friendship over so many years. John-Michael Dumais, for his expertise in the copyediting phase of the book.

My husband, philosopher George Yancy, whose passion and drive are truly inspirational. He continues to be a wonderful supporter and valuable critic of my work and the way I live my life. He encourages me to transcend old ways of viewing the world and to live each day anew, with fresh eyes, and with the courage to help others expand their vision. For this, and so much more, I love you.

Our children, Adrian, Gabriel, and Elijah, for their ongoing support and for helping me to keep everything in a healthy perspective. You bring me such joy and fulfillment.

My parents, Lillian and Geoff, for their love and support. Also, Mum for her help in formatting the front pages for me when I was at a loss for how to get it all to work. And my mother-in-law, Ruth, for always being there for us.

Cindy Lacom, my colleague and friend, who provided valuable feedback on my chapters. Cindy embodies the type of teacher and person I am striving to become.

My students, who continue to teach me, to challenge me, and to remind me in subtle ways why this work is so rewarding.

The faculty, staff, and administration at Slippery Rock University.

My family and friends, who have been supportive in various ways: Peter, Jennifer, Emma, Thomas, and Sonya Hadley; Ruth, Michael, Charles, Megan, Geoffrey, and Susan Sutherland; Mark Hadley; Lib, Don, Jane, Richard, and Cath Allen; Ros and Ray; Pauline and Kevin; Artrice and Carson; Mika, Alonso, and Kaleena; Brother El; Caroline Cusack; Susan Young; Jo Randell; Andrea McCallum; Emma Collins; Kylie Johnston-Leek; Toni Lalich; Nick, Vik, Max, and Lexi Haslam; Tony Meadows; Mechelle and Steve Hawk; Barb Frankenburg; Stacey and Terry Steele; Denise Grocke; Beth and Ian Dunn; Don and Natalie Petesch; John and Debbie McClendon; Serena Hughes; Jo Lawler; Janet and Ted McDade; Linda Bamberger; and, Sheryl Ogburn.

I also want to thank the many feminists and critical theorists who already have touched my life and those who, in the future, will move me through their writing, their music, and the ways they live their lives.

CONTENTS

CONTRIBUTORS

Jennifer Adrienne, M.A., M.M.T., is an adjunct professor in sociology and in women's studies. She has taught at Lehigh University and is currently teaching at the Community College of Baltimore County. She received her master's degree in music therapy from Temple University and her master's degree in sociology from Lehigh University. Her professional experience includes the creation and management of a therapeutic arts program in a shelter for survivors of domestic violence and sexual assault. She has done research on community domestic violence prevention and education, cognitive sociology, and quality of life for women and children.

Dorit Amir received her doctorate in music therapy at New York University. Since 1982 she has been coordinating the music therapy program at Bar Ilan University, Israel. She has worked with a rich variety of populations, has published many articles, and has given lectures on various subjects in Israeli, European, and American congresses. Her book, *Meeting the Sounds: Music Therapy Practice, Theory and Research* was published in 1999 in the Hebrew language. She co-edited a book entitled *In Another Language—Art Therapies—Therapeutic Stories* that was published in 2005 in the Hebrew language. Dr. Amir served as the European Editor of *Voices* and currently serves on the editorial boards of *The Arts in Psychotherapy* and Barcelona Publishers' Monograph Series *Qualitative Inquiries in Music Therapy*.

Joke Bradt, Ph.D., MT-BC, is assistant professor of music therapy at Montclair State University, New Jersey. She has taught a variety of undergraduate and graduate music therapy courses in the US and in Europe. Since 1996, she has been a visiting specialist in the music therapy programs at the Hogeschool of Nijmegen and Arnhem in the Netherlands and at the Hogeschool of Sciences and Arts, campus Lemmensinstituut, in Belgium. Each year, Dr. Bradt gives lectures and workshops in Belgium on music therapy-related topics. After earning her Master of Music Pedagogy degree from the Lemmensinstituut in Belgium, Dr. Bradt was twice awarded a Fulbright Grant to study music therapy at Temple University, Philadelphia, where she earned her Master of Music Therapy degree and her doctoral degree in Music Therapy. Since that time, her work has focused on medical music therapy, specifically as it relates to music entrainment for pediatric pain management. As a researcher, Dr. Bradt has been involved in several music therapy research studies. Dr. Bradt has been author and co-author of several music therapy articles and chapters.

Sandra L. Curtis, Ph.D., MT-BC, MTA, is an internationally trained music therapist with 20 years of experience in clinical practice, teaching, and research. A board-certified music therapist and past president of the Southeastern Region of the American Music Therapy Association, Dr. Curtis is a strong advocate for and practitioner of the use of the creative processes of music to empower people in their daily lives. Drawing from her most recent years of clinical practice with women's groups and from her doctoral research with abused women, Dr. Curtis has laid clear and well-grounded foundations in the specific uses of music by and for women to transform their lives. Dr. Curtis has published and presented extensively in professional circles, with speaking engagements throughout Canada and the United States, as well as in Australia and Ireland.

Cheryl Dileo, Ph.D., MT-BC, received her Ph.D. in Music Education from Louisiana State University and her Bachelor's and Master's in Music Therapy from Loyola University of the South. She is a board-certified music therapist with several years of experience as a clinician and consultant. At Temple, she has served as Coordinator of Music Therapy and on several college and university committees (e.g., Institutional Review Board, Alternative Medicine Committee). Dr. Dileo currently serves as Coordinator of the Master's degree program in music therapy. Previously, she has also been on the music therapy faculty at the University of Evansville and Loyola University. She is a consulting editor for the *Journal of Music Therapy*, the *International Journal of Arts in Psychotherapy*, the *International Journal of Arts Medicine*, and the *Journal of Music Therapy and MusicMedicine* (Germany). She has held a variety of leadership positions in the National Association for Music Therapy, including President, and is the Immediate Past-President of the World Federation of Music Therapy. She has given numerous lectures and workshops in the USA and around the world. She is very widely published. One of her primary interests and specialties is professional ethics.

Jane Edwards, Ph.D., is Senior Lecturer and Course Director for the MA in Music Therapy at the Irish World Music Centre, University of Limerick, Ireland. She holds a Guest Professorship in the Institute for Music Therapy at the University of the Arts, Berlin, and is a former By-fellow of Churchill College, University of Cambridge, UK. She regularly contributes to *Voices* (www.voices.no) and has published in German, British, New Zealand, Australian, American, and Nordic journals of music therapy; and on a range of clinical, research, and theoretical topics in *The Arts in Psychotherapy*.

Michele Forinash, DA, MT-BC, LMHC, is associate professor, coordinator of the Ph.D. program, and coordinator of the music therapy specialization in the Division of Expressive Therapies at Lesley University in Cambridge, Massachusetts. She is past president of the American Music Therapy Association. Dr. Forinash is the editor of the book *Music Therapy Supervision* (Barcelona Publishers) and co-editor of the book *Educators, Therapists, and Artists on Reflective Practice* (Peter Lang Publishers). She has published articles and chapters on phenomenological research, arts based research, supervision, and qualitative research in music therapy. She is the North American Editor for the online international music therapy journal *Voices: A World Forum for Music Therapy* (www.voices.no).

Frances Smith Goldberg, MA, MT-BC, FAMI, MFT, is a graduate of Indiana University and Lone Mountain College. She is Director of the Therapeutic Arts Institute, an international postgraduate training institute in the Bonny Method of Guided Imagery and Music. Fran is a licensed psychotherapist and retired from a 47-year clinical practice in 2005, after working in adult psychiatry for 34 years and maintaining a private music psychotherapy practice with adults for the last 27 years. She also retired as Associate Clinical Professor in the Department of Psychiatry at the University of California San Francisco and Associate Professor at the California Institute for Integral Studies in the Expressive Arts Therapy program. She has served on the editorial boards of three professional journals, has published many journal articles and book chapters, and has presented widely in national and international professional conferences. She recently relocated from San Francisco to Indianapolis, haunts opera houses worldwide in search of the ultimate performance and loves playing with her grandchildren

Susan Hadley, Ph.D., MT-BC, associate professor of music therapy at Slippery Rock University, received her bachelor's degree in music therapy from the University of Melbourne, Australia. She received her master's and Ph.D. degrees in music therapy and psychoeducational processes from Temple University. As a music therapy clinician, Susan has worked with a wide variety of clients. She is editor of *Psychodynamic Music Therapy: Case Studies* (Barcelona Publishers, 2002) and co-editor (with George Yancy) of *Narrative Identities: Psychologists Engaged in Self-Construction* (Jessica Kingsley Press, 2005). She has published journal articles, book chapters, and book reviews. Currently she serves on the editorial board of Barcelona Publishers' Monograph Series *Qualitative Inquiries in Music Therapy*.

Laurie Jones, M.M.T., MT-BC, is assistant professor and coordinator of the music therapy program at Seton Hill University. She received her bachelor's degree in music education/vocal performance from West Virginia University and her master's degree in music therapy from Temple University. Her current clinical experience includes work with older adults with dementia, adults with psychiatric illnesses, and medical patients. Laurie has established a contracting business, Expressive Therapy Consultants. She is also actively involved in a variety of volunteer efforts throughout the community. She is a regular speaker on music and wellness for numerous special interest groups and frequently facilitates community drum circles. In addition, she is a core vocalist and soloist with the Westmoreland Choral Society.

Carolyn Bereznak Kenny, Ph.D., MT-BC, MTA, is a Senior Research Scholar at the Institute for Social, Behavioral and Economic Research at the University of California Santa Barbara. She is a Professor of Human Development and Indigenous Studies for the Antioch University. Dr. Kenny holds a Ph.D. in Human Development from The Fielding Institute; a Master of Arts in Interdisciplinary Studies (Psychology, Anthropology, Ethnomusicology) from the University of British Columbia; a Bachelor of Arts in History and Philosophy from Loyola University; and an Associate of Arts in Music Therapy from Loyola University, New Orleans. She has also trained extensively in Dance Therapy and Multicultural Counseling. She is co-editor-in-chief (with Brynjulf Stige) of *Voices: A World Forum for Music Therapy* and serves on the editorial board for the *Journal of Music Therapy*. She is the former editor of the *Canadian Journal of Music Therapy*. She was the co-founder of the first music therapy training program in Canada (with Nancy McMaster) and founded the first master's program in music therapy in Canada. She is a member of the International Scientific Board for the University of the Arts in Berlin, Germany and is a member of the Music Therapy Qualitative Research Symposium Group. She has published and lectured extensively in the United States, Canada, Europe and New Zealand in Music Therapy and Indigenous Studies. She also conducts a private practice in music therapy. Her ancestry is Choctaw/Ukranian and she was adopted into the Haida Nation by a Haida elder.

Seung-A Kim, M.A., LCAT, MT-BC, is an adjunct faculty member at Molloy College and a member of the clinical staff at the Rebecca Center for Music Therapy. She received her master's degree in music therapy from New York University, specializing in the influence of culture on music therapy and in clinical work with people living with dementia and Alzheimer's disease. She completed postgraduate studies in advanced clinical training in Analytical Music Therapy, studying with Benedikte Scheiby. Her recent research has focused on the effect of culture on music therapy. In addition, she has created an innovative Creative Arts Therapy program for the Korean-American community at Bethpage, New York. She is currently pursuing the music therapy Ph.D. program at Temple University.

ChihChen Sophia Lee, Ph.D., MT-BC, is the Director of Music Therapy at the Southwestern Oklahoma State University, Weatherford, Oklahoma. Professionally active at the local, regional, national, and international level, Dr. Lee has provided various workshops and in-service presentations to healthcare professionals and educators. She has also presented papers and continuing education for music therapists workshops at regional, national, and international music therapy and expressive art therapy conferences. Currently she serves on the Academic Program Approval Committee of the American Music Therapy Association and is a member of the Music Therapy Association of Taiwan. A graduate of University of Minnesota (Ph.D., M.A.) and Ohio University (B.M.), Dr. Lee's research interests include Music Therapy Distance Education, human psychophysiological reactions and processes to music stimuli, international music therapy, and ethnomusicology. Clinically, Dr. Lee has worked in long-term care, hospice care, early intervention, and with rural at-risk youth.

Katrina McFerran received both her Ph.D. and Bachelor of Music therapy from the University of Melbourne, Australia. Her professional experience has focused on working with children in a range of settings, including special education, palliative care and medical settings. Katrina currently works on the Adolescent Ward at the Royal Children's Hospital in Melbourne where she works with young people on an individual basis, as well as facilitating some group work on the ward. Katrina also lectures at the University of Melbourne. In addition, she works with chronically ill children at Very Special Kids house, running programs for those staying at the house for respite or palliative care purposes as well as providing services to families wanting to access music therapy. She has published extensively in international journals and has presented at conferences both nationally and internationally. Katrina is the current Chair of the National Education Committee of the Australian Music Therapy Association and operates a music therapy clinic in the inner western suburbs of Melbourne where she conducts ongoing individual and small group work. Katrina also maintains a private practice in short term group work for organisations such as Canteen, YSAS, Outreach Grief Services and others.

Theresa (Terra) Merrill received the Bachelor of Music Therapy degree from Capilano College, Vancouver, B.C. (Canada), the Master of Music Therapy degree from the British Columbia Open University, and is completing the Ph.D. in music education/therapy at Michigan State University. Her research topic is an exploration of mentoring relationships between music therapists. She is also completing advanced GIM studies. Terra is Assistant Professor and Clinical Coordinator of Music Therapy at Marylhurst University in Portland, Oregon. She comes to this position after 19 years of clinical practice in Canada and the US with adults in medical, elder-care, and end-of-life care settings. She has published in the *Canadian Journal of Music Therapy*, the *Nordic Journal of Music Therapy*, *Private Practice*, and the *Journal of Long Term Care*. She has presented at numerous conferences throughout the world. Her supervisor's training course has been offered and well received by professional organizations such as CAMT, OAMT, CTRA, BCTRA, and CSWA. Terra is currently the editor-in-chief of the bilingual *Canadian Journal of Music Therapy* after serving three years on its review board. She also serves the Association for Music and Imagery as Ethics chair. She maintains a private Bonny Method of Guided Imagery and Music practice in Portland that focuses on supporting individuals through life transitions. She performs and records music for meditation in the Sikh sacred tradition of Naad Yoga.

Lucy O'Grady completed her bachelor's degree in music therapy (with Honours) and master's degree in music therapy, both at the University of Melbourne, Australia. She has been working within music in community contexts for five years. Her main focus in this area has been facilitated by her role as the musical director of a community theatre company that devises new works with young people who are outside the school system and with women in prison. Her master's thesis examines the relationship between community music and music therapy and offers new perspectives on how the two disciplines can both unite and differentiate themselves. She has presented at various Australian music therapy conferences and has published in a variety of arenas.

Colleen Purdon, MTA, completed an Honours Bachelor of Music at Queen's University, Kingston, and a L.G.S.M. diploma in music therapy from the Guildhall School of Music and Drama in London in 1975, where she studied with Juliette Alvin and completed Analytic Music Therapy training with Mary Priestley. She taught at the Mentorenkurs Musiktherapie (1978–80) as a member of an international faculty at Germany's first music therapy program, and worked in Germany for over six years as a clinician, clinical supervisor, educator, and Lehrmusiktherapeutin. Colleen has over 20 years' experience as a music therapist with a broad range of clients. For eight years she was the Executive Director of a multi-service agency for abused women and children, while remaining active in music therapy as a board member of Canadian Association of Music Therapy. Colleen has presented at national and international conferences and seminars on music therapy and abuse-related issues. In addition, she works as a freelance researcher and organizational consultant on national, provincial, and local projects on women's equality, violence against women and children, and rural women and poverty.

Randi Rolvsjord is associate professor of music therapy in the Grieg Academy, Department of Music, at the University of Bergen, Norway. Her clinical practice as a music therapist has been in the areas of psychiatry and geriatric care. She has published several articles in international journals. Her book, *Når Musikken Blir Språk* (*When Music Becomes Language*) (2002), explores theoretical perspectives and clinical methods in music therapy. She is currently completing her doctoral research on resource-oriented music therapy in mental health care at Aalborg University, Denmark.

Sue Shuttleworth, Ed.D., M.M.T., FAMI, MT-BC, is assistant professor and coordinator of music therapy at Slippery Rock University. She holds a bachelor of science in music education from Morehead State University. She received her master's degree in music therapy from Florida State University and her Doctorate of Education in health care education from Nova Southeastern University. For her applied doctoral research she developed an Experiential Learning Formative Assessment Instrument for Undergraduate Music Therapy Clinical Students. Dr. Shuttleworth has presented at regional and national music therapy conferences and currently serves on the Academic Program Approval Committee of the American Music Therapy Association.

Elaine Streeter undertook music studies in piano and composition at the Guildhall School of Music and Drama where she studied composition with Edmund Rubbra and Buxton Orr. She undertook her music therapy training with Paul Nordoff and Clive Robbins in 1974. After working with severely disabled children at Goldie Leigh Hospital, and preschool children at Charing Cross Hospital, she undertook a master's degree at the University of York. In 1980, she was invited to develop a new music therapy training course at the Roehampton Institute of Higher Education, which she led for several years. She has lectured and taught on a number of other music therapy training courses both in the UK and abroad, recently heading the music therapy department at the Guildhall School of Music and Drama after fifteen years as a senior clinical tutor there. Elaine has worked extensively with children with special needs. She has also worked with self-referred adults and as a training therapist with individual students and with groups of music therapy students. She has experience working in private practice as a psychodynamic counselor. She currently supervises music therapists in London and has been accepted for Ph.D. studies at the University of York.

Barbara L. Wheeler, Ph.D., MT-BC, is Director of Music Therapy at the University of Louisville. Prior to this she spent 25 years on the faculty of Montclair State University in New Jersey, where she was given the honor of being designated Professor Emerita. Dr. Wheeler has been active in music therapy since 1969 and her clinical work has been with children and adults with a variety of problems. In addition to being a music therapist, Dr. Wheeler is a licensed psychologist in New York (license currently inactive), where she worked with people with drug addictions and with elderly people. Dr. Wheeler edited the internationally acclaimed book *Music Therapy Research: Quantitative and Qualitative Perspectives*. She has written a number of articles and chapters on music therapy and her research interests include both quantitative and qualitative research. She serves on the editorial boards of *Voices: A World Forum for Music Therapy*, for which she is a Discussion Editor, and the *British Journal of Music Therapy*. She was honored with the 1999 Publication and Research Award given by the American Music Therapy Association. She has been active in music therapy organizations on the international and national levels. She served as Vice President of both the AMTA and the National Association for Music Therapy. She was recently Chair of the AMTA International Relations Committee and was Chair of the Commission on Education and Training of the World Federation of Music Therapy. Dr. Wheeler is frequently asked to speak both in the US and abroad. She serves as examiner for degrees in Music Therapy and is also a consultant for the National Music Therapy Research Group (NAMTRU) in the Faculty of Music, University of Melbourne, Australia.

Elizabeth York holds a Bachelor of Music in Music Therapy from the University of Georgia in Athens, Georgia. Both her Master of Music in Music Therapy and Ph.D. in Music Education are from the University of Miami, Coral Gables, Florida. In 2005 she was chosen to begin the Music Therapy Program at Converse College. Before coming to Converse, she served for ten years as Director of the Music Therapy Program at Utah State University, Logan, UT. Her career spans the breadth of music therapy experience as a clinician, educator, researcher, and performer. Dr. York has worked clinically in music therapy for more than thirty years, the majority of which has been devoted to working with adults with psychiatric illnesses, including schizophrenia, depression, bipolar disorder, and dementia. As a long-time member of the National Association for Music Therapy and the American Music Therapy Association, she has presented at international, national and regional conferences. Topics of recent presentations include qualitative research with the women served at the Community Abuse Prevention Services Agency; the development of a music therapy assessment tool for Alzheimer's patients, the *Residual Music Skills Test* (*RMST*, York, 1995, & York, 2000 and Lipe & York, in press); and improvisational methods of music therapy with adults. Dr. York currently serves on the editorial board of Music Therapy Perspectives, the Ethics Board of the American Music Therapy Association, and the Education Council for the World Federation of Music Therapy.

Introduction

EMBRACING FEMINISM: AN OVERVIEW

Susan Hadley

[A]nd people bin raising up their voices
since it just ain't bin right
. . . like, say, the women who gave their lives
so that I could have one
. . . people, we are standing at ground zero
of the feminist revolution
yeah, it was an inside job
stoic and sly
one we're supposed to forget
and downplay and deny
but i think the time is nothing
if not nigh
to let the truth out
coolest f-word ever deserves a f---ing shout!
i mean
why can't all decent men and women
call themselves feminists?
out of respect
for those who fought for this

—Ani DiFranco
(Lyric excerpts from Grand Canyon)

Simone de Beauvior (1953/1989) stated that "one is not born, but rather becomes a woman" (p.267). bell hooks (2000) stated that "feminists are made, not born" (p.7). Although I was born female in terms of my biology, I have become the woman who I see myself as and who others see me as through a complex process of socialization.[1] Just as I am not *fully* aware of my process of becoming a woman, I am not *fully* aware of my process of becoming a feminist. I do know that I am not a feminist by virtue of being born female. There are

[1] Singer-songwriter Dar Williams describes this process of socialization that both males and females go through in her song "When I was a Boy," on her album *The Honesty Room* (1995).

many females I know who are not feminists and who distance themselves from feminism, while there are males I know who are feminists and strongly align themselves with feminism.

To trace my journey toward becoming a feminist, I must look at the context in which I grew up, that is, make sense of my personal history. It is not that I said to myself one day, "I want to be a feminist and these are the steps I must take to become one." I believe that "it is the *lived* context of history, both immediate and distal, that constitutes the background of the self's intelligibility" (Yancy & Hadley, 2005, p.10). By that, I mean that I am born into a socio-cultural-historical matrix which has already shaped or positioned me. Within this inherited framework, though, there are many possibilities for how I narrate who I am. In other words, "we create as we are also created" (Yancy & Hadley, 2005, p.11). There are various discourses and ideologies that we may adopt or reject which play a part in structuring our "personal" identities. These discourses and ideologies also play a part in structuring societies. As Tod Sloan (2005) states, "in relations with others over the years we develop fairly fixed modes of organizing affect, ideation, [and] action and these modes can be seen as ideological structures in that they tend to play a part in sustaining social relations" (p.236). Although many of these social relations are hierarchical, there are non-exploitative and non-oppressive frameworks that are concurrently available which encourage mutual respect. Thus, we can "choose" to re-narrate our identities in ways in which we can strive to lessen our gender, race, class, age, ability, sexual, religious, and national privileges, and work toward ending all types of oppression.

So, why do I find it important to share selective experiences from my personal history? How will these first-person accounts function? Susan Brison (2002) notes that it is "not out of sloppy self-indulgence," but that "feminist theorists are increasingly looking at first-person accounts to gain *imaginative access* [italics mine] to others' experience" (p.25). Thus, I am writing the following account not only to contextualize my own process of becoming a feminist and to give you, the reader, a greater understanding of my evolving process, but I am writing in the hopes that you, too, will be encouraged to reflect on your own experiences, how they have shaped and continue to shape your evolving identities, and how they contribute to your investment in your gender, race, class, age, ability, sexual, religious, and national identities.

I believe that aspects of my feminist consciousness were shaped by my maternal grandmother who was born at the turn of the twentieth century, during the "first wave" of modern feminism. She was raised by her *grandmother* (who must have been very progressive) who nourished my grandmother's intellectual desires and encouraged her to pursue a career before concerning herself with marriage and children. My grandmother became a teacher and then travelled[2] from England to Singapore, where she taught, married, and had two daughters. During World War II, she was evacuated with her two young children to Australia. Subsequently, my grandfather died as a prisoner of war and my grandmother raised my mother and my aunt alone. As had her grandmother, my grandmother nourished her daughters' intellectual and creative desires and encouraged them to complete a University degree and pursue their careers before having a family, if they so chose. Having grown up in an all-female household and having attended an all-female school, my mother had a very healthy sense of her identity as an independent woman. She studied science and mathematics, which were not traditional areas for women of her generation to study, and became a high school mathematics teacher. Teaching, of course, was a traditional career choice for women. My aunt became a social worker (but would have become a music therapist had it been available when she was attending University).

The status of women was different in my father's family. My paternal grandmother, although she, too, had been educated at an all-female school, believed that it was more important for males to be educated than females. Thus, my father was sent away to a boarding school at the age of 12, while his two sisters attended local high schools. In addition, his musical talents were nourished. My father went on to obtain University degrees, including a Ph.D., whereas his sisters did not.

I was born in the 1960s during the "second wave" of modern feminism, when my mother was in her mid-30s, and my maternal grandmother was in her 60s. When I was four, I began attending the all-female school at which my mother taught. The following year, my father became the principal of this school and my mother had to find another job because the school did not want the appearance of nepotism. I could not comprehend the claim of nepotism when my mother had a history of working there prior to my father's appointment. I remember always feeling incensed that my mother's position was "taken" from her. Although she had been there first, she was in the less powerful position, was working part-time, was earning less money, and therefore obviously felt that it was her "duty" to comply.

My experiences at an all-female school allowed me to experience myself as full of possibilities. Like my mother, I was drawn to mathematics, physics, and chemistry. Like my father, I was drawn to music. Many of my teachers were progressive in their politics and encouraged critical reflection on a range of topics. I remember one of the first topics that I explored on the debating team was women's rights to have abortions. I also remember one of my teachers, who

[2] In respect of the diversity of countries and cultures represented by the authors in this book, I have decided to keep the cultural spellings of authors within the chapters.

had lived on a Kibbutz, getting us to reflect critically on capitalism. One of my teachers stimulated me to reflect critically on the hierarchical structures within our school when she encouraged us to question longstanding traditions and call her by her first name. She also had many other unique approaches to teaching that I did not realize at the time were feminist in nature. Although many of my teachers obviously held to the liberal views with which, given the political values of my family, I aligned myself, many of my fellow students did not. Most of them were from white upper-middle-class families with conservative political values. Many were outwardly racist and elitist. I found that in response to their dogmatic and myopic political views, my political views became more progressive. There were many times when I questioned their assumed right to class privilege, when I was appalled by their racist assumptions, and when I critiqued their sexist practices. I began to question why women wore make-up, shaved, had their hair styled and their nails manicured, etc., or at least for whom. I wondered why certain women dressed the way they did and then began to look at the ways in which I, too, was adopting what I now deem oppressive social practices.

Of course, I did not create these questions or even the position I took in relationship to them from thin air. There already were feminist, socialist, anti-racist, etc., frameworks through which I could view the world. But, oddly enough, as passionate as I was in my views, I did not realize the extent to which I was, and am still, in many ways, unwittingly upholding various dominant oppressive ideologies. I remember several experiences where I found myself in a state of cognitive dissonance, where what I assumed to be "a given" came up against a different perspective which challenged my assumptions. I will provide three examples. The first was my assumption that only "weak" women remained in abusive relationships. When I found myself in an abusive relationship in my early twenties, my beliefs and understanding shifted. I began to understand the complexities involved in abuse and in relationships. I began to understand how the sexist discourses of males and females shape how we view the victim of abuse as being partially, if not fully, responsible for the abuse. I found that these discourses become internalized in detrimental ways.

My second example involves the way that I see the physical layout of the world and my assumption that how *I* see it is how it *actually* is. One day I was helping a friend to rearrange her bedroom in order to maximize the small space. I found a perfect solution and began to assert my viewpoint. When she looked at me and asked how she would get her clothes out of her wardrobe or get into bed, I replied that it was easy and proceeded to show her. As she looked at me and shook her head in tolerant amusement, the ignorance of my suggestions became embarrassingly clear. I had not taken into consideration that her wheelchair would not fit into the tight spaces that my upright ambulatory body did!

My final example is from when I first moved from Australia to the USA. I moved into a neighbourhood in which the majority of the residents were African-American. For the first time in my life, as a white woman, I was in the racial minority. I was struck by how I was constantly aware of the colour of my skin. I felt that negative assumptions were being made about me based purely on the colour of my skin, and I felt angry that I was not being seen for the person I felt I was. For a while, I was under the erroneous assumption that I now understood what African-Americans or Native Americans or Indigenous Australians or other non-white people must experience in North America, in Australia, and in other countries dominated by white ideology. Of course, I came to understand that this was a naive assumption because I was still living in white skin in a culture that privileges whiteness. To be in a context where one is the racial minority does not mean that one is oppressed. One only has to think of South Africa to see the absurdity of such a belief.

I am often aware of how I am perceived as a woman in relation to men. It happens in various social contexts in the form of not having my hand shaken, having my spouse spoken to rather than me when in a discussion of a financial matter, being looked at, spoken to, or whistled at on the street by men I do not know (an object of their gaze, something for their pleasure), having people who are working on some part of the house ask to speak to my husband in order to explain the problem, having the restaurant bill handed to my spouse, etc. It also happens in healthcare settings. One notable experience was when I went to the doctor because I knew I was seriously ill. I was falling asleep all the time, even in the middle of teaching half hour cello lessons. I had been getting plenty of sleep, but found it extremely difficult to get myself physically out of the bed. I asked the doctor to give me a blood test and he felt it was unnecessary and implied that I was "just a stressed woman looking for time off." Angered by his implication, I insisted on the blood test. Continuing to believe this was unnecessary he mockingly asked what I thought was wrong. So, I diagnosed myself with mononeucleosis (also known as glandular fever). He again was adamant that he doubted that this was what I had, that even if it was it would not show up yet on a blood test. However, he begrudgingly allowed me to have the test that I was demanding. Sure enough the results proved my diagnosis to be correct.

This type of sexism is also very evident in the academy. Although I have earned a high educational "status" as a Ph.D. holder, this is regularly undermined by my "status" as a woman. Once, while being interviewed for a teaching position, the provost of the University frequently called me "sweetie," "honey," and "love," with condescending "kindness." When I had major difficulties in my first pregnancy and had not yet accrued enough sick days to cover the months of bed rest that the doctors insisted on, with no paid maternity leave available, the people in the state office told me that I should have *planned* to have my children in the summer. Also, although titles can be argued to be problematic in terms of power and privilege, it is disappointing to note that I have witnessed female colleagues who have earned doctorates being referred to as "Ms." and male colleagues who have not earned doctorates being referred to as "Dr." by students and faculty alike.

Gender stereotypes are constantly reinforced by the media. When I watch a movie, I see *my* status as woman in relationship to men. When I glance at magazines when I am in line at the grocery store, I see how *I* am supposed to look, I see what *is* beautiful. When I hear songs, I understand how *I* am to experience love and loss. When I see music videos, my role as woman is ever reinforced. In all of these media, I see how men and women are viewed from the *spectatorship* of men. It is not for *my* gratification that I see women in these ways. As singer-songwriter Dar Williams says in her song "When I was a Boy":

> *And now I'm in the clothing store, and the signs say Less is More*
> *More that's tight means more to see, more for them, not more for me*
> *That can't help me climb a tree in ten seconds flat.*
> (The Honesty Room, 1995)

Over the last decade, I am not only more aware of how I am oppressed as a woman, but I have become more and more aware of the multiple ways in which I am a part of, and in many ways unconsciously perpetuate, the dominant oppressive ideologies that I so passionately critique and wish to reject. I find myself continually questioning my assumptions, my actions, my reactions, my practices of Othering and oppressing others, overtly or covertly. I feel it is my ethical obligation to do what I can to contribute to ending sexism, sexist exploitation, and other forms of oppression. This is what defines me as a feminist. What we say and what we do can perpetuate or disrupt existing oppressive ideologies. As music therapists, what we say and what we play can also do the same. This is why I feel that there is a great need for music therapists to embrace feminism.

In order to provide a larger historical framework for the chapters that are to follow, I will present a brief outline of the history of feminism, describe some of the major approaches to feminism, and explore the impact of feminism to date in the music therapy literature.

What is Feminism?

I grappled with whether or not to define feminism in this book because it is so diverse and has so many forms that I could not imagine doing it justice. However, realizing the importance of explaining the terms that we use, I will try to define it in its broadest sense, including core ideas that most forms of feminism have in common. A basic assumption of feminism is that gender inequality exists and that this is problematic. In other words, feminism is "a critique of misogyny, the assumption of male superiority and centrality" (Beasley, 1999, p.4).

Allan Johnson (1997) distinguishes among branches of feminism according to the degree to which:

- they understand various aspects of social life—such as sexual domination and violence, religion, warfare, politics, economics, and how we treat the natural environment—in relation to gender;
- they explicitly recognize patriarchy as a system, as problematic, as historically rooted, and in need of change; and
- they see men as a dominant group with a vested interest in women's subordination, the perpetuation of patriarchal values, and control over the political, economic, and other institutions through which those values operate. (p.112)

Thus, some forms of feminism do not have a strong focus on patriarchy and avoid challenging men, while others view patriarchy, male privilege, and gender oppression as central. For some forms of feminism the focus is narrow (on certain select issues, for instance, feminist ethics), while for other forms the focus is global and multidimensional (for instance, post-colonial feminism). Although there are many strands of feminism, they are not mutually exclusive. While there are significant differences, they share commonalities and have grown from similar roots. One can find aspects of various forms of feminism useful in various situations. Therefore, I like Johnson's analogy of the various feminist approaches as "threads woven together to form a whole. While the threads are distinctive in many ways, they are strongest in relation to one another" (p.113). Or as Alice Paul (1885–1977) stated, "I always feel the movement is a sort of mosaic. Each of us puts in one little stone, and then you get a great mosaic at the end" (Kroløkke & Scott Sørensen, 2005, p.3).

Although there are many approaches to feminism and enactments of feminisms—liberal, socialist, Marxist, radical, psychoanalytic, standpoint (identity and difference feminisms), spiritual, ecofeminism, postmodern, post-structuralist, postcolonial, narratological, etc.—one can say that feminism is an embodied, flesh-and-blood, socio-cultural, political, philosophical movement predominantly created by and for women's liberation/emancipation from various forms of male hegemony. Some forms of feminism even call into question the definition of woman. A central goal of feminism is to unmask forms of male hegemony at various sites (in the home, workplace, academy, the street, doctor's

offices, within academic and non-academic professional settings, in the bedroom, in the media, in the area of theory construction, research, methodology, epistemology, ontology, aesthetics, theology, sexuality, identity formation, interaction with the earth, interaction with other human beings, and so on) that *parade* as neutral and/or objective when in fact they hide profound levels of male interest, male norms, and male value-laden assumptions.

The feminist movement is most often referred to in terms of the three modern feminist waves or movements, although it is better understood as existing along a continuum that spans a far larger timeframe. If we start with the first wave, we are ignoring voices from throughout earlier history. Eileen O'Neill discusses the absence of women in history, specifically in the history of philosophy, and stresses that it was not that women scholars did not exist, but rather that their work is treated as if it was written in disappearing ink (O'Neill, 1998). She attributes the dramatic disappearance of women from the histories of philosophy in the nineteenth century to the ideals that grew out of the French Revolution, ironically, ideals of humanism and egalitarianism (pp.37–39). Addressing this contradiction, she writes:

> How to embrace the ideals of a common humanity and egalitarian social order while at the same time preserving a system of sexual [and racial] difference that underpins [white] masculine hegemony? Since reason was the property essential to human nature, and since it was the sole requirement needed by a man to be admitted as a citizen, the texts of this period are filled with debates about the precise character of a [white] woman's [and of a non-white man's or woman's] exercise of reason, and thus her [or his] rightful role as citizen. (p.37)

These texts showed a widely held belief that white women and non-white men and women were not capable of reason. There were widespread practices preventing white females and non-white males and females from learning to read, and from participating in civic, economic, and political spheres. O'Neill (1998) writes:

> Perhaps all of this should make us suspicious about our histories; about the implicit claim that our criteria of selection justify our inclusion of philosophers [or composers, etc.] as major, minor, or well-forgotten figures; about our ranking of issues and argumentative strategies [or compositions, etc.] as central, groundbreaking, useful, or misguided. (p.39)

The disappearance of certain histories has had a significant impact on how white women and non-white men and women view themselves and their roles in relationship to white men. This phenomenon is not specific to philosophy; it is also evident in music and most other disciplines. Thus, the process of making these histories visible is a vital component in the process of healing for historically oppressed groups.

In order to make the history of the women's movement more visible, Charlotte Kroløkke and Anne Scott Sørensen state:

> We could go as far back as antiquity and the renowned *hataera* of Athens, or we could go even further back to prehistoric times in Mesopotamia and the Mediterranean regions and discuss goddess religions and matriarchy. Or we could examine the European Middle Ages and the mystical rhetoric of holy women like Hildegard von Bingen (1098–1179). (Kroløkke & Scott Sørensen, 2005, p.2)

There was also the French poet and author Christine de Pizan who wrote *The Book of the City of Ladies* in 1405 in which she questioned the widely held assumption that women were inferior to men because of their sex. Pizan argued that it was inequities in education and training that created the *illusion* of male superiority. In short, she rejected male ideology masquerading as nature. In her work, Pizan gave attention and credence to her own experiences and the experiences of other women instead of uncritically accepting the opinions of male authorities. She trusted her own voice. She critically analysed attitudes about women and did research that uncovered the contributions of other women, thereby modelling important feminist strategies characteristic of contemporary feminism. Other notable figures are Olympes de Gouges (1748–1793), who drafted a *Declaration of the Rights of Women* (1791) in response to the French revolutionaries' *The Declaration of the Rights of Man* (1789), and Mary Wollstonecraft who wrote *A Vindication of the Rights of Woman* (1792) in response to Edmund Burke's *Reflections on the Revolution in France.*

While there is much to write about feminism prior to the 1800s, in this introduction, due to space limitations, I will provide only a brief synopsis of the three waves of modern feminism and then will explore some of the major approaches to feminism.

The Three Waves of Modern Feminism

Each wave of feminism became known by the predominant issues it addressed. The first wave (mid-1800s–1920) has primarily been associated with access and equal opportunities for women, specifically the drive for women's suffrage. However, Judith Hole and Ellen Levine (1990) describe the women's movement that emerged during the 1800s as "a more multi-issued campaign for women's equality" (p.452). In the 1800s there was a growth of social reform movements and "a philosophical emphasis on individual freedom, the 'rights of man' and universal education" (Hole & Levine, 1990, p.453). The "first wave" of modern feminism in the US had its roots in the abolition movement of the 1830s. Although women were actively involved in the fight for the abolition of slavery, there is evidence that they were not respected as equals by their fellow male abolitionists. According to Hole and Levine, "the brutal and unceasing attacks (sometimes physical) on the women convinced the Grimkes [Sarah and Angelina] that the issues of freedom for slaves and freedom for women were inextricably linked" (p.453). Some of the issues with which the early feminists were concerned included challenging the assumption of the natural superiority of man; challenging the social institutions predicated on that assumption, such as religious dogma and the institution of marriage; challenging stereotypes of women (such as claims of proper female behaviour and talk); equal pay for equal work; state legislative reforms on woman's property rights, rights to divorce, abortion rights, rights to guardianship of their children; non-legislative partnership; temperance (especially in terms of the physical and sexual abuse that resulted from alcohol consumption by men); dress reform; and, women's suffrage—although some felt that suffrage was less important than some of these other issues (Hole & Levine, 1990, pp.454–455; Kroløkke & Scott Sørensen, 2005, p.5–7).

After the Civil War and the resulting abolition of slavery, women were deliberately excluded in the amendments to the Constitution. Women activists therefore came to see the vote as the means to achieving other rights and thus suffrage became the main focus of the women's movement at that time. This focus on suffrage was seen by many as more respectable and conservative than many of the other issues, and support for the women's movement grew. Results did not come quickly. "The woman suffrage Amendment . . . , introduced into every session of Congress from 1878 on, was finally ratified on August 26, 1920" (Hole & Levine, 1990, p.458).

The "second wave" of modern feminism (1960s and 1970s) grew out of related emancipation movements in postwar Western societies, including the US civil rights movement, the Black power movement, student protests, anti-Vietnam war movements, lesbian and gay movements, and the Miss America Pageants protests. Women of the second-wave of feminism revived women's political struggles for civil rights. They found that there was still a large gap between what they were told women had achieved and their experiences of their own situations. This was the time when expressions articulated by the radical feminist group, the Redstockings, became popular—expressions such as "sisterhood is powerful," "consciousness raising," and "the personal is political" (Kroløkke & Scott Sørensen, p.9). It was at this time that various approaches to feminism—liberal, socialist, radical—developed, the seeds of which had been planted in the first wave; each of which emphasized different explanations of and remedies for patriarchy and androcentrism.[3] Many of the same issues that were of concern to the early feminists continued to concern second-wave feminists. What many of the second-wave feminists overlooked, however, was the significance of race, class, age, sexual orientation, and ability that contributed to the intersectionist dimensions of oppression, and thereby they universalized the experiences of oppression had by middle-class white women. Moreover, given the lack of critical attention to the differential ways in which male oppression operates along lines of race, differential class positions, and such considerations, these middle-class white feminists privileged the types of oppression enacted by men who were well-educated, white, and who occupied a middle-class position. In eventual reaction to such a monolithic presentation of concerns, various strands of "identity" feminisms began to emerge, such as womanism (black feminism), Mujerista feminism (Latina feminism), Sephardic feminism (Israeli Jewish feminism), Third-World feminism, and lesbian feminism as some examples (Kroløkke & Scott Sørensen, p.12–13). Thus, in the second wave, many feminist groups acknowledged that patriarchal oppression is not experienced in a homogeneous fashion.

The "third wave" of modern feminism (1990s) has been marked by "the need to develop a feminist theory and politics that honor contradictory experiences and deconstruct categorical thinking" (Kroløkke & Scott Sørensen, p.16). These authors have embraced the significance of "acceptance of a chaotic world, while simultaneously embracing ambiguity and forming new alliances" (Kroløkke & Scott Sørensen, p.18). The third-wave is marked by a "performance turn." This turn "marks a move away from thinking and acting in terms of systems, structures, fixed power relations, and thereby also 'suppression,' and toward highlighting the complexities, contingencies, and challenges of power and the diverse means and goals of agency" (Kroløkke & Scott Sørensen, p.21). Thus, there is a shift from what has been defined as structuralism to post-structuralism. This wave of feminism includes *postcolonial feminism*, which establishes a critical global perspective and creates alliances between diasporic and subaltern feminisms, and emphasizes issues of race, political power, and geographical concerns; *queer and transgender feminism*, which attacks heteronormativity; *transfeminism*, as articulated by Emi Koyama, which believes that individuals should be free to construct their own gender identities, rejecting medical and cultural (essentialist) notions of gender; *feminist disability studies*, as articulated by Rosemarie Garland-Thomson (1996), Susan Wendell (1996), and Simi Linton (2005), which considers feminist theorizing to be skewed

[3] By patriarchy I am referring to *male-dominated* structures and social arrangements, and by androcentrism I am referring to that which is *male-centered*, that is, when male norms become the standard.

toward the non-disabled experience, disability studies to be skewed toward non-gendered, non-raced disability experiences, and which understands the complexity of disability experience to be integrally related to other aspects of one's life such as gender, race, and class; *Grrl feminism*, as articulated by feminists such as Jennifer Baumgardner and Amy Richards (2000), which has criticized sexist language while at the same time using mimicry and subversion in terms of exaggerating stereotypes that traditionally have been used against them and appropriating and resignifying the meanings of "derogatory" terms for women (such as girl, slut, bitch, and ho), and also inventing self-celebrating words and forms of communication; the "*new feminism*" in Europe which is characterized by local, national, and transnational activism, in areas such as violence against women, trafficking of female bodies, body surgery, self-mutilation, and the overall "pornofication" of the media; *performance third-wave feminism*, as articulated by feminists such as Judith Butler, which understands gender as a set of discursive practices that are a hegemonic, social matrix and a "performative gesture" with the power to disturb the chain of social repetition and open up new realities; *cyberfeminism*, as articulated by Donna Haraway, which is also aligned with post-structuralist thought and thus understands classifications between society and subject, materiality and sociality, flesh and soul, as well as other demarcations to be arbitrary rather than natural (Kroløkke & Scott Sørensen, pp.15–21); and, *postfeminism*, a term which is sometimes used to describe a time when women's issues and feminism are no longer relevant and sometimes used to describe the views of a group of conservative women who define themselves in opposition to and criticize feminists of the second-wave (Heywood & Drake, 1997, p.1; Rosen, 2001, pp.274–276).

Some Major Approaches to Feminism

Although there are many different approaches to feminism, I will outline major approaches that have had a significant impact on feminist thought: liberal, radical, Marxist/socialist, psychoanalytic (Freudian, Lacanian), Black/Asian/Latina/Indigenous/Sephardic, postcolonial, and postmodern feminisms.

In *liberal feminism* the explanation for why women have a lower position in society is because of "unequal rights or 'artificial' barriers to women's participation in the public world, beyond the family and household" (Beasley, 1999, p.51). Liberal feminists believe that women are basically the same as men, but are not given the same opportunities. Thus, the solution is to provide women with freedom of choice, to challenge sexist stereotypes, and to demand equal access and treatment. The main aim of liberal feminism is to "accord to women the rights that men hold 'naturally'" (Whelehan, 1995, p.29). This is primarily achieved through legal and political avenues. The emphasis is on "reform of society rather than revolutionary change" (Beasley, 1999, p.52).

Radical feminism, by contrast, focuses on the underlying patriarchal system as that which helps to maintain male privilege. They see the problem as "a cultural ideology that serves male privilege and support's women's subordination . . . *it is prejudice plus the power to act on it*" (Johnson, 1997, p.122). There is a strong emphasis on sisterhood based on the shared oppression of women. According to Beasley (1999), they encourage "some degree of 'separatism' from men, which may range from simply supporting other women to living as far as possible in the exclusive company of women" (p.54). Sexual oppression is seen as the main oppression of women and all men are viewed as having power over at least some women (Beasley, 1999, p.55). They critique heterosexuality as giving men priority. Radical feminists call for revolutionary social change.

Marxist/Socialist feminism emphasizes the hierarchical class relations as the main source of other forms of oppression. Gender oppression is believed to be linked to capitalism, in that women are exploited in terms of free or cheap labour. Marxist/socialist feminists emphasize the complex combination of patriarchy and economic systems that need to be dismantled in order to transform the existing social and economic order. They support the view that "only an alliance that included women and men, black and white, poor and middle class had the possibility of developing a strategy, a program, and a vision that would lead to freedom and justice" (Chafe, 1991, p.30). For Marxist/socialist feminists, it is the class system which creates divisions between men and women (Beasley, 1999, p.61).

Psychoanalytic feminism (Freudian) links "unconscious mental phenomena (sexed subjectivities) . . . with conscious concrete macrosocial relations between men and women" (Beasley, 1999, p.69). Critically reassessing Freud and challenging Freudian notions of women being deficient, psychoanalytic feminists, largely from the US, have described differences between men and women in woman-friendly terms and explored both the positive and negative consequences of these differences on women. Nancy Chodorow has suggested that "the feminist political agenda should be directed towards feminizing men" by developing their nurturing capacities and in sharing child-rearing responsibilities; Carol Gilligan described a "different form of moral reasoning employed by women"; and Sara Ruddick writes about "maternal thinking" (Beasley, 1999, pp.67–68). They believe that in order to effect meaningful change, it is imperative to intervene in the psychological development of girls and boys.

Psychoanalytic feminism (Lacanian & post-Lacanian) holds the view that "the self and sexuality are socially constructed in that there can be no (sexed) self—no masculine or feminine person—prior to the formation of the subject in language" (Beasley, 1999, p.71). Psychoanalytic feminists from France such as Hélène Cixous, Luce Irigaray, and Julia Kristiva explore the possibility of a discourse that is capable of expressing women's unique experience. This approach is known as *l'écriture feminine*—embodied feminine writing or writing from the position of the woman. This writing "challenges the way in which woman is construed in language/culture" (Beasley, 1999, p.71). The French feminists critique the hierarchical binarisms of Western thinking which they describe as "phallocentric" ways of thinking. They "explored Western *universalism* [italics mine] and its paradoxical articulation through dualisms such as mind/body, man/woman, and White/Black and their hierarchical ordering, in which one element is not only *different from* but also *less than* the other" (Kroløkke & Scott Sørensen, p.14).

Black/Asian/Latina/Indigenous/Sephardic feminisms share in common a critique of the universalization of women's experiences. They assert that mainstream feminism has been inattentive to race and ethnicity, exclusionary, and either implicitly or explicitly racist/ethnocentric (Beasley, 1999, p.104). They acknowledge their multiple identities and argue that "race, class and gender are *interlocking* systems of oppression not additive systems" (Humm, 1992, p.122). They delineate their distinctive experiences of oppression drawing on their particular shared history of struggle.

Postmodern feminism holds the view that identities are discursively constructed and are multiple and malleable in nature.[4] It emphasizes the "positionality of subjectivity within history" (Nicholson, 1997, p.5). Postmodern feminism rejects grand and essentialist narratives of "womanhood." That is, they believe that even the understanding of the meaning of "woman" changes in various contexts and at different points in history. Postmodern feminists also challenge notions of reality, truth, objectivity, and standards for evaluating knowledge claims. Unlike standpoint feminists who take women's experience as the basis for knowledge claims, postmodern feminists emphasize discursive constructions that shape experience which is then interpreted by the individual. Addressing and critiquing this shift, philosopher Linda Martín Alcoff (2000) claims that "experience sometimes exceeds language; it is at times inarticulate . . . . [So,] to claim that discourse is the condition of intelligibility for all experience, is to erase all of those kinds of experiential knowledges unsusceptible to linguistic articulation" (p.256).

[4] The emphasis placed on the discursive dimensions of sexual identity has been influenced by philosopher Michel Foucault, particularly in terms of his view that "the sexed body cannot be located outside of discursive frameworks" (Beasley, 1999, p.96). Judith Butler's work on the sexual self as a set of performances is similar to Foucault's emphasis on the power of discursivity.

Feminism and Music Therapy

When I originally conceived of this book several years ago it was because I began to wonder in what ways we as music therapists might be unwittingly perpetuating the oppression of our clients. I felt that given the contemporary social and political importance of feminist thought both inside and outside of academia, it was not only surprising but also disheartening that in the twenty-first century there was so little in terms of research in feminist music therapy and that there was not a single book dedicated to demonstrating and exploring the feminist dimensions of music therapy. Given that the music therapy profess-sion is made up of over 80% women, one might expect that feminist perspectives in music therapy would have emerged by now. Perhaps, however, because of the disproportionate number of females in the profession, we have taken for granted that many of the assumptions operating within the theoretical and practical spheres of music therapy have nothing to do with issues of male power and hegemony. It is important to be aware, however, that sites of power are concealed through norms that structure relationships as "natural," as a given. This is why it is imperative that we make the effort to analyse our own cultural, ideological, and pedagogical practices. What is clear is that despite the large percentage of women in music therapy, we have not yet experienced a collective effort to articulate a critical link between feminist theory and practice in relation to music therapy.

Although this book is unprecedented in terms of its exploration of approaches to feminist music therapy, there are some feminist explorations in the music therapy literature. For example, Sandra Curtis (1990) surveyed 836 women music therapists with questions that examined role models, awareness of bias (in general and in their own work situations), the effects of sex-role stereotyping, and general satisfaction with the profession of music therapy. Curtis (1990) found that "their views and their perceptions were almost as diverse as their work situations . . . [but that] [t]he most prominent concerns . . . were inadequate salary and lack of advancement opportunities, leisure time, time or money for continuing education, prestige, and professional recognition" (pp.61–62). Curtis (1990) sees women's issues as having "an impact on both men's and women's lives, clinicians' and academicians' lives, and in our personal and professional lives" (p.65). In her conclusion, Curtis expressed her hopes that through open dialogue women would become more aware of how they are victims of gender bias and, when denying its existence, perpetrators of it. She expressed her hope that such dialogues will inspire women to become advocates for change.

Susan Baines (1992), in describing a feminist framing of music therapy, encouraged music therapists to take a sociological and political perspective on their work in order to become aware of sexist biases. She maintained that music therapists should accept the clients' perceptions as the most valid and that music therapists should establish egalitarian relationships with their clients. Although Curtis (2000) categorizes Baines' approach as one that is nonsexist rather than one that is feminist per se (p.4), it uses certain feminist assumptions and demonstrates their relevance to music therapy. Curtis has stated that in order for therapy to be *feminist*, more is needed; for example, music therapists must advocate for social as well as personal change for both the client and the therapist herself (Curtis, 2000, p.4). Curtis (2000) developed a model of feminist music therapy for the empowerment of women, specifically for increasing the self-esteem of women who have been abused by their intimate male partners. Her model integrates principles and practices of feminist therapy with those of music therapy. In this model, she advocates the use of innovative techniques of feminist analysis of power and gender-role socialization through lyric analysis and song writing.

In a parenting program for women abused in childhood who were either pregnant or had young children, Toni Day and Helen Bruderer (2002) provided song writing as a means to give voice to the experiences of this group of women. These inspirational songs are now part of a training resource for workers. These women's songs give voice to their pain, distrust, anxiety, and to their power and determination to live and have different lives. Day, a music therapist, and Bruderer, a social worker, employed feminist principles in order to provide a space for agency and determination in this group.

More recently, feminist perspectives in relation to music therapy have been explored by Curtis (2003), Susan Hadley and Jane Edwards (2004), and Michele Chestnut (2004). Elizabeth York and Maureen Hearns (2005) conducted research with women survivors of intimate partner violence which incorporates feminist perspectives. In this research, York and Hearns worked with a group of women for a period of eight months which resulted in the development of a performance piece/"ethnographic drama." This was later performed around the state by the women themselves and recorded onto a CD (See York's chapter in this book).

Although not explored from a feminist perspective, music therapists have written on topics that are of interest to feminists, including:

- male violence against women (e.g. Cassity & Kaczor-Theobold, 1990; Rinker, 1991; Curtis, 1994; Wallace, 1995; Whipple & Lindsey, 1999; Montello, 1999; Amir, 2004; and, Hernández-Ruiz, 2005);
- abused children/adolescents (e.g. Clendenon-Wallen, 1991; Lindberg, 1995; Rogers, 1992, 1994, 1995, 2003; Purdon and Ostertag, 2000; Ostertag, 2002; Purdon, 2002; Robarts, 2003; and, Edwards & McFerran, 2004)

- eating disorders/body image (e.g. Parente, 1989; Nolan, 1989; Robarts & Sloboda, 1994; Ventre, 1994; Justice, 1994; Rogers, 1998; Robarts, 1998, 2000; Sloboda, 1998; Hilliard, 2001; Trondalen, 2003; and, McFerran, 2005);
- empowerment (e.g. Daveson, 2001; Proctor, 2001; Rolvsjord, 2004; Rolvsjord, Gold, & Stige, 2005);
- sexual orientation and related health issues (e.g. Bruscia, 1991; Lee, 1996; and, Chase, 2004);
- gender (e.g. Bruscia, 1995; Brooks, 1998; Körlin & Wrangsjö, 2001; Meadows, 2000, 2002);
- childbirth (e.g. Clark, McCorkle, & Williams, 1981; Hanser, Larson, & O-Connell, 1983; Allison, 1991, 1994; and, Browning, 2001);
- culture and community (e.g. Troppozada, 1995; Bradt, 1997; Ruud, 1998; Darrow & Molloy, 1998; Stige 2002, 2003; Kenny & Stige, 2002; Chase, 2003; and, Pavlicevic & Ansdell, 2004;); and
- critical reflexivity (e.g. Kenny, 1989; Aldridge, 1996, 2000; Pavlicevic, 1997; Ruud, 1998; Ansdell, 1999, 2003; and, Stige, 2002).

Evolution of this Book

When I conceived of this first book on feminism and music therapy, I envisioned a critical mass of women working together. Given my own political awareness of how women's voices have been marginalized historically, the idea was to allow women music therapists a safe space within which their voices could be heard as they struggled—many for the first time—to articulate how they understood the relationship between feminism and music therapy. As I thought of women to ask to contribute to the book, I began with those who I knew were already interested in feminism. In addition, I asked women who were working with women on issues which are particularly relevant to women. I also asked women who had a strong interest in a particular area of music therapy (research, supervision, ethics, pedagogy, assessment, lyric analysis) and who might be interested in exploring that area from a feminist perspective. I asked women from a variety of countries, cultures, and religious groups, in the hopes of a greater diversity of voices and experiences. As I approached these women, they recommended other women to ask, given the work they are doing. Some people even asked to be included once they heard about the development of this book project. The number of contributors grew rapidly. The composition of the book continued to change as new people came aboard and as others dropped out due to personal and professional reasons unrelated to the book. It was also important to me that I include not only women who have published extensively in music therapy, but also those who had not previously published in music therapy.

As the book evolved, I was interested in many of the responses to what I was doing. The statement "the personal is political," and even "the political is personal," took on a new meaning for me. I have since tried to understand the many responses to the book in terms of the implicit assumptions and the discursive function of various comments that were made. I have decided to include some of these responsive comments (which I have italicized) and to explore them in an attempt to understand, and openly dialogue about, some of these important issues. I will also draw on some feminist literature to explore the implications of these responses. These responses show that although there have been many "successful challenges to 'old' sexism (overt justification of gender inequalities), [these have] . . . simply paved the way for the equally powerful, naturalized and invisible 'new sexism'" (Riley, 2001, p.58). The two main themes that emerged were: 1) resistance to a book on feminist perspectives in music therapy; and 2) the perception that I have adopted the same patriarchal practices that I wish the book to explore and critique.

> Comment: *I would think that the types of males that go into music therapy are very sensitive. Therefore, what is the need for a book on feminism in music therapy?*

The assumption here is that it is men only, and only of a particular type, who perpetuate sexism. Statements of this kind minimize the pervasiveness of sexism in our society. Another assumption is that the main purpose for a feminist exploration/critique in music therapy is to examine gender inequities/sexual exploitation within the profession. This assumption, however, shows little understanding of the complexities involved in terms of the expression and maintenance of hegemony in the therapeutic relationship, the gender stereotypes which are communicated through the music we select and use, our discursive practices, the concepts we employ, the theoretical orientations we adopt, the ways women's health issues are perceived in the medical and wider communities, the continuing gendered socialization and institutionalized oppression of women, etc.

With regard to gender inequities within the music therapy profession, there are many unsettling statistics that I recently obtained from the American Music Therapy Association and the Certification Board of Music Therapists. In 2004, the ratio of females to males in the AMTA membership was 88% to 12%. Of the 1317 board-certified music therapists with a master's degree, 88% are female and 12% male, reflecting the ratio of females to males in the AMTA membership. Of the 148 board certified music therapists with a doctoral degree, however, only 74% are female and 26% are male. Similarly, of the 146 AMTA members who indicated their job title as "Faculty (University/College)" on their most recent survey, only 73% are female and 27% are male. In both cases, there are a disproportionate number of males in music therapy in the United States who earn doctorates and who hold University positions. Why this is the case is a question that needs to be addressed.

Furthermore, in terms of the salary of the survey respondents who indicated they work full time (34 hours or more) and who provided an annual income estimate on their most recent survey, the average for females was $41,265.35 as opposed to $52,500.00 for males. For those who indicated their job title as Faculty (University/College), the average salary for females was $50,690.91 as opposed to $61,166.67 for males. From these figures it appears that the average salary for males still exceeds that of females by about $11,000 within the music therapy profession, outside and within academia, and that proportionally more males than females hold faculty positions.

Along similar lines, in 1985 Mark James noted that, in the music therapy literature in the United States, women authored 10% more articles than men between 1974 and 1984, and came to the erroneous conclusion that "general parity exists between men and women authors, with a recent trend for more articles to be authored by women." Curtis (2000) insightfully turned this conclusion around by stating, "While this is indeed an improvement over the past, this '*parity*' looks quite different if the 90:10 female to male music therapists ratio is taken into consideration."

More recently, Edwards and Hadley (2006) examined the gender of authors of articles published in the years 2000–2005 in the *Journal of Music Therapy* (JMT), the *Nordic Journal of Music Therapy* (NJMT), and the *British Journal of Music Therapy* (BJMT), three major music therapy journals published in English. They found that in JMT 61.5% of the authors were female and 30% were male;[5] in NJMT 44% were female and 56% were male; and in BJMT 62% were female and 38% were male. Pooling the data from all three journals, 60% were female and 40% were male. Although an improvement over earlier statistics, this still does not reflect the ratio of females to males in our profession. Edwards and Hadley conclude by stating, "When combined with the information about salaries and academic appointments in the US it is cause for concern that gender seems to correlate with salary, attainment of doctoral qualifications, and employment in an academic post. This is a worthy topic for ongoing comment and discussion."

[5] In 8.5% the gender of the authors could not be determined from the name or affiliation.

> Comment: *Is there really a need for it anymore? I mean, we have come a long way from what it used to be.*

Unfortunately, many people, male and female, feel that feminism has already achieved its goals. Many people believe that they live in a "post-feminist" era, one in which equal opportunities have replaced the sexist practices of old. Paul Peace (2003) refers to this type of response as belonging to the "equality as imminent/achieved" repertoire. He states that this premature celebration diverts attention from inequalities which continue to exist and "conceals, absents and makes less urgent the continuing need for change" (p.167). Many people now tend to advocate a gender-neutral perspective as opposed to a feminist perspective. This gives the impression of egalitarianism which "functions to marginalize any continued feminist voice" and as such the "underlying power structures can remain stable" which reduces the need for "further initiatives for social change" (Riley, 2001, p.55).

Addressing this issue, hooks (2000) states:

> Since masses of young females know little about feminism and many falsely assume that sexism is no longer the problem, feminist education for critical consciousness must be continuous. Older feminist thinkers cannot assume that young females will just acquire knowledge of feminism along the way to adulthood. They require guidance. (p.17)

hooks' comment in fact exemplifies the need for such a book.

> Comment: *I was always taught that feminism was something, you know, bad.*

I was interested in how many young women who have benefited substantially, whether consciously or not, from the feminist movement, had a negative view about it. Although they readily admitted only to vaguely understanding what feminism is, and although they believe that there is still a lot of prejudice against women, they often had strong negative opinions about feminists. I found that many of them characterized feminists in stereotypical ways as extreme, aggressive, overly ambitious, unreasonable, men-haters, unfeminine, unattractive, demanding, uptight, dogmatic, radical, and lesbian. From my experience, I found this was widespread, that although both males and females strongly support values associated with feminism, feminists are often constructed in negative ways. Accounting for this decoupling of feminist values from feminists, Riley (2001) argues that it serves five major functions. By negatively characterizing feminists and positioning them as extremists, it:

1) minimizes the impact that such individuals and associated social movements have had on creating social change,
2) minimizes the historical oppression of women, thus masking the effects of this in contemporary society,
3) minimizes the privileges that men have received in the past and the present,
4) marginalizes any voice for continued change by representing it as not credible, and
5) allows for the reformulation of feminist values into gender neutral constructions of equality or discourses of liberal equality, which can function to maintain existing male power and privileges.

A vast number of people believe that feminism (or pro-female) is anti-male. hooks (2000) states that "their misunderstanding of feminist politics reflects the reality that most folks learn about feminism from patriarchal mass media" (p.1).

> Comment: *If you don't include men's voices, fewer people will read/buy the book.*

Again, from my experience, it is fascinating how many people actually agree with this statement. I wonder how many times each of us has picked up a book with all white authors without giving it a thought. How many times have we picked up a book with all male authors and not given it a thought? If the topic of this book was not about feminism, I wonder whether it would have been a concern whether or not male contributors had been included.

On the issue of inclusion of males in women's groups, Riley (2001) conducted a study in which she provided male participants with a vignette about a male researcher in gender issues who was excluded from a women's research group. She then asked the research participants to discuss the vignette. Through her discourse analysis, several interesting themes emerged. One example is that although many of the men recognized a need for or supported the idea of women's groups, she found that many felt that excluding males was hurtful to the agenda of the women. "(Open-minded) men's roles in such [groups] are . . . presented in terms of acting as power brokers for women, so that 'women's issues' need to be communicated through a male spokesman, based on the premise that men are more likely to believe each other than women (a meeting of equals?)" (p.64). This type of response shows support for women's issues or feminist values—the message—while in some ways criticizing the messenger (Riley, 2001, p.65).

> Comment: *By only choosing women to contribute, you are engendering feminism, which has the direct implication that you have marginalised men. You are controlling how and when men can speak!*

In his critical discourse analysis of predominantly women participants, Peace (2003) identified three main discourse repertoires—"equality as imminent/achieved" (mentioned in an earlier example), "women as oppressors/ men as victims," and "women as manipulators,"—which women are said to engage in, and "which play a part . . . in bolstering gender relations that ultimately oppress them" (p.160). The above response falls into the repertoire of "men as victims." The function is for us to feel sorry for men. The trouble with this type of comment is that it suggests "that equality has actually been overshot in favour of women" (Peace, 2003, p.168). Men, particularly white men, have not traditionally been silenced or had their opinions trivialized. Peace (2003) notes, "it is progressive to recognize sexism as a two-way street (even if most of the traffic travels one way). However, what *is* problematic is when particular *instances* are used to make *general* points that lament the 'poor man' and celebrate women's greater power" (p.169). It points to a conservative fear of women going "too far." In addition, there are a multiplicity of other venues where men can and have had their voices heard and privileged.

> Comment: *My issue is that by only choosing women to write the book you are implying to me that women own feminism and that male voices are not relevant. I find this very surprising, especially if one of the original tenets of the feminist movement, as I understand it, was a fight for equality of voice.*

Many people equate feminism primarily with a fight for equality. And many people believe that by allowing for an all female space it is disenfranchising the male voice. This suggests that it is hypocritical to argue for equality of rights while also advocating special needs (Riley, 2001, p.70) and that by carving out a space for women to explore feminism in music therapy, I am putting up barriers that will thwart the fight for equality, thus creating a contradiction. Riley (2001) states:

> The construction of such groups as "putting up barriers" positions "real" equality as one in which women/gays/non-white groups fit into "normal" society presenting equality and progress in terms of all people assimilating to the male/heterosexual/white norm, rather than, for example, men/heterosexuals/whites engaging in social diversity. This masks any work that men/heterosexuals/whites may need to do,

> avoiding a reassessment of, for example, the roles and privileges associated with being male/heterosexual/white. (p.71)

Also, the claim that by choosing only women I am implying that "women own feminism and that male voices are not relevant" again falls into the "men as victim/women as oppressors" repertoire. I am actually a strong advocate of "men doing feminism." Again, the relevance of white male voices has not been in question historically. When various people were suggested for this book, I took into account the topics that they would write on. Actually, the topics suggested for the men who were recommended were gender, feminist perspectives in the *other* creative arts therapies, and queer theory, all of which are very important topics, but the specific areas these men cover were not congruent with the focus of this book. I certainly encourage male music therapists to approach their work from a feminist consciousness and to explore ways to empower women and other oppressed groups.

While men/whites/heterosexuals "may grant that women/[non-whites/GLBTs] are disadvantaged," many are unwilling "to grant that they [men/whites/heterosexuals] are over-privileged" (McIntosh, 1997, p.291). Peggy McIntosh asserts that when we belong to the dominant group we are carefully taught not to recognize and even to *deny* the unearned privileges of that group. She describes such privileges as "an invisible package [or knapsack] of unearned assets which I can count on cashing in each day, but about which I was 'meant' to remain oblivious" (McIntosh, 1997, p.291). It is very difficult to admit the ways in which we are oppressors, even if we can admit that certain groups are indeed oppressed. It is easy to distance ourselves from these oppressive groups without realizing the benefits we continue to reap as members of the oppressor group. It takes continual critical reflexivity to identify the daily effects of privilege in our lives and then to go about trying to challenge and "weaken these hidden forms of advantage" (McIntosh, 1997, p.299). It is much easier to deny our status as privileged or even to claim a disadvantaged status. For example, many white males feel like they are now the most discriminated against group, because of the efforts being made to "level the playing field." What has historically represented their "entitlement," is not so readily accessible today. Many even suggest that women, non-white, and disabled people are *given* positions instead of white males simply because they are women/non-white/disabled, suggesting that in fact women/non-whites/disabled are inferior and are given "special" treatment (so-called reverse discrimination). This denies the actual abilities and qualifications of women/non-whites/disabled and downplays the lack of educational/economic/social opportunities that adversely impact the lives of women/non-whites.

Exploring the Process for the Contributors

As each contributor was going through the process of writing her chapter, she made comments to me about the writing process. Some found it a very challenging process, while for others it brought them a sense of belonging that they had not felt previously. I faced a personal challenge involving some contributors with whom I have existing relationships outside of this project. For those with whom I have friendships there was an interesting perception of power/hierarchy that emerged in terms of editor/contributor relationship. For others, the existing relationships were ones in which the contributor had held a "higher"/more powerful position in relationship to me and the dynamics arising from this new relationship were at times challenging. In order to provide a sense of how the contributors felt about writing their chapters, the following are some of their personal reflections.

> *As you know, I never considered myself to be a feminist, but as I was reading books/articles in preparation for this chapter, I realized that I am very much a feminist.*

> *I knew at the outset that this would be difficult for me because I come very much from the praxis in music therapy, not research. . . . The bigger problem in the writing was the fact that I worked very intensely as a music therapist for 11 years, then changed professions and immersed myself in violence against women work for the past 20 years, while carrying on with some limited music therapy with various client groups. . . . The work I did [with those in this chapter] was a few years ago, and I never did sit down and think about it from a theoretical or feminist perspective at that time. I simply worked in the way that made sense to me, given the fact that I had done lots of sexual abuse counselling.*

> *For me it was hard because I didn't feel I had the expertise to do this. I haven't spent years reading the feminist literature, I haven't been defining myself outwardly as a feminist and I feel so far behind many of my colleagues who have done so much work in this area. It was actually in the process of writing this chapter and doing all the reading that gave me a sense of competence—but that was slow in coming. I think this helped me grow in a very positive way but this growth was difficult. I found it helpful to talk to some of the other authors who also felt less competent . . . when I was struggling. So, now in retrospect I am glad that I did this and it has changed the way I think and act in the world both personally and professionally. I'm*

also sure that this has helped and will help me view my three daughters' (ages 11, 9, and 6) development in a new way.

What I really appreciated in the process was the opportunity to learn of so many others interested in feminism in music therapy.

During the past 15 years, I have been writing and editing books, articles, and chapters on the subject of music therapy. However, I have never written about music therapy from a feminist point of view. When the invitation to write a chapter for this book came, it was a challenging task for me. Even though I do have a feminist world-view, I realized I had some resistance to do it. Some feminist activities and definitions don't suit me and don't represent my belief system. I accepted the invitation since it forced me to think, re-think, examine, and articulate my feminist values. Even more challenging was to look at my practice and examine it from this perspective. While the evolution of feminism continues to invite me to question my practice as a woman therapist, writing this chapter encouraged me to get into a dialogue with myself, to question my perceptions, and to understand more deeply what my feminist values are and how they are interwoven in and contribute to my life and work. In this way, writing this chapter was an enlightening process.

Although I have benefited from feminism both personally and musically (and professionally, only peripherally at best), it was not until writing the proposal for my sabbatical year that I began to envision music therapy research that would integrate my feminist values, women's music and a feminist clinical approach with women survivors of domestic violence . . . . I had not experienced consciousness raising with my professional peers . . . . I had never attended a conference presentation on [feminist practice] or been asked to engage in such a discussion . . . . My work in the women's music network seemed "a thing apart," separating me rather than connecting me with like-minded women in my professional life. I assumed that I was a solitary practitioner, an anomaly. After spending a painstaking year compiling data from [my research], a male colleague told me about [this book] in progress. A synchronistic meeting at the 2004 AMTA conference finally brought Sue Hadley and I together. Literally with manuscript in hand, I asked her to take a look. Suddenly, I found myself coming out into a circle of peers of which I am proud to be a part . . . . May the voices in this book resonate with the voices of other women and men who have yet to identify themselves as feminist music therapists!

As I got into the writing about feminism . . . , I felt as though I was writing about something that I was such a "baby" in understanding. It has been a several-year process and I have started to get a grasp of some of the concepts. There are some that I still don't understand, although I have tried to understand them. It has been a gratifying process in that I have learned a lot.

It was a profound experience for me. At times, it was overwhelming when I got in touch with the intense feelings that were evoked by the events and conditions that I was describing. I felt a great responsibility to report everything with accuracy, and to be comprehensive in what I covered. One of the challenges that I had during the writing process was that feminism in ____ is fairly new and is vigorously moving forward. So, every time that I had thought I had finished the writing, I found something new to add or delete from my writing. The other challenge was my anticipation of many varied strong reactions from ____ and ____-American people, both men and women. Some men would not like to read the truth of what has been going on, and some would be in denial that the things I described ever happened. Not only men, but some women also would be in denial about ____ society's treatment of women. Other women would be resistant to change. In the end, I had to write what I knew to be true. This is the privilege of being an author. I deeply appreciate the opportunity—to reflect, to examine my cultural roots. It was both bitter and sweet! I hope that my writing will be helpful for music therapists who encounter ____ people in their practice and in their supervision. Further, I hope that it will help people, in general, to understand the situation of women in ____ , and that this will lead to change.

I characterize the process of writing this chapter as one of integration. In a sense, I am so many different people. And because I am an interdisciplinarian, I am also working in extremely diverse disciplines. I find it very interesting that I did not even realize the degree to which I have been functioning in a fragmented state until I had the opportunity to write about my work and myself as a whole woman, through a feminist lens.

> *I have to admit that I felt challenged by this process. Writing in an area I can talk about at the drop of a hat but which I have never written in in such a way before was very difficult. I began to perceive myself as a writer and scholar quite differently in trying to handle new materials as well as link some concepts I know about in a broad way to the specific work of music therapy . . . . Sometimes I felt like an infant stumbling over my first words, pointing to an object because I had no words to describe or name it . . . . It took me an inordinate amount of time and along the way I cursed that I had ever said yes . . . . I hope to include feminist ideas in further writings on topics where I am in more familiar territory.*

Outline of the book

As you read through this book you will find that the contributors have differing conceptions of feminism, which brings to the foreground that feminism is not monolithic. You will also find that there are very different degrees to which the contributors take on a feminist identity—from those who do not consider themselves as feminist to those who no longer feel comfortable calling themselves therapists precisely due to their feminist world-view. For me, an important aspect of this book is that is reflects a range of viewpoints.

As to the layout of the book, I had an original conception of the book in three sections that were clearly delineated. As the chapters came in, I found that I was trying to force chapters into these little boxes that I had set up. It felt awkward and imposed. So, I have decided to group chapters together in terms of themes covered. To introduce each group of chapters, I have inserted interludes that will help to contextualize the chapters within that section.

Final Thoughts: Motivation for a Better Future

Knowledge about issues of oppression does not in itself lead to change without the desire to change, the desire for something better. Philosopher Susan Babbitt (2005) points out that "histories of marginalized groups are often known, but play no role in national identities or agendas . . . . [W]ithout such a role, such histories are not really understood." Babbitt goes on to explain that in order to deal maturely and honestly with the past it is not just a matter of telling our stories differently or incorporating aspects that have previously been omitted, but having expectations for a better future. She makes three important claims:

1) We can know many things intellectually and understand little if we do not recognize how what we know bears upon who we are.
2) Expecting a better future is also an acknowledgement of the present and our responsibility for it.
3) Histories, or the personal stories of others, are understood when they are relevant, but they become relevant when there is a need, and there is only a need to fully understand others' histories when we recognize and take responsibility for where we are now. We do not act upon the information that we possess unless we recognize that it matters to who we are and where we want to go.

Thus, in order to be motivated to change, we need a reason to change. As long as we believe that we are fine as we are then there is no reason to change. We can know many facts, recognize their significance, even be morally outraged by them, and yet still not be motivated to *do* things differently, especially if we see them as about others and not about us as well. And, it is very difficult to own something that contradicts our expectations about ourselves. For example, we can be outraged about racism and view ourselves as not racist. As such, we take no responsibility for the perpetuation of racism and thus have little motivation to *be* different. The same can be said of patriarchy. Indeed, the same can be said of our understanding of our clients. Again, to quote Susan Babbitt (2005):

> Trust is not built by knowledge of others' stories; rather, it is built when such stories motivate us, when they can become reasons for acting, and can define the path of development, individual or social. But stories cannot become *reasons* unless there is something that needs to be understood which is not likely if . . . we are fine as we are.

To challenge the status quo can frighten us and make us feel uncomfortable, but it can also be exciting, challenging, and empowering because it is about having expectations for a better future. I hope that this book does not just provide knowledge, but that it helps us all imagine and expect a better future and as such motivate all of us to see how we are responsible for both our present and our future. May it provide reasons to do things differently—and for the betterment of us all.

REFERENCES

Alcoff, Linda Martin (2000) Merleau-Ponty and feminist theory on experience. In Fred Evans and Leonard Lawlor (eds.) *Chiasms: Merleau-Ponty's Notion of Flesh*. Albany, NY: State University of New York Press.

Aldridge, David (2000) *Spirituality, Healing & Medicine: Return to the Silence*. London: Jessica Kingsley Publisher.

Aldridge, David (1996) *Music Therapy Research and Practice in Medicine: From Out of the Silence*. London: Jessica Kingsley Publisher.

Allison, Dianne (1991) Music therapy at childbirth. In Kenneth E. Bruscia (ed.) *Case Studies in Music Therapy*. Phoenixville, PA: Barcelona Publishers.

Allison, Dianne (1994) *The use of programmed music versus non-programmed and no music, during childbirth*. Unpublished Master's Thesis, University of Melbourne, Australia.

Amir, Dorit (2004) Giving trauma a voice: The role of improvisational music therapy in exposing, dealing with and healing a traumatic experience of sexual abuse. *Music Therapy Perspectives, 22*, 96–103.

American Music Therapy Association (2005) *Resource Directory*. Springville, MD: American Music Therapy Association.

Ansdell, Gary (2003) The stories we tell: Some meta-theoretical reflections on music therapy. *Nordic Journal of Music Therapy, 12*, 152–159.

Ansdell, Gary (1999) *Music therapy as discourse & discipline: a study of the music therapist's dilemma*. London: Unpublished PhD Dissertation, City University.

Babbit, Susan E. (2005) Collective memory or knowledge: "Covering reality with flowers," Lecture Presented on October 1, 2005, for the 2005 Conference of the Canadian Society for Women in Philosophy, Halifax, NS, Canada.

Baines, Susan. (1992) *The sociological and political contexts of music therapy: a question of ethics*. Unpublished Master's Thesis, New York University, New York.

Baumgardner, Jennifer & Richards, Amy (2000) *Manifesta: Young Women, Feminism, and the Future*. New York: Farrar, Straus, and Giroux.

Beasley, Chris (1999) *What is Feminism? An Introduction to Feminist Theory*. London: Sage Publications.

Beauvior, Simone (1953/1989) *The Second Sex*. New York: Vintage Books.

Bradt, Joke (1997) Ethical issues in multicultural counseling: Implications for the field of music therapy. *The Arts in Psychotherapy, 24*, 137–143.

Brison, Susan (2002) *Aftermath: Violence and the Remaking of a Self*. Princeton, NJ: Princeton University Press.

Brooks, Darlene (1998) *Anima Experiences of Men in Guided Imagery and Music (GIM)*. Dissertation Abstracts International-A (6), 1957.

Browning, Caryl Ann (2001) Music therapy in childbirth: Research in practice. *Music Therapy Perspectives, 19*, 74–81.

Bruscia, Kenneth (1995) Modes of consciousness in guided imagery and music: A therapist's experience of the guiding process. In Carolyn Kenny (ed.), *Listening, Playing, Creating: Essays on the Power of Sound,* 165–197. New York: State University of New York Press.

Bruscia, Kenneth E. (1991) *Case Studies in Music Therapy.* Gilsum, NH: Barcelona Publishers.

Cassity, Michael David & Theobold, Kimberly A. Kaczor (1990) Domestic violence: Assessments and treatments employed by music therapists. *Journal of Music Therapy, 27,* 179–194.

CBMT – Statistics provided through personal communication with staff at CBMT.

Chafe, William H. (1991) *The Paradox of Change: American Women in the 20th Century.* Oxford: Oxford University Press.

Chase, Kristen (2004) Therapy with gay and lesbian clients: Implications for music therapists. *Music Therapy Perspectives, 22,* 34–38.

Chase, Kristen (2003) Multicultural music therapy: A review of the literature. *Music Therapy Perspectives, 21*, 84–88.

Chestnut, Michelle (2004) *Family music therapy: family work in music therapy from a feminist perspective.* Unpublished Master's Thesis, New York University, New York.

Clark, Michael E., McCorkle, Ronald R., & Williams, Sterling B. (1981) Music therapy-assisted labor and delivery. *Journal of Music Therapy, 18*, 88–100.

Clendenon-Wallen, Joy (1991) The use of music therapy to influence the self-confidence of adolescents who are sexually abused. *Music Therapy Perspectives, 9*, 73–81.

Curtis, Sandra L. (2000) Singing subversion, singing soul: Women's voices in feminist music therapy. (Doctoral dissertation, Concordia University, 1997). *Dissertation Abstracts International, 60* (12-A), 4240.

Curtis, Sandra L. (1994) Killing us softly: Male inner violence against women. In Stanley G. French (ed.) *Interpersonal Violence, Health and Gender Politics*. Dubuque. IA: W.C. Brown.

Curtis, Sandra L. (1990) Women's issues in music therapy. *Music Therapy Perspectives*, *8,* 61–66.

Darrow, Alice-Ann & Molloy, Della (1998) Multicultural perspectives in music therapy: An examination of the literature, educational curricula, and clinical practices in culturally diverse cities of the United States. *Music Therapy Perspectives, 16,* 27–32.

Daveson, Barbara (2001) Empowerment: An intrinsic process and consequence of music therapy practice. *Australian Journal of Music Therapy, 12,* 29–38.

Day, Toni & Bruderer, Helen (2002) *A Journey of Healing and Hope Through Song*. Brisbane: Queensland Government.

DiFranco, Ani (2004) Grand Canyon. On *Educated Guess* [CD] Buffalo, NY: Righteous Babe Records.

Edwards, Jane & Hadley, Susan (2006) expanding music therapy practice: Incorporating the feminist frame. Unpublished manuscript.

Edwards, Jane & McFerran, Katrina (2004) educating music therapy students about working with clients who have been sexually abused. *The Arts in Psychotherapy*, *31*, 335–348.

Estrella, Karen (2001) Multicultural approaches to music therapy supervision. In Michele Forinash (ed.) *Music Therapy Supervision.* Gilsum, NH: Barcelona Publishers.

Garland-Thomson, Rosemarie (1996) *Extraordinary Bodies*. New York: Columbia University Press.

Hadley, Susan & Edwards, Jane (2004) Sorry for the silence: A contribution from feminist theory to the discourse(s) within music therapy. *Voices: A World Forum for Music Therapy.* http://www.voices.no/mainissues/mi40004000152.html

Hanser, Suzanne, B., Larson, Sharon Cotteral, & O-Connell, Audree S. (1983) The effect of music on the relaxation of expectant mothers during labor. *Journal of Music Therapy, 20*, 50–58.

Heineman, Michelle (1982) *A study of career aspirations and perceived career success in female and male registered music therapists.* Unpublished Master's Thesis, Florida State University, Tallahassee, FL.

Hernández-Ruiz, Eugenia (2005) Effect of music therapy on the anxiety levels and sleep patterns of abused women in shelters. *Journal of Music Therapy, XLII*, 140–158.

Heywood, Leslie & Drake, Jennifer (1997) *Third Wave Agenda: Being Feminist, Doing Feminism*. Minneapolis: University of Minnesota Press.

Hilliard, Russell (2001) The use of cognitive-behavioral music therapy in the treatment of women with eating disorders. *Music Therapy Perspectives, 19*, 109–113.

Hole, Judith & Levine, Ellen (1990) Historical precedent: Nineteenth-century feminists. In Sheila Ruth (ed.) *Issues in Feminism*. Mountainview, CA: Mayfield Publishing.

hooks, bell (2000) *Feminism is for Everybody: Passionate Politics.* Cambridge, MA: South End Press.

Humm, Maggie (1992) *Modern Feminisms: Political, Literary, Cultural*. New York: Columbia University Press.

Irigiray, Luce (1994) *Democracy Begins Between Two*. Translated by Kirsteen Anderson. New York: Routledge.

James, Mark R. (1985) Sources of articles published in the Journal of Music Therapy: The first twenty years, 1964–1983. *Journal of Music Therapy, 22*, 87–94.

Johnson, Allan G. (1997) *The Gender Knot: Unraveling Our Patriarchal Legacy*. Philadelphia, PA: Temple University Press.

Justice, Roberta Wigle (1994) Music therapy interventions for people with eating disorders in an inpatient setting. *Music Therapy Perspectives*, *12*, 104–110.

Kenny, Carolyn & Stige, Brynjulf (2002) *Contemporary Voices in Music Therapy: Communication, Culture, and Community*. Olso, Norway: Unipub Forlag.

Kenny, Carolyn (1989) *The Field of Play: A Guide for the Theory and Practice of Music Therapy*. Atascadero, CA: Ridgeview Publishing Company.

Körlin, Dag & Wrangsjö, Björn (2001) Gender differences in outcome of Guided Imagery and Music (GIM) therapy. *Nordic Journal of Music Therapy, 10*, 132–143.

Kroløkke, Charlotte & Scott Sørensen, Anne (2005) *Gender Communication Theories and Analyses: From Silence to Performance*. New York: SAGE Publications.

Lee, Colin (1996) *Music at the Edge: The Music Therapy Experiences with a Musician with AIDS*. New York: Routledge.

Lindberg, Katherine A. (1995) Songs of healing: Songwriting with an abused adolescent. *Music Therapy, 13*, 93–108.

Linton, Simi (2005) *My Body Politic: A Memoir*. Ann Arbor, MI: University of Michigan Press.

Loth, Helen (2003) There's no getting away from anything in here: A music therapy group within an inpatient programme for adults with eating disorders. In Allison Davies & Eleanor Richards (eds.) *Music Therapy and Group Work: Sound Company*, London: Jessica Kingsley Publishers.

McFerran, Katrina (2005) Dangerous liaisons: Group work for adolescent girls who have Anorexia Nervosa, *Voices: A World Forum for Music Therapy*. http://www.voices.no/mainissues/mi40005000173.html

McIntosh, Peggy (1997) White privilege and male privilege: A personal account of coming to see correspondences through work in women's studies. In Richard Delgado & Jean Stefancic (eds.) *Critical White Studies: Looking Behind the Mirror*. Philadelphia, PA: Temple University Press.

Meadows, Anthony (2002) Gender implications in therapists' constructs of their clients. *Nordic Journal of Music Therapy, 11*, 127–141.

Meadows, Anthony (2002) *Gender implications in Guided Imagery and Music therapists' constructs of their clients*. Doctoral Dissertation, Philadelphia, PA: Temple University.

Montello, Louise (1999) A psychoanalytic music therapy approach to treating adults traumatized as children. *Music Therapy Perspectives, 17*, 74–81.

Nicholson, Linda (1997) *The Second Wave: A Reader in Feminist Theory*. New York: Routledge.

Nolan, Paul (1989) Music as a transitional object in the treatment of Bulimia. *Music Therapy Perspectives*, *6*, 49–51.

O'Neill, Eileen (1998) Disappearing ink: Early modern women philosophers and their fate in history. In Janet A. Kourany (ed.) *Philosophy in a Feminist Voice: Critiques and Reconstructions*. Princeton, NJ: Princeton University Press.

Ostertag, Joachim (2002) Unspoken stories: Music therapy with abused children, *Canadian Journal of Music Therapy, IX*, 17–27.

Parente, Alice B. (1989) Feeding the hungry soul: Music as a therapeutic modality in the treatment of Anorexia Nervosa. *Music Therapy Perspectives, 6*, 44–48.

Pavlicevic, Mercedes & Ansdell, Gary (2004) *Community Music Therapy*. London: Jessica Kingsley Publishers.

Pavlicevic, Mercedes (1997) *Music Therapy in Context: Music, Meaning, and Relationship*. London: Jessica Kingsley Publishers.

Peace, Paul (2003) Balancing power: The discursive maintenance of gender inequality by wo/men at university. *Feminism & Psychology, 13*, 159–180.

Proctor, Simon (2001) Empowering and enabling: Improvisational music therapy in non-medical mental health provision, *Voices: A World Forum for Music Therapy*. http://www.voices.no/mainissues/Voices1(2)Procter.html

Purdon, Colleen (2002) The role of music in Analytical Music Therapy—Music as a carrier of stories. In Johannes Eschen (ed.) *Analytical Music Therapy*. London: Jessica Kingsley Publishers.

Purdon, Colleen & Ostertag, Joachim (2001) *Music therapy and abuse: training package for Wilfred Laurier Music Therapy Department*, Owen Sound, Ontario, Canada (unpublished).

Purdon, Colleen & Ostertag, Joachim (1999) Understanding abuse: Clinical and training implications for music therapists. *Canadian Journal of Music Therapy*, *VI*, 9–23.

Riley, Sarah (2001) Maintaining power: Male constructions of 'feminist' and 'feminist values.' *Feminism & Psychology, 11*, 55–78.

Rinker, Rhonda Lineberg (1991) Guided Imagery and Music (GIM): Healing the wounded healer. In Kenneth E. Bruscia (ed.) *Case Studies in Music Therapy*. Gilsum, NH: Barcelona Publishers.

Robarts, Jaqueline (2003) The healing function of improvised songs in music therapy with a child survivor of early trauma and sexual abuse. In Susan

Hadley (ed.) *Psychodyanmic Music Therapy: Case Studies.* Gilsum, NH: Barcelona Publishers.

Robarts, Jacqueline (2000) Music therapy and adolescents with Anorexia Nervosa. *Nordic Journal of Music Therapy, 9*, 3–12.

Robarts, Jacqueline (1998) Towards autonomy and a sense of self: Music therapy and the individuation process in relation to children and adolescents with early onset Anorexia Nervosa. In Ditty Dokter (ed.) *Arts Therapies and Clients with Eating Disorders: Fragile Board.* London: Jessica Kingsley Publishers.

Robarts, Jacqueline & Sloboda, Ann (1994) Perspectives on music therapy with people suffering from Anorexia Nervosa. *Journal of British Music Therapy, 8*, 9–15.

Rogers, Penny (2003) Working with Jenny: Stories of gender, power and abuse. In Susan Hadley (ed.) *Psychodyanmic Music Therapy: Case Studies.* Gilsum, NH: Barcelona Publishers.

Rogers, Penny J. (1998) Sexual abuse and eating disorders: A possible connection indicated through music therapy? In Ditty Dokter (ed.) *Arts Therapies and Clients with Eating Disorders: Fragile Board.* London: Jessica Kingsley Publishers.

Rogers, Penny J. (1995) Childhood sexual abuse: Dilemmas in therapeutic practice. *Music Therapy Perspectives, 13*, 24–30.

Rogers, Penny J. (1992) Issues in working with sexually abused clients in music therapy. *British Journal of Music Therapy, 6,* 5–15.

Rolvsjord, Randi, Gold, Christian, & Stige, Brynjulf (2005) research rigour and therapeutic flexibility: Rationale for a therapy manual developed for a randomized controlled trial. *Nordic Journal of Music Therapy*, *14*, 15–32.

Rolvsjord, Randi (2004) Therapy as empowerment: Clinical and political implications of empowerment philosophy in mental health practices of music therapy. *Nordic Journal of Music Therapy, 13,* 99–111.

Rosen, Ruth (2001) *The World Split Open: How the Modern Women's Movement Changed America.* New York: Penguin Books.

Ruud, Even (1998) *Music Therapy: Improvisation, Communication, and Culture.* Gilsum, NH: Barcelona Publishers.

Shiraishi, Iris M. (1997) A home-based music therapy program for multi-risk mothers. *Music Therapy Perspectives, 15*, 16–23.

Sloan, Tod (2005) Life reflections of a nomadic subject. In George Yancy and Susan Hadley (eds.) *Narrative Identities: Psychologists Engaged in Self-Construction.* London: Jessica Kingsley Publishers.

Sloboda, Ann (1998) Individual music therapy with Anorexic and Bulimic patients. In Ditty Dokter (ed.) *Arts Therapies and Clients with Eating Disorders: Fragile Board.* London: Jessica Kingsley Publishers.

Stige, Brynjulf (2003) *Elaborations Toward a Notion of Community Music Therapy*. Oslo, Norway: Unipub forlag.

Stige, Brynjulf (2002) *Culture-Centered Music Therapy*. Gilsum, NH: Barcelona Publishers.

Trondalen, Gro (2003) "Self-Listening" in music therapy with a young woman suffering from Anorexia Nervosa. *Nordic Journal of Music Therapy, 12*, 3–17.

Troppozada, Manal (1995) multicultural training for music therapists: An examination of current issues based on a national survey of professional music therapists. *Journal of Music Therapy, 32,* 65–90.

Ventre, Madelaine E. (1994) Healing the wounds of childhood abuse: A Guided Imagery and Music case study. *Music Therapy Perspectives, 12*, 98–103.

Wallace, Terra Eve (1995) *The use of music therapy with a domestic violence support group in a women's prison*. Unpublished Master's Thesis, Florida State University, Tallahassee.

Wärja, Margareta (1999) Music as mother: The mothering functions of music through expressive and receptive avenues. In Stephen K. Levine & Ellen G. Levine (eds.) *Foundations of Expressive Arts Therapy.* London: Jessica Kingsley Publishers.

Wendell, Susan (1996) *The Rejected Body: Feminist Philosophical Reflections on Disability*. New York: Routledge.

Whelehan, Imelda (1995) *Modern Feminist Thought: From the Second Wave to 'Post-Feminism'*. New York: New York University Press.

Whipple, Jennifer & Lindsey, Rebecca (1999) Music for the soul: A music therapy program for battered women. *Music Therapy Perspectives, 17,* 61–68.

Williams, Dar (1995) When I was a Boy. On *The Honesty Room* [CD] New York: Razor and Tie Music, L.P. & Burning Field Music.

Yancy, George & Hadley, Susan (2005) *Narrative Identities: Psychologists Engaged in Self-Construction*. London: Jessica Kingsley Publishers.

York, Elizabeth & Hearns, Maureen (2005, July 20) *A music therapy research protocol with women victims of intimate partner violence.* Presentation at the 11th World Congress of Music Therapy, Brisbane, Australia.

PART ONE

PART ONE

INTERLUDE I

The six chapters included in this section have sociological threads that tie them together. In the first chapter, Jennifer Adrienne traces her departure from the field of music therapy for what she describes as specifically feminist and sociological reasons. She applies ideas of sociologists and feminist sociologists to the field of music therapy and proposes four principles for a feminist music therapy. Envisioning a way of practicing music therapy which takes into account sociological and feminist values, she suggests looking to earth-based traditions. In these traditions, the life cycle of birth, death, and regeneration is celebrated; the divine feminine is still a part of the ceremonies or rituals; and, typically there are non-hierarchical forms of shared leadership.

In the second chapter, Lucy O'Grady and Katrina McFerran explore the potential of community music therapy, practiced within a feminist worldview, to free itself and its agents from the oppressive potential of therapy, society, and the self. They suggest that the value of a feminist community music therapy is that it works with people within the context of their *gendered* social, cultural, and political environments.

Coming from an indigenous tradition, in the third chapter Carolyn Kenny describes an ecological worldview that grows out of the spiritual belief that the Earth is our Mother and that we are in relation to all things. She shows that within this tradition, this ecological view informs all of our actions as ethical human beings. She states that women are viewed as special in indigenous societies because they are the same gender as the earth and because they are the guardians of the children. Carolyn Kenny brings a critique to feminist theories that are advanced by white women academics and especially to those who romanticize and commercialize Native beliefs and practices.

Like Carolyn Kenny, the feminist movement that was advanced by white women meant little to African-American Frances Goldberg. In the fourth chapter, Frances Goldberg discusses her approach to music psychotherapy from a feminist perspective and describes how the ancient Goddess tradition informs her work with women clients. Throughout the chapter, she weaves stories of her personal feminist and spiritual awakening. She illustrates how the archetype of the Great Goddess emerged in and drove the therapy process in BMGIM sessions with one of her clients.

In the fifth chapter, Seung-A Kim describes the centrality of Han (sorrow and anger that grows) in the lives of Korean women because of their oppressive life circumstances. She describes the circumstances of traditional Korean women, and provides a brief overview of the feminist movement and feminist therapy in Korea. Seung-A Kim also provides a brief overview of the role of music in healing and therapy in traditional Korean society, including shamanistic rituals and folk music of healing. This is followed by a brief history of music therapy in Korea. Finally, she explores the suitability of music as a form of expression in therapy for Korean women and suggests various music therapy methods that would work well for a Korean feminist music therapy.

Finally, in the sixth chapter, ChihChen Sophia Lee explores feminist music therapy in Taiwan. Like Seung-A Kim, ChihChen Lee provides a brief overview of the role of music in healing in Taiwan, distinguishing between the indigenous, Chinese, and western cultural traditions that make up Taiwanese culture as a whole. Again, shamanism and folk medicine are prominent in the traditional approaches. The role that women played in these rituals was central. ChihChen Lee also provides a brief history of the feminist movement in Taiwan and a brief overview of music therapy in Taiwan. To conclude, she explores what would be required for the formation of feminist music therapy in Taiwan.

Chapter One

A FEMINIST SOCIOLOGY OF PROFESSIONAL ISSUES IN MUSIC THERAPY

Jennifer K. Adrienne

I began this chapter with the question posed by Sue Hadley: Could I imagine a music therapy in which, as a feminist, as a sociologist, as a musician, and as a former music therapist, I could work and feel true to my sociologically minded ethics? Answering this question was personally as well as professionally and academically interesting and difficult. At the completion of the chapter, I had not worked in music therapy for five years. I had since begun a career as a sociologist, working primarily in domestic violence shelters and teaching. I consciously left the music therapy field for specifically feminist and sociological reasons. This article is undoubtedly guided by my ideals. I have worked in environments where feminist ideals were addressed in daily operations, so I believe this imagining is worth the effort.

The structure of this chapter is succinct. In the first section, I introduce and apply some ideas of founding sociologists as well as feminist sociologists to training and professional issues in music therapy. I include some reflections on my personal work experience as well. In the second section, I propose four principles for a feminist music therapy.

I. SOCIOLOGICAL FOUNDATIONS

Feminist sociologists, like feminists in most disciplines, have many diverse voices. Janet S. Chafetz (1988) defines four criteria for feminist sociological theory that are helpful in analyzing music therapy theory and practices. These are summarized by Sara Delamont as: "1) that gender is a central focus, 2) that gender is systematically related to social contradiction, inequalities and pressure points, 3) that the theory accepts that gender relations are mutable, have changed and will change, 4) that it can be used to challenge, counteract, or change a situation in which women are devalued or disadvantaged" (2003, p.18). These are underlying guidelines throughout this chapter.

I propose that a feminist music therapist must be competently trained in basic sociological theories as well as sociological theories of gender. The psychoanalytic and general counseling psychology orientation of music therapy, whether formally or inadvertently learned, is lacking in education about the political context in which clients are engaged. The field of sociology has contributed a breadth of research on the intersections of race, class and gender. A clinical perspective that is informed by the pervasiveness of these social structures would more justly serve clients.

Charles Horton Cooley theorized that we see ourselves as society reflected back to us—known as the "looking-glass self" (Cooley, 1964). Socialization research states that our personality is constructed and formed by our relationships, experiences, and social problems (Erikson, 1976; Shibutani, 1961). For this analysis, the question must be asked: what is the music therapy experience reflecting back to our clients about gender?

Clients are essentially in a social position in which they are perceived as having difficulty managing social forces, whether drug addiction, illness, or family issues. Music therapists' insight into these social forces shapes the course that these social forces take. Peter Berger and Thomas Luckmann (1966) assert that we are socially constructing our reality, communally. In other words, we are together—music therapists and clients—building our knowledge and our reality of the present and the future, through our daily interactions. We must understand the impact of our professional social position in this reality construction. We are socially constructing race, class, and gender together with our clients.

The artifacts of culture are the very items of evolving culture. In music therapy, the basic artifacts are the instruments, the printed music, the therapy room, the case notes. A sociological dramaturgical analysis (Goffman, 1959) would examine the music therapy session and institutional surroundings as if it were a drama. Who are the actors? Who plays the leading role? Who are the supporting actors? What are the costumes? What are the props? What is happening upstage . . . downstage . . . backstage? What is the script? What does all this communicate about the values and norms of the culture of music therapy or the culture of the particular institution? In the examination of daily life, we can observe how culture in constructed.

Music therapy is part of the evolution of cultural values, including gender norms and values. It is not an oasis from cultural construction. My feminist perspective asserts that we are accountable and responsible because of our social position. If we do not actively work toward systemic change, represented in our own interactions as well as in our institutional policies and procedures, clients will be offered a small helping of the human potential for change. If we keep in mind the concept of the looking-glass self, we note that inner cognitive and inner emotional adjustment to social forces would only help a client adapt to a difficult societal environment. This would alter the personality toward this end only, and ultimately.

Gender Research in Sociology

Female clients are raised in a cultural context in which domestic violence, rape, sexual abuse as children, and sexual harassment lead to cumulative experiences and consequences that create gendered differences (Kelly, 1999, p.121–125). Women restrict their movements and involvements in public life far more than men (Stanko, 1990). The prevalence of violence against women affects "personal safety, routine decision-making to long-term mental health problems" (Kelly, 1999, p.125). This prevalence makes it a "citizenship issue" (Kelly, 1999, p.125). In a feminist sociological perspective, the personal consequences of this violence are not individual therapeutic issues.

"That sexual violence is so pervasive supports the view that the locus of violence rests squarely in the middle of what our culture defines as 'normal' interaction between men and women" (Johnson, 1980, p.146). For women, the most significant predictor of psychiatric treatment, suicide attempts, criminal convictions and involvement in the sex industry is prior victimization (Kelly, 1999, p.132). As therapists, our manifest societal function is to help normalize clients to society to the best of their abilities. In essence, we are helping clients adjust to these realities, rather than demanding new realities. Music therapists work in institutions that sociologists refer to as "total institutions." The societal function of total institutions is to completely resocialize the personality, to reconstruct the intellect, the emotions, and behavior patterns to make one a successful social being in the present state of society. If "normal" is so violently gendered, feminist music therapists need to create a different role with different job responsibilities; otherwise we are participating in and approving of the current violent gender norms.

> As awareness of the extent of sexual violence has developed, so have professional responses to it. In many Western societies this response has become increasingly therapeutic and individualized, (Dobash & Dobash, 1992) displac-ing feminist frameworks, which stress collect-ive support and response through self-help groups and political activism. The last decade could be described as the "decade of disorders" . . . and personal healing has eclipsed the stress on social justice and collective action. (Kelly, 1999, p.138)

Unfortunately, from a feminist perspective, the profession of music therapy has followed this trend. However, the possibilities for a social justice, collective action music therapy still exists if we find and follow the examples of music that have historically accomplished such goals, rather than music which has supported social institutions that upheld unequal and violent race, class, and gender ideologies.

Liz Kelly states: "The barriers which are created for black and migrant women, disabled women, young and elderly women, women in the sex industry, and women with mental health problems must be explored and addressed at all levels" (Kelly, 1999, p.138). For our profession, we first must examine the position and the role in the social systems in which we work and ultimately, we must examine the layers of the music that we trustingly apply. These barriers are embedded in the music as well.

As well-trained music therapists, we continue our professional, ethical-as-trained role as part of the bureaucratic structure of our therapeutic institutions. We believe that if we are professionally ethical that gender oppression or any form of socially constructing gender is minimized. In contrast, feminist sociology illuminates systemic, institutional gender oppression.

Dorothy Smith (1987) is a feminist sociologist who defines her sociology as "explaining sociology to people," "sociology beginning in the actualities of people's lives and exploring the actual social relations and organizations in which they participate." For example, our social class shapes how we think, feel and behave, yet social class is rarely examined or challenged in the therapeutic environment. Social class influences, if not determines, where or if we work, what we wear to work, what schools we went to, how much school we finished and what careers we considered, how professionally or academically we are able to communicate, what cars we drive, whether or not we take the bus or subway, where we buy groceries, what food we eat, what religion we practice, how we raise children or who raises our children for us, what we think of people who have more or less wealth than ourselves, who we know and how we know them, our mannerisms, how we relate to authority, and how we arrange our living environment, to name a few examples. Our social class guides our gender construction, including our values, norms, and perceptions of events related to gender roles. In *Feminist Theory: From margin to center,* bell hooks (1984) describes the complex social realities of class and race applied to feminist issues such as the nature of work, childcare and the (false) idea of a common oppression among women.

Woman on the Edge of Time, by Marge Piercy, is a story defined by feminist ideologies, about a woman who is institutionalized and labeled insane, yet throughout the book she is sanely tuned into the future and alternative ways of life. Piercy explores equal and peaceful gender relations in her characters' lives. As I read this book, I began to imagine clients on the edge of bureaucratic time, with music therapy placating, soothing, and softening the edges of overmedication, ritualization, and institutional rules. Music therapy relaxes the urge to question diagnoses and other issues considered not relevant to the defined therapeutic goals. As feminist therapists, we ought to continue to ask who is doing the problem defining.

The formal systems for problem defining in therapeutic institutions for mental health—namely the DSM and related pharmaceutical companies—have remained unchallenged by the profession of music therapy, yet these systems structure the focus and direction of much of our work. Sociologists and anthropologists have compiled quite a bit of evidence about the relativity of the DSM. The social construction of mental illnesses as symptom-based disease entities is a new system of classifying behavior and human conditions tied to "specific social and historical circumstances and from the interests of particular groups that benefit from classifying psychological conditions as states of illness" (Horowitz, 2002, p.208). Third-party funding, the desire to acknowledge psychiatrists and social workers (and allied mental health workers) as legitimate medical professionals, and corporate pharmaceutical interests required a "rational, quantitative system of thought about mental disorders" (p.209). Many new jobs, professions, and medications have been created as a result.

This system provides health care professionals with a sense of objectivity, reason, and truth (music therapists often 'apply' music with this sense as well), yet close examination reveals categories with egregious logical flaws and a system of knowledge lacking research validity. This perspective of pathology has only been firmly in place since 1980, yet it is the standard. It is not seen as one possible view of human distress, but the truth of human dysfunction. More recently, the President's New Freedom Commission on Mental Health, begun in 2002, serves to benefit pharmaceutical companies and mental health professions far more than people with so-called mental illnesses. Allan Horowitz (2002) concludes that we ought to "consider when restoring normality is best accomplished by changing individuals and when it is best done by transforming social conditions" (p.229). Remember, of course, that violent gendered relations are considered normal, so we have one more layer to consider.

The DSM does indeed point to what we consider deviant in our particular society. But, the medicalization of deviance creates social problems including the individualization of social issues and the depoliticization of deviance (Conrad & Schneider, 1992). Within the ideals of corporate patriarchy, the female gender is a category defined as deviant. Diagnoses, psychiatrically, psychologically, and medically, explain more about our fears as a society than about the individuals themselves. Medical diagnoses often serve to silence explanations that point to social problems. Feminist music therapists cannot accept this.

One of the most striking examples I personally witnessed occurred throughout the time I managed programs in a domestic violence shelter. I was deeply saddened to see the quantity and types of psychotropic medications regularly prescribed to survivors of domestic violence. Accompanying the medications were the usual personal statements about their diagnoses, contributing to their disempowered self-concept. In medical environments in which these surviving women seek assistance, they are considered "needy," typically requiring a little more time in their appointments.

We must take this reality painstakingly further into the analysis of the music that we are using with clients. We need to facilitate an understanding of the sociology of music to our clients, at least the social relations and gendered organization of the music itself. If this task is not accessible or difficult to accomplish with clients, the gendering continues unexamined, particularly due to our status in the institutional hierarchy.

Are we using music to help people adapt, and make sense of how the world sees them, rather than "explaining society," specifically in terms of gender stratification and interrelated socioeconomic stratifications? As I will discuss further, music, unanalyzed for gender in form, is doing just that: reconfirming the position of the client in society, and perhaps resocializing her to be better at it.

In university, I was enrolled in a course in disability rights. Introducing myself on the first day, I proudly said I was studying music therapy and the professor responded, "Isn't that interesting, if I'm normal it's called listening to or engaging in music, if I'm defined by society as not normal, it's called music therapy." This began my search for an understanding of how helping professions, in their usual form, actually perpetuate social inequalities.

I believe our intentions as music therapists are hopeful and sincere, as I also believe music can help transcend and confront social problems. At the same time, I also believe that music can be an integral part of gendering, especially in the therapeutic relationship where the client has a label and thus a stigma. According to labeling theory, people become what we socially imagine them to become, particularly when one is labeled deviant (Becker, 1963) (see, for example, Herman, 1993). What do we imagine for our clients? What relationships, professions, skills, ambitions, loves, do we imagine are possible? A part of music therapy training is to learn to minimize the unequal power relationship of the therapeutic dyad, or to use the interpersonal dynamics of this to the client's advantage. Although this is a good start, this does not change the institutional hierarchy of power, also paralleled and experienced in the music. Thus, social construction of violent gendered relations persists.

Bureaucracy, feminism, and music therapy

We work in industrialized societies where bureaucracies are the ideal models of providing care. One characteristic of bureaucracy is specialization of professions (Blau & Meyer, 1987) for the purpose of rational institutional functioning. In my work as a music therapist, I was always struck by a sense of over-specialization. Specialization is prone to missing the big picture. Even if we have the big picture, within an institution it is theoretically not our position to think about this. In bureaucratic structures, we do not hold the authority to have legitimate knowledge of functioning beyond music.

Smith (previously mentioned) studies issues in the sociology of knowledge and the social construction of reality from a feminist perspective. Sociologists examining the construction of knowledge, such as Smith, are interested in how we arrive at knowledge socially. I suggest that therapy is a form of knowledge production, the production of knowledge about one's life. It is that particular therapist/client dyad, that particular music, that particular institution that produces a specific knowledge about oneself. A different institution, a different dyad, a different music thus equals different knowledge about oneself. Gender hierarchy and subsequent oppression are part of our health bureaucracy. Being an unaware part of the bureaucracy contributes to the construction in everyday life and activities of gender oppression. Gendering in music recreates gendering in the therapeutic experience.

Another characteristic of bureaucracy is the significant effort spent defining job descriptions (Blau & Meyer, 1987). The professionalization of music therapy may actually be part of the reason it cannot be feminist in model. Professionalization has included aligning ourselves to similar adjunct mental/ social health professions, as we create acceptance for our work. Our therapeutic processes, models, and daily activities closely resemble recreational therapy, art therapy, social work, counseling, etc. Is this really how music works when used as a part of healing?

The construction of assessments, goals, objectives, evaluations, clinical notes, and insurance diagnoses, are all how we socially create what is necessary in order to legitimate our profession and to legitimate the need for our job. Professionally, we must also construct the body of knowledge, including our journals and research venues, to legitimate the likelihood of pay. If we were just helping someone on our instinct, our intuition, our biased care, we would not be granted the authority within the bureaucratic hierarchy. So, there are experiences in music that we have cut out of sessions because what remains must be able to be written in case notes and thus remunerated. Our beloved music is being used to maintain client status.

Sociological thought and research (Marx, 1844, Simmel, 1902–1903, Weber, 1905) provides evidence that industrialization and globalization have brought about increases in alienation and weak social bonds. Under patriarchal systems, which are the only systems that currently exist, where power, prestige, and privilege are part of any social construction of reality, women as a gender category, and women/girls as mental health clients, are alienated to a greater degree from power, prestige, and privilege (Stefan, 1996, pp.195–218).

As we write our case notes and plans, we are part of the "practices of ruling" in our kind of society (Smith, 1990, p.24). We are "rewriting the other's world and imposing upon it a conceptual framework that extracts from it what fits with ours" (p.25). Smith is critiquing the sociology of knowledge and sociological inquiry. I find parallels relevant to our jobs as therapists.

> As professionals we know how to practice and preserve the rupture between the actual, local and historically situated experience of subjects and a systematically developed consciousness of society . . . . We must be competent performers of this severance. (Smith, p.52)

Smith examines the texts of the relations of ruling, such as the reports of ceremonies, task forces, and ad hoc committees. I find similarities to case notes, session plans, and reports for health insurance.

> The immediate and concrete features of experience become a resource for the expression of the conceptual version; the particularities fall away and only what can be grasped and interpreted, divested of its material basis remains. (Smith, 1990, p.52)

The presence and actualities of our clients' daily activities are subsumed into our professional schema of interpreting. Our theories produce knowledge for organizational relevance and purposes (p.145). "Setting up categories, development of methods, filling categories . . . these are integral to the organization of the state . . . and the relations of ruling" (p.144). Importantly, Smith finds that the results of this are damaging: detaching mood and feelings from "lived actualities disconnects them from possibilities of change, action and of power" (p.137).

Smith (1990), in distinguishing between feminist sociology of knowledge and traditional sociology of knowledge, believes that as women, we inquire into the particulars of knowledge, the social organization of knowledge. She offers an alternative: knowledge is not transcendent of local and particular worlds; instead, "knowledge can be investigated as the ongoing coordinated practice of actual people" (p.62).

Music has become a text in the "relations of ruling."

"Objectified forms of knowledge structure the relation between knower and known" (Smith, 1990, p.63). In our profession, an objectified form of knowledge, a text of ruling, is our music. The music and the production of knowledge about the music is a "virtual" reality. We are trained how to read our "texts," our music. We know our clients through a "textually" mediated reality. They become an "objectified form of knowledge constituent to the contemporary organization of ruling" (p.63).

Thus, music becomes a text of relations of ruling. The technical knowledge we have of the music is not accessible to the majority of clients. They are on the receiving end and we seek to understand them through the lens of music, as we know it. As music therapists, our knowledge of the client outside the "textual presence" is not relevant to our specific job in the institution. We apply our schema. Clients have some response—sometimes profound. Even if we claim that we don't interpret, we still must place our knowledge somewhere within the institutional structure above them. We begin to produce an account of their behavior from our viewpoint. Often, we don't offer assistance with a client's social situation, only with the emotions.

As we translate music therapy sessions to our colleagues or multi-disciplinary teams, our knowledge of the client becomes dislocated from the lived actuality with the music. The music experience has a situation-specific quality that is also dislocated from the situational specifics of a person's actual life. Yet, our music therapy assumption and ideology are that these are related.

Music has become a "bureaucratically controlled text" (Smith, 1990, p.65). Our professional procedures legislate a reality rather than discover one.

> The objectified forms, the rational procedures, the abstracted conceptual organization create an appearance of neutrality and impersonality that conceals class, gender, and racial subtexts. Institutionally differentiated spheres of bureaucratic, managerial, and professional control manage the local situations that people experience as a totality . . . the domestic situation of women is parceled out into issues of housing, mental illness, child neglect, poverty, welfare, and family violence. The actualities of class, gender, and race are dispersed over a range of sites within the institutions of ruling. (p.65)

II. PRINCIPLES FOR A FEMINIST MUSIC THERAPY

Drawing on the work of feminist musicologist Susan McClary, feminist sociologist Dorothy Smith, and feminist linguist, Genevieve Vaughn, I argue for these introductory principles:

1. A feminist music therapist is well trained in the social premises of music and challenges the social functions of music that unconsciously perpetuate gender oppression.
2. A feminist music therapist practices friendship in music.

3. A feminist music therapist understands that music out of a bonded community context is dissociative and disembodied.
4. A feminist music therapist works to make music free from the capitalist patriarchal paradigm of economic exchange.

Principle: Be well-trained in the social premises of music.

Conventional Wisdom by Susan McClary and *Music and Society* edited by Richard Leppert and Susan McClary are recommended reading for those interested in beginning to listen to music in a sociologically minded manner. McClary summarizes the focus of her own work as exploring "the social premises of music." As she demonstrates throughout her music analyses, "gender-related issues have intersected with music at different historical moments" (2000, p.1).

As a graduate student in music therapy, I surveyed all available recorded music by women composers in an attempt to find suitable pieces for Guided Imagery and Music programs. In the process, I was trying to discern what qualities make good music for GIM. Although there were hundreds of recordings by women from which to choose, the musical canon of GIM was following the musical canon of the performance world of Western "art" music. GIM was culturally wedded to the masterpieces, which historically were all by male composers. Some questions that I grappled with were: what did this mean for clients when the gender of all the music was male-composed? I knew from my classical music studies that gender relations for the specific historical period, as well as the gender construct of the individual composer, are indeed embedded in the form of the music, but how does this translate to the therapeutic experience and how do people begin to reinterpret their lives through this process?

Historically, women did not have the same access to compositional opportunities as men and the gendered social history of the classical music canon cannot be changed, so I did not have as much accomplished material to consider, although I made some recommendations. If therapy is resocializing a client to society, what was this unarguably gendered music resocializing her to? These are particularly important questions for GIM because the method lends itself to trusting in the music on the part of the therapist and the client. Trust the masterpieces.

This project led me into the sociology of music. McClary always does a brilliant job of arguing against the claim that there is anything "purely musical" about any piece of music. Traditionally trained music therapists, like our music performance colleagues, have been taught that the structure of music is just "forms, chords, and pitch-sets" (2000, p.2), not gender, not narratives, and not politics. Music therapists have extended the idea to imagine and perceive the possible psychotherapeutic connections to musical structures—without much solid research underpinning the nuanced ideas we have of particular pieces, or passages or even instruments—which calls upon the question, what is ethical in the professional "ruling-relations" (Smith, 1990) in which we work? Imagination, well-educated ideas, and intuition are all wonderful if we were helping a friend in an equally powerful situation. But, this is not the case. Music therapists work in hierarchical bureaucratic structures in which our interpretations become record, add evidence to diagnoses, to treatment plans, to medication prescriptions. Ultimately, we influence the life course of our clients and the social construction of their particular illness. We influence their path to wellness, which really goes against the motivation of bureaucratic institutions. We need *ongoing*, *chronic* illness in order to keep our institutions and our professions running.

Describing her standpoint, McClary writes, "I have found it impossible to accept any kind of bedrock certainty, anything natural or purely formal in the realm of human constructs" (2000, p.2). Music, gender, and therapy are the human constructs for our consideration. Since the nineteenth century, Western art music has striven to go beyond convention, toward the purely musical. My experience as a music therapy student, and thus part of my orientation to my practice, was that these purely musical moments were somehow related to the healing potential in music. In GIM training this applied very specifically to music that is believed to be non-representational. My perception was that we were to prepare sessions that could create maximum interface for clients with these moments in music. From my feminist orientation, I felt that I could not be certain that these definitely palpable moments of validation, insight, and intuition occurring in the relationship trio—client, therapist, music—were purely helpful. What if this experience was not really change for the better? Who was defining better? Even if a client is defining change as better—*what are we socialized to believe is better*? Of course, much of our socialized beliefs are for the betterment of human progress. However, looking at the socioeconomic status and quality of life indicators for women, our socialized beliefs about gender are not serving us well. Thus, gender analysis of music is required for feminist work in this field.

Within our clinical dialogue, some of us are able to be sensitive in our speech and are situationally open-minded, trying to avoid socializing our clients back into unhealthy gender norms. But, can we do that with the music that we choose, create, or listen to in therapy? Are necessary situational issues not changing because these moments in music are in effect recreating the bond to society with all of its gender hierarchies? Rather, therapeutic goals ought to analyze to what type of society we are re-bonding and how we are constructing everyday life. Having studied the prolific sociological data about the lives of women, I have come to the conclusion that reorganizing ourselves and clients back into these norms is actively anti-feminist.

Principle: Challenge the social functions of music that unconsciously perpetuate gender oppression.

A significant image was passed on to me in the course of my music therapy training: the belief that male therapists and female therapists are different in essentialist ways. I do see sociological evidence for some essential differences between the genders but the current understandings of the differences are the ones I disagree with. We construct reality in everyday interactions. We can change gendered realities in every interaction. The conventional differences are the oppressive forms. Based on an analogy of the male or female in sexual intercourse, homosexual or heterosexual, it was suggested that male therapists know how to help clients push through issues, to pierce through, penetrate, etc. and female therapists know how to surround, to hold, etc. It was also suggested that you could identify these properties in music—male or female qualities, mother or father qualities. It may be that gendered qualities describing these exist representationally in the music (McClary would probably support exactly that), but is this the engendering that we want to continue—has this helped us? Is this then the music that is healing? Using music that is unconsciously gendered in the same oppressive forms with which we have been gendered is powerfully (because we know the encompassing effect of music on the organism) *resocializing a person to the same thing all over again.* It is dissociative to think that music has separate qualities from those in society.

Having just birthed a baby one year prior to the completion of this chapter, I have birth analogies running parallel in my mind. This belief system I mentioned is also suggestive of the crisis related to our divorce from natural birth. If you know natural birth, you know that the power of women to birth the divine into physical form takes quite a bit more intensity, strength, focus, and love than the pacified, receptive, holding qualities we associate with the feminine. Not to mention that this original idea of women in sexual intercourse is a false understanding of the anatomy and physiology of female sexual experiences. I don't fault the person for passing on this analogy, but rather, I point to the sickened gendered state of humanity. This is just one example of how cultural practices, values, and beliefs intersect with therapy decisions and musical perceptions.

Music performs social functions. What are these functions? What dominant cultures are upheld? What dominant gender ideologies are upheld? If these questions are unexamined, music therapists can't deny our role in perpetuating these social functions.

I return to the problem of analyzing the social function of music for use by therapists. In the GIM canon example, it is easy to assume that Western "classical" music belies interpretation of cultural constructedness because of its supposed non-representational qualities. However, I quote McClary (2000) at length as she introduces her feminist musicology and highlights the functions we need to be interested in as well.

> I want to explore in music history the kinds of processes Raymond Williams calls "structures of feeling," Fredric Jameson the " political unconscious," Roland Barhes "mythologies," Thomas Kuhn "paradigms," Kaja Silverman "dominant functions," or Ross Chambers simply the "social contracts" that establish the conditions for the production and reception of artworks. Whatever we label these structures, they are intensely ideological formations: whether noticed or not, they are the assumptions that allow cultural activities to "make sense." *Indeed, they succeed best when least apparent, least deliberate, most automatic* [italics, mine]. Although musicologists and theorists often grant these kinds of formations the status of the "purely musical," I will treat them as conventions—albeit conventions that so permeate human transactions that we usually fail to notice their influence. And I want to examine the values they represent, the interests they reinforce, the activities they enable, the possibilities they exclude, and their histories within the contested field that music inevitably is. (p.4)

Conventions in music—the songs we take for granted, the phrases we assume to signify certain feelings, the rhythms we believe represent certain states of experience—McClary says are "nothing less than the premises of an age, the cultural arrangements that enable communication, co-existence and self-awareness" (2000, p.6). Masterfully describing the argument and complexities of form versus content in music analysis, she encourages us to move beyond just methods for skepticism and to "consider how music actually operates as a cultural practice" (2000, p.8).

She asks the questions I believe we need to ask about gender. "What social needs did musical conventions satisfy, what functions did they serve, what kinds of cultural work did they perform?" (2000, p.65). She goes on to discuss the convention of tonality, on which much of our work is based, as constructing the ideals of rationality, individualism, progress, and centered subjectivity. She argues that music is not just reflecting the times, but also that "these musical procedures participated actively in shaping habits of thought on which the modern era depended" (2000, p.65).

Our tonal and timbral system of music helped construct the values required to build an industrialized, corporate, patriarchal society. John Shepard concludes that the "vast majority of music consumed in the Western world is concerned with articulating, in a variety of different ways, male hegemonic processes" (1987, p.171). He documents how classical music through its "insistence on standardized purity . . . gives expression to the closed, finite and infinitely repeatable nature of capitalist social relations (p.161)," including our constructions of gender. Classical music is not neutral, safe, harmless, or innocent, but alienating to all but the bureaucratized norm. He examines the parameters of timbre, pitch, and rhythm in classical and popular music and finds male hegemonic processes dominating and recreating the traditional ideas of gender, despite the conventional associations. He claims that the "technical characteristics of music represent little more than sites over and through which power may be mediated textually" (p.172).

Principle: A feminist music therapist is to practice friendship in music.

I remember one client I was going to visit in the AIDS unit of a nursing home. I was properly trained and knew my professional role well; I was to walk in the room with my goals, objectives, and empathies squarely ready for the session. I walked in and found the client distressed that her long hair was severely matted, from roots to ends . . . her room and body neglected by family and staff. Was I to facilitate or support her in expressing her distress toward this situation—how might that be handled by staff and psychiatrists? To help her relax, be comforted? Would this physical neglect be continued then? What did I do? I gently combed her hair for an hour and chatted. This, I know, is not reimbursable music therapy.

I argue that we have taken a wrong turn in the professionalization of our field. Our human species has survived difficulties up to this point, through kinship relationships, friendship relationships, and shared community concern, not through time slots, goals and objectives, and specialized people for specialized purposes. Friendship in music is the only humane, musically moral option. We have taken preindustrial practices of music, that of music for community bonding and physical healing by a known community member, and tried to fit this into the systems of industrial/postindustrial "health" institutions. Therapeutic relationships, and the necessary codes of ethics, have been designed as just a blip in time, a substitute relationship, typical for industrialized societies that have lost community, generational, and familial roots and ties.

In the movement against domestic violence, the empowerment model of counseling is espoused. This model is a good place to start in finding a way to practice friendship within social service settings. A basic tenet of this model is that a counselor does not need a certification or professional license to help another woman find safety and make choices. In my experience, counselors adopted the following nuanced assumptions as part of this model:

1) The woman is the authority on her own life, not just ideologically, but as a matter of life and death. Only she knows what is and is not possible for her own individual situation of surviving violence. Following the advice of a "professional" can put a woman in danger because she does not follow her own instincts.
2) Advocates minimized their own personal details that might otherwise intimidate a woman or indicate to her that the advocate knows better. Generally, education and socioeconomic differences were deemphasized.
3) Advocates fought to maintain as much privacy for the woman as possible, from the state and from other helpful people. The details of conversations were not shared among staff, casually or formally, and the absolute minimum was recorded in a file.
4) The advocate clearly indicated the optional nature of the relationship. There were no requirements. In other words, the message was not: "we will give you shelter but you must meet with a counselor once a day. . . ."

To generalize these ideas to the practice of friendship, I suggest these qualities that are found in the literature on the sociology of friendship:

1) The relationship is personal in the sense that it is one individual to another individual. It is not the individual to the group (hospital, nursing home, school, etc.). Non-kin relationships form on a one-to-one basis not a one-to-group, or a one-to-place relationship. Often the client is asked to form a trusting relationship with the group of people providing care, and each individual that provides care represents the group. The therapist should not use the power of the group or institution as an assumed basis for a therapeutic relationship. How would you converse or interact with this woman if she was in your community of relationships?
2) The therapist should seek to protect the privacy of sessions as you would an important conversation with a friend. I always personally felt that I was betraying the confidence of a client when I wrote case notes and shared information with treatment

teams. Certainly there is a short-list of information that ought to be passed on; we can work toward that short list.

3) The relationship must be voluntary.
4) The relationship should be non-exploitive. The relationship should not serve any instrumental purpose for the therapist. (This is a whole article topic in itself.)
5) The relationship should be equal in status.
6) Recognize that in many cultures if you have truly helped her, in her eyes, you have surpassed friend status to one of kin. Honor this.
7) The relationship should have some reciprocity. As therapists we like to imagine that we don't seek to gain anything from a client, that the relationship cannot be mutual. But, bottom line, it is. It pays our salary; that is a reciprocal relationship. In a more subtle line, a woman will feel embarrassed for always being helped or receiving services without feeling that she can repay. For example, regarding the practice of not accepting gifts—although I certainly know the pitfalls—there needs to be some method that a client can feel that she is giving back. Otherwise, the "we can't accept gifts" serves to indicate to the woman that she is in the helped status and the therapist is in the helper, thus the status difference (Allan, 1979, pp.35–47).

Historically, feminism has sought to equalize power relations or radically shift institutional conventions. Unfortunately, the more the movement against domestic violence has become bureaucratized, the less this model has been accepted, and violence against women and their children is still raging in increasingly severe methods.

I worked in domestic violence shelters for years, and of course, we had ethical guidelines for behavior and wonderfully professional staff. However, our allegiance to our job, the administration, the funding streams in non-profit work, and our field undoubtedly resulted in times where we had to choose against the *truly* ethical (versus the professionally ethical—most of the time they are the same, but there is a distinction), in service of preserving our place in the professional hierarchy. As the course of professionalization goes, we have all mastered the ways of interpreting events and of explaining knowledge of an experience to rationalize why we could not follow a certain course of action over another. Again, in a feminist orientation, the humanely, truly ethical and the professionally ethical are not always the same. In a friendship model, the client supersedes the bureaucracy or the institution in importance.

I don't think combing this client's hair was the bureaucratically or professionally ethical decision—I don't properly recommend this to music therapy students. However, what does it say about the role of music in institutions? It is applied at ordained, efficient times. It is routinized, it is gendered. Statistically, we the female support staff serve to legitimate the authority of psychiatry. (Personally, I don't have experience in health institutions where psychiatry was not a key component of the team; so, extend my ideas only to this type). A staff member saw me doing this and the next time I came to visit this client her hair was shaven.

Principle: Music out of a bonded community context is dissociative and disembodied.

Experiences of dissociation and disembodiment are qualities of everyday life documented throughout the ethnographic record of patriarchal society. Music outside of a mutually bonded community is artificial. It is mechanized. Returning to the birth analogy, consider what we have done to birth in this culture . . . mechanized it, medicalized it, theorized it, diagnosed it, disintegrated the flow into sections, parts, different rooms, different locations, taken it out of the natural, lived setting, introduced different professionals for different purposes throughout the process, and made it "The Norm." We have done the same to music in institutions. I ask the feminist reader this: Is this the music that inspired you to become a therapist?! Entrenching ourselves in professionalizing and legitimizing our field is in my opinion not feminist and not the potential of musical intelligence for our species. It is trapping it. It only serves to maintain the status quo.

In my understanding, a feminist music therapy seeks to transform, relating at all levels of society. Music should be restored to its flow in natural time and in its natural communities. Music that socially acknowledges life passages, facilitates community bonding and personal wellness can only wield its power under these conditions. I ask myself, after examining gendered emotional barriers, if I were instinctively creating a social ritual using music to facilitate healing, would it really require, for example, ongoing, scheduled sessions of 50 minutes, with assessments, evaluations, goals and objectives, with a suggested length of 6 months or more? Sometimes one embodying experience is all that it takes to move on. However, this in not the basis for a job, and thus my point of caution. Be alert to how clients are becoming part of the construction of our job. However, we should be embracing the essential, authentic community-supported path toward the client's own true healing and confronting/changing systematic oppression.

If music could be researched and proven to help heal the neurological damage done to each individual in this culture of violence (beginning with our culture of violent birth and the template this creates for the rest of our lives, see, for example, the works of Joseph Chilton Pearce); if music could work toward a culture of connection and mutual bonds; if music could reverse the social damage from this past Century of Violence, and be done in a way in which the music relationship was not unequally powered through money, or status, or authority, or engendered to current gender relations; if music could strengthen common bonds between women and allies of women and decrease the alienation that is symptomatic of patriarchal institutions (the family, education, religion, politics), then we might have a feminist music therapy.

Principle: A feminist music therapist works to make music free from a capitalist patriarchal system of exchange.

Through the work of her foundation and her writing, linguist Genevieve Vaughn has identified and described two economies that operate in capitalist patriarchal economies. One is the known economy based on exchange and the other is the hidden economy based on gift-giving. In industrialized countries, the volunteer work, social bonding work, mothering, and household work of women is the hidden economy. In developing countries, the unpaid work of women supports the economies of industrialized countries. Feminist political scientists have analyzed the sacrifices made by women in this hidden economy (see, for example, the works of Maria Mies). Usually, this is presented as a problem to be corrected. Vaughn, however, theorizes that this may be one of the ways out of capitalist patriarchal systems and all of the accompanying violence and oppressions. She labels this model the "gift paradigm." "It is a way of constructing and interpreting reality that derives from the practice of mothering and is therefore woman-based (at least as long as women are the ones who are doing most of the mothering)" (1997, p.30). She starts from the premise of gift-giving in language, extending this to the values of mothering, making suggestions for a new, valued economy.

Vaughn demonstrates how the patriarchal exchange economy is a parasitic system. "Those above are nurtured by the free gifts of their 'hosts' below. Profit is a free gift given to the exchanger by the other participants in the market and those who nurture them. Scarcity is necessary for the functioning of the system of exchange and is not just an unfortunate result of human inadequacy and natural calamity" (1997, p.34). Similarly, therapists and policy makers have made sanity a scarcity (see Presidential Commission on Mental Health) in order to make a profit. I was recently in a conversation with a counselor in private practice and noted the language as she described the challenges of "growing her practice." Clients give therapists free gifts in the form of their difficulties, and therapists are nurtured; although in our exchange economy it looks as though the flow goes in the other direction.

The more we quantify, evaluate, and analyze music and musical responses by clients for institutional purposes, the more we participate in the exchange economy. A gift-paradigm of music would be need-based, and given without needing an equal return, or a "fair" exchange. Therapists' fair exchanges are our texts in the "relations of ruling" (Smith, 1990). As Vaughn eloquently explains, the exchange paradigm is really more about the gift-giver than about the one supposedly receiving the gift. In other words, we give only to get something back. In capitalist thinking, we are trying to find the parts of music, the phenomena of music that occur in relationships with clients that can be captured and replicated easily and cheaply for profit, if not for ourselves, for our institutions.

This does not rule out the possibility of work in music therapy. I believe it just requires that we offer a different paradigm for the functioning of music to the places in which we see a true, not just professional, need. In trying to imagine how this might exist in the world today, I envision a cross between the role of a hospital chaplain and the role of the facilitator in earth-based traditions. A chaplain role maintains flexibility in the timing of meetings, no-bureaucratic-strings-attached (ideally), and a voluntary nature of the relationship. The space of a chapel would be a better model for a music therapy room: honoring life passages, facilitating community bonds, and encouraging personal wellness as understood in a broader social context beyond the institution providing care. Earth-based traditions encompass indigenous traditions, pagan, goddess, and wicca spiritualities. The life cycle of birth, death, and regeneration is celebrated. The divine feminine is still a part of the ceremonies or rituals. Typically there are non-hierarchical forms of shared leadership. The interdependent nature of our existence is honored. These traditions are often community- and/or location-dependent, and not viewed as universal to all human beings. The traditions are flexible, creative, and dependent on the needs and desires of particular communities. Starhawk and Hilary Valentine (2000) provide a model for facilitating reclaiming rituals. In facilitating rituals, the psychological privacy of the participants is respected and protected, sharing one's process is optional but still deeply transforming. The facilitator is well trained in setting up the space and flow of the ritual, yet there is no observer status that will be documenting progress or level of connection to the event or material. Starhawk and Valentine do not separate the spiritual, or psychological from the political, and participants have power as a group.

In this type of role, music therapists could question the efficacy of insurance systems, the nature and hierarchy of treatment teams, and the standard concepts of mental health, with a focus on unhealthy gender norms. If the APA, as a group, can challenge and even politically encourage the legalizing of gay marriage, then music therapists and allied expressive art therapists can certainly challenge the hegemonic sterilization of creativity as it is expressed within health care institutions.

CONCLUSION

In conclusion, I hope this chapter encourages a sociologically-inspired interpretation of gender in the professional context of music therapy, and in the larger institutions in which we work. I hope the principles for a feminist music therapy are a strong enough foundation on which to begin building a new paradigm of music therapy. Thank you, Sue Hadley, and the reader, for offering me the opportunity to imagine this possibility.

REFERENCES

Allan, Graham A. (1979) *Sociology of Friendship and Kinship*. London: George Allen & Unwin, Ltd.

Becker, Howard S. (1963) *The Outsiders*. New York: Free Press.

Berger, Peter & Luckmann, Thomas (1966) *The Social Construction of Reality*. Garden City, NY: Doubleday.

Blau, Peter M. & Meyer, Marshall W. (1987) The concept of bureaucracy. In Richard T. Schaefer & Robert P. Lamm (eds.) *Introducing Sociology*. New York: McGraw-Hill.

Chafetz, Janet S. (1988) *Feminist Sociology: An Overview of Contemporary Theories*. Itasca, Illinois: Peacock.

Conrad, Peter & Schneider, Joseph W. (1992) *Deviance and Medicalization: From Badness to Sickness*. Philadelphia: Temple University Press.

Cooley, Charles Horton (1902) *Human Nature and the Social Order*. (1964 ed.) New York: Schocken Books.

Delamont, Sara (2003) *Feminist Sociology*. London: Sage Publications Ltd.

Dobash, Rebecca & Dobash, Russell (1992) *Women, Violence and Social Change*. London: Routledge.

Erikson, Kai T. (1976) *Everything in Its Path*. New York: Simon and Schuster.

Goffman, Erving (1959) *The Presentation of Self in Everyday Life*. Garden City, NY: Doubleday.

Herman, Nancy J. (1993) Return to sender: Reintegrative stigma-management strategies of ex-psychiatric patients. *Journal of Contemporary Ethnography*, *22*, 29–30.

hooks, bell (1984) *Feminist Theory: From Margin to Center*. Cambridge, MA: South End Press.

Horowitz, Allan V. (2002) *Creating Mental Illness*. Chicago and London: The University of Chicago Press.

Johnson, Allan Griswold (Autumn 1980) On the prevalence of rape in the United States. *Signs*, *6*, Women, Sex and Sexuality, Part 2, 136–146.

Kelly, Liz (1999) Violence against women. In Sylvia Walby (ed.) *New Agendas for Women*. New York: St. Martin's Press, Inc.

Leppert, Richard & McClary, Susan (eds.) (1987) *Music and Society: The Politics of Composition, Performance and Reception*. New York: Cambridge University Press.

Marx, Karl (1844) *Economic and Political Manuscripts of 1844*. (1964 ed.) New York: International Publishers.

McClary, Susan (2000) *Conventional Wisdom: the Content of Musical Form*. Berkeley and Los Angeles, California: University of California Press.

Newman, David M. (2004) *Sociology: Exploring the Architecture of Everyday Life*. London: Sage Publications, Inc.

Piercy, Marge (1976) *Woman on the Edge of Time*. New York: Ballantine Books.

Shepard, John (1987) Music and male hegemony. In Richard Leppert & Susan McClary (eds.) *Music and Society: The Politics of Composition, Performance and Reception*. New York: Cambridge University Press.

Shibutani, Tamotsu (1961) *Society and Personality: An Interactionist Approach to Social Psychology*. Englewood Cliffs, NJ: Prentice Hall.

Simmel, Georg (1902–1903) Metropolis and mental life. In Kurt H. Wolff (1950 ed. and trans.) *The Sociology of Georg Simmel*. New York: The Free Press.

Smith, Dorothy (1990) *The Conceptual Practices of Power: A Feminist Sociology of Knowledge*. Boston: Northeastern University Press.

Smith, Dorothy (1987) *The Everyday World as Problematic, A Feminist Sociology*. Boston: Northeastern University Press.

Stanko, Elizabeth (1990) *Everyday Violence: How Women and Men Experience Sexual and Physical Danger*. London: Pandora.

Starhawk & Valentine, Hilary (2000) *The Twelve Wild Swans: A Journey to the Realm of Magic, Healing and Action*. New York: Harper Collins.

Stefan, Susan (1996) Reforming the provision of mental health treatment. In Kary L. Moss (ed.). *Man-Made Medicine: Women's Health, Public Policy, and Reform*. Durham and London: Duke University Press.

Vaughn, Genevieve (1997) *For-Giving: A Feminist Criticism of Exchange*. Austin, TX: Plain View Press.

Walby, Sylvia (1999) *New Agendas for Women*. New York, NY: St. Martin's Press, Inc.

Weber, Max (1905) *The Protestant Ethic and the Spirit of Capitalism.* (1958 ed. Trans. Talcott Parsons.) New York: Scribner's.

Chapter Two

BIRTHING FEMINIST COMMUNITY MUSIC THERAPY: THE PROGENY OF COMMUNITY MUSIC THERAPY PRACTICE AND FEMINIST THERAPY THEORY

Lucy O'Grady and Katrina McFerran

Though still in its infancy, the burgeoning discourse concerning community music therapy already has many parallels with the basic tenets of feminist therapy theory. Both share an oppositional stance to many of the underlying principles of psychotherapy and medical models of therapy, principles that Gary Ansdell (2002) draws together and refers to as the "consensus model" of music therapy. Similarly, the culture-centered approach to community music therapy championed by Brynjulf Stige (2002) encourages our awareness of the influence of culture and context upon an individual, and thus aligns itself with ideas that women put forward as early as the first wave of feminism.

However, the union between community music therapy and feminist therapy theory would not be without its tensions. As will be detailed later in this chapter, the manifestations of such tensions spawned our current research into the relationship between community music therapy and community music practices. Through an examination of the relationship between music therapy, community music therapy, community music, and feminist therapy, we argue that feminist therapy theory has already infiltrated community music therapy discourse in many ways but can extend it much further. Most importantly, feminist therapy theory strives far more radically than current community music therapy discourse to free itself and its agents from the oppressive potential of therapy, society, and the self. If the voice of feminist therapy theory was heard more in community music therapy practice, we believe the union between the two would give birth to a beautiful, feminist model of community music therapy.

MATCH MADE IN HEAVEN? LINKING FEMINIST THERAPY THEORY WITH COMMUNITY MUSIC THERAPY.

The neglect of social and cultural dimensions in contemporary accounts of music therapy (Ansdell, 2004; Stige, 2004) may be implicated in its dismissal by a South African musicologist as nothing "other than some colonial import" (Pavlicevic, 2001). Lately, however, the influence of culture within therapeutic practice is beginning to be acknowledged more profoundly within music therapy discourse. Heralded as the fifth force in music therapy by Kenneth Bruscia (2002) as well as a metatheory for community music therapy by Gary Ansdell (2003), culture-centered music therapy goes beyond the assumption that culture is "a coat that we may take off" (Stige, 2002a, p.2) and involves an awareness of the impact of factors such as history, environment, race, language, beliefs, and values upon an individual (Bruscia, in Stige, 2002a). This closely aligns community music therapy with the feminist viewpoint that places individuals within the context of their *gendered* social, cultural, and political environments.

A feminist perspective is also implicated in the stance taken by community music therapy advocates who oppose the individualistic approaches inherent in the psychotherapeutic and medical models of therapy. Both Stige and Ansdell draw these approaches together to represent a "universally" accepted model of music therapy. Stige refers to this model as "conventional music therapy" (2002b) even though he acknowledges that music therapy is actually practiced and discussed in a variety of ways and therefore "conventional music therapy" may be more of an idea than a reality. Ansdell is less apologetic about the vague and problematic nature of such an idea, drawing on everyday examples of music therapists who question whether their broader practices could be classed as music therapy. He believes these examples support the existence of a "consensus model" of music therapy, one that has been arrived at by a sizeable international body of music therapists, and is typically individualistic in nature, insensitive to context, unnecessarily unequal between therapist and participant, and focused on illness rather than ability (2002). As we will now show in more detail, community music therapy and feminist therapy theory are, at first sight, very well matched in their stance on these issues.

Individualism vs. Culture-Centeredness

Feminist therapy theory criticizes the tendency of humanistic and psycho-analytic therapies to focus on the individual as separate from their history and culture, thereby assuming that an individual is entirely free and responsible for their own happiness (McLellan, 1995; Ballou, Matsumoto, & Wagner, 2002; Marecek & Kraetz, 1998). Israeli music therapist Dorit Amir (2004) attaches this concept of "individualism" to music psychotherapy, referring to it as "Individualized Music Therapy" (IMT). Although IMT can "help identify, understand and resolve intrapersonal and interpersonal conflicts, unresolved emotional issues and enhance personal growth" (p.250), the client is treated as an isolated being and consequently experiences a gap between their therapy experiences and their everyday life. In this context, Amir asserts, "there is no active connection between therapy and community" (pp.250–1). This is despite the fact that:

> . . . sometimes we work with clients whose problems may be deeply interwoven with the material and economic structure of society, or whose problems are shaped more by their own attitudes and reflections, as well as by the attitudes of others, rather than by their individual or objective biological constitution. (Stige, 2002b, p.19)

Sidney Bloch and Bruce Singh (2001) argue that cultural context plays a role in any illness regardless of its causes, thereby identifying a culture-centered perspective as relevant to any health problem. According to Lia Rejane Mendes Barcellos (2002), the acknowledgement of this by Brazilian music therapists has lead them to embrace their role in preparing choirs, festivals, workshops, bands and facilitating other forms of cultural expression, whereas they had previously questioned the therapeutic value of such activities. The therapeutic value of performance, in particular, has been given increasing consideration in music therapy discourse. This has required a reconsideration of essential elements of the consensus approach and an increasing emphasis on the importance of connection between therapy and everyday life (Turry, 2004; Maratos, 2004; Zharinova-Sanderson, 2004).

Systematic vs. Context-Dependent Processes

Feminist and community music therapy discourse has criticized the use of the expert-patient dichotomy within medical and psychotherapeutic models of therapy. This split emphasizes the need for professional "treatment" and tacitly implies that the therapist has a superior ability to diagnose the individual and devise a system of therapy that corresponds to this label (Proctor, 2002; McLellan, 1995). According to Mercedes Pavlicevic (2004), this systematic treatment typically involves:

- procedures of referral—by colleagues who know the client, or by the client themselves
- assessment—which involves a consideration of the client's diagnosis and the formulation of goals and objectives
- the intervention—which can be varied, and
- evaluation—which involves the therapist's reflections and interpretations of the client's response to the intervention.

Community music therapy, on the other hand, "is not characterized by a pre-defined set of procedures and techniques" in treatment (Stige, 2004, p.103). Instead, it follows where the client and the music lead (Pavlicevic & Ansdell, 2004).

Expert vs. Collaborator: Resetting the Power Differential

Proponents of community music therapy and feminist therapy theorists are also united in criticizing the expert-patient dichotomy within psychotherapy and medical models for attributing unnecessary power to the therapist. This power is maintained by the hierarchies inherent in the psychiatric and medical professions and is supported by an unequal exchange of personal information between therapist and client (Proctor, 2002; McLellan, 1995). The therapist has traditionally been required to maintain a "posture of distance" (Greenspan, 1983) and to set strict boundaries that involve conducting therapy within a set period of time and place in order to distinguish it from other types of social, personal, or professional encounters (Dileo, 2000). According to Simon Proctor (2002), the power differential that results from these boundaries is particularly unhelpful in mental health, since problems in this area are related to self-perception and experience of relationships with others.

It is important to be aware of the cultural implications of such boundaries. Pavlicevic describes how it would have been "culturally violating" (2004, p.41) to implement conventional therapeutic boundaries in her work with black African women, since sharing meals and moving fluidly between inside/outside spaces are natural and important aspects of their culture. In cultures where such boundaries are not so alien, it can be helpful to explicitly acknowledge the power differential that inevitably exists between the client and therapist. Irish music therapist David Stewart (2004) finds this in his community music therapy work within the homes of clients. Proctor (2004), in his English community mental health workplace, demonstrates how the power differential is reduced by minimal record-keeping, sharing meals between workers and service-users, involving the latter in overseeing committees and attributing little importance to diagnosis.

Diagnosis vs. Ability

Psychotherapeutic and medical models of therapy typically target an individual's diagnosis and symptomatology, thereby labeling the individual as "ill" and focusing on their disabilities (Proctor, 2002; Ballou, Matsumoto, & Wagner, 2002). This has caused problems for music therapists who prefer to work more holistically and focus on the "well" parts of their clients. For example, Oksana Zharinova-Sanderson's colleagues initially felt that her music therapy work with torture victims in Berlin missed the main issue of the work, being trauma itself. This, she felt, was due to music therapy's limited role in diagnosing and working directly with the symptoms of post-traumatic stress disorder (2004). Interestingly, it could be argued that Zharinova-Sanderson's work would be better understood by her colleagues if she didn't attach the word "therapy" to it. According to Stige, music therapists should only use the term "therapy" when they are dealing directly with the symptoms of disease and disorder:

> I consider it rather important that we go beyond "watering down" the notion of therapy in order to make it broad enough for inclusion of other health-related practices. When music therapists actually are working with treatment and cure of disease or disorder they will need a language enabling them to communicate that that is what they are doing. (p.200)

He develops this argument by suggesting that the health-promoting activities of the music therapy profession will belong in the future to several categories, with therapy—in the conventional, contemporary sense of the word—as only one of the possibilities.

SPARKS FLY: WHEN FEMINISM MEETS AUSTRALIAN MUSIC THERAPY

These issues are not only ideas; the tensions they create have manifested in the reality of our own personal and professional lives. The cultural context within which we practice is Australian music therapy, which tends to occur mostly in metropolitan centers, often in institutions, and is largely practiced by women. This acknowledgement is particularly important as Pavlicevic and Ansdell (2004) recognize that the very term "Community Music Therapy" can be considered a "Eurocentric and ill-informed" (p.18) re-naming of established international practices. Australian-born Jane Edwards (2002) has argued this point in a web-based discussion stating that, for her, music therapy had always been a socio-political work. In the same debate, Katrina McFerran-Skewes (2003) contends that Australians have been practicing "community" music therapy for years, but this work had not been revered in international theoretical discourse. Australian practitioners such as Catherine Threlfall, Dianne Allison and Anja Tait have been advocating community music therapy work for the past decade, emphasizing the importance of the wider community to our clients and the role of music in helping to reintegrate the disenfranchised. Many other clinicians have, without public comment, incorporated performances, choirs, and other non-traditional practices into their work in response to the needs identified within their institutions.

Working Within an Australian Feminist Organization—A Personal Experience

Somewhere within the local and varied contexts of Australian music therapy practice, situations exist where the tensions between feminist principles, therapy, community music, and community music therapy manifest. The following personal experience of Lucy O'Grady is an example of this:

> *For a year, I had been working as a community musician with a theatre company that devises plays with women in prison, having recently completed undergraduate studies in music therapy. During that year I had been constantly reflecting on my work with the women and had begun to feel that a more formal reflective practice, in the form of research, would help me to be better at my job. After discussing my intentions with one of the creative directors, I applied for a place in the master's research program at the National Music Therapy Research Unit, at the University of Melbourne. Upon acceptance, the director of the theatre company decided that she could not allow me to research the work through the music therapy department. Her reasoning, reflecting feminist principles, was that such research would entail the use of a therapeutic framework, a framework that was at odds with the theatre company's own creative approach. She explained that this approach was, amongst other things, an alternative to the oppressive nature of many models of therapy.*

This vignette describes a personal experience where music therapy was perceived as being anti-feminist. The director had made it very clear that the use of the word "therapy" was not acceptable in working with the women, and her response to the research proposal further clarified this position. The oppressive potential of therapy, referred to by the director in the vignette, has been called "psychopression" by Australian feminist theorist, Betty McLellan (1995). Drawing from many feminist critiques of therapy, McLellan notes the oppressive potential of humanist and psychoanalytic therapies in their encouragement of individuals "to look within themselves for the cause of their unhappiness and . . . to take full responsibility for their own pain and despair" (McLellan, 1995, p.45). Such an intrapsychic focus labels the individual as sick or responsible for their own problems, sees the autonomous individual as separate from history and culture, and assumes that free choice is possible (Marecek & Kravetz, 1998).

The oppressive potential of therapy is considered to be of particular concern when working with disempowered minority groups such as women in prison. As an example, Norwegian music therapist Ruud Nilsen notes that the female prisoners he works with object strongly to the use of the term "therapy" when it is used in a professional sense even though the women use it themselves in a vernacular manner (Stige, 2002). Trygve Aasgaard (2004) also notes that he presents music therapy as a project rather than a music therapy session because of the different associated meanings of therapy in a pediatric oncology ward (p.157). We, the authors, have often discussed this issue when working with groups of adolescents who may become defensive at the inherent suggestion that they need "help." The term can imply an unnecessarily skewed power differential that does not sit easily within a feminist perspective (McLellan, 1995; Ballou, Matsumoto, & Wagner, 2002; Brown, 1994; Marecek & Kravetz, 1998; Chrisler & Howard, 1992).

Is this Work Therapy?—A Professional Experience

Do feminist ideals and therapeutic principles constitute an unhappy marriage? If the oppressive shackles of the therapeutic framework are abandoned in favor of a creative approach, does it cease to be therapy? The tensions involved with such questions can be seen in the following narrative, which is a continuation of the experience previously outlined.

> *When I first accepted the position at the prison, I agreed that my work would not be music therapy—I would work as a community musician. While I understood the director's reasoning, my own approach to my work in the prison was informed by my training in music therapy, both in overt ways such as the improvisation and song-writing techniques I used, as well as more subtly in my attunement to group dynamics and ways of understanding and*

> *working with psychological issues. However, there were marked differences to my experiences as a music therapist in previous employment situations. My role and the associated expectations of my employers were different. The relationships I had with the women seemed to be based on artistic collaboration rather than the conventions of a therapeutic relationship. My aims and intentions were conceptualized with more focus on the end product, i.e., the play, and any therapeutic benefits seemed to occur as unplanned offshoots of this creative work.*
>
> *"What exactly am I doing when I'm in the prison?" I asked myself. "Why am I doing it?" Like a leopard who never changes her spots, I didn't feel that I had to change the ways I liked to work in order to accommodate my new job as a "community musician-NOT-music therapist," even though the external aspects of the job were different to those of music therapy. Had I ever really been a music therapist, or was I more of a community musician with music therapy training? Is there really a difference between musicians and music therapists working in the community? How would a music therapist, employed as such, work in the women's prison?*

These questions led Lucy O'Grady, supervised by Katrina McFerran, to research the relationship between community music and community music therapy. The international discourse on community music therapy also pays tribute to the need to understand ourselves in relation to community musicians. Englishwoman Harriet Powell (2004) considers her own work in both roles as having many overt parallels, "but how it happens is different" (p.181). Her decision to train as a music therapist was influenced by a desire to work in more long-term relationships and to use improvisation rather than preplanned performance. Ultimately, however, even these simple differences were not played out, and her music therapy approach incorporated both improvisation and performance. Prior to the discourse on community music therapy, many clinicians who worked in nontraditional ways questioned whether this would be classified as music therapy (Pavlicevic & Ansdell, 2004). When Lucy first approached the University of Melbourne to consider a research topic, she also hesitated to label her work as such, although she was clearly influenced by her therapeutic training. This kind of dilemma is familiar territory for feminist researchers, who often address tacit issues while raising uncomfortable and difficult questions (Olesen, 1994). With this in mind, feminism emerged as the most appropriate framework from which to conduct the investigation.

Experiences Lead to a Radical Response—The Generation of Theory

These personal and professional experiences led us to undertake research that examines the relationship between community musicians and community music therapists, from a feminist perspective, and within the context of Victoria, Australia. Currently underway, the qualitative research project involves the generation of data from in-depth, semi-structured interviews with community musicians and community music therapists. These interviews include discussions of each research participant's aims and intentions, their role, the role of music, their influences, the methods and techniques they use, the outcomes of the work, the nature of their relationships with participants, and their perceptions of the other field.

The data is being analyzed using techniques of grounded theory in order to identify a theoretical framework for Australian community music therapy practice. We have chosen to formulate our findings as theory, however we acknowledge that it is located in our own perspectives and those of our participant contributors. The decision not to utilize the thick descriptions typical of postmodern feminist research is significant. Although theories have historically been built by those "who believe that universal truths both exist and function in human nature" (Ballou, Matsumoto, & Wagner, 2002, p.118), our theory will be offered as an interpretation rather than absolute truth. We perceive this as a radical reaction to the postmodern tendency of presenting descriptions of multiple realities rather than drawing together their theoretical underpinnings. While such descriptions have great explanatory power, some feminists argue that their failure to make a stand on any issue limits their potential to bring about transformative change (Ballou, Matsumoto, & Wagner, 2002; McLellan, 1995).

In addition to emphasizing the importance of gender and subjectivity, the current research methodology also views bias and knowledge construction from a feminist perspective. Rather than denying the existence of the researcher's bias, which often occurs in quantitative research (Denzin & Lincoln, 1994), or attempting to set aside bias through the epoché in phenomenological research (Polkinghorne, 1989), the role of the feminist researcher in data analysis is to use her biases as a resource (Olesen, 1994). This is done by tracing and documenting the choices she made during data analysis, "so that other researchers and interested parties can see for themselves some of what has been lost and some of what has been gained" (Mauthner & Doucet, 1998, p.138).

COURTSHIP: DOES THE RELATIONSHIP BETWEEN COMMUNITY MUSIC THERAPY AND FEMINIST THERAPY THEORY WITHSTAND THE REALITY TEST?

Although we are still in the early stages of theory development, our research supports a tenuous relationship between principles of feminist therapy theory and community music therapy practice. It seems to be strongest when examining music therapists' non-adherence to the traditional therapeutic conventions previously discussed. For example, one music therapist working in community mental health describes steering away from any systematic approach to therapy.

> *I really think that [for] the work that you do . . . in the community, you can only devise what you're doing as you go along anyway because you can't decide what your aims and goals and outcomes are. You can only decide that or be conscious of them as they evolve . . . I really think that those things come out of the actual doing of it, not the planning of it.*

Some of the music therapists interviewed place little importance on knowledge of a person's diagnosis or history.

> *I haven't felt that I needed to know their diagnosis, or wanted to know their past history . . . I don't think it matters, really.*

and another says,

> *I knew that most of them had schizophrenia, but that wasn't really an important thing for me to know.*

Some music therapists try to redress unnecessary power imbalances between clients and themselves:

> *I would just rock up in, probably not a singlet [tanktop], but casual clothes. What I wore was quite important to me. I certainly wouldn't have worn something too dressed up because that puts me on a pedestal. So, I wore clothes similar to what they would wear.*

Interestingly, the stronger, more oppositional language used by many of the community musicians interviewed can be used to argue that the relationship between community music and feminist therapy theory is more pronounced. For example, a community musician states:

I don't want to have the medical model appropriate this in any way, shape or form. I want it to stay something ingenuous and kind of, I don't know, from . . . almost a childlike discovery direction . . . and the community element is really important to me, that it becomes something that we do, not that is done to us or for us, you know, and that we discover that really important human connection by doing it, not by being told that we should do it.

With similarly strong language, another community musician talks about how therapeutic intent can actually be an obstacle:

The mindset of "I'm helping this person" can sometimes be an impediment to the relationship. It's not equal. You know, "You're being acted upon, I'm the actor. I'm the therapist. You're the sick person. I'm the healthy one." That doesn't work for anyone, really.

Another musician, from a community theatre company that devises plays with young people who are no longer in the school system, describes this therapeutic intent as limiting.

I don't know if you saw the question and answer at the end of this morning's play where there was a question targeted at the kids by a woman who I in fact know happens to be a senior nurse and is deeply involved in working with disturbed adolescents. So she was using the language of therapy. I mean, she asked a very simple question which was "Do you kids feel that it is helping you in some way?" And there was stony silence. You'd think that'd be the easiest question for them to answer: "Oh yes, it's wonderful, we get so much out of it, rah, rah, rah." Now, maybe a few years ago some of those kids may have said that but they've matured so much that they realize that what we're doing is beyond that, see?

TRIAL SEPARATION: FEMINIST THERAPY THEORY AND COMMUNITY MUSIC THERAPY HAVE THEIR DIFFERENCES

While community music therapists who have participated in our research do share some underlying concerns about traditional therapeutic conventions, feminist therapy tends to be more radical in the alternatives it offers. Both community music therapists and feminist therapy theorists call for more egalitarian relationships between therapist and client, but feminist therapy seems to diverge from the community music therapy practice captured in the research by encouraging far more therapist disclosure in an effort to enhance reciprocity, thus strengthening and normalizing the relationship (Dileo, 2000). In contrast, the therapists interviewed as part of the research disclose far less than their clients, even though their boundaries are more relaxed than is typical. For example, one music therapist says:

> *It's not an area where I've set myself really strict boundaries. I haven't felt the need to do that, but then I don't disclose many aspects of my own life.*

Similarly, another music therapist says,

> *Because I work with people and their therapeutic issues and their inner landscape to such an intense degree, they don't know anything about me. They know I'm the music therapist and I do a little bit of therapist self-disclosure when the time is right, but nothing personal. So, I know so much about them and they know so little about me.*

Furthermore, feminist therapy diverges from the community music therapy practice captured in our research by not only actively trying to change the oppressive elements of society but also by working with an individual to change their responses to such oppression. This is often attempted by encouraging the individual to examine the influence of social roles and norms on their personal experience (Dileo, 2000). The only example of this contained in the research data is from a community musician who devises songs with young people who are outside the school system. This musician encourages participants to examine the socio-cultural elements that contribute to their alienation and channel these issues into the creation of their own songs so that they are able to be more objective about the social constructs that they find themselves in.

THE UNION: WHAT WOULD FEMINIST COMMUNITY MUSIC THERAPY LOOK LIKE?

In view of this, it is probably safe to argue that a "feminist" community music therapy does not yet exist. What follows is the creative vision of the authors as they contemplate the matrimony of these powerful individual forces—community music therapy and feminist therapy, from the data collected from Australian musicians and music therapists. The authors believe that, since the basic tenets of feminism have already been integrated into community music therapy theory, envisioning a model of community music therapy that is uniquely feminist now demands a more radical approach. The following suggestions therefore adopt an exclusive approach that focuses on the needs of women as they respond to dominant forces in patriarchal society. This is in spite of the fact that we fully support feminist therapist Laura Brown's acknowledge-ment that "issues of culture . . . cannot be of lesser importance in a feminist analysis than gender and . . . if our theories are to advance social change and undermine patriarchy we must include all categories in our analysis" (1994, p.70). Despite this, feminist therapy remains focused on the impact of gender stereotypes upon an individual (Chrisler & Howard, 1992) and we believe that, by relating this focus particularly to women in our vision of feminist community music therapy, we are creating a specific model of therapy that is easily distinguished from prevailing community music and music therapy practices while providing a much-needed service to those who choose to contribute to it.

Saying "No" to Referral Processes

Within a feminist approach to community music therapy it is not appropriate for individuals to be instructed to see another "specialist" who will help them. Participation is based on the interest of individuals and groups and begins with a process of information sharing between potential participants and their supporting agency. If there is interest in involvement, the individual is recommended, or assisted as appropriate, to make contact with the facilitators. No background information is sought from other professionals, as this is considered irrelevant to the needs of those involved. Nor does the facilitator seek these details from participants; rather it is left to be shared by those involved at a time of their choosing. As noted in the interviews collated, a diagnosis offers very little insight into a person and may even limit others' ability to see them for who they truly are.

Identifying Those who May Wish to Contribute

This model of music therapy does not sit easily within institutional settings. It is positioned within the community and is based on an established network with organizations concerned with the health of women. Information will be made available about musical participation through these organizations and specified groups will be considered as potential contributors, rather than as clients or people with needs. The link with women's health organizations may elicit contributions from women who have suffered abuse at the hands of individuals or society. These women may have resultant eating disorders, mental illness, or may continue to struggle in abusive relationships. They may have fled their own countries to escape atrocities or they may have fled their own families. These women may be of any age and their contributions will be a direct reflection of who they are and what they desire from society.

Being Involved in Multi-Leveled Relationships

A respect for the capacity of women to be involved in multi-leveled relationships will be engendered in the participatory musical process. The facilitators will be whole and authentic in their relationships with other women, drawing on their own life experiences as well as their understandings of how others have coped with their responses to oppression/abuse. Musical experiences will occur in various settings, both public and private, based on the needs and desires of the contributors. Because of this, it is possible that the contributors and facilitators may work in partnership to present musical material at public events and in these situations social interactions are likely to occur naturally. They will work together to agitate at local, state, and federal levels to change oppressive policies and in doing so will share their thoughts and feelings in responding to this process. This is considered both appropriate and necessary for addressing issues of relationship—both with society and individuals.

A Focus on Active Music Making

Receptive music therapy methods are likely to have reduced importance in a feminist community music therapy framework. Instead, active methods of participatory music making will be made accessible to contributors. The role of song in society has been powerful historically, both in reflecting the current state of society and provoking serious debate about suppressed issues. Song writing is likely to be popular within the work and is a modality that has powerful communicative intent with a wider audience that will be utilized to change current societal views. This strategy promotes an altered focus from internal responsibility to external forces. It supports participants to objectify the cause of their struggle and to decrease their sense of victimization in responding to it. Contributors may elect to reproduce songs written through performance or recorded mediums. These processes will be facilitated through the available networks of the music facilitator, which will then become networks that are available to the participants in future actions.

The Potential Outcomes

Changing the oppression of women in society is the focus of our vision of a feminist community music therapy. In addition, individual benefits are anticipated, with women developing a greater understanding of the role of society in contributing to their sense of victimization. The focus on the societal responsibility will be highlighted during sessions, with contributors being encouraged to debate and articulate their opinions on this topic. Participants will develop strategies to navigate societal expectations and beliefs without taking responsibility for its dysfunctional aspects. It is hoped that the musical creations of those involved will achieve small attitudinal changes in those who witness the work, and ultimately, contribute to changes in society.

Feminist Community Music Therapy: To Be or Not to Be?

As this chapter has hopefully demonstrated, the label "therapy" is extremely problematic when paired with feminist ideals, largely due to its inextricable and longstanding association with the patriarchal implications of psychotherapeutic and medical models of therapy. There are two ways to deal with this label when envisioning a feminist model of music therapy: 1) we can drop the label entirely and focus more on music-making (which is what some community musicians do) or 2) we can persevere with the label, despite its heavy baggage, in an effort to remain explicit about our intention to work specifically and directly with the health issues caused by patriarchal oppression. We choose the latter option for two reasons. First, we acknowledge that there are times when individuals need to work directly with the issues that are preventing them from maintaining full health. It is at these times where we believe the term "therapy" is likely to be understood and warranted by all contributors, including the therapist. Second, it is important that a feminist model of community music therapy is easily distinguished from community music practices for reasons of communication, outcomes, legal and ethical obligations, and funding. Attaching the label "therapy" to our feminist practices will enable us to be explicit about our intentions to alleviate health issues related to patriarchal oppression, and will therefore attract individuals who overtly seek this service as opposed to a community music experience where such outcomes are often perceived as unplanned offshoots of music making.

CONCLUSION

A feminist model of community music therapy that is specifically for women may remain a theoretical entity rather than a practical reality. In its struggle to free women from patriarchal oppression, feminist theory empathizes with and embraces the plights of all minority groups who suffer at the hands of the same dominant force. This natural affinity makes it difficult to exclude potential contributors on the basis that they are male. However, we maintain that it is important to consider, at least theoretically if not practically, the potential of music therapy for women. The theoretical position presented serves to underline the most significant feature of a feminist approach to community music therapy practice—the rejection of an unequal distribution of power. Whether this occurs through referral processes, diagnoses, or unequal levels of disclosure, feminism values women's abilities and scrutinizes patriarchal processes that serve to discredit and victimize them. Feminist community music therapy considers women as active beings who can respond to the patriarchal forces of society through creative expression. Music can serve as a force for change when directed by women who refuse to sit quietly on a couch and share their secret pain with a stranger who offers little in return. Feminist community music therapy can be a vehicle for the multitude of women's voices that still remain unheard.

REFERENCES

Aasgaard, Trygve. (2004) A pied piper among white coats and infusion pumps: Community music therapy in a paediatric hospital setting. In Mercedes Pavlicevic & Gary Ansdell (eds.), *Community Music Therapy.* London: Jessica Kingsley Publishers.

Ansdell, Gary (2002) *Do we puncture the balloon or let it fly? Some thoughts by Gary Ansdell on the reception of his article 'Community Music Therapy and the Winds of Change'.* www.voices.no/discussions/discm4_03.html

Ansdell, Gary (2003) *An Oslo community dinkum experience—Response to Katrina McFerran-Skewes: "A Brisbane community dinkum experience."* www.voices.no/discussions/discm25_04.html

Ansdell, Gary (2004) Rethinking music and community: Theoretical perspectives in support of community music therapy. In Mercedes Pavlicevic & Gary Ansdell (eds.), *Community Music Therapy.* London: Jessica Kingsley Publishers.

Amir, Dorit (2004) Community music therapy and the challenge of multi-culturalism. In Mercedes Pavlicevic & Gary Ansdell (eds.), *Community Music Therapy*. London: Jessica Kingsley Publishers.

Ballou, Mary B., Matsumoto, Atsushi, & Wagner, Michael. (2002) Toward a feminist ecological theory of human nature: Theory building in response to real-world dynamics. In Mary Ballou & Laura S. Brown (eds.), *Rethinking Mental Health and Disorder*. New York: The Guilford Press.

Barcellos, Lia Rejane Mendes (2002) Carnival and music therapy. *Voices: A World Forum for Music Therapy.* http://www.voices.no/columnist/colbarcellos071002.html

Bloch, Sidney & Singh, Bruce, S. (2001) *Foundations of Clinical Psychiatry* (2nd ed.). Melbourne: Melbourne University Press.

Brown, Laura S. (1994) *Subversive Dialogues: Theory in Feminist Therapy.* New York: BasicBooks.

Bruscia, Kenneth E. (2002) "Introduction" in Brynjulf Stige *Culture-Centred Music Therapy.* Gilsum, NH: Barcelona Publishers.

Chrisler, Joan C. & Howard, Doris (1992) *New Directions in Feminist Psychology.* New York: Springer Publishing Company.

Denzin, Norman K. & Lincoln, Yvonna S. (eds.). (1994) *Handbook of Qualitative Research.* California: Sage Publications Ltd.

Dileo, Cheryl (2000) *Ethical Thinking in Music Therapy.* Cherry Hill, NJ: Jeffrey Books.

Edwards, Jane (2002) Untitled. *Voices: A World Forum for Music Therapy.* http://www.voices.no

Greenspan, Miriam (1983) *A New Approach to Women and Therapy.* New York: McGraw-Hill.

McFerran-Skewes, Katrina (2003) Untitled. www.voices.no/discussions/discm25_03.html

McLellan, Betty (1995) *Beyond Psychoppression.* North Melbourne: Spinifex Press.

Marecek, Jeanne & Kravetz, Dianne (1998) Putting politics into practice: Feminist therapy as feminist praxis. *Women and Therapy, 21*, 17–36.

Maratos, Anna (2004) Whatever next? Community music therapy for the institution! In Mercedes Pavlicevic & Gary Ansdell (eds.), *Community Music Therapy*. London: Jessica Kingsley Publishers.

Mauthner, Natasha & Doucet, Andrea (1998) Reflections on a voice-centred relational method: Analysing maternal and domestic voices. In Jane Catherine Ribbens & Rosalind A. Edwards (eds.), *Feminist Dilemmas in Qualitative Research—Public Knowledge and Private Lives.* London: Sage Publications Ltd.

Olesen, Virgina L. (1994) Early millennial feminist qualitative research: Challenges and contours. In Norman K. Denzin & Yvonna S. Lincoln (eds.), *Handbook of Qualitative Research,* California: Sage Publications Ltd.

Pavlicevic, Mercedes (2001) Music therapy in South Africa. *Voices: A World Forum for Music Therapy.* http://www.voices.no

Pavlicevic, Mercedes (2004) Learning from *Thembalthu:* Towards responsive and responsible practice in community music therapy. In Mercedes Pavlicevic & Gary Ansdell (eds.), *Community Music Therapy.* London: Jessica Kingsley Publishers.

Pavlicevic, Mercedes, & Ansdell, Gary (2004) *Community Music Therapy.* London: Jessica Kingsley Publishers.

Polkinghorne, Donald (1989) Phenomenological research methods. In Ronald S. Valle & Steen Halling (eds.) *Existential-phenomenological perspectives in Psychology.* New York: Plenum Press.

Powell, Harriet (2004) A dream wedding: From community music to music therapy with a community. In Mercedes Pavlicevic & Gary Ansdell (eds.), *Community Music Therapy.* London: Jessica Kingsley Publishers.

Proctor, Simon (2002) Empowering and enabling—Music therapy in non-medical mental health provision. In Brynjulf Stige & Carolyn Kenny (eds.), *Contemporary Voices in Music Therapy.* Oslo, Norway: Unipub Forlag.

Stewart, David (2004) Narratives in a new key: Transformational contexts in music therapy. In Mercedes Pavlicevic & Gary Ansdell (eds.), *Community Music Therapy.* London: Jessica Kingsley Publishers.

Stige, Brynjulf (2002a) *Culture-Centered Music Therapy.* Gilsum, NH: Barcelona Publishers.

Stige, Brynjulf (2002b) The relentless roots of community music therapy. *Voices: A World Forum for Music Therapy.* http://www.voices.no

Stige, Brynjulf (2004) Community music therapy: Culture, care and welfare. In Mercedes Pavlicevic & Gary Ansdell (eds.), *Community Music Therapy.* London: Jessica Kingsley Publishers.

Turry, Alan (2005) Music psychotherapy and community music therapy: Questions and considerations. *Voices: A World Forum for Music Therapy.* http://www.voices.no/mainissues/mi40005000171.html

Zharinova-Sanderson, Oksana (2004) Promoting integration and socio-cultural change: Community music therapy with traumatised refugees in Berlin. In Mercedes Pavlicevic & Gary Ansdell (eds.), *Community Music Therapy.* London: Jessica Kingsley Publishers.

Chapter Three

THE EARTH IS OUR MOTHER: REFLECTIONS ON THE ECOLOGY OF MUSIC THERAPY FROM A NATIVE PERSPECTIVE

Carolyn Bereznak Kenny

My center does not come from my mind. It feels in me like a plot of warm, moist, well-tilled Earth with the sun shining hot on it.

—Georgia O'Keefe

We return thanks to our mother, the Earth, who sustains us.
We return thanks to the rivers and streams, who supply us with water.
We return thanks to all herbs, which furnish medicines for the cure of our diseases.
We return thanks to the corn, and to her sisters, the beans and squashes, which give us life.
We return thanks to the wind, which, moving the air has banished diseases.
We return thanks to the moon and stars, which have given to us their light when the sun was gone.
We return thanks to the sun, that he has looked upon the Earth with a beneficent eye.
Lastly, we return thanks to the Great Spirit, in whom is embodied all goodness, and who directs all things for the good of his children.

—Iroquois Prayer

Music therapy is not my only work. I continue my practice, but as an inter-disciplinary scholar, I am interested in many disciplines and fields. I only write and publish in two fields—Music Therapy and Indigenous Studies. Much of my work in Indigenous Studies is unknown to my colleagues in Music Therapy. One of my areas of expertise is gender-based analysis of policy for Native women, or as we say in Canadian Policy work, Aboriginal women. I have conducted research and written policy documents for the Status of Women Canada (Kenny, 2002a; Kenny, 2004).

The words of Native Elders and friends have always been and will always remain the primary influence for all of my work.

> When I listen to an Elder, I do not always understand what is said. Yet there is a presence that holds me in aesthetic arrest. I do not move. I attempt a deep listening. I sense qualities. I perceive the many lines on a face. I open my heart to voice, to tone. I watch arms move and laughter flash. I pay attention to regalia. When Elders depart, not only have I gained information on practical things, but I also feel rejuvenated by their qualities, the echo of their spirits. No one can steal this from me. And this sense does not diminish over time, nor is it altered by new ideas, new technology. It is a constant and persists. (Kenny, 1998, p.80)

Born in 1946, in the midst of one of the great waves of feminist discourse, I came of age reading books like Rachael Carson's *Silent Spring* (1962). When I developed as a scholar I became aware of certain essential readings like Carol Gilligan's *In a Different Voice* (1993), and Mary Field Belenky, Blythe Mcvicker Clinchy, Nancy Rule Goldberger, and Jill Mattuck Tarule's *Women's Ways of Knowing* (1986). Other texts like Susan Griffin's *Woman and Nature* (1978) and Charlotte Spretnak's *Dimensions of Spirituality* (1986) and *States of Grace* (1991) were important to me. These readings supported my struggles and helped to shape my identity in what my Native mother called "a man's world."

Yet, sitting in the presence of Native Elders and participating in ceremonies were even more significant because these were holistic influences that engaged my mind, but also my body, heart, and soul. Dancing at the Pow Wows reminded me that the Earth is indeed, our Mother. For Native peoples, there is an intimate relationship with all of the forces of the living world. There is an interdependence among these forces that sustains us. Our lexicons are elaborate when it comes to scholarship. But the elegance of the Native experience of music, dance, and other arts is so powerful, so direct, that this has been the single most important influence in my life, including my work in music therapy.

As one of the few women working in the area of theory in music therapy, I have become acutely aware of the different ways in which men and women describe their experiences. Let me offer a few examples.

My own theoretical framework, *the field of play*, is about safe space for human growth and development. This field is similar in character to the spaces I create for my children and grandchildren. In his classic treatment of modes of consciousness in Guided Imagery and Music (1995), Kenneth Bruscia brings up the gender issue. He contrasts the conceptual and theoretical ideas of female therapists with his own gender orientation as a male therapist asserting that a spatial orientation like *the field of play* that creates a contained space for nurturing might indicate a female orientation to theory in music therapy. He writes: "As a male therapist, the idea of creating a musical space and locating a field of play is quite different from moving my consciousness in and out of various experiential spaces—they both seem to come from different archetypal patterns of helping others" (p.195).

In a text titled "Death and Rebirth Experiences in Music and Music Therapy" (1995), Benedikte Scheiby describes herself as a midwife in the music therapy process. She offers a series of four graphics to illustrate her music therapy process with clients. The graphics are surrounded with staffs and notes in an oval. In the center of the ovals are fetuses in utero. The graphics are named sequentially as:

- Total Symbiosis in the Sound Field
- Heart Beats Faster in the Sound Field
- Fighting for Life in the Music
- Getting Born in the Sound

In my own session notes I write poems to help me process the music therapy work. Because the space is so subjective in my version of music therapy, I must go through the process of redefining myself through a separation between my patient and me. We have been through a very intimate space together—all the while coming and going, in terms of the depth of intimacy. In order to create clear boundaries after sessions, the artist in me turns to comment or interpret the experience. This, I would say, is a type of aesthetic distance. Often in these poems, I refer to myself and my music as a "wall of sound."

Example 1

The clock is ticking
Time goes by
Take the time to play
Find a place
Back
Go back
Hesitate
Measure each step
Find the time
To play
Now play

I will be the hard ice
Upon which you skate
I will be the wall of sound
Upon which you throw yourself
And wait
Breathe

Example 2

Come play with me
Hold my hand
Come walk with me
And we will go
Skipping into the Wood
Take a slow step here
And yes jump there
Over the damp rolling logs
Stumble lightly
Fly
Skip, laugh, scream, cry
I will be the wall of sound
Upon which you reach to tickle the wind
Chase a dream
Run and play
Chase me
I chase you
Hide behind a dark tree
For a time

Marginalities and Feminisms

Most Native women have an ambivalent relationship with feminist theories. The romanticizing and commercializing of Native beliefs and practices is apparent in the Women's movement. Of course, these abuses are prevalent in many sectors of society. White women's use of Native ritual structures has been a source of discomfort for Native peoples who are in a struggle to save their own languages and customs and who are reluctant to allow the marketplace to co-opt the very foundations of their cultures and societies.

The overall perception of Feminist theories is that they were invented by white women academics. Hence, many Native women intentionally distance themselves from Feminist ideas.

Grace Ouellette (2002) conducted a study of Canadian Aboriginal Women to learn something about their views on feminism. She titled her work *The Fourth World: An Indigenous Perspective on Feminism and Aboriginal Women's Activism* (2002). In this study, there was a range of responses to Feminist theories. But the majority of Native women distanced themselves in one way or another from the mainstream of feminism, choosing instead to create a parallel movement, an Aboriginal Women's Movement, in which they could create their own discourses about how to improve the lives of Aboriginal women.

In general, the Aboriginal women's movement is much broader in context than the Feminist Movement. It is not concerned solely with sexism and male dominance. And in the critique of society, colonization takes a much higher profile than the dominating practices of men, though colonization and domination by men are undeniably related. There may be a great diversity of worldviews and cultural practices among Indigenous peoples around the world. But all Indigenous peoples share the experience of colonization.

Maori scholar Linda Tuhiwai Smith has written a very successful book titled *Decolonizing Methodologies: Research and Indigenous Peoples* (1999). In this work she explains why "research" is a dirty word to many Aboriginal people. She favors qualitative methods, stories in particular, and documents how quantitative studies have only served to continue colonizing processes in Native communities. Because I work in the policy area with Aboriginal women, I have seen statistics and demographics used in unethical ways to shape policy and funding. Methods that reduce peoples' lives to algorhythmic formulas are obviously offensive to people who have experienced the taking away of their names, their stories, their languages, their religions, even their children. Not only must these stories be told, but they must form the foundation of all future work.

Another constant is the spiritual belief in the Earth as Mother. Ouellette (2002) writes:

> The most common theme and teaching is a respect for nature, which means that all things in nature are connected and dependent upon each other. Everything in the universe was put here for a reason by the Creator, and Mother Earth has to be taken care of to ensure the survival of future generations and the world. In the many conversations that I have had with Aboriginal women, this idea has often been referred to as "connectedness." Therefore, it is no surprise that Aboriginal women think in these terms about their relationships with men. Aboriginal women believe that they were put on Earth for a purpose, to give life, but they also believe that they cannot act alone. (p.86)

Native women who are academics often have a rather cynical attitude about the self-in-relation theory coming out of the feminist school of thought. White Feminist academics are perceived as claiming to have "invented" this idea, while it was an idea that has been at the heart of the Native worldview from the beginning. This might be one case in which the colonizers made a big mistake, ecologically speaking. In the Native world, there is no self, if not in relation. Whatever one does, one does on behalf of the others in the community. In healthy communities, there is a profound sense of morality in the principle of connectedness. And when this principle is allowed its full expression, it functions in a more comprehensive way than feminist theorists have ever imagined.

Kim Anderson, a Cree/Métis writer, educator, and leader in Aboriginal women's organizations in Canada, has written a wonderful book about the identities of Native women titled *A Recognition of Being: Reconstructing Native Womanhood* (2000). In this work, she states:

> Our relationship with creation involves connecting with all that exists around us: plants, animals, land, water, sun, moon and the sky world. Because the land is our Mother Earth, and the moon is our Grandmother, Native women have a special relationship with these parts of creation. To many Native women, reclaiming a relationship to land is as important as recreating Indigenous social and human relations, because the land is something through which we define ourselves, and it is essential in our creation. Aboriginal women do not see the land as a wild material resource that needs to be developed, possessed, or controlled; rather, the land is a relative with whom we have a special relationship. (p.180)

This interpretation of Aboriginal women's identity comes with a tremendous amount of responsibility. In my study for the Status of Women Canada, one of my participants quoted a very old Ojibway saying:

> *When the women heal, the family will heal. And when the family heals, the nations will heal.* –Margaret Lavalle

Furthermore, Ouellette (2002) writes:

> Motherhood is an important concept in Aboriginal thought and is inherent in the Circle of Life philosophy. It is the women's qualities that form the foundation of this belief. A woman gives and supports life through nurturing. She is important for the continuance of future generations. By the same token, Mother Earth is seen as a woman who gives and supports life to all people. Mother Earth is a nurturer, but she must also be nurtured in return to ensure future generations and survival. A woman's role as childbearer, nurturer and custodian is perceived as central to survival. (p.90)

Standards of Conduct

My Choctaw mother always used to say, "Let people do what they want and things will always go better." Yet this was a woman with a strong and solid morality. In most Indigenous cultures, women serve explicitly or implicitly as the moral guardians. Though they may not be visible in positions of leadership, they stand in a circle around the male leadership creating a strong accountability structure. Though Native societies are famous for being permissive when it comes to the raising of young children, there are rules, and these rules are taught, usually, by example. Moreover, there is certainly a code of conduct exemplified by healthy and strong Elders and leaders in each community. Some of the most basic rules are:

> *Know yourself*
> This is always the first rule. Permissive child-rearing practices are usually a way for children to find out who they are through their successes and through their mistakes. Opportunities always present themselves for you to find out about your "true nature." Every person is unique. The journey of a life is to discover who you are and to remember who you are.
>
> *Honor the gifts the Creator has bestowed upon you*
> It is always assumed that the first gift we acknowledge is Mother Earth. Then beyond knowing oneself in a general sense, in terms of our nature, we must recognize our individual talents and qualities and make an effort to develop those gifts to the best of our abilities for ourselves and the members of our communities.
>
> *Stay in balance*
> In the Native world, balance is an extremely important concept. Balance means that we give attention to our whole selves—body, mind, heart, and spirit. If we go too far in one direction or another, we can get into trouble. Staying in balance also means that we direct our sincere efforts to sustaining balance with all of the living forces of the world.
>
> *Show respect*
> Respect for Mother Earth and all living things on the Earth is the imperative. We give particular respect to Elders, too. And we try our best to give respect to all people. But most of all, respect yourself. If you decide that you can't respect someone, they can't hurt you.

> *Stand tall*
> Always be proud in a good way because you are a beautiful expression of the genius of the Creator. And you represent all of your ancestors and relatives. But don't puff yourself up and act with self-importance. Wait until you are chosen as a leader. Never waive your own flag. Your voice is only one voice. And all voices are equal.

These standards of conduct are examples of the teachings of the Elders. Rules like these have been passed down in a steady stream of succession for centuries. They have endured genocide, colonization, even internalized oppression. They are not as simple as they would appear to be. They are highly complex as moral imperatives. In Native communities, the women are the guardians of the morality of the people.

In my music therapy practice and my scholarly work, as in all areas of my life, I try my best to embody these standards.

The Ecological Nature of the Field of Play

In the text, *The Field of Play* (1989), I invite music therapists to imagine their patients and clients as bioregions. This is not a fanciful suggestion. Rather it is a suggestion rooted in the ethical imperatives expressed above. It is also in the spirit of the principles of the Deep Ecology movement (Drengson & Inour, 1995). This movement, initiated by Norwegian philosopher Arne Naess in 1973, and greatly influenced by Carson's *Silent Spring* as well as several ecofeminists, reflects feminist principles and also principles that form the foundation of the worldview of Native Peoples around the world. Deep Ecology is a commitment to being in the world in the best possible relationship with the Earth.

For me, the articulation of *the field of play* is a personal and professional imperative that was born out of a series of epiphanies[1] about the state of our

[1] In *The Power of Myth* (1988), Bill Moyers asks Joseph Campbell about James Joyce's definition of epiphanies. I completely agree with Campbell's description of epiphanies, inspired by James Joyce. He replies: "Joyce's formula for the aesthetic experience is that it does not move you to want to possess the object. A work of art that moves you to possess the object depicted, he calls pornography. Nor does the aesthetic experience move you to criticize and reject the object—such art he calls didactic, or social criticism in art. The aesthetic experience is a simple beholding of the object. Joyce says that you put a frame around it and see it first as one thing, and that, in seeing it as one thing, you then become aware of the relationship of part to part, each part to the whole, and the whole to each of its parts. This is the essential, aesthetic factor—rhythm, the harmonious rhythm of relationships. And when a fortunate rhythm has been struck by the artist, you experience a radiance. You are held in aesthetic arrest. That is the epiphany."

world and the state of our profession. It is difficult to identify a "first epiphany." The fact that these epiphanies have existed for the duration of my memory may indicate a phenomenological attitude[2] from the beginning of memory. However, I am able to identify many of these moments in time.

As a young child I came to know Nature as a safe refuge. In times of trouble and in times of joy, I was compelled to enter the forest to surround myself with the rich possibilities of mountain streams, bird songs, gentle breezes, rustling leaves, a myriad of colors and sounds. Natural places became resource pools of images that I carried around with me into the world. They were always available internally. The social world was an extension of these rich landscapes. And as I grew and changed, I came to understand that both the social and natural worlds could be turbulent and peaceful. My epiphany was that they were reflections of each other and always in relation.

I understood this relationship as one of Beauty. And at sixteen, this Beauty was transferred into my relationships with patients at Our Lady of Perpetual Help Cancer Home when I sat beside the beds of patients to sing songs. The epiphany here was that I recognized how beauty could be present, even in the face of tremendous suffering, and that the music could help us to recognize these possibilities.

The Navajo Blessing Way

With beauty before me, I walk
With beauty behind me, I walk
With beauty above me, I walk
With beauty below me, I walk
From the East beauty has been restored
From the South beauty has been restored
From the West beauty has been restored
From the North beauty has been restored
From the zenith in the sky beauty has been restored
From the nadir of the Earth beauty has been restored
From all around me beauty has been restored. (Kenny, 1989)

After practicing music therapy for seven years, once again, I found myself daily in the presence of death. I was working at the Danish Convalescent

[2] The "phenomenological attitude" is a formal term in phenomenology. It indicates a perceptive capability that is free from the mere appearance of things and favors the lived experience of perception. It is distinguished from "the natural attitude," which is more influenced by sensory data or the limitations of the physical world.

Hospital in Atascadero, California. There I met a young woman who was not an Elder. In fact, she was a young woman, aged 32, who had been in a seriously debilitating car accident. She was sent to our hospital because she did not respond to the standard rehabilitation treatments. For many weeks, we sat at the piano together. I improvised and she remained hunched over in her wheelchair. Then one day she reached up to the keyboard and began to play. After one year of working with Debbie intensively at the piano, and after she had started to speak again, another epiphany arrived. On this day, my hands could not write the standard medical terms in her chart because these words did not accurately describe my experience with her. This was the day when I realized that I would have to create a new language to describe my music therapy practice (Kenny, 1996).

A slow and steady disillusionment with the language of psychology, medicine, and in general, the clinical world, had been growing in me for many years. Not only had I studied psychology at the graduate level, but I had worked in psychiatric settings where I had opportunities to learn about the application of the concepts, theories, and general principles of psychology as a practitioner. At Riverview Hospital in New Orleans, I had worked in a milieu setting, supervised by several brilliant psychiatrists. At the University of British Columbia Health Sciences Centre, I had worked at a very innovative day treatment centre called The Dayhouse, in which we had weekly staff supervision meetings (Knobloch and Knobloch, 1979). Both of these settings were guided by psychoanalytic approaches to treatment. Eventually, I developed a healthy respect for psychological theories and other theories related to treatment and care, but I felt that they were limited in their scope. I began to consider them as interpretive art forms, each fascinating in their own way. They were expressions of worldviews. But none of them represented a more holistic and elaborate approach to care than any of the others. The epiphany arrived when I came to understand that all of these theories were based on an image of the person that was an "ideal type."[3] They were designed, not so much as emergent approaches, but as ways to control patients and clients to make them more acceptable to society and to live what society considered to be a better and healthier life.[4]

[3] An *ideal type* is an analytical construct that serves the investigator as a measuring rod to ascertain similarities as well as deviations in concrete cases. It provides the basic method for comparative study. "An ideal type is formed by the one-sided accentuation of one or more points of view and by the synthesis of a great many diffuse, discrete, more or less present and occasionally absent *concrete individual* phenomena, which are arranged according to those one-sidedly emphasized viewpoints into a unified *analytical* construct." (Max Weber, http://www2.pfeiffer.edu/~lridener/DSS/Weber/WEBERW3.HTML)

[4] Of course, I was confirmed in my skepticism about the grand narratives of personality theory and psychological treatment by popular spokesmen like Thomas Szaz and Ivan Illich, both of whom I had read and heard.

While working on my research for my Ph.D., I took a trip to England to observe Nordoff Robbins Music Therapy. I traveled around to many residential treatment facilities and met many music therapists. I also spent time at the Nordoff Robbins Music Therapy Centre in London, observing the work of Sybil Beresford-Pierce and Rachael Verny. While watching Rachael work with a young developmentally disabled boy, I began to see the music space that she created as a field of possibilities—an environment that was rich in sound. I observed the young child select various melodies, harmonies, and rhythms from this resource pool. Then I observed Rachael and the child creating music together.

During this period, I also participated in my own Guided Imagery and Music sessions with Helen Bonny, Sara Jane Stokes, Lisa Summer, and Fran Goldberg. Many epiphanies arrived in these sessions. But the theoretical notion of space was the outstanding feature of these sessions when I reflected on their many dimensions. Everything changed.

As a scholar/practitioner, many ideas emerged in these years that contributed to *the field of play*. After deciding that music therapy was an interdisciplinary field, I had read the current literature in many fields related to our work. As a doctoral student, I had accumulated 250 pages for my dissertation literature review. Another epiphany arrived while I was in the desert working on my dissertation. I realized that it was time for music therapy to stand on its own two feet, in relation to other fields, by building its own concepts and principles from within its own discipline. I burned my literature review in a ceremony in the desert, keeping only a few fragments of theory from our field. My primary source was the work of Bill Sears. [5]

While studying in the desert, reading the works of Maurice Merleau-Ponty and also studying the New Physics, I realized that the best way for theorists to serve humanity and the future was to design theories around concepts of space and time. And this was easy for me to imagine at this stage of my work and my studies because I had already come to know about safe space. My earlier metaphor for the best conditions for growth and change, and one which continued to embrace me, was Nature.

In 1995, while teaching students at Sandane University in Norway, my colleague Brynjulf Stige asked me, while we were hiking near the largest glacier in Europe, to define what I meant by "Nature." The question was an epiphany and still has not been adequately answered. However, it was partially answered

[5] "Sears describes three classifications that underlie the processes of music therapy: '1) experience within structure; 2) experience in self-organization; 3) experience in relating to others.' On the theoretical level, Sears provides an environmental approach—one which offers fields, conditions, relationships and self-organization. Explicit within his three classifications are self-organization and relationships (relating). Implicit are fields and conditions." (Kenny, 1989, p.27–8)

when I realized that my concept of Nature was deeply rooted in my feeling as a Native person, and as a woman. The senses are much more essential than we usually imagine. They are part of who we are as Earth.

Another epiphany arrived when I recently came to understand the history of Western Civilization as one of control over Nature and over people. Though there are many fine examples of cooperation and consensus, if you take a course in the history of Western Civilization, you study war. We need theories that are non-hierarchical. We need theories that are about mutuality and respect.

Women Must Wait

Where is the man who in the middle of the water goes while I meanwhile am crying into the long Winter nights with screams which barely cut through times in space where shifts of Earth surprise babes in the night and innocence of all souls?

Is there the sound of blood on some distant fields of sand where gods are more human than we dare to imagine on desert nights?

I wait
And shake
In long nights of grieving women who scream and thrash at old stories we thought would never return from ancient wounds of Earth our ground of being we thought long would be healed now.

Who are these men, my son?
In your voice I hear the call of the old drum that no longer need be played for killing things.

Go away you into the hills now from the sound of blood spilling in spaces where we could embrace and eat Earth.

I am woman who wants to melt away these killing metals though it be in ancient screams and hot tears in caves where bewildered spirits crouch in fear of what man has made upon us the Earth.
It is the longest night beyond the Winter Solstice Feast beyond some babe who spoke of love and died beyond the Full Moon when mothers wait for signs of life from distant lands where young men do some useless old piece of hopefully soon to be forgotten thing called war.

Your eyes reach out for my anger at this
You are not afraid.
Can you say the names of all of those who have died?

My scream is reaching out into the night for existence in time itself and after the first rain a dewdrop comforts me and dolphins swimming in waters by my tent on that first day of some new hope for peace to the sound of tears of mothers of sons.

Take me to salt and sea and the dissolution of old ways, of killing things.

Where is the man who waits for peace on sandy shores of quiet places and lights on my fear in a boat where fog and mist cover the edges of harsh words and the letting go of old ways? (Kenny, *Voices, 2002b*)

These are a few of the spontaneous epiphanies that have helped to inform my work. They are emergent ideas that continue to grow. I have often said that theories are defense mechanisms for the therapist.[6] And I need my theory, just like everyone else. My theory places my feet on the ground, literally. I am part of a constantly evolving and changing interrelated and interconnected ecological zone. My client and I constitute a small part of that zone when we meet. But we are also an essential part of it. Every human encounter is a part of it.

Though my work with clients can be interpreted in many ways, and it is certainly complex, it is also simple. It is an ecology that encourages my clients to survive and thrive, based on the conditions in the space. These conditions can be imagined like a field of daisies, or any bioregion. [7]

My epiphanies have been triggered both by my direct experience and scholarly readings. But I find that often, scholarly ideas relate only to each other, not to people, and certainly not to the Earth. In fact, there is a prejudice about relating to the Earth. Relating to the Earth is somehow considered to be primitive at worst and idealistic at best. However, if we don't we are truly lost.

I started out my theoretical work long before *the field of play*. In a graduate class in Cultural Anthropology, I wrote a paper titled "The Death/Rebirth Myth as the Healing Agent in Music." This paper later formed the foundation of my Master's thesis. The basic premise of the paper was that the ecological processes

[6] This comment, in an article titled "The Dilemma of Uniqueness: An Essay on Qualities and Consciousness" in the *Nordic Journal of Music Therapy*, was greatly criticized. But we must remember the positive aspects of defense mechanisms.
[7] This is the central metaphor in the theory of the Field of Play and in my understanding of an ecological model of Music Therapy (Kenny, 1989).

of constant death and rebirth in Nature were integral to our experiences in life and in music therapy.[8]

I am the tree
And in this moment of being tree
I experience both the endless struggle and profound beauty of life in the same breath.
We are engaged in a quest for survival and balance.
I hear the music of our dance even through the silence of dark hours.
Soon the leaves on my brother will turn
And leave . . . to replenish the Earth again.
I too change
I sometimes die and am reborn,
As long as we share connecting patterns we are One.
Not I, nor He . . . but whole and sweet life. (Kenny, 1982)

CONCLUSION

When Native people say that the Earth is our Mother, it is true. A deep traditional ecological worldview springs from this spiritual belief. It is one that informs all of our actions as ethical human beings. And it is one that women must relate to as a constant.

Women have a special place in healthy traditional societies because they are the same gender as the Earth and because they are the intimate guardians of children, who are, in most Native societies, the center of the culture.

In 1969, I started my career using music in a special education setting. Then in 1970 I asked Walker Stogan, a Musqueum Elder, if he thought I should take my training as a music therapist. On this day, we had just completed our work in the Longhouse on the Musqueum Reserve in Vancouver, British Columbia (Kenny, 1982). I had been playing music with the Musqueum children in a project called The Children's Spontaneous Music Workshops. Walker took a long draw on his cigarette and looked toward the River. He didn't speak for what seemed like a long while. Then he said: "For you, it makes sense." That same year, I began my music therapy education under Charles Braswell at Loyola University in New Orleans.

[8] In *The Mythic Artery* (1982) I emphasize the sensory aspects of the music therapy experience in the elements of the music. These sensory elements are our direct relation to the physical world, and therefore to the Earth.

The worldview that I have brought into my music therapy practice has worked very well for me. I feel that I have honored the moral imperative of my Elders and ancestors. I can walk tall in my own communities. My Haida mother, who adopted me several years after my birth mother died, gave me the name Nang Jaada Sa-ẽts, meaning "Haida woman with a mind of the highest esteem."

My theoretical work in music therapy must stand tall in front of the standards that I have learned from my Native mother and from all of the Native Elders, particularly the women, who have taught me. The Earth is my Mother. And I am in relation to all things.

REFERENCES

Anderson, Kim (2000) *A Recognition of Being: Reconstructing Native Womanhood.* Toronto, Ontario: Sumach Press.

Belenky, Mary, Field, Blythe, Mcvicker Clinchy, Nancy, Rule Goldberger, Jill, & Mattuck, Tarule (1986) *Women's Ways of Knowing: The Development of Self, Voice, and Mind.* New York: Basic Books.

Bruscia, Kenneth (1995) Modes of consciousness in Guided Imagery and Music (GIM): A therapist's experience of the guiding process. In Carolyn B. Kenny (ed.) *Listening, Playing, Creating: Essays on the Power of Sound.* Albany, NY: State University of New York Press.

Carson, Rachel (1962) *Silent Spring.* New York: Houghton Mifflin Publishing.

Drengson, Alan & Inour, Yuichi (1995) *The Deep Ecology Movement: An Introductory Anthology.* Berkeley, CA: North Atlantic Books.

Gilligan, Carol (1993) *In a Different Voice: Psychological Theory and Women's Development.* Cambridge, Mass: Harvard University Press.

Griffin, Susan (1978) *Woman and Nature: The Roaring Inside Her.* San Francisco: Sierra Club Books.

Kenny, Carolyn (2005) When the women heal: A gender-based analysis of the research principles of ownership, control, access, and possession (OCAP). Vancouver, British Columbia: Aboriginal Women's Health and Healing Research Paper (in review).

Kenny, Carolyn (2002a) *North American Indian, Métis, and Inuit Women Speak About Culture, Education, and Work.* Ottawa: Status of Women Canada. http://www.swc-cfc.gc.ca/pubs/pubspr/0662318978/index_e.html

Kenny, Carolyn (2002b) Women music wait. *Voices: A World Forum for Music Therapy.* http://www.voices.no/mainissues/Voices2(3)editorial.html

Kenny, Carolyn (2004) *A holistic approach for Aboriginal Policy Research.* Ottawa: Status of Women Canada. http://www.swc-cfc.gc.ca/pubs/pubspr/0662379594/index_e.html

Kenny, Carolyn (2000) The sense of art: A First Nations perspective. *Canadian Journal of Native Education, 22*, 77–85.

Kenny, Carolyn (1996a) The dilemma of uniqueness: An essay on consciousness and qualities. *Nordic Journal of Music Therapy, 5*, 87–96.

Kenny, Carolyn (1996b) The story of the field of play. In Mechtild Langenberg, Kenneth Aigen, Jörg Frommer (eds.) *Qualitative Music Therapy Research: Beginning Dialogues.* Gilsum, NH: Barcelona Press.

Kenny, Carolyn (1989) *The Field of Play: A Guide for the Theory and Practice of Music Therapy.* Atascadero, CA: Ridgeview Publishing Company.

Kenny, Carolyn (1982) *The Mythic Artery: The Magic of Music Therapy.* Atascadero, CA: Ridgeview Publishing Company.

Knobloch, Ferdinand & Jirina Knobloch (1979) *Integrated Psychotherapy.* London and New York: Jason Aronson.

Ouellette, Grace J.M.W. (2002) The Fourth World: An indigenous perspective on feminism and aboriginal women's activism. Halifax, NS: Fernwood Publishing.

Scheiby, Benedikte (1995) Death and rebirth experiences in music and music therapy. In Carolyn B. Kenny (ed.) *Listening, Playing, Creating: Essays on the Power of Sound.* Albany, NY: State University of New York Press.

Smith, Linda Tuhiwai (1999) *Decolonizing Methodologies: Research and Indigenous Peoples.* London and New York: Zed Books Ltd.

Spretnak, Charlene (1986) *The Spiritual Dimension of Green Politics*. Santa Fe: Bear and Co.

Spretnak, Charlene (1991) *States of Grace: The Recovery of Meaning in the Postmodern Age.* San Francisco: Harper/Collins Publishers.

Chapter Four

DESCENT TO THE GODDESS: A SPIRITUAL AND PSYCHOLOGICAL JOURNEY TO THE FEMININE

Frances Smith Goldberg

Lady of blazing dominion
Clad in dread
Riding on fire-red power

Inanna
Holding a pure lance
Terror folds in her robes
Flood-storm-hurricane adorned
She bolts out in battle
Plants a standing shield on the ground

Great Lady Inanna
battle planner
foe smasher

Praise to Her
My lady
Godly child nursed in heaven
Inanna
Godly maiden ripened on earth
YOU ARRIVE
Your spread-out arms
Wide as the Sun King

When you wear fearsome dread in heaven
Crystal brilliance on earth

When you unfold from the mountains
Your woven net of blue lapis cord

when you bathe in clear mountains
you, mountain born in a crystal-pure place
when you wear
the robes
of the old, old gods

when you slice heads
like a scythe cuts wheat swaths

then the black-headed praise you with song
the Sumerians sing in one voice
everyone sings sweetly a joy song

Queen of battle
The Moon God's oldest Child
Maiden Inanna
I worship you
Here is my song.

This poem
spoken for the sacred Woman
is exalted
praise the mountain destroyer
praise Her who received the unchanging powers
praise my Lady wrapped in beauty
PRAISE BE TO INANNA

Excerpted verses from three poems by Enheduanna, translated by Betty De Shong Meador, 2000.

The Goddess, Inanna, along with other ancient Goddesses, has burst into the consciousness of modern women and men in recent years through dreams and images, paintings and poetry. In this chapter, I address this awakening of the Goddess through stories—stories of Goddesses, stories of women who lived millennia ago, my stories, and one of my client's. I discuss my particular approach to music psychotherapy from a feminist perspective, how the Goddess informs my work with women clients, and what She offers music therapy. Interwoven throughout are stories of my personal feminist and spiritual awakening.

For many thousands of years, a woman, a Goddess, was the main deity worshipped by humans. Our history of worshipping a male, a god, as the main deity is relatively quite short (Woodman & Dickson, 1996; Meador, 2000). This shift in the gender of deities has had a profound impact on women. Women have been made subservient to men, to the extent that they have been considered the property of men. Although in current Western society we are no longer considered the property of men, we are still carrying chains in the form of low self-esteem and lack of confidence in our abilities, and this often leads to difficulties in relationships and depression. My personal response to this has culminated in my paying attention to those issues when they surface in psychotherapy with women, which have their roots in this patriarchal cultural heritage. In this small way, I am just one of millions of women throughout the world who are working to redefine themselves and their cultures to foster and support women's full creative potential.

Personal Context

Like many African American women, probably most, the feminist movement of the 1960s and 1970s meant little to me. The civil rights movement of the sixties had much more personal meaning for me. I was a young mother with a fulfilling career as a music therapist. After all, I thought, as a third generation college graduate and the granddaughter of a college president, my family abounded in women with professional identities. These were not the suburban self-medicating women whose ambition in the world was stymied by being relegated to the home with only children and other depressed, home-bound women to talk to. Neither was I. I did not join a consciousness-raising group; these were the province of middle-class white women. However, in the early seventies, a white friend, wanting to be part of the women's movement, asked me to share a subscription to "New Woman" magazine. She was worried that her husband would disapprove if the magazine came to her house, so I agreed. I had no such worries that my husband would disapprove. And in that way I was exposed to the feminist voices of the 1970s as they were expressed on the pages of "New Woman." Though I was interested, those voices still were far away from me.

The overriding experience in society for me was that as an African American. In her book *Ain't I a Woman, Black Women and Feminism* (1981), bell hooks comments on the massive silence among Black women at the beginning of the women's movement. She states, "We clung to the hope that liberation from racial oppression would be all that was necessary for us to be free" (p.1). And indeed that was my view at the time. hooks, however, reminds us that Black women in the 19th century were conscious of the need for liberation from sexism as well as racism. Women like Anna Julia Cooper, Mary Church Terrell, Sojourner Truth, and others spoke out about their experiences as Black Women and the need to rid our country of sexism.

I was well aware of the heavy burden society placed on my parents, grandparents, and my ancestors before them; their struggles and sacrifices leading to the opportunities that were open to me were palpable elements in my life. But I did not fully take in the difference between the experiences of my motherline and that of my male ancestors. And despite the continuing limitations placed on me because of the color of my skin and my ethnic origin, I was determined to succeed in my life—for them as much as for myself.

hooks points out that romanticizing the Black woman's experience by feminists, who emphasized Black women's strength, stood in the way of the feminist movement embracing racism and classism as a purview of feminist theory. This view of Black women is also an issue in society at large and is addressed by Alice Walker in her book *In Search of our Mothers' Gardens* (1983). We Black women have been glorified as superwomen, matriarchs, etc., without acknowledgement of the real victimization and oppression that Black Women have suffered ever since the first woman was kidnapped out of Africa and brought to this country enslaved. I think many of us bought into that story of the extraordinary strength of Black women, and even wore it as a badge of honor. But that was to deny the horror of the reality of the experiences of those women who bore the brunt of slavery and its aftermath. Toni Morrison's *Beloved* (1987), which was highly successful as a novel, was a disappointment at the box office because of that denial. The horror of the mother, running away from a slave master and knowing the fate that awaited her girl child, led her to kill her child to save her from that fate. Morrison painted a true picture of the agony of a Black mother that most of us, white or Black, are not yet ready to fully face.

I found myself facing some of that horror in my personal Bonny Method of Guided Imagery and Music (BMGIM) sessions. I had images of processions of people walking in rain and cold on a dark night, so weary they fell down from exhaustion, but had to get up and keep walking. I was in that procession of struggling, faceless people. Later in my image I was holding my small child self by the hand and walking on a narrow desert path surrounded by high mountains. My heart ached for this innocent girl child who had come into this world full of possibilities and expectations, still innocent of the racism that would impact every aspect of her life. Soon my anguished cries were accompanied by the crying of the mountains; then the wailing of the whole world joined in; and soon the stars and the heavens added their mournful voices. The entire universe reverberated with the sounds of deep sorrow. I felt that sorrow in every cell of my body, in the very core of my being. And my experience doesn't begin to approach that of my female ancestors.

Although both hooks and Walker decry the romanticizing of the Black woman's ability to survive her use and abuse as a denial of real oppression that Black women have suffered, there may be another aspect to this idealization. As a BMGIM practitioner, I have noticed that some women have images of Black women when dealing with deep pain. One of the most common archetypal images of suffering is Christ on the cross, but in my work I have observed enough images of Black women—images which carry that same symbolic meaning of suffering—to begin to wonder about it. This phenomenon has been observed in women in different countries, in clients of my GIM students as well as my own clients. These images have been of both anonymous and famous Black women. They were images of pain as well as comfort in times of great sorrow or crisis. Could it be that, even though we as a society are not yet able to face the unspeakable acts visited upon Black women in reality, the Black woman's experience of beatings, rape, and having her children ripped from her, never to be seen again, has seeped into our unconscious and taken on the weight of an archetype of suffering? I can't answer that question, but it seems worth further research.

As mentioned earlier, when the women's movement came along, my identity as an African-American was primary and my identification as a woman was secondary. In her book, *Feminist Theory from Margin to Center* (2000), bell hooks makes an important point regarding identity. She describes a discussion about the origins of domination in a college women's studies class where she objected to a statement that gender was the most important factor when a baby is born. She pointed out that in Black families, when a child is born, the first consideration is skin color and gender is second (2000). For most African Americans, gender identity is second to race and color. In large part, due to the misogynist and racist practices of white slave owners, African Americans exhibit a beautiful rainbow of colors, ranging from cream to black coffee. And in this American racist society, color continues to be a defining factor. I would venture that race and color are equally significant to gender in the identity of many of the darker peoples who make their way in the dominant Eurocentric American culture. This experience of walking within two different cultures also brings a unique perspective. That of being able to see each culture from some distance because we know both worlds, giving us a view that may be broader than that of those who live in just one of these cultures (hooks, 2000; Bolen, 2001).

When hooks experienced that narrow definition of identity, the women's movement had not yet broadened to include race and class within the scope of feminist theory, thought, and action. Black feminists felt ignored, overlooked and marginalized. As hooks points out, no other group in America has had their identity socialized out of existence as have Black women. We are rarely recognized as distinct from Black men, and we are often not seen as part of the culture of women (1981, p.7). At the insistence of feminists of color, the movement began to examine how it thought and wrote about gender and eventually the "interlocking nature of gender, race and class changed the direction of feminist thought" (hooks, 2000, p.xii). Now that the interface of gender, race, and class is mainstream in the feminist movement, I can finally relate. My personal consciousness raising, though, came through another route, but that story will come later.

Feminist Psychotherapy

A sense of identity is crucial to a person's development and is often central to psychotherapy. The view of women's development by a therapist of women has a profound impact on her therapy process and ultimately on her sense of identity. Early feminists including Betty Friedan, considered the psychotherapy process to be damaging to a woman, not only because of Freud's Victorian views on women (embedded in his Judeo-Christian culture), but also because of the perceived power differential between client and therapist. In response to this criticism, many feminist psychotherapists initially adopted a role that was more friend than therapist, they socialized with their clients, and blurred boundaries in other ways that were not in the best interest of their clients.

I agree with the view of Charlotte Prozan (1992) that there is a difference between the therapist and the client, but it need not result in a power differential that makes the client feel inferior. The therapist has training from which the client is seeking to benefit and the client pays the therapist a fee in acknowledgement of that fact. I also agree with Hannah Lerman (1976) that the therapist need not take the position of expert, but that of supporting the client's self-empowerment as she gains insight through self-exploration. This is not only consonant with my practice of music psychotherapy, it is inherent in BMGIM, my major approach as music psychotherapist. Carolyn Kenny's *Field of Play* (1989), with the metaphor of an aesthetic for both the client and the therapist, is another music therapy theory in which a more egalitarian relationship between client and therapist is promoted. Client empowerment is embedded in the process as Kenny describes it.

Prozan (1992) discusses the work of women psychoanalytic theorists, such as Karen Horney—who dared to dissent with Freud's views on women's development and debated with him in papers written during the 1920s and 1930s—Melanie Klein and her followers, and more recent writers such as Carol Gilligan and Nancy Chodorow. In Prozan's view, Chodorow's revision of Freud's Oedipal theory (1978) and Gilligan's revision of Freud's theory of an inferior superego in girls and women (1982), taken together, are revolutionary in the reformulation of the psychoanalytic view of female development. They make current feminist psychoanalytic thinking about women both viable and clinically useful (p.137). Jean Shinoda Bolen, a Jungian analyst, has also challenged the old order. In her book *Goddesses in Every Woman* (1984), she describes her sense that the Jungian concept of the animus, a woman's inner male aspects, is not adequate for all women. She has developed a new psychology of women based on the Greek and Roman goddesses as feminine archetypes that challenge the idea that goal directed, assertive, and aggressive behavior are provinces of the animus. Further discussion of these specific theories is beyond the scope of this chapter. The reader is referred to the above authors' respective books and papers. The intention here is to demonstrate that at least some current psychodynamic psychotherapy theories are consistent with and complement feminist theory.

The first major influences on my thinking were the contributions of women archaeologists, mythologists, historians, and religious scholars. Later, I had the opportunity to study with the feminist thinkers, Jean Shinoda Bolen, Betty De Shong Meador, and Naomi Lowinsky of the San Francisco Jung Institute, which deepened my convictions regarding psychotherapy with women. As I learned from all these sources, my approach to therapy evolved. Understanding the impact of our patriarchal society on women's development, their self-esteem, their ability to achieve, and their relationships, I paid close attention to these issues. Furthermore, I realized the importance for women to break out of their constricted roles and to develop autonomy, to be able to make conscious choices, and to understand that they need not be limited to a so-called predefined role of serving men and children. According to Prozan (1992), these are the tenets that all feminist psychotherapists acknowledge. This conclusion certainly follows once one fully understands the issues faced by women in our society and the concurrent impact on men as well.

My consciousness raising came through my interest in mythology as it relates to psychotherapy. With the Bonny Method of GIM, many images come to clients that are similar to myths, legends, and fairy tales. I became more interested in Jungian theory and practice as Jung understood the importance of myths and archetypes to psychology and the psychotherapy process. I began reading books on mythology and was drawn in particular to the stories of Goddesses. I eventually came upon Martha Ann and Dorothy Myers Imel's *Goddesses in World Mythology* and Carolyne Larrington's *The Feminist Companion to Mythology*. And later, I discovered *Ancient Mirrors of Womanhood* by Merlin Stone (1990). These books opened new worlds to me. I found stories of Goddesses from all over the world, Goddesses who reflected the full range of human complexity, way beyond the Greek and Roman pantheons that had been the subject of my high school Latin texts. And, most importantly, I was introduced for the first time to the idea that these myths were the sacred religious stories of the cultures in which they were created.

Most of the transcription of myths was done by male researchers, archeologists, and linguists, who *tended to play down the roles of Goddesses in comparison to gods.* Church scholars and missionaries *whose bias was for strong males and weak females, in keeping with their worldviews,* did most of the earliest recording! This was life-changing news for me. I had never thought of "male bias" and how that has profoundly influenced our cultural views of women and my view of myself. I remembered that in college I so enjoyed my work in the student senate that I said, "If I were a man, I would study law and go into politics." It was shocking to me that I actually thought that way; and then I understood how insidiously patriarchy has shaped our ideas about ourselves as women, my ideas about myself. Although I did not join a consciousness-raising women's group, clearly I could see in society and in myself profound effects of the feminist movement.

Early Christianity

Because of the connection between religion and myth, I soon found myself reading about the early Christians as well. It is well known among religious scholars that many gospels circulated during the first two hundred years after Christ's death, and many of these writings were excluded from the Bible. The scripture as we know it today emerged at the end of the second century, two hundred years after the death of Jesus. All that was known about these other writings were through those who refuted them, such as Bishop Irenaeus, in Lyon c.180 CE, so their contents could only be inferred. Clearly, there had been an organized attempt to destroy these gospels. In 1945, an Arab peasant found thirteen leather-bound books hidden inside a large earthenware jar that had been buried in a cave near the town of Naj Hammadi in Egypt. Some eventually were sold on the antiquities black market and finally, after many years, some made their way into the hands of scholars who could translate them (Pagels, 1979). These turned out to be some of the rejected gospels (apparently having been hidden for safekeeping), and are now called the Gnostic Gospels. What was left out of the Bible scriptures as we know them makes for very interesting reading regarding women. They reveal that there was a split among early Christian communities over the role of women in the church. The communities that respected women and in which women played significant roles were ignored, not only by those who "won" the argument over the roles of women in the church, but also by the male writers of history. There also seems to be evidence that Mary Magdalene may have been a disciple, loved by Jesus over the others (Pagels, 1979). I was taught in Sunday school that she was a prostitute. It is likely she had been a priestess in a temple of the Goddess before her encounter with Jesus.

There is also clear evidence that the writers of the Bible deliberately obscured the fact that the "pagans" referred to over and over again were Goddess worshipers. Even though archeological evidence shows that most of the idols had breasts, the Goddess is referred to as Elohim, in the masculine gender. Only the Koran makes it clear: "Allah will not tolerate idolatry . . . the pagans pray to females" (Stone, 1976, p.xviii). I saw the archeological evidence for myself at the Israel Museum in Jerusalem. And when I saw the tiny Goddess figure dated 250,000 BCE that was found in Berekhat Ram, Israel, the profound sense of the Divine Feminine was overwhelming. At that moment the Goddess became real for me.

With all this information, the relationship between the monotheistic dogma of the Judeo-Christian-Islamic religions and the disparagement of women became obvious to me. Male religious scholars, and even the early church fathers, had demeaned the Divine Feminine by labeling those religions cults of prostitution and the priestesses as prostitutes. Worse still, they deliberately wrote them out of history. I found myself becoming more and more outraged.

The Cost to Women of the Dominance of Male Consciousness

Lowinsky (1992) discusses the great cost to women of the eruption of masculine consciousness, which placed god and man above nature, "demeaning and denying the body and the mother, creating a language which splits the world" (p.187). She quotes Ursula LeGuin:

> His language expresses the values of the split world, valuing the positive and devaluing the negative in each redivision: subject/object, self/other, mind/body, dominant/submissive, active/passive, man/nature, man/woman, and so on. The father tongue is spoken from above. It goes one way. (LeGuin, 1989, p.149)

This hierarchical view of the world is the basis of the splits between races, religions, and countries—Black/White, me/you—and all the other divisions of man. *This is the very root of oppression.* In the world of the Goddess, nature was prime and humans were not separate from nature. There is evidence that Goddess cultures were not matriarchal in the same sense as patriarchy because there was not a hierarchy. Men and women were equal, even though those societies were matrilineal, meaning that family lines were traced through the mother. Bodies were celebrated as manifestations of the Divine; women's bodies were understood as the sacred living genesis of life, and the sex act was seen as sacred, a mirror of creation.

The writing of history from a masculine hierarchical view, ignoring female contributions to culture, is an old recurring story. Parallels are found in nearly every avenue of human activity. Riane Eisler, in her seminal book *The Chalice and the Blade* (1987/1995), writes that historians continued to deny the fact of both women pharaohs and Black pharaohs in Egypt long after historical and visual evidence was very clear regarding their existence. Even Darwin, after seeing the statue of a pharaoh with Negroid features, qualified what he had seen with his own eyes, which was corroborated by two people with him, and maintained that the statue was definitely not of "Negro intermixture" (p.40). Women composers, painters, warriors, religious thinkers, inventors, scientists, and others have been given short shrift by history as told by men. A paradigm that has reigned for more than two thousand years has relegated women to invisibility at worst and insignificance at best.

From the Great Mother to the Great Goddess

The first mother was a Black woman in Africa. Archeologists, ethnographers, and DNA studies have verified this fact. Her descendants migrated into Sicily and beyond into Europe, West Asia, and the Levant (Birnbaum, 2001), taking with them their Goddess. Evidence of the ancient reign of the Goddess in Africa twenty thousand years ago or more is engraved in rock walls of African countries. The ancient stone Goddess figures found throughout Europe, the Middle East, and Asia bear a striking resemblance to one another, even though they were found thousands of miles apart. It is as though there was an ideal image of the Goddess that was already known (Frobenius, 1927, cited in Ford, 1999). German researcher, Leo Frobenius suggested in 1927 that an African Goddess was that ideal. He proposed that these figurines had initially been fashioned of wood in Africa and were carried in the African migration to other parts of the world, their African roots lost to history. The African images having been made of wood, not stone, would have deteriorated over time (cited in Ford, 1999). Clyde W. Ford points out the similarities of rock carvings and cave paintings throughout primitive Europe to those of the San in Africa as evidence this might be so. He also reveals through the African myths he has collected that the Goddess in Africa was symbolized primarily in the tree, the earth, the stone, the snake, and the buffalo. Stones and rocks often were considered sacred manifestations of the Goddess. Given this, he says:

> Perhaps the appearance in Eurasia of these very same forms of the Goddess, etched and carved in stone, were vestiges of a more ancient time in Africa when it was wholly unnecessary to create the Goddess out of stone because the Goddess was already enshrined in the stone unadorned, already experienced in ritual, already felt in the forest hunt. (p.140, 1999)

In her book *dark mother, african origins and godmothers* (2001), Lucia Chiavola Birnbaum also holds the view that Africa is the origin of the ancient Goddess. She, too, cites rock art along the African migration routes as evidence of their source in African countries. She notes that the rock paintings in central and south Africa are "characterized by a predominance of the color red or purple as well as spirals, straight or wavy lines, petals, and concentric circles—signs, according to Marija Gimbutas, Judith Grahn, and other feminist scholars—of the goddess" (p.45). Birnbaum also traces the origins of the Black Madonnas found throughout Europe to Isis, the Black Goddess in Egypt, and other dark Goddesses, in her book *Black Madonnas: feminism, religion and politics in Italy* (1993). She also notes that sites of the Black Madonna are frequently ancient sites of Goddess worship.

In the many books that have been written about the Goddess in recent years, there is relatively little on African Goddesses. We know the names of many and some of their stories and attributes, such as Nyame, the one supreme deity without beginning or end, who was initially reported by missionaries as a "Sky God" of the Ashanti or the Horned Goddess from the Tassili Mountains, dating from 8000–6000 BCE. Missionaries who were biased regarding women deities, changing the sex of some and disregarding others, were early collectors of the African myths, the religious stories of the African countries. And unfortunately, most of the original stories are now lost in the systematic destruction of those cultures by European colonialists and missionaries (Ford, 1999). Many Africans, however, are reclaiming their history and their cultures, and are unearthing some of the old stories of the religions of their ancestors. It does appear, however, that the first Goddess was also a Black woman.

Marion Woodman and Elinor Dickson, in their book *Dancing in the Flames: The Dark Goddess in the Transformation of Consciousness* (1996), speak of the appearance of an unknown feminine figure in the dreams of many contemporary men and women. This is the Goddess coming to people of various faiths and different walks of life. She is appearing in art all over the world, and in novels. This is the Dark Goddess, the hidden Goddess, resurfacing in contemporary consciousness from antiquity where she has been buried for more than two thousand years.

Many years ago, in my late twenties, I had a dream in which I was helping my mother and grandmother care for my great grandmother and my great-great grandmother. They were all familiar to me in real life except the great-great grandmother, and she was curled up like a baby on the bed, completely helpless. At the time, I attributed this dream to the impending birth of my first child. Now, I understand that in addition to this, the dream was a beginning awakening of my feminine consciousness. I connected with my motherline and the oldest mother was the Dark Goddess, curled up asleep and waiting for me to open myself to Her. She came to me two more times years later in BMGIM sessions, both times in a spiritual context. My opening to Her occurred very slowly, over a period of more than twenty-five years.

The ancient Goddess was originally a mother Goddess, rooted in nature. All things flowed from Her, and all things returned to Her at death. As human consciousness evolved from the literal to the symbolic, the Goddess was consciously articulated at a high level of consciousness. And she appeared in many forms. She was called Ayeba, Isis, Inanna, Sophia, Perimbo, Jalang, Devi, Maya, and many other names. She was the Supreme Being, the Holy One, the Creatrix, the All in All. The sense of oneness, the sense of absolute authority within Her milieu was evident in Her descriptions (Woodman & Dickson 1996), an example of which is at the beginning of this chapter in relation to Inanna. I refer to these Goddesses collectively as the Great Goddess. When referring to the hidden Goddess specifically, I name Her as the Dark Goddess or the Dark Feminine.

The Great Goddess is often referred to as the Triple Goddess. These three aspects are the maiden/virgin, mother, and crone (Woodman & Dickson, 1996). Our patriarchal culture elevates the mother over the other two. This is often seen as the rejection/fear of death by patriarchy. The Goddess and women are associated with death. Traditionally, women have attended the dying, and prepared the dead for burial. The ancient rites of the Great Goddess included death/rebirth rites, first as concrete reminders of the power of the Goddess to both give and take life, and later as transformational, initiation rites. An example of a death/rebirth initiation is Inanna's Descent to the Underworld, which will be discussed later in this chapter. The wise old woman, the crone, has been demonized as a witch because of the association with death. Denial of the maiden/virgin is a rejection of our female bodies, our cycles, and sexuality. The exclusive idealization of woman as mother/madonna is to deny our complete life cycles and our feminine aspects.

We, as women, have now lost sight of our own cyclical nature, and use drugs to eliminate the effects of our cycles on us. We deny our passion, our blood, our temperament, and our underworld, death-dealing aspects. All these aspects have been demonized. It has been said that women's bodies are "the devil's gateway," associated with hell. We have forgotten the transformational mysteries of the descent to the underworld, the ritual of death and rebirth. We suffer shame about our natural bodily functions and pathologize our menstrual experience, calling it PMS (Lowinsky, 1992). We deny our basic nature as fully human, with all the emotions and capabilities inherent in our feminine condition.

With the rise of masculine consciousness, the status of the Great Goddess began to erode. She was given a son or lover, or made a partner of a god, and later she was downgraded to wife or mother of the supreme god, then to daughter or sister. The Greek/Roman pantheon is an example of this degradation. Finally, the sacred Goddess was demonized as a prostitute, witch, or monster; trivialized as an angel, nymph, or fairy; demoted to a subservient and docile saint or "good" wife; and dichotomized as a madonna/whore (Ann & Imel, p.xx, 1993). The lone male god reigned supreme.

This masculine consciousness also gave rise to the Hero Myth, reaching its peak in the 12th and 13th centuries. These are stories in which the hero triumphed over the Great Goddess, Her consort, a derivative of the Great Goddess, or other representations of Her. Examples of these are the stories of Medusa, the killing of the dragon/serpent, and driving the snakes out of Ireland.

Tragically, with the rise of masculine consciousness and repression of the Great Goddess as well as the Great Mother, there was "a gradual eclipse of the understanding of the unifying light in creation, the subtle Oneness of the Goddess that had begun to break through into human awareness" (Woodman & Dickson, 1996, p.22).

The Goddess in Contemporary Society

In spite of the overwhelming influence of patriarchy the Goddess lives on in the twenty-first century. Many women are reclaiming their bodies and helping their daughters do the same by celebrating their daughters' menarche with parties or rituals. Monthly bleeding is no longer "the curse" to these women, rather this blood is a welcome sign of womanhood. Women are learning about themselves through celebrations of the Goddess, and going on pilgrimages to discover Tara, Kali, Inanna, the Black Madonna, African Goddesses, Mary Magdalene, and the Divine Feminine for themselves.

The Hindu Black Goddess, Kali, has been worshipped continuously in India for thousands of years to the present. Her primary followers traditionally are women and people of the servile and untouchable classes, who were excluded from the Vedic rites (Cleary & Aziz, 2000). Her blackness symbolizes absolute transcendence beyond all qualities. According to Hindu tradition, we are now in the Kali Age, a time of resurgence of the Divine Feminine spirit (Mookerjee, 1988). Kali, who is often pictured in her warrior aspect with her lolling red tongue and necklace of severed heads, is also Divine Mother, creator and nourisher. She represents the never-ending cycle of birth, death, and rebirth. Her role in the present is the same as when she initially sprang from the brow of the Great Goddess Durga during a battle to annihilate demonic male power:

> In the present Kali age, Kali is the answer, and she will have to annihilate again in order to reveal the truth of things, which is her mission, and to restore to our natures that divine feminine spirituality which we have lost. (Mookerjee, 1988, p.9)

In recent years, interest in Kali has expanded to women and men around the world in recognition of her ability to bring much-needed balance to patriarchy. Woodman and Dickson (1996) point out that Kali represents chaos, and that the chaos we fear is the very thing that can free us. Within chaos a deeper, intrinsic order is revealed, and if we enter into it, chaos can resurrect us into a higher wisdom, rooted in the wisdom of the creative process (p.45).

The Great Goddess is also alive in the Black Madonnas found in Catholic churches and cathedrals throughout Europe. Among the best-known are the Black Madonna of Einsiedeln in Switzerland, our Lady of Czestoshova, "Queen of Poland" in the Jorna Gora monastery, and *La Moreneta*, the Black Madonna of Montserrat in Spain. Thousands of pilgrims pay homage to these and other Black Madonnas each year. Other Black Madonnas are in small village churches, cathedral basements, and private collections. More than four hundred were catalogued by Ean Begg (1985), and in the forward to the 1996 edition of his book he noted that he had found many, many more around the world. I have visited *La Moreneta* in Spain and was amazed to see busload after busload of pilgrims standing in line for up to two hours just to file slowly past Her. I also studied with Karlyn Ward, a Jungian analyst and BMGIM Fellow, who led us through Provence in Southern France, visiting the many Black Madonnas in the area. They included Sarah, *La Vierge Noire* in the small beach town of *Les Saintes Maries De La Mer* in the church of the same name, named after the three Marys said to have landed there in a boat after the death of Christ. The Roma (Gypsies), who gather there each year to honor Her, call her Black Sarah.

Some attribute the Black Madonnas to smoke from incense over the centuries, but they do not explain why only their faces and hands are black and not their clothes. Most of the Black Madonnas can be traced back more than a thousand years, but their origin is unclear. Some researchers believe their origin is in the Black Goddess (Begg, 1985/1996; Gustafson, 1990; Birnbaum, 1993, 2000). The fact that many of the sanctuaries of the European Black Madonnas were sites of ancient Goddess religions (Birnbaum, 1993, 2000) perhaps supports that idea.

Whatever their origins, there are hundreds of them, and they are revered by thousands of people. That alone is meaningful. Fred Gustafson, a Jungian analyst and protestant pastor, believes they represent the Dark Feminine, "a phenomenon that transcends local boundaries and relates to Western spirituality in general" (p.xi). In his view the Black Madonnas speak to the area of the soul that "hungers for value and hope, in the midst of the indefinition and incomprehensibility of life" (p.xii). The Black Madonnas seem to carry the transformative aspects of the Great Goddess into Western Society in the twenty-first century.

Growing numbers of women feel that patriarchal traditions have alienated them from their deepest spiritual connections. And for many women of today, there is a conscious need to reclaim the holiness of female embodiment and acknowledge the Sacred Feminine. The issue for some is not so much about gender, but about rectifying historical imbalance. For others the Divine Feminine is a deeply personal lived experience of the sacred. Many churches acknowledge this need by referring to "Mother God" and "Father God" in church services. In the introduction to her beautiful book, *The Mother's Songs, Images of the God the Mother* (1988), Meinrad Craighead, artist and former nun, writes:

> I believe in her because I experienced her . . . . My Catholic heritage and environment have been like a beautiful river flowing over my subterranean foundation in God the Mother. The two movements are not in conflict, they simply water different layers of my soul.

The Goddess Inanna

Inanna came into the consciousness of people more than 6,000 years ago. The word Inanna in Sumerian means Queen of Heaven and Earth. She was worshipped in Sumer for thousands of years. Inanna rose to supremacy above all the other gods and Goddesses. The excerpts at the beginning of this chapter show how the poetry of Enheduanna captures the paradoxical nature of Inanna that "mirrors a wide range of characteristics all the way from the most horrendous, vicious, cruel, destructive, and violent to the most beneficent, glorious, and creative" (Meador, 2000, p.10). "More than any other Sumerian god or Goddess she embodies the totality of 'What Is'" (Meador, 2000, p.12). In this way, Inanna carries all the elements necessary for a woman's full identity that are missing in patriarchal systems.

In her book *Inanna, Lady of the Largest Heart, Poems of the Sumerian High Priestess Enheduanna* (2000), Meador tells about Enheduanna. She lived in the city of Ur about 2300 BCE and is the earliest writer known to be identified by name in the poems and hymns she wrote. She lived 1700 years before Sappho and about 500 years before Abraham, who, probably not coincidentally, also lived in Ur. The first alabaster discs with Enheduanna's writing, along with her image, were discovered by a team of archeologists in the 1920s as they excavated the ancient city of Ur in modern day southern Iraq. To date, three long poems to Inanna, three poems to Nanna, and forty-two temple hymns by Enheduanna—more than 4,500 lines of writing—have been discovered. What an impressive body of work, and produced by a woman who lived more than 4,000 years ago.

Enheduanna was the daughter of Sargon, a Sumerian king, who appointed her High Priestess of the moon god, Nanna, a position traditionally given to the king's daughter. By Enheduanna's time, the shift from a single Goddess to both gods and Goddesses had already occurred, but Inanna continued to be a whole Goddess—meaning She carries all aspects of human kind, rather than split-off parts or stereotypes that are characteristic of god and Goddess pantheons developed in patriarchy. Through her poems, Enheduanna's personal and intimate relationship with her Divine is revealed. She prays to Inanna in one of her poems for help as patriarchy was eroding the Goddess culture; and she remained faithful as she suffered the overthrow of her Temple and the loss of her position as priestess. Her devotion was complete.

Inanna's Descent to the Underworld

Inanna's Descent is told here using translations from the clay tablets from ancient Sumer by Diane Wolkstein and Samuel Kramer (1983).

> From the Great Above she opened her ear to the Great Below.
> From the Great Above the goddess opened her ear to the Great Below.
> From the Great Above Inanna opened her ear to the Great Below.
>
> My Lady abandoned heaven and earth to descend to the underworld.
> Inanna abandoned heaven and earth to descend to the underworld.
> She abandoned her office of holy priestess to descend to the underworld. (p.52)

As Inanna set out for the underworld, She instructed her servant, Ninshubur, to set up lamentations for Her, and then to go to the gods for help if She did not return.

> When Inanna arrived at the outer gates of the underworld,
> She knocked loudly.
> She cried in a fierce voice:
> "Open the door, gatekeeper!
> Open the door, Neti!
> I alone would enter!" (pp.54, 55)

The gatekeeper of the *kur* asked who She was. She replied, "I am Inanna, Queen of Heaven." Neti asks if she is truly Inanna Queen of heaven, why is She on the road from which no traveler returns. Inanna answers that it is because of her older sister Ereshkigal, Queen of the Underworld, whose husband has died, and she has come to witness the funeral rites. Neti goes to Ereshkigal, who tells Neti to let Inanna enter and as She enters to remove Her royal garments, She must enter bowed low.

At the first gate, Inanna surrenders the *shugurra,* the crown of the steppe. At the second, Her small lapis beads. And so it went as she passed through each of the seven gates until she arrived naked and bowed low in the throne room of Ereshkigal.

> The Annuna, the judges of the underworld passed judgement against her.
> Then Ereshkigal fastened on Inanna the eye of death.
> She spoke against her the word of wrath.
> She uttered against her the cry of guilt.
>
> She struck her.
>
> Inanna was turned into a corpse,
> A piece of rotting meat,
> And was hung from a hook on the wall. (p.60)

When after three days and three nights Inanna had not returned, Ninshubur began lamentations. Then she approached the gods, Enlil, then Nanna, who refused to help. Finally, the god of Wisdom, Enki, was troubled and grieved by the news. From the dirt under his fingernails, Enki fashioned two creatures whom he sent into the underworld to rescue Inanna. The very small creatures easily slipped past Neti and arrived at the throne room where Ereshkigal moaned and groaned loudly in mourning for her husband. The creatures moaned and groaned with her. At last Ereshkigal stopped and asked who they were. She offered them a gift in thanks for their empathy. The creatures responded that they only wanted the corpse and it was given to them. They brought Inanna back to life.

As Inanna ascended from the underworld, she was accompanied by demons from the underworld whose task it was to bring a replacement for Inanna. The entire city was in mourning for Inanna, except Dumuzi, her husband, who was sitting on the throne dressed in his shining garments.

> Inanna fastened on Dumuzi the eye of death.
> She spoke against him the word of wrath.
> She uttered against him the cry of guilt:
> "*Take him! Take Dumuzi away!*" (p.71)

Dumuzi escaped the demons several times with the help of the gods, but finally he was caught. His sister, Geshtininna, wept for him and begged to share his fate. When Inanna saw Geshtininna's grief, Inanna took Dumuzi by the hand and said:

"You will go to the underworld
Half the year.
Your sister, since she has asked,
Will go the other half.
On the day you are called,
That day you will be taken.
On the day Geshtininna is called,
That day you will be set free."

Inanna placed Dumuzi in the hands of the eternal. (p.89)

Inanna's descent and return was celebrated for over five thousand years. Inanna willingly went into the underworld and there she arrived naked and was forced to face herself. She was judged and found guilty, just as we must look at ourselves naked and pronounce ourselves guilty of whatever we find. This story is about letting go of layers of defenses and owning the parts of ourselves we don't like. It means working to bring to consciousness the repressed feelings and issues that drive our behavior in unwelcome ways. It is a story of transformation. When Inanna returned she took charge of her fate. She punished Dumuzi for his lack of concern for her even though she loved him, and showed compassion to his sister, Geshtininna. She made hard choices. Inanna's descent is an ancient story of modern psychotherapy.

I first met Inanna when I found myself in despair over my growing antipathy toward the Christian church. I found myself rejecting all I had been taught in the Methodist church in which I was raised. I, who had joyously sung in and conducted church choirs for so many years, now found my favorite holiday, Christmas, empty and meaningless. The music I had loved so much now sounded hollow. This was my descent into the underworld. There I had to face the reality that all the love and security I had experienced in my faith was gone. I felt utterly betrayed. I had encountered what Fowler (1981) calls the "broken symbol"; I was immersed in the dark night of the soul. This was very frightening, disorienting, and even shameful.

A friend recommended the book *Descent to the Goddess: A way of Initiation for Women,* by Sylvia Perera (1981). This book brought a ray of hope into my darkness. Perera views Inanna's descent as the revelation of an initiation ritual that is directly relevant to the feminine experience of today. The feminine aspects, instincts, and values have been pushed underground and Perera views the descent to the Goddess as a necessary initiation for most modern women to retrieve what has been lost. Her view is that this retrieval is necessary for women to become whole. She states:

> In those depths we are given a sense of the one cosmic power; there we are moved, and taught through the intensity of our affects that

> there is a living balance process. On those levels the conscious ego is overwhelmed by passion and numinous images. And, though shaken, even destroyed as we knew ourselves, we are recoalesced in a new pattern and spewed back into ordinary life. (p.14)

Modern woman's descent to the underworld carries both spiritual and psychological significance. Sometimes one is more prominent than the other, but they always proceed hand in hand. The separation of the two aspects in contemporary society is simply another hierarchical split by patriarchy. Some women seek that space in order to grow. Others, like me, are catapulted into it by a life crisis. I had to allow the death of the old and make space for the new.

Women's Spiritual Journeys

Through Sherry Ruth Anderson's and Patricia Hopkins' book *The Feminine Face of God: The Unfolding of the Sacred in Women (1991)*, I found kindred spirits. Anderson and Hopkins conducted over one hundred in-depth interviews with women across the United States about the unfolding of the spiritual in their lives. They spent two days with each of the women who represented a variety of faiths, including nuns, medicine women, rabbis, ministers, but primarily ordinary women. Inspired by Carol Gilligan's *In a Different Voice: Psychological Theory and Women's Development* (1982), which found that women approach morality differently from men, their objective was to find out if women's spirituality unfolded in different ways from the patriarchal path of leaving home, families, and loved ones to find god. The concept of the spiritual as it is used in this context, as well as in this chapter, is broader than religion. Religion consists of an organized set of beliefs, whereas the concept of the spiritual refers to a personal relationship with the Divine, within or outside of an organized religious practice.

They found that few of these women left home to find their spiritual paths; these women did not sever relationships. Women spoke of finding themselves moving away from what had once been a secure spiritual home into the unknown, being in a place of not knowing, and encountering "something unspeakably, and sometimes almost unbearably new" (p.48). Many of them experienced descents where they struggled with learning to trust the neglected or rejected parts of themselves. They had profound encounters with a new reality, a sense of true authority that enabled them to live through the depths of feelings. Each woman had to come to terms with her own lived experience and learn to trust it (p.55).

These experiences ultimately resulted in an intimate relationship with the Divine. But the process was fraught with fear, anxiety, loneliness, and sometimes depression. One woman said, "We want to know whether we're going through a 'dark night of the soul' or a depression. If it's a 'dark night,' we'll try to get through it. If not, we want Elavil" (p.65).

Anderson and Hopkins believe the paths were so difficult for women because of the patriarchal culture that not only teaches that men are the authorities in spiritual and religious matters, but that women are not to be trusted or have no role at all in spiritual or religious matters. Therefore women have to work very hard to trust their unfolding processes. These women clearly went through a descent to find their spiritual paths.

Women's Psychological Journeys

Therapist Maureen Murdock (1990) described a pattern in modern women that she calls the Heroine's Journey, which she likens to Inanna's descent. She has observed this pattern in many of her women clients as they grapple with achieving in our male-dominated society. The circular journey begins with separation from the feminine, which the woman views as weak, dependent, and/or over-controlling. This usually takes the form of rejection of her mother. The woman identifies with the masculine, embarking on the familiar hero's journey out into the world (Campbell, 1965) and gathers male or male-identified women allies. This leads to the road of trials as she makes her way in the world. She then finds the boon of success, achieving independence, prestige, money, or power. Feelings of spiritual aridity and death, a sense of dryness and sometimes despair eventually follow. These feelings herald the initiation and descent to the Goddess, the "inevitable descent to the underworld to meet the *dark feminine"* (p.4). Out of this darkness, according to Murdock, comes the next stage, a yearning to reconnect with the feminine, which eventually leads to working on the mother-daughter split. The final stages of the Heroine's Journey are healing the woman's wounded masculine and finally integration of the masculine and feminine within herself (p.5). In therapy, the woman who has embarked on this Heroine's Journey presents as feeling dissatisfied with life in spite of her success and is often depressed.

Some years ago as I was preparing a case study for publication, I recognized a pattern in my client similar to the Heroine's Journey described by Murdock. My work with this client had ended several years prior to writing the case study and to Murdock publishing her book, so I did not have that perspective during the therapy process. In retrospect, however, the overall pattern was clear, even though some details were different. Since the purpose of the published case study (2000) was to describe and demonstrate the clinical efficacy of the Bonny Method of Guided Imagery and Music, I chose not to include the descent aspect of the case. I will present it here.

Jan

Jan was a 37-year-old white, separated, registered nurse living with her seven-year-old son. In the initial interview her speech was rapid and pressured, but clear and coherent; she was quite anxious and rather hyperactive, with much nervous laughter. She was preoccupied with her husband, whom she planned to divorce, his new girlfriend, and her own issues of control. As the session progressed, she became more serious and looked depressed. She had some insight into her hyperactive behavior as a defense against her anxiety about having left her marriage of ten years, and the interpersonal problems brought on by her need to control.

Jan felt her controlling behavior was her major problem, but felt she could not give it up. She realized this conflicted with her need for intimacy, which was missing from her marriage, and was focused on finding a new and better relationship.

Jan is the oldest of four children, with one brother and two sisters. Her father was a truck driver; her mother, who died of an aneurysm when Jan was 13 years old, was a housewife. Jan described her mother as a "wonderful, intelligent person, yet she was very content to be a mother." Her lack of respect for her mother's choices was evident. After her mother's death, Jan felt very responsible for the family and, although a paternal aunt came nearly every day to help, Jan took on many of the responsibilities and chores of running the family. She noted that her father "took care of our physical needs," but withdrew into alcohol and a protracted grief reaction to his wife's death. She attended Catholic schools through college where she completed a degree in English.

Jan had seen a therapist several times over the last three years to deal with her troubled marriage, and returned to the same therapist two months before that therapist's departure and being referred to me. Jan had no other treatment. She reported being depressed about her mother's death until about age 23, and that she'd had a hyperactive period similar to her current one immediately following the birth of her son. She also became somewhat depressed when she was unable to become pregnant a second time in an effort to save her marriage. Family history includes her alcoholic father and an aunt whom she described as manic-depressive.

In summary, this was a woman who was in crisis as the result of the breakup of a marriage that had been deteriorating for several years. She was angry, rigid, and controlling, and seemed to be covering a depression by becoming hyperactive. Her strengths were a wonderful sense of humor, above-average intelligence, a capacity for insight, and a genuine desire for change.

Her stated therapy goals were to (1) form a new relationship with a man without the problems of her marriage, (2) decrease her controlling behavior, (3) allow her needs for nurturance to be met, and (4) relieve her guilt. My additional goals were to increase her awareness of her dependence/independence issues as they related to her need to control and find a man, and to relieve her underlying depression and anxiety. A concern was the history of affective disorder in the family coupled with her history of depression and manic-like defenses. This would require careful management.

In retrospect, I could see that Jan's disdain for her mother's choice to be a housewife signaled a break with the feminine. And although her father had failed her emotionally, she had identified with the masculine. Murdock refers to Linda Schierse Leonard (1982), who says that inadequate attention from a father can lead a woman to armor herself in an attempt to father herself. This also cuts off her feminine feelings, creativity, spontaneity, and healthy relationships with men. In the absence of her father as an ally, Jan looked to herself for protection and to male relationships for a sense of self. She had already gone through the trials of the heroine's journey as she struggled to assert herself in the world and had found a measure of success. She had begun the descent with the dissatisfaction in her marriage and the underlying depression.

Course of Therapy

The first phase of Jan's therapy consisted of talk therapy. Through her dream work, it became quickly apparent to me that she was a good candidate for BMGIM therapy. However, she was resistant to this suggestion. She was clearly concerned about maintaining control and needed time to develop trust in me. Her therapy at this time focused primarily on current problems coping with living on her own and her contentious relationship with her husband, especially around practical issues involving their son. We also touched on the loss of her mother, the subsequent disappointment with her father, and her experiences in her family as a child. Finally, after three months she said, "I'm all talked out, let's do music."

I will discuss four of Jan's BMGIM sessions here. Italics indicate her words describing her imagery experience during the music. Highlights from her first session included sliding down a rainbow slide, seeing a waterfall on a creek with a rainbow in the spray, saying, *I feel a surge of energy, power of life—endless, miracle of life. Energy flows like water, never runs out. You can do whatever you want to do, the possibilities are limitless.* She saw butterflies, rode a dolphin, saw a dogsled team in a vast white open field, and rugged mountains. Then she became a hawk, saying, *Everything belongs to me. Kind of sad, the hawk is all alone, vastness all around, desolate feeling. The hawk enjoys power, it flies alone.* (Crying)

Jan liked being the hawk, but reflected, "it was very sad, the hawk didn't want to change." The hawk turned out to be a symbol of her self that recurred in both her music experiences and her drawings throughout her therapy. The rainbow, too, became a recurring image, later becoming obviously a symbol of the feminine. Jan was also able to connect with her strengths through the power of the waterfall and the hawk.

The following week she brought in the first mandala drawing. At the center was an eye surrounded by yellow light, with a red heart for a pupil and a teardrop. At the top were a hawk and a rainbow. On the left side were a dolphin in water and a naked woman running, seemingly toward the fire at the bottom. There was a large blank space on the right. A border around the mandala consisted of leaves of different colors representing the four seasons. She identified very strongly with the hawk, his strength and power, and to a lesser extent, his loneliness. The crying eye represented her sadness and she said the eye drew energy from the fire. The woman running toward the fire may also have symbolized the danger that her feminine self experienced, and possibly her descent into the underworld.

In her next BMGIM session the major images were a small boy that others were picking on, tension and feeling overwhelmed when she was trying to change linens on hospital beds that went on and on, becoming Icarus flying, and a chapel in an abbey.

She associated the small boy with a childhood neighbor, an only child, whom Jan felt was lonely and abandoned. This was an expression of her own feelings, both in the present and in her childhood after the loss of her mother. This session also revealed symbolically how out of control her life felt. Icarus, who in the myth flew too close to the sun, was a warning sign.

Her next mandala provided the basis for the balance of her work. The hawk is at the top of the mandala; in the middle, a strong-looking cypress tree *clinging to the side of a hill. Only one root goes into the ground and it's shaped by the winds and other external forces.* A stone (which looked very much like a tombstone) was on the left with a hammer and a chisel representing a rigid, cold, strong man who works hard to make things. On the right side, a potter's wheel with a pot on it represents a woman. *The pots flow from her, she doesn't work hard like the man. She's warm and weak.* The toys at the bottom represent the little boy playing in the sand. Jan strongly identified with the man who *acts on the world.* The potter represented her repressed feminine aspects. And the fact that she could not relate to the woman potter at all was an indicator of Jan's damaged feminine.

At this point, Jan was enjoying the BMGIM sessions so much that she had begun to add music to her regular practice of meditation, using her favorite relaxation music. These "self-guided sessions" were very important to her therapy as they helped her feel in control of her therapy and herself. They also greatly accelerated her process. Given my concern about the possibility of her going into a full blown manic state, when she presented at our next session very pressured and hyperverbal, I made the decision to discontinue the BMGIM sessions for a while.

She had continued her "imagery with music" process at home in which she took the child, whom she named Felice, to visit the sculptor, named Dominic, and the woman potter, named Serena, the characters from her mandala. She spent the most time with Serena. *She's harder to know, but she's more real to me now.* Jan realized they were all parts of her and expressed the fear that she wouldn't be able to work them through sufficiently to have satisfactory intimate relationships with men.

Over the next few sessions, Jan was hyperactive, but not clinically manic. *I still take out the garbage and put dinner on the table.* I felt she still needed to be more grounded before continuing with BMGIM so our sessions were verbal. She continued to meditate with music at home, connecting with Dominic and Serena. She wanted to know if everybody got as involved with their images as she did, wondering if she was "crazy."

During this period she had a significant dream. She, her husband, son, and some friends had just finished painting a room. They disagreed on whether it was a good job or not, each viewing the work from a different perspective. Jan wanted to take care of everyone, and realized she had to speak to *each person, in their own language.* Jan understood this to mean that she needed to speak to and learn from the characters representing parts of herself "in their own language."

At this point, Jan was beginning to undergo major change. She was softer and less controlling with her husband and son. She began to take bubble baths, surrounded by candles, which she had never done before. Jan was more pensive, very concerned with problems like the leaky roof, problem patients, etc. *Nothing like reality to ground you.* As her hyperactive behavior decreased over the next few weeks, she was more in touch with her sense of loss. We decided it was time for more BMGIM sessions.

Her next BMGIM session began in a chapel from a previous session and morphed into a cathedral. There was a wedding party where she felt a strong sense of community among the women, but the men were all very vague. She said it was an odd wedding, with no bridegroom. Then she realized the bride was becoming an adult member of the community of women. As the bride stood at the altar with a priestess presiding, a movie played behind the priestess, showing women doing domestic things and taking care of babies. Everyone watched entranced. The priestess and bride drank wine from a goblet, which was passed to all the women like communion at mass. The women, in beautiful colored dresses, made a circle around the bride and the priestess. The beauty of the experience brought tears to Jan. Light streamed through stained glass windows and she had a *feeling of communion and support, like you would always want to be enclosed in this circle.*

The next image was of a house with smoke coming from the chimney and breakfast was starting. A peasant woman in a long skirt lived there by herself in harmony with nature, growing food and also roses for beauty. Inside the cottage were roses, a fireplace, and books for *comfortable, solitary pleasures.*

In the final images Jan was a bird or angel, flying. *Light, a cosmic aurora borealis; I'm a see-through person flying through a tunnel of light. I'm drawn upward to the source of the light. It's very spiritual. I'm watching giant butterflies with wings like Waterford crystal; now I'm the butterfly with wings of beveled glass with a thousand prisms.*

Jan's response was, *What a wonderful ritual I devised for myself.* She now fully realizes she has made great progress in integrating her feminine self. The mandala she brought the following week featured a beautiful "Butterfly Woman" with yellow light surrounding her head in the middle, the peasant woman's cottage on the left, Serena's potter's wheel with a rainbow behind it on the right, and the hawk flying at the top. A flower border around the mandala represented the colors in the women's dresses. The ritual reminded her of African rituals, and the gowns were like African dress, except made of chiffon. I wondered to myself if that represented a positive transference to me as an African American. We discussed the symbolic meaning of the wedding—an integration with her feminine self, and the peasant woman as a symbol of a self-sufficient woman. Jan as the butterfly, a symbol of transformation, reinforced the message in the ritual. She was not hyperactive, only excited at feeling her progress.

Over the next few sessions, Jan dealt with anger with her father over abandoning her emotionally, and grief at her mother's death. She continued to deal with her issues in terms of Dominic and Serena. She also began to paint (her mandalas were all done in oil pastels, not paint) something she had never done. She was amazed to discover she not only enjoyed painting, but also was fairly good at it. She was discovering her creativity.

During this period Jan had an important dream in which she was awakened by the wind chimes in her garden. A man stole her bicycle, then she turned over and found he was in bed with her. He had a "satanic" look and was about to rape her when she woke up. To her, the theft of the bicycle represented stealing her balance and freedom to move about in the world. She saw him as Dominic about to overpower her new-found feminine self. This was her first genuine realization of Dominic's negative side, and we remembered the tombstone-like stone associated with Dominic in her second mandala. At this time Jan began reading some of the popular books about goddesses in relation to feminine psychology. Her mood began to stabilize and she was neither hypomanic nor depressed.

The final BMGIM session that I will discuss here found Jan in a field with dark storm clouds above and thunder and lightning in the distance. It was raining hard, but not on her. Bolts of lightning released tension and everything was becoming green. Scary and majestic women, harpies like the Valkyries, were coming out of the sky. As it began to clear, a rainbow appeared. Everything was very green, with flowers, a brook, frogs, and a waterfall. A woman spirit lived in the waterfall, which was very big over a deep gorge. The woman spirit emerged with enormous energy, holding a rainbow in one hand and a thunderbolt in the other. After a while she went back in, all was quiet and the water was a very deep green.

Jan realized she had made a quantum leap, and the following week she brought in a drawing of the "Waterfall Woman." This drawing was completely different from all previous ones in that it was not in circular form and there was no border. It had a large green stalk, and large green leaves that reached upward and fanned out at the top. On either side of the fan at the top were black strokes that were reminiscent of the hawk's wings. It was a very strong image that completely filled the paper.

Jan explained that the waterfall was first a *giant phallus,* then the Woman spirit sprang out with enormous energy and power, the full length of the waterfall. *A very, very powerful woman!* She understood that she no longer needed a phallus because she was now stronger than Dominic.

Jan's therapy ended shortly after this last BMGIM session. She achieved her goal of letting go of her most rigid, controlling behavior. She began to relate to her ex-husband comfortably, and no longer felt compelled to control his behavior in relation to other women or visiting with their son. She felt ready for a new relationship, but was no longer driven to find a man. Both the hypomanic and depressive symptoms abated and her mood stabilized as genuinely bright.

Discussion

Jan's imagery went right to the heart of the matter. The hawk, a symbol of her Self, the rainbow, a symbol of her lost feminine aspects, the butterflies, precursors of the Butterfly Woman, and the waterfall, a precursor of the Waterfall Woman, were all present in that very first session. Her words in that session were prophetic: *I feel a surge of energy, power of life—endless, miracle of life. Energy flows like water, never runs out. You can do whatever you want to do; the possibilities are limitless.* Jan descended to the Dark Goddess and through her transformational images she underwent an initiation ceremony where she reclaimed her feminine aspects and returned with a transformed and more balanced personality.

My sense is that the Great Goddess archetype was activated in Jan. In other words, she was infused with the energy of the archetype and that energy drove her therapeutic process. According to Bolen (1994), a goddess archetype can become activated and "spring into life when the archetype is called forth by a person or event" (p.30). The event in Jan's life was leaving her husband, coupled with the realization that she needed to come to terms with her over-controlling behavior in order to establish better interpersonal relationships. Her psyche understood that the primary work lay in integrating the feminine aspects that she had shut down long ago. The activation of the Great Goddess archetype would explain the intensity with which she worked with her imagery, did her own music sessions, and made so many symbolic drawings. Her therapy lasted only six months, including the first three months that were only verbal sessions. This was remarkable progress. One does not have to be familiar with archetypes for one to be activated. Archetypes carry their energy on an unconscious level. The BMGIM sessions were the vehicle through which she accessed the archetype, but it was her own inner direction that led her to the Great Goddess.

Jan's therapy also illustrates an important point on which I disagree with Murdock. The last two stages of Murdock's Heroine's Journey are healing the woman's wounded masculine and integrating the masculine and feminine within herself. In my view, a woman does not have to look to something labeled masculine to find parts of herself. As Bolen (1984) asserts, the concept of the animus as the masculine aspects in a woman does not fit every woman. What Jan did was heal her wounded feminine and then integrate it fully through the Great Goddess with all her creativity and strength, not the feminine *and* masculine. Jan's image of the harpies and Valkyries symbolized the vengeful and warrior aspects of the feminine, and the Waterfall Woman held both the rainbow and the thunderbolt—the soft, intuitive and the wild, spirited feminine attributes. This is the Great Goddess, the complete woman. When we look back into antiquity, beyond European cultures, we find models of the whole feminine. Inanna and the other ancient Great Goddesses were complete as women, with all the human attributes, positive and negative. These are the models I look toward in psychotherapy with women.

These, indeed, are the models for all women. Women come from varying backgrounds and have different life experiences; however, to quote Luisah Teish (2005):

> [E]very woman must make her own choices and experience the consequences. But it is important to know that we have more than just a few ancestral biographies and mythic models to feed our imagination. And we must have the power and the processes to transform our inherited images into contemporary reality. When we analyze the stories we can understand our inheritance; when we study the symbols we can enrich our Imaginations, and when we act upon this enrichment . . . we can enjoy a healthier life and leave a richer inheritance for the coming generations. This is not only the right, but also the responsibility, of woman. (p.35)

As the mother of daughters and sister to women around the world, I take this responsibility seriously. This responsibility is the primary message of this chapter.

Music Therapy

What does the Great Goddess hold for music therapy? The Great Goddess holds the paradox of life/death, light/darkness, and mind/body. She demands that we go into the underground and grapple with the depths of our souls. Music therapy in the United States has been mired in the mechanistic view of the world, the patriarchal split of mind vs. body, emotion vs. rationalism. To embrace the Great Goddess, to honor the feminine, music therapy must, to use the words of Woodman and Dickson (1996), ". . . establish a balance, a reconnection with our own deepest nature that can root us in a world of meaning and imagination" (p.36). Music therapy and music therapists must be rooted in the full range of experience that our music holds and expresses.

This need is evidenced in the split between music therapists who use music in a mechanistic way, to act upon clients, and those who recognize the deep connection of music to the realm of feeling, the disturbing sides as well as the loving aspects of human nature, feeling that is rooted in the body. There is a split between those who acknowledge music's ability to illuminate our deepest nature, both our highest aspirations and the shadow which carries our malevolent leanings, our destruction of the earth and our inhumanity to each other, and those music therapists who do not or cannot tolerate this application.

I have practiced music therapy for nearly 49 years, and I have witnessed this struggle firsthand. I have marveled at the strength of the resistance to embracing the depth potential of music in therapy, reactions ranging from ignoring, marginalizing, or denigrating these methods, to personal attacks on those who have brought these methods to us as well as their practitioners. The only way I can understand this is the absence or marginalization of Great Goddess energy, the Feminine in music therapy. This is ironic in a female-dominated profession.

But the hidden Feminine is surfacing in music therapy, just as She is in society at large despite the strong resistance. She is seen in the large numbers of music therapists studying a variety of music and imagery techniques, the much greater acceptance of all forms of music and imagery, and the increasing embrace of depth-oriented music improvisation methods. She is found in those therapists who tolerate chaos in improvisational music and allow structure to emerge from the process, rather than insisting on imposing structure on the improvisation.

Music holds it all. It reflects light and shadow, our dreams, our fears, our deepest emotions, and our beauty. Music therapy will evidence the Great Goddess when the breadth and depth of music and music therapy practices are accepted and taught in ALL music therapy programs, not just a handful. Music therapy will reach its full potential when the hidden Dark Goddess who lives in music is allowed to shine forth in all of Her beauty and Her terror, Her generativity and Her destruction, Her fierceness and Her love, embracing all of her wondrous glory.

REFERENCES

Anderson, Sherry Ruth & Hopkins, Patricia (1991) *The Feminine Face of God: The Unfolding of the Sacred in Women.* NY: Bantam.

Ann, Martha & Imel, Dorothy Myers (1993) *Goddesses in World Mythology: A Biographical Dictionary.* NY: Oxford University Press.

Begg, Ean (1985/1996) *The Cult of the Black Virgin.* London: Penguin Books.

Bolen, Jean Shinoda (1984) *Goddesses in Every Woman: A New Psychology of Women.* San Francisco: Harper & Row.

Bolen, Jean Shinoda (2001) *Goddesses in Older Women, Archetypes in Women over Fifty.* NY: HarperCollins.

Birnbaum, Lucia Chiavola (1993, 2000) *Black Madonnas: Feminism, Religion & Politics in Italy.* NY: toExcel.

Birnbaum, Lucia Chiavola (2001) *Dark Mother, African Origins and Godmothers.* NY: Authors Choice Press.

Campbell, Joseph (1949) *The Hero with a Thousand Faces.* Princeton: Princeton University Press.

Chodorow, Nancy (1978) *The Reproduction of Mothering: Psychoanalysis and the Sociology of Gender.* Berkeley: University of California Press.

Cleary, Thomas & Aziz, Sartaz (2000) *Twilight Goddess, Spiritual Feminism and Feminine Spirituality.* Boston: Shambhala.

Craighead, Meinrad (1986) *The Mother's Songs, Images of God the Mother.* Mahwah, NJ: Paulist Press.

Eisler, Riane (1987/1995) *The Chalice & the Blade, Our History, Our Future.* NY: Harper.

Ford, Clyde W. (1999) *The Hero with an African Face, Mythic Wisdom of Traditional Africa.* NY: Bantam Books.

Frobenius, Leo (1927) *Das Unbekannte Afrika*, cited in Campbell, *Historical Atlas, 40.*

Gilligan, Carol (1982) *In a Different Voice, Psychological Theory and Women's Development.* Cambridge: Harvard University Press.

Goldberg, Frances Smith (2000) I am the creator and the created: A woman's journey from loss to wholeness. In *Beitrage zur Musiktherapie* 10:47–58.
Gustafson, Fred (1990) *The Black Madonna*. Boston: Sigo Press.
hooks, bell (1981) *Ain't I a Woman: Black Women and Feminism.* Cambridge: South End Press.
hooks, bell (1984, 2000) *Feminist Theory: From Margin to Center.* Cambridge: South End Press.
Kenny, Carolyn (1989) *The Field of Play*: *A Guide for the Theory and Practice of Music Therapy.* Atascadero: Ridgeway.
Larrington, Carolyne (1992) *The Feminist Companion to Mythology.* London: Pandora Press.
LeGuin, Ursula (1989) *Dancing at the Edge of the World.* NY: Harper and Row.
Leonard, Linda Schierse (1982) *The Wounded Woman.* Boston: Shambhala.
Lerman, Hannah (1976) What happens in feminist therapy? In Sue Cox (ed.), *Female Psychology: The Emerging Self.* Chicago: Science Research Associates.
Lowinsky, Naomi Ruth (1992) *Stories from the Motherline, Reclaiming the Mother-Daughter Bond, Finding our Feminine Souls.* Los Angeles: Tarcher.
Meador, Betty De Shong (2000) *Inanna, Lady of the Largest Heart, Poems of the Sumerian High Priestess Enheduanna.* Austin: University of Texas Press.
Mookerjee, Ajit (1988) *Kali, the Feminine Force.* London: Thames and Hudson.
Morrison, Toni (1988) *Beloved*. NY: Plume Books.
Murdock, Maureen (1990) *The Heroine's Journey.* Boston: Shambhala.
Pagels, Elaine (1979) *The Gnostic Gospels.* NY: Vintage Books.
Perera, Sylvia (1981) *Descent to the Goddess, A Way of Initiation for Women.* Toronto: Inner City Books.
Prozan, Charlotte Krause (1992) *Feminist Psychoanalytic Psychotherapy*. NJ: Jason Aronson.
Stone, Merlin (1976) *When God was a Woman.* NY: Harvest/Harcourt Brace.
Stone, Merlin (1979) *Ancient Mirrors of Womanhood.* Boston: Beacon.
Teish, Luisah (2005) The stained glass whore and other virgins, In Lucia Chiavola Birnbaum (ed.), *She is Everywhere!* NY: iUniverse.
Walker, Alice, (1983) *In Search of Our Mother's Gardens.* NY: Harvest/Harcourt Brace.
Wolkstein, Diane & Kramer, Samuel (1983) *Inanna, Queen of Heaven and Earth, Her Stories and Hymns from Sumer.* NY: Harper Row.
Woodman, Marion & Dickson, Elinor (1997) *Dancing in the Flames, The Dark Goddess in the Transformation of Consciousness.* Boston: Shambhala.

Chapter Five

FEMINISM AND MUSIC THERAPY IN KOREA

Seung-A Kim

They have long been silenced by physical and psychological intimidation, and actual bodily violence by the oppressor. When there is no place where [Korean women] can express their true selves, their true feelings, the oppressed become "stuck" inside.

— Hyun Kyung Chung, 1990

HAN

A central theme in women's lives in Korea is captured by the Korean word, "*han*." Symbolically, it represents the image of traditional Korean women's suffering, pain, and crying, as well as their resilience throughout Korean history. A loose translation of the term would be, "the sorrow and anger that grows" (E. H. Kim, 1995, p.160). Due to many invasions by other countries, *han* is a quality that has become deeply embedded in Koreans from one generation to the next. In fact, *han* is a term that applies to both women and men. However, it has special application to women because of their oppressive life circumstances.

Therefore, *han* has emerged in various ways in the lives of Korean women. Historically, there have been few outlets for women to directly express their grief and sorrow over their personal life situation, or life in general. This has resulted in psychosomatic illness being common among Korean women: "Korean women's life experience is *han* itself. The resentment, indignation, sense of defeat, resignation and nothingness in *han* make many Korean women brokenhearted and physically sick" (H. K. Chung, 1990, p.66).

In addition to manifesting as a mental and emotional state, this idea of suffering has emerged in various forms of art. To express an intense emotion in a nonverbal form is considered socially acceptable in Korea. Accordingly, there is much traditional Korean music, dance, and rituals entitled, *Han*. This is also expressed indirectly, as many poems and songs incorporate the phrase, "women's cries" or "women crying" (S. C. Choi *et al.,* 2001; Ho. Kw. Chung, 1972; Noh, 2001).

On the other hand, Korean women have progressively chosen more active ways to express their "grief and sorrow," by participating in the women's movement or in social and political movements. This quality of bearing with almost unbearable inner anguish is something that has characterized the resilience of Korean women.

TRADITIONAL KOREAN WOMEN

Philosophy of Confucius—The Basis of Social Ideology in Korea

Since the Chosun dynasty (1393–1910), Koreans have been deeply governed by the ideology of Confucius. The principles of Confucius provided guidelines for the ways that people should interact in society. The proper relationship between husband and wife is well described in *Samkangoryoon,* which was written by Confucius to characterize the relative social positions of each: "the husband is the mainstay of the wife; between husband and wife, there is a distinction in position" (Ho. Kw., Chung, 1985, p.89). While the ideas of Confucius served to establish social stability, these ideas clearly regarded women as being unequal to men. Confucian philosophy supported the idea of a patriarchal society in which women were accorded a low status and a subservient role. According to Confucius, it was the natural order of things that males should lead and be in charge and that women should be silent and essentially limited in their functioning to the home.

Additionally, it was Confucius's idea that a society should function according to high moral standards. Originally, Korea was an agricultural country and maintained a collective social philosophy, which is typical of Asian countries. Having the political and social power vested in males, and having the society stratified, supported Korean society as a whole. However, "proper conduct" within the societal structure was itself considered a moral value. Therefore, to act in any other way was considered a disruption of the natural order of things and a violation of correct moral standards. These standards of behavior were supported by those in authority, by those of the upper classes, and by males in general.

Traditionally, the Korean woman[1]has been viewed and treated as a subordinate in the various phases of her life. This is well described in the

[1] In this chapter, I refer to "the Korean woman" when giving examples of how the culture has socialized and oppressed women. However, I do not wish to indicate that we all

Trilogy of Obedience: "when she is a child, a woman must obey her parents; after marriage, she must submit to her husband; and in old age, she must yield to her son" (Ho. Kw. Chung, 1985, p.94).

From the moment that she was born, the Korean woman had to face gender discrimination due to the clear strong preference for sons within families. Simply because she was female, her status within her family was always lower than that of her brothers. During childhood, she was indoctrinated in the clear distinctions between the roles of women and men. According to traditional social standards, a Korean woman could not speak with a loud voice and could not be assertive. She could not study and receive the same education as boys. Further, it was not only what she was "taught," it was what she experienced all around her—in her family, in her community, and in her society as a whole. These roles were explicitly and implicitly delineated in every aspect of her experience.

At a certain age, girls were expected to get married. If the woman did not get married at that point, this became a serious concern of the whole family. Once she got married, by virtue of her marriage the Korean woman became an "'un-person' until she produced a son" (Crane, 1967, p.95). In addition, she was no longer referred to by her own first name, but as the mother of her children—for example, "Emily's Mother." So, she lost her personal identity, and was affirmed only in having given birth to children. This is still common today.

A woman was in charge of matters inside the home, and that was regarded as a woman's job. However, this refers to her husband's home, and her husband's family. It was often far from her family of origin. In practical reality, this was often not so clear and not so easy. Being in the family home of her husband meant living with her mother-in-law, who had been the female in charge until her son's marriage. Often, the mother-in-law did not want to relinquish her authority or her position of importance when the daughter-in-law moved in.

Seven Evils for Exile is yet another example by which the Confucian view of women resulted in severe limitation, restriction, and unfair treatment: "if a woman failed to honor her husband's parents, did not bear any children, committed adultery, expressed intense jealousy, became seriously ill, talked incessantly, or engaged in stealing, then she was immediately driven from her home" (Ho. Kw. Chung, 1985, p.94). The underlying idea was that any of these seven acts brought shame upon the family. Exiling her from the family not only embodied punishment, but also absolved the family of shame by disconnecting the family from the woman. Within this code of thought, women's sexual

experience oppression in the same ways or that there are no variations in our experiences as Korean women.

fidelity was overly emphasized. A woman was not simply judged by the behavior that she initiated, but was judged responsible for anything that happened to her. For example, if a woman was raped, she was encouraged to commit suicide for the sake of preserving the family's honor.

Therefore, traditional Korean women were expected to devote themselves to the good of the family. They were even forced to sacrifice themselves in the service of their husband and family. Within this social context, feminist ideas were met with a great deal of resistance. Social change that involved even modest recognition of women and their rights as human beings was not only regarded as socially disruptive and unacceptable, but it was considered morally wrong.

Even though the royal class no longer exists in modern Korean society, the influence of Confucius is still deeply embedded in Koreans. Moreover, because of the great respect for Confucius, it has significantly hindered genuine fundamental social change, especially for women (H. K. Chung, 1990; S. H. Chung, 1986; Jung, 2003; Ro, 1998).

OVERVIEW OF THE FEMINIST MOVEMENT IN KOREA

The feminist movement in Korea needs to be examined within the historical context of Korean society (Edwards & Roces, 2000; Hampson, 2000; Jung, 2003; H. J. Lee, 1996). In most Asian countries, feminism has often been criticized as an aspect of Western thought, which is discordant with traditional Eastern thinking. However, it is important to note that Korea has developed its "own feminist practice, rooted in [its] specific socio-political and cultural context" (Jung, 2003, p.261). For example, as Hyo-Jae Lee (1996) has pointed out, when certain rights for women were initially enacted into constitutional law, this was not achieved by the efforts of social movements, but rather came about through particular political-social circumstances.

In addition, discussing the feminist movement in Korea is quite complicated, due to several factors that impact it. Issues of nationalism, capitalism, modernism, democracy, and social class structure, as well as the issue of the reunification of North and South Korea have all intertwined with the feminist movement to varying extents at certain points in time. This has hindered the development of feminism as its own independent movement in Korea (Hampson, 2000; H. J. Lee, 1996). Women's issues have often been "hidden" behind other issues mentioned above, which were considered more "acceptable" at the time. This is another example of the uniqueness of the development of the feminist movement in Korea.

Historical Perspectives

The history of feminism in Korea is not extensive, yet it has developed actively. One can view women's participation in Nationalism during the 1900s as the seed of the feminist movement in Korea. Additionally, the Women's Labor Movement during the 1970s can be seen as the first step in that feminist movement.

Since 1975, which was proclaimed by the United Nations as International Women's Year, the principles of feminism have grown in Korea. To develop this movement in a more organized way, the Korea Women's Associations United (KWAU) was established in 1987. Since 1990, as the result of a more democratic social atmosphere, this organization has become more focused on gender-specific issues, such as sexuality and family law reform (Jung, 2003).

In the late 1970s, Western theories on women's issues were formally introduced to the country, and colleges in Korea created departments of Women's Studies. After that, the women's movement in Korea actually branched into two different groups, each pursuing their own aims. One group was composed of educated and intellectual individuals, who pursued women's studies, and developed their theories in support of family law reform, human rights and democratization. The other group was composed of individuals from the lower socio-economic classes, who focused on the real life situation of women in the labor force (Jung, 2003; Y. S. Kim & M. H. Han, 2000).

Korean Women and Patriotism (National Liberalism)

Traditionally, Korean women have taken the role of keeping their family together and helping the next generation to succeed, regardless of the personal sacrifice involved. Although women advocated ideas such as laws permitting women to remarry and equality of social classes, when Japan invaded and colonized Korea, the issue of immediate importance became the education of women in order to "properly raise their children." Under the colonization by Japan in the 1900s, it was believed that the efforts toward independence and nationalism could best be promoted by educated women properly educating their children, and avoiding indoctrination by the occupying country. It is striking that the perception of the need for women's education came from nationalism, not the direct idea of women's rights or the furthering of the individual. In addition, it should be noted that there were also men who advocated the need of education for women. For instance, influenced by his studies in America, Pil Se Jae introduced and discussed the importance of women's education through the newspaper of which he was the editor, *Independence* (H. J. Lee, 1996).

Korean Women and Religion

Influenced by Shamanism, Buddhism, and Confucianism, Korean women have been religious and spiritual throughout history. Their faith in God also has a strong relationship to their endurance of the societal restrictions and attitudes concerning women. In 1885, ministers from the West arrived in Korea. At that time, the nation was going through the process of modernization, and the socio-political situation in Korea was unstable. At this point in history, women were desperately looking for something to give them hope (H. J. Lee, 1996). This is one of the reasons that Christianity was successful in Korea. Christianity, which taught the principle of equality under God, regardless of gender or class, was appealing in a country that was dominated by the idea of class structure. It was particularly appealing to women, who were oppressed as a group. This religion, which was new to Korea, brought them new hope. It presented ". . . an inclusive image of God . . . which promotes equality and harmony between men and women: a partnership of equals" (H. K. Chung, 1990, p.48). On the other hand, introducing Western culture and capitalism to Korea contributed to the lessening of traditional Korean culture and an imitation of Western values.

Rapid Economic Growth and Political and Social Changes

The development of the women's movement in Korea has been shaped by Korea's economic, political and social situations. In 1948, the republic of Korea was established. As part of the new constitution, the basic rights of women were protected, such as equal opportunity in employment and education. During the 1960s and 1970s, Korea accomplished a "miracle of economic growth." Women's labor contributed greatly to this. Many young women left home and moved to urban areas to make money. However, their work situation was poor, receiving low wages and working in poor environments that were hazardous to their health. Additionally, when a woman worked, it was regarded as a temporary job. That is, once a woman got married, she left work. If a woman continued to work after marriage, it was seen as a sign of the family's financial need (Y. S. Kim & M. H. Han, 2000). This was considered shameful.

Along with this rapid economic development, there were also governmental policies that suppressed freedom of speech, and criticism of those in power. When they occurred, labor strikes by female factory workers were seen as challenges to governmental authority. Therefore, in reality, "it was an exercise of trying to break a rock with an egg" (Y. S. Kim & M. H. Han, 2000, p.504).

However, the political and social situation in Korea drastically changed in the late 1980s and early 1990s. The first civilian (non-military) president was elected in 1993. "Nationalism (*Minjok*), Democracy (*Minju*), and People (*Minjung*)" was the main slogan that focused the entire Korean society. Accordingly, it is only recently that gender-specific issues, such as sexuality and sexual violence, have been openly discussed in Korea.

Korean Women and Sex

In Korean society open talk about sex, especially by women, was regarded as improper. Within the traditional norms, women in Korea were not allowed to express their sexuality. If a Korean man was not satisfied in his marriage, he could look to a woman outside his marriage for companionship or sex, without much consequence. On the contrary, a woman would be judged by Confucius's *Seven Evils for Exile.*

A female's body was regarded as belonging to her husband, as a medium of the husband's pleasure and as the vehicle for bearing a son. Therefore, "women are not encouraged to have control over their bodies or their sexuality and many unmarried women are still ignorant about sex and contraception" (Hampson, 2000, p.174). Consequently, Korea has a high abortion rate (Korean Women's Development Institute, 2005). It is interesting to note that in the West abortion is considered a matter of a woman's choice. However, in Korea the high abortion rate is driven by the desire to have sons and avoid giving birth to daughters (Hampson, 2000).

A case of sexual assault by the police (Jung, 2003) dramatically brought to light the issue of women's rights. In 1986, Kwon In Sook, a student activist, was arrested by the police. She was brutally, sexually assaulted by the arresting officers. The officials dismissed it as false accusations by the young woman. Women's groups and the general public were so outraged that reform followed. As a result, many social movement organizations united through this incident, regardless of sex. However, even then, the incident was seen as a political issue rather than a case of sexual assault against a woman, and a violation of fundamental human rights.

The women's Sexual Violence Relief Center (SVRC) and the Sexual Assault Center (SAC) were established in 1990s. They have provided education to the public, and have encouraged people to bring incidents of sexual violence to public attention. As a result, the seriousness of sexual assault issues in Korea has been discussed more in public.

Comfort Women

"Comfort women" is another example of an issue that helped the Korean people to unite by embedding the concern for women's abuse within the context of a broad social issue—in this case, nationalism (J. M. Kim & C. Y. Chung, 2005). During World War II, Japan collected young Korean girls and forced them into sexual slavery, for use by their military. These young women were referred to as "comfort women." For many years, they were treated in Korea as social outcasts. Although they had been brutalized and repeatedly violated, these women were unable to talk openly about what had happened to them, because of the prevailing attitudes of the Korean people toward women. The events were treated as a source of "national shame" (Y. J. Choi, 2002). Therefore, the "comfort women" had to endure their physical and sexual trauma in silence.

The feelings in Korea toward Japan were that it had committed a political atrocity, not an atrocity against women and their rights as human beings. It was not until 1990 that these events were discussed openly. Public recognition and support for the "comfort women" led to the creation of *the Korean Council for Women Drafted for Military Sexual Slavery by Japan* (Hankuk, 2001). Although the emphasis has still remained political, the Korean society as a whole has become more supportive to these women, and more open to viewing the events from a feminist perspective.

The Concept of Family in Korea

Within the Confucian system of thought, the family unit is the core of society. The family came to be regarded as almost a sacred element of Korean society. For Koreans, as with many Asian cultures, the idea of "family" is not the nuclear family that is the model in the West, and especially in America. It refers to an extended family system that includes husband and wife, their children, grandparents, and sometimes uncles and aunts. Further, it involves a hierarchical system of relationships, with males holding principle importance, and the elderly being accorded respect. Beyond this, the family even includes persons who are no longer living, as the family's ancestors are regarded as part of the family, and are revered and prayed to in worship ceremonies. In Korea, this is what is considered the "traditional family system."

While Korea was under occupation by the Japanese in the 1900s, Japan reinforced the "family headship" system (the *hoju* system), because they believed that centralizing family authority and responsibility in the male head of extended families made control of the society easier for them. This family headship system prescribed the structure of families and society as a whole. The aim was to support the Japanese military rule of Korea, and to promote an agricultural society (Oh, 2002).

Within this system, in the case of the death of the husband/father, the eldest son of the family inherited all the property, and any other assets of the father, as well as the father's authority as head of the household, regardless of the son's age or that of his female siblings. Anything having to do with the family was always referenced back to the father. Children of a widowed or divorced mother were still considered to belong to the father. This was true even when the children were being raised by a divorced mother, and had no contact with the father. This caused many practical social problems, such as not being able to receive social welfare, in the case of divorce or adoption (Oh, 2002). Prejudice against women, their low social status, and their limited legal rights, all resulted in a strong preference for sons in families, and a desire to avoid having daughters.

The constant efforts of feminist groups, as well as evolving social awareness, have combined to change the social system in Korea. It has been only recently in 2005 that the national assembly passed a bill that revised constitutional law and resulted in the abolition of the family headship system. This bill will take effect in 2008 (S. H. Lee & J. J. Choi, 2005). These new laws have been considered a significant victory for Korea's feminist groups.

Are These Changes Real Feminist Changes?

One of the practical strategies that the women's movement in Korea had to employ is to avoid pursuing feminist goals directly, and to attach their issues to other social movements. Nonetheless, these "back door efforts" have resulted in more opportunities for women to get higher education, and greater job opportunities for women. As part of this legal change that is still going on, Korea has enacted many laws. Among the most important of these is the Prohibitional Law Regarding Discrimination between Men and Women (1999), a law that clearly promotes feminist principles.

However, legal change does not necessarily bring about a corresponding change in thinking, or actual social change. Unfortunately, this process has led to the perpetuation of feminist issues being viewed as general social or political problems, instead of being seen as issues pertaining to women and their rights as human beings.

Modern Korean Women

On the other hand, these legal changes have been accompanied by changes in the thinking of many women. As women have progressively embraced feminist ideas, they have been socially freed by no longer being "locked" into marriage. There has been a significant trend for women to choose not to live in male-dominated extended families. Living on their own, choosing not to get married, refusing to accept the traditional Korean family and social systems, have all embodied radical breaks with the cultural past.

As younger women have been exposed to ideas from outside their traditional culture, and as they have traveled to and lived in Western countries, they have come to embrace feminist ideas from these countries, and have become dissatisfied with the traditional Korean social values. As a result of exposure to new ideas, along with changing economic conditions, women engage in subservient family duties or domestic work less and less. Instead, they choose to pursue education and personal careers with increasing frequency. In addition, men and the society as a whole are more receptive to feminist ideas. Consequently, the family structure has changed, and "hierarchical family relations have changed into relatively equal ones" (H. J. Lee, 1989, p.85).

Social changes in attitudes and values have been rapid and recent. Accordingly, it is common to see differences in the views between generations. This was evident in the research of Gyesook Yoo (2004), who conducted research on the attachment between Korean mothers and their adult daughters. She found that mothers are "less concerned about reciprocation of attachment and interaction than their daughters are" (p.29).

For traditional mothers, the primary attachment is to their sons, especially the first son. The closeness between mother and son continues after the son's marriage. As a result, conflict between the new wife and the mother-in-law is often the consequence. However, the modern Korean woman does not accept this situation, and this, in turn, can lead to marital discord. These generational differences are also evidenced in living situations. Modern women no longer accept the separation from their family of origin that was traditional for a young woman once she got married. Instead, they prefer to maintain a closer relationship with their own mothers.

In addition, those modern women who have accepted feminist principles are changing the traditional hierarchical family attitudes. These daughters no longer accept the roles that their mothers played in the family, which was submissive and sacrificing. They no longer accept the idea that marriage is an opportunity for upward social mobility. Moreover, the idea of living as a single woman living outside of the family home is a new social pattern for Korea, and has been occurring with increasing frequency.

Overall, Korea is in the process of revising the traditional structure of the family (Hampson, 2000; H. J. Lee, 1996; J. K. Lee, 1999). Outwardly, the family structure appears to be changed from the extended, male-dominated, hierarchical family system to the Western nuclear family. However, in practice, the parent-child relationship is still considered more important than the wife-husband relationship. Fundamental social change is still in progress. As with many fundamental social changes, these differences in women's attitudes and behavior and lifestyle have met with conflicts within the family.

The Rapidly Rising Divorce Rate

In the past 20 years, the divorce rate in Korea has been continuously increasing. It is only in recent years that the divorce rate seems to have stabilized (*The Korea Times*, March 30, 2005). This is a major social issue for the country, because the permanency of the family has been the foundation of the Korean social system. Sung-Soo Bang & Bo-Im Jang (2003) identified the causes of the rising the divorce rate as the increase in the socio-economic status of females, changes in marriage ideology, increasing public acceptance of divorce, the revised family law, and fewer children being born into families.

Since laws and attitudes have been changing quite recently, it is not surprising that the divorce rate is especially high among elderly couples. Women who had been putting up with abusive or patriarchal husbands now refuse to accept the conditions anymore. Leaving the marriage is made even easier now that their children are grown.

Divorce is not only an issue for the married couple, but also for the children. In addition to the issues of physical and emotional dysfunction that occur when a family breaks up, there is the problem of child rearing, as well as the financial difficulties which usually accompany being a single parent. Therefore, there is a great need for social and psychological services, as well as social welfare support.

Domestic Violence

Domestic violence is also a serious feminist and social issue in Korea, as it is in many areas of the world (E. S. Choi, *et al.*, 1996). Many abused women hide the fact of their physical abuse, because of their feelings of shame. They suffer the physical injury, as well as the emotional trauma, and try not to let anyone know about it. This often becomes expressed through a somatization of their symptoms—the emergence of psychosomatic illness. The violence also affects children growing up in the family. They witness or hear the violence and rationalize it taking place. Unconsciously, it becomes the model for husband-wife behavior that the children learn (G. S. Kim, 2003).

In 1985, a *Women's Hotline* was created, and reportedly it has been effective in dealing with cases of domestic violence and sexual abuse. However, feminist groups are attempting to intervene before the incidents of abuse take place. Rather than trying to undo the effects of abuse, they are attempting to provide programs of education aimed at prevention, such as education about family life, and a couples-relationship program (E. S. Choi, *et al.*, 1996).

FEMINIST THERAPY IN KOREA

With the growth of the women's movement in Korea since the 1980s, the field of counseling and therapy has begun to pay attention to women's issues. The terminology "feminist psychotherapy" first appeared in Korea when the Korean Women's Development Institute published the book, *Theories and Practices for Counseling Women*, in the mid-1980s. It began with treatment for abused women (Chang, 2000).

Although there have been some psychological services available to women, such as feminist-oriented family therapy, group counseling, and anger management, there are some difficulties with women being able to utilize these services. Korean women have been culturally conditioned to blame themselves for anything that goes wrong. Additionally, in Korea, talking about problems outside of family is regarded as shameful behavior. Further, although the new generation of Korean women is learning to think in a new way, traditional women, who tend to be the most abused, are least able to take care of themselves financially. And, if she needs them, social welfare services are not sufficient for a woman to be able to sustain herself, especially if she has children.

It is yet another practical reality that there are few therapists in Korea who are adequately trained in feminist therapy and the issues which can arise in the therapy (K. Park, 2003). Women's issues have a close relationship with social and cultural issues. If therapy deals with a woman's thoughts and feelings, but the social environment and the "socio-cultural stress" remain unaltered, it will be difficult for the woman to effect enduring change in her personal life.

Psychological Disorders

There are certain psychological disorders that are commonly found in Korean women: depression, anger disorder, somatization, and anxiety disorder. This is the result of socio-cultural factors which exist in Korea (Spector, 2004; Yu, 2003).

Depression

Depression is the most common psychological disorder found in Korean women (E. J. Choi, 2003; H. E. Kim, 2003; K. S. Kim, et al., 1999). Depression is suffered by twice as many Korean women as Korean men (K. Park, 2002). This was shown in 1998 when Korea held the Nation-Wide Depression Screening Day to assess the extent of the national problem, and to provide diagnostic assistance to its citizens. However, despite its prevalence, less than one third of those diagnosed had been treated. Those who had not received treatment were either unaware of their psychological condition, or did not think that they needed clinical assistance. Also, many did not receive proper treatment to begin with (K. S. Kim, *et al.*, 1999). The suppression of the expression of strong emotions may be the primary cause for the prevalence of depression. This has made it a feminist issue, as well as a general cultural issue.

Anger Syndrome

Anger Syndrome (Hwa-Byung) (Han, 2002) is one of several psychological disorders that have been identified as "culture-bound mental health syndromes." It appears in both genders, but much more so in women. Seventy-seven percent of those diagnosed with the disorder were women, while 23% were men (K. Park, 2002). Women especially are expected to conduct themselves in a restrained and undemonstrative way. To do this, they repress strong feelings, including anger. This may give rise to hostile and aggressive attitudes, which are diagnosed as inappropriate behaviors. These intense emotions may come out as psychosomatic symptoms. These symptoms include shortness of breath, insomnia, fatigue, fear of impending death, indigestion, and anorexia (Spector, 2004, p.227).

Psychosomatic Symptoms

Much literature has reported that Korean women suffer from psychosomatic symptoms (Chang, 2000; H. K. Chung, 1990; J. S. Kim, 1994; K. Park, 2003). Additionally, since the etiology of these syndromes has been linked to repressive Korean attitudes toward women and the reactionary codes of behavior demanded of women, these disorders have become feminist issues. In addition to those symptoms already identified, the repression of women has led to the psychosomatic emergence of pain in the extremities, shortness of breath, amnesia, burning sensations, and painful menstruation. According to Jin-Sung Kim (1994), psychosomatic symptoms are found in Korean women to a greater extent than they are in Korean men or in Western individuals. In Eastern cultures, an individual's suffering or psychological difficulties are often expressed as psychosomatic symptoms. It is primarily the result of trying to avoid blame. It is also the consequence of avoiding the shame that Koreans ascribe to having psychological problems. Furthermore, it is due to the social oppression imposed on women by the patriarchal family system.

Anxiety Disorder

Anxiety Disorder is another possible result of not being able to express or release strong emotions. Accordingly, women in this situation have developed anxiety, along with depression, anger, and psychosomatic illness (J. S. Kim, 1994).

Additional Psychological Causes

Kyung Park (2002) identified the following additional psychological causes of psychological difficulties in women: the passive-dependent socialization of women in their sex roles, the severe difference in the power positions of men and women within society, difficulties in women maintaining healthy husband-wife interpersonal relationships in married life, and the loss of supportive relationships that takes place in a women's life once she gets married.

Treatment

According to K. Park (2002), the treatment goals of Feminist Therapy for Korean women are:

- to lessen their suffering
- to lessen their social-political oppression

In order to do this, women need to raise their awareness of the importance of their participation in the feminist social movement. As stated earlier, it is not enough for the client to experience emotional change. It needs to be accompanied by change in the social-political structure. Along with this, there needs to be fundamental change in women's thinking. Therefore, the traditional patriarchal viewpoint of therapy is not suitable for women. Rather, therapy for women needs to be based upon a feminist philosophy that understands and respects women as human beings, and acknowledges their value.

BRIEF HISTORY OF THE DEVELOPMENT OF MUSIC THERAPY IN KOREA

Music and Healing

Throughout Korean history, music has played an important role as an instrument of therapy and healing. There were two types of music that existed in traditional Korean society: royal class music and folk music. Whereas royal class music served the function of maintaining the hierarchical social system, folk music was a means of public expression (E. H. Ihm, 1993). "Ordinary people," who did not have much control over their lives, expressed their emotions through folk music. The origin of Korean folk music derives from the same musical tradition as the music that is used in the shaman's rituals of Korea.

Kut Ceremony in Korean Shaman's Rituals

Many aspects of the *Kut* ceremony in shaman's rituals are relevant to music therapy (H. S. Kang, 2000). In fact, a shaman's ritual is a therapeutic process that has significant similarity to music therapy (Aigen, 1991; H. S. Kang, 2000; Moreno, 1997). For example, as Hyo Sun Kang points out (2000), it contains many elements of psychotherapy, including transference and counter-transference, empathy, compassion, projection, catharsis, and identification. In addition, the roles of shamans and therapists are similar—helping the patient/client to achieve relief from physical, mental, or emotional distress, from life difficulties, or from relationship problems. To this end, the therapeutic relationship with the client is important to both of them. In addition, both music therapy and shaman rituals use improvisation in their music, but the shaman's music has a heavy rhythmic component, and is much freer in structure than the improvisation used in Western music therapy.

Interestingly, many of the Korean shamans are female. Female shamans are regarded as "wounded healers," who have special insight into illness, injury, and disease, because of having been wounded, themselves. This actually entails a subtle recognition of the position of women in Korean society:

> Korea also retains continuing and fascinating traditions of music as therapy in popular culture, in the practice of primarily women shamans, known as *mudangs*. *Mudangs* are called upon to carry out ritual healing ceremonies called *kuts*, which are most typically carried out for Korean women and their households. (Moreno, 1997, p.61)

When these shamans conduct their healing rituals, their insight into physical sickness and mental problems is believed to come from God's rage. The shaman uses music and ritual to communicate with God. This is outwardly different from modern psychotherapy, which is built on a foundation of systematic, scientific methods. As opposed to music therapy sessions, which usually are conducted for extended periods of time, the shaman's ritual is a ceremony that takes place only briefly. The ritual ceremony is performed at a gathering of the individual plus the family or community (H. S. Kang, 2000). While there is no specified time frame, these meetings typically take place from one to a few times.

In traditional Korean society, the extended elements of families lived close to one another. Therefore, the whole community, in effect, functioned very much like an "extended family." Neither the shaman nor the community made any distinction between mental or emotional problems, and physical illness. In this regard, there is an old Korean saying, "Illness has to be outwardly spoken to be expelled." They believed that it was necessary to talk about their physical illnesses in order to recover from them, even with the help of the shaman. This may be seen as the physical counterpart to psychological catharsis. In both cases the idea is that talking about the problem results in the patient purging herself of that problem. This traditional attitude has changed over time, due to the modernization of society.

Poongmulnori—Korean Folk Music of Healing

There is a type of music used in rituals called *Poongmulnori,* which is used in combination with dance and acrobatics. It also originated from shamans' music. The composer or composers of the music are unknown. The music has never been written down. In effect, it is the musical aspect of the "oral tradition" that exists in so many cultures. However, instead of cultural myths and legends that are passed from one generation to the next by the retelling of stories and ancient histories, it is unique healing music that is passed on to the next generation through listening to it and playing it.

Ancient Korean society, an agricultural society, believed in the power of music and dance. This power was thought to be more than just ritual. It was thought to be much more than just some traditional procedure that the shaman performed to bring comfort to the suffering person. The ritual was thought to have healing power and spiritual power deriving from something inherent in the resonant sound of the music and from the physical movement of the dance. In effect, it can be regarded as a spiritual foundation of music therapy.

Day and night, the music was played continuously. The purpose of the ritual could be for any reason that was considered to be important to the community. In addition to its use for the healing of the physical and mental/ emotional issues of individuals, the music and dance were used to repel evil spirits, to celebrate the planting of crops at the beginning of the growing season, and the harvesting of the mature crops.

As found in both the shaman's music and *Poongmulnori*, another aspect of the shamanistic ceremonies was the sense of unity and community that it generated—everyone united and focused on a common goal. While there was certain music that only the shaman could play and sing, everyone was a musician and dancer. Four different kinds of instruments were used in these ceremonies, which intentionally symbolized what were considered to be the 4 elements of nature: earth, wind, thunder, and rain. While these ceremonies may have been "primitive" by Western standards, they embody the power, the support, the intention and the therapeutic underpinning of modern music therapy.

As with most cultures, music and the arts have been used as a form of social expression in Korea. Hyun Mi Paek (1998) examined Korean popular music and drama of the 1930s, and found that they reflected the patriarchal nature of Korean family structure, and the image of modernized women in tragedy. As a result of the prevailing social values, a number of songs described women who gave "everything" because of loving a man. In these songs they were seen as immoral and were blamed for their loss of virginity.

There is another form of music that has been used to address social issues since the 1970s. It is referred to as a "song for the masses" (*Minjung Gayo*), and was begun by university students who believed that "the main purpose of music is the honest reflection of our lives, and should be a help to its listeners in overcoming their personal problems" (S. C. Choi *et al.*, 2001, p.165). This can also be seen as a forerunner of music therapy.

In recent years, feminist values have begun to emerge in the popularity of female performers who are openly sexy and provocative, like Madonna. Accompanying this is a new generation of free-spirited teens, who have embraced feminist values, such as not being dependent on a man, and who do not believe in a "forever love."

The Music Therapy Profession

Beginning in 1960, the concept of using music in therapy was introduced to Korea by other professionals, such as psychiatrists, special educators, and nurses (Y. J. Chung, 2001). At this early point, they used music in conjunction with other therapies, and conducted research on the therapeutic effect of music. It is only recently in 1997 that graduate programs of Music Therapy were established at universities in Korea. Since then, the field of music therapy has been developing rapidly.

Music Therapy educators and music therapists who have studied in the United States have imported ideas mostly from America. There are now a few music therapy organizations that support research in the field and advocate for the profession of music therapy (H. K., Kwon & H. J. Chung, Personal Communication, 2005). They aim to educate other health-related professionals, as well as the public, about music therapy through the publication of articles and through programs broadcast on television and radio. However, acceptance of music therapy by the Korean government, by other therapy professionals, and by academia is still limited. Similarly, the range of problems treated in Korea through music therapy is limited.

At this point there are several needs among Korean music therapists: ongoing efforts in conducting systematic research, advocacy for music therapy and dissemination of information about the field of music therapy as an independent profession, as well as a unifying music therapy organization (Y. J. Chung, 2001).

There are some Korean music therapists who believe in the importance of "culturally-sensitive music therapy" (Y. J. Chung, 2001; H. S., Kang, 2001). They think that music therapy is a Western idea, based on Western thinking. Therefore, it needs to be modified in the way that it is practiced with Korean clients. As a reflection of this thinking, one of the universities in Korea has created a graduate program in *Healing Music Therapy*, based on religious music in Korea. Another effort to develop a music therapy program that is sensitive to Korean culture, is the attempt to combine the Korean tradition of acupuncture with music therapy, but at this writing it is at a preliminary stage.

Similarly, to properly conduct feminist music therapy, a variety of music therapy approaches may need to be explored. Even more specifically, it is important to find the Korean women's voice in music therapy. There is much to learn from Western music therapy. However, since women's issues in Korea cannot be separated from Korea's social and cultural factors, the proper and effective treatment may need to be developed independently.

Feminism in Music Therapy

Since the field of music therapy in Korea is still developing, there has been very little research done in which clinical practice has focused on gender-specific issues (H. J. Chong, Personal Communication, 2005). One interesting research study was conducted by Eun Jin Choi (2003), who examined the prevalence of depression in Korean women living in the United States, who were accompanying their families for various reasons. From this study, she concluded that the major cause of their depression comes from their reason for living abroad: being in America is not for themselves, but for their families. As a result, the Korean women studied felt disconnected from home and from that which was familiar. This resulted in depression. This study shows that there is a significant need for proper treatment services for Koreans who live abroad.

Suitability of Music as a Form of Expression in Therapy for Korean Women

What can music therapy offer Korean women? Korean women are in crisis, and there is a great need for music therapy. By coincidence, Koreans have traditionally used music in a therapeutic way. Since music is used as nonverbal communication, I strongly believe that music therapy is ideally suited for Korean women. To openly express oneself and to reveal one's thoughts and feelings to another person is a violation of Korean cultural norms—especially for a Korean woman. Moreover, since they are governed by a strong superego, it is most difficult for them to express negative thoughts and feelings. The fact of being in a therapy situation does not make much difference to Koreans. This is Western thinking. Music can be less threatening for Korean people.

Following is a list of suggested feminist music therapy goals for Korean women:

- to promote the empowering of the client and to help her participate in social change
- to foster the development of the client as a human being, including the development of a healthy sex role
- to assist the client in overcoming the inequalities toward women in Korean society
- to overcome dependence, and the idea that a woman needs a man to survive in society

Orientation and Values of the Music Therapist

Many feminist therapists discuss the importance of the therapist's orientation and system of values (Hadley & Edwards, 2004; Chang, 1996; K. Park, 2003). As Susan Hadley and Jane Edwards (2004) have pointed out, a music therapist should be aware that "perhaps, given women's proportional dominance in music therapy, we have taken it for granted that many of the assumptions operating within the theoretical and practical spheres of music therapy have nothing to do with issues of male power and hegemony." Particularly in Korea, it is necessary for the music therapist to have a feminist agenda in mind.

Therefore, the therapist should have an understanding of the social context of the client. For example, it is not genuinely therapeutic to help the client blindly fit in with an individual, with a family, or with a social system, if that person, family, or system is based on principles that are not in harmony with the client. This, of course, includes accommodating a patriarchal social system. Regardless of the music therapist's approach, she/he should respect women as they are and should understand clinical issues that are particular to women.

One way to view women (or any other group) is as a specific culture. With this in mind, we need to consider developing a *culture-centered music therapy* specific to Korean women. In discussing this therapeutic orientation, Julie Brown (2002) states that the music therapist needs to have cultural empathy, both idiographic and nomothetic. Idiographic events are individual events, which one understands in that way—unique, personal, individual. Nomothetic events are those that can be viewed as specific occurrences of general laws, patterns, and universals. She emphasizes that to truly understand a culture, a music therapist must understand both; only then can she/he understand what a client is going through.

Community Music Therapy

Community Music Therapy is a recent development in the field. An example of community music therapy is the music therapy work that was done after the World Trade Center attack. As Gary Ansdell (2002) defines it:

> Community Music Therapy is an approach to working musically with people in context: acknowledging the social and cultural factors of their health, illness, relationships and music. It reflects the essentially communal reality of "musicking," and is a response both to overly individualized treatment models and to the isolation people often experience within society. (p.120)

Due to Korea's cultural history, this may be an effective form of working with Korean people. Since the issues of feminism are so embedded in the societal structure, the community music therapy approach may be particularly effective in dealing with these issues.

The use of music in Korean shaman's rituals and *Poongmulnori* involves similar concepts to community music therapy. In community music therapy, the whole community is involved. Within this setting, one person's issue becomes the whole group's concerns. In general, music therapists who do this work conduct therapy along a continuum from individual to communal therapy (Ansdell, 2002). This format offers women an opportunity to work on their issues within the context of the community. I believe that the Korean psychological makeup and cultural history, and the nature of feminist issues, give the music therapist the opportunity to work with the individual within the actual social context for the particular problem. Additionally, music therapy that deals with the social system and not just the individual makes it less likely that the individual client will undergo insight and inner change, but only succumb again to the pressures of the same unchanged social context.

Couples Music Therapy and Family Music Therapy

Treating couples and families in music therapy are two approaches that may be effective for working with a Korean population, considering the relational nature of the culture. In particular, attention must be given to the way in which the construction of gender roles in our society organizes women's lives and men's lives in many different ways. These roles are most often disadvantageous to women. Couples music therapy and family music therapy give the client(s) the opportunity to explore personal factors, as well as the interactions that take place within the respective system, the couple's dyad or the family (Leigh & Clossick, 1992; Skerrett, 1996).

Feminist Narrative and Music Therapy

Deriving from the philosophy of social constructionism, the idea behind the therapeutic use of narratives is that our lives are not made meaningful by the facts of the events that take place, but by the meaning that we ascribe to them. In fact, it is argued by social constructionists that it this attributing of meaning to the events of our lives that creates our reality (Gottlieb & Gottlieb, 1996 & J. Lee, 1997).

This philosophy of narrative therapy can be used as a form of feminist therapy, including music therapy. It begins with the client's current narrative, a story, detailing her life and the meaning of the things that happened over her lifespan. Then, a process begins in which client and therapist work as co-collaborators to renarrate the client's life story progressively. The majority of the therapist's work is to help the client see new, alternate meanings in the same life events: ". . . new narratives provide alternative frames for attributing meaning to experiences that can help clients understand the gendered and politicized nature of their everyday lives" (Gottlieb & Gottlieb, 1996, p.6).

In so doing, the nature of the client's life is changed, through new insight and understanding, and ultimately by experiencing her life in a different, more constructive way. The use of improvisational exploration and Analytical Music Therapy would seem to be key here.

Analytical Music Therapy

The analytical approach to feminist therapy has been criticized by some feminist therapists (Chang, 2000; O. H. Ihm, 2003, K. Park, 2003). According to YeonJip Chang (2000), Freud's theory is a male-dominant theory, so for women it is not equal. She believes that it serves to maintain Korea's patriarchal social structure. She suggests that Karen Horney's psychoanalytic theory was a first step toward the development of a feminist theory of therapy. Many go even further, seeing Horney's break with Freud over his view of women as a true expression of feminist principles. In her psychoanalytic theory she attributed the differences between females and males not to biological factors, as Freud did, but instead to societal and cultural factors. It is important to note that while these ideas are considered fundamental to the feminist perspective today, at the time that Horney was writing about these issues, these ideas were not linked to the feminist movement.

I believe that Analytical Music Therapy (AMT) is an effective form of music therapy for both women and men, and can provide a great deal of benefit to Korean women and their families (Scheiby & S. A. Kim, 2006). It is a form of music therapy that seeks to understand the client's problems, her/his intrapsychic dynamics, as well as the client's social and environmental context.

I believe that analytical music therapy is especially suited to deal with the issues and intrapsychic dynamics that occur frequently within Korean families. Earlier, the Korean woman's relationship to her son was identified as the source of strife between the wife and her mother-in-law, as well as the source of marital conflict. In addition, there often develops a "triangular struggle" for affection and power within the family system between mother, new wife, and son. Analytical music therapy, with its foundation in psychoanalytic principles, lends itself to the identification and treatment of these issues.

For the Korean woman, there has been a dual sense of what she wants in the ideal, contrasted with what she experiences as the practical reality of her life. On the one hand, she may believe that she should be treated in a certain way as a human being. On the other hand, the elements of the traditional oppressive, patriarchal society are still strong in Korea. Therefore, her reality is radically different and even opposite to her ideal.

Many Korean women have been so oppressed for long that they might not see the true nature of their situation. They believe that they are to blame, or that they are thinking in a distorted way. Therefore, in general, a first step would be bringing the client's thoughts and feelings from the unconscious to the conscious, in order to help her see and identify the problem(s).

In Analytical Music Therapy, both the music therapist and the music are used in the therapy to facilitate the client's exploration of fundamental relationships, situations, and patterns in the client's life, as well as specific current problems that the client brings to therapy (Priestley, 1975; 1994). This is similar to the Korean tradition of healing through shamanistic ritual ceremonies, where both the shaman and the music are considered the medium of the healing. Also, while it is more apparent in the case of AMT, both the shaman and the analytical music therapist seek to bring unconscious material to the conscious level of awareness in order to work with it. The shaman seeks to uncover "diseased thoughts" within her client, to help the suffering individual talk about them, and to then expel them from the person who is suffering. In addition, there are certain similarities in the improvised music in analytical music therapy and the music that is improvised during the shamanistic rituals. Both can be chaotic at times, as music reflects the client's state of mind.

For the abused/oppressed woman, the analytical music therapist would strive to bring repressed thoughts and feelings to consciousness, along with the forgotten memories of events, as well as those blocked from consciousness because of denial. In this process, musical countertransference is often the key:

> . . . we can actually listen to the unconscious—manifest in the form of music—[it] is a unique and fascinating phenomenon in the field of psychotherapy. . . . The client can directly hear the musical transference and be helped to draw important insights through these realizations. The music therapist can become aware of musical countertransference reactions and either correct these or use them as useful information as they relate to the client. (Scheiby, 2005, p.9–10)

Improvisational music can be used to stimulate the client's thoughts and feelings associated with her life events. Additionally, personal, individual issues will be explored and brought to consciousness by music. As the music therapy continues, repressed desires are identified, and unhealthy gender roles are analyzed. As the music therapy proceeds, Mary Priestley's interventions, aimed at identity integration, are often effective and helpful: somatic communication, dream work, exploring relationships, reality rehearsal, etc. (Priestley, 1994).

The collaborative and egalitarian relationship between therapist and client that is usually the goal of early feminist music therapy might be hard for oppressed/abused women to accept at the beginning of therapy. In addition, the client may feel lost when she finds herself in the position of being encouraged to move from dependence to independence. Therefore, gradual independence might be more effective. They are so used to being in an oppressive, hierarchical relationship, that being on an equal footing with the therapist might cause many Korean women to leave therapy prematurely (Byon, Chan & Thomas, 1999; Wong & Tsang, 2004).

CONCLUSION

The feminist movement in Korea needs to be understood within the specific social, political, and cultural contexts of the country. In Korea, promoting feminist issues has intertwined with other social issues, such as nationalism and the transition to genuine democracy. It is only recently, in the 1990s, that gender-specific issues were brought to public attention on a broad scale. As Korean women have struggled against the culturally imposed limitations on their rights as human beings, more and more Korean men, especially the new generation, have also advocated feminist ideas. It is time that both men and women develop a "partnership" in society.

Korean society is in the progress of change, as a whole (*The Korea Times*, 2004, December 31). The rapid fluctuations that have transpired in the past have brought change to the family structure, and to the traditional roles of men and women. As a result, the old values and traditions are confronted by new values and traditions, and are often in conflict with them. While the status of women has been raised within Korean society, Confucius and his patriarchal ideas regarding the proper, moral functioning of families, still deeply influences Korean individuals and families. This has resulted in a variety of social issues, including a high divorce rate, and domestic violence. Health-related professionals have attempted to provide treatment for these needs.

Music therapy is a relatively new profession in Korea. However, in our spiritual tradition, Koreans have used music therapeutically. There is a great need for feminist music therapy services in Korea. At this point, it is necessary to develop clinical theories and music therapy practices for Korean women, taking into consideration their specific social and political situations. Additionally, more research is needed, focusing on the specific needs of women. Moreover, proper training for feminist music therapists is needed, to heal wounded minds and to raise women's awareness of their fundamental human rights.

REFERENCES

Adleman, Jeanne & Enguidanos, Gloria M. (1995) *Racism in the Lives of Women: Testimony, Theory and Guide to Antiracist Practice.* New York: Harrington Park Press.

Aigen, Kenneth (1991) The voice of the forest: A conception of music for music therapy. *Music Therapy: Journal of the American Association for Music Therapy*, *10*, 77–98.

Ansdell, Gary (2002) Community Music Therapy and the winds of change—A discussion paper. In Carolyn Kenny & Brynjulf Stige (eds.), *Contemporary Voices in Music Therapy: Communication, Culture, and Community*. Olso, Norway: Unipub Forlag.

Bang, Sung-Soo & Jang, Bo-Im (2003) Social welfare approach for divorce increase. *Journal of Welfare Administration,13*, 159–175.

Brown, Julie M. (2002) Towards a culturally centered music therapy practice. In Carolyn Kenny & Brynjulf Stige (eds.), *Contemporary Voices in Music Therapy: Communication, Culture, and Community*. Olso, Norway: Unipub Forlag.

Brown, Laura S. (2001) Feelings in context: Countertransference and the real world in feminist therapy. *JCLP/In session: Psychotherapy in Practice, 57*, 1005–1012.

Byon, Kyong Hee, Chan, Fong & Thomas, Kenneth R. (1999) Korean international students' expectations about counseling. *Journal of College Counseling, 2*, 99–109.

Chang, YeonJip (1996) Feminist counseling and psychotherapy. *Yeusung YeungooNonchong, 11*, 5–25.

Chang, YeonJip (2000) Feminist psychotherapy. *Women's Health, 1*, 13–29.

Choi, Eun Jin (2003) *A study of the effects of music therapy for mental depression of middle-aged women (middle-aged Korean women residing in the United States)*. Unpublished Masters Thesis, Chonnam: Chonnam National University.

Choi, Eu-Soon, Ko, Myungsook, Lee, Gu-Eun & Guil, Sook-Young (1996) The study on woman's health problem in the view of battering, sexual violence and divorce. *Journal of Women's Health Nursing, 2, 92–107.*

Choi, Sang-Chin, Cho, Yoon-Dong, & Park, Cheong-Yeul (2001) An investigation of Korean's affection reflected in popular song's lyrics. *Korean Journal of Psychology, 20*, 41–66.

Choi, Young Ju (2002) Theatrical representation of 'comfort women.' *Korea Drama Review, 18,* 89–118.

Chong, Hyun Ju, Chung, Hee Jin, & Kwon, Hye Kyung (2005) Personal Communication.

Chung, Hong Kwon (1972) *Faith and Literature.* Pusan, Korea: AJoo Publishing Co.

Chung, Hong Kwon (1985) *Generational problems in the Korean immigrant churches of Philadelphia.* Unpublished Doctoral Dissertation, Philadelphia: Westminster Theological Seminary.

Chung, Hyun Kyung (1990) *Struggle to Be the Sun Again: Introducing Asian Women's Theology.* Maryknoll, NY: Orbis Books.

Chung, Sei-Wha (1986) *Challenges for Women: Women's Studies in Korea.* Seoul, Korea: Ewha Womans University Press.

Chung, Youngju. (2001) *The history of music therapy in Korea.* Unpublished Masters Thesis, Seoul, Korea: Ewha Womans University.

Crane, Paul S. (1967) *Korean Patterns.* Seoul, Korea: Holly Corporation Publishers.

Edwards, Louise & Roces, Mina (2000) *Women in Asia: Tradition, Modernity and Globalization.* Ann Arbor: The University of Michigan Press.

Funderburk, Jamie R. & Fukuyama, Mary A. (2001) Feminism, multiculturalism, and spiritualism: Convergent and divergent forces in psychotherapy. *Women & Therapy, 24*, 1–18.

Gottlieb, Diane T. & Gottlieb, Charles D. (1996) The narrative/collaborative process in couples therapy: A postmodern perspective. *Women & Therapy, 19*, 37–47.

Hadley, Susan & Edwards, Jane (2004) *Sorry for the silence: A contribution from feminist theory to the disclosure(s) within music therapy.* Voices: a World Forum for Music Therapy.
http://www.voices.no/mainissues/mi40003000152.html

Hampson, Sasha (2000) Rhetoric or reality? Contesting definitions of women in Korea. In Louise Edwards & Mina Roces (eds.), *Women in Asia: Tradition, Modernity and Globalization.* Ann Arbor: The University of Michigan Press.

Han, Il Kyu (2002) *Feministic pastoral counseling.* Unpublished Masters Thesis, Seoul, Korea: Ewha Womans University.

Hankuk Comfort Women's Issues Counterplan Organization. (2001) *Requiring the Responsibility for the Comfort Women of the Japanese Military: Historical and Social Study.* Korea: Pulbit Publisher.

HankukYeuSungYeunGooSo. (1994) *Women's Studies.* Seoul, Korea: Ewha Woman's University Press.

HankukYugyohakhae. (2001) *Confucius and Feminism.* Seoul, Korea: Philosopy and Reality Publisher.

Ihm, Eun Heui (1993) Music therapy in Korea. In Cheryl Dileo Maranto (ed.), *Music Therapy International Perspectives.* Pipersville, PA: Jeffrey Books.

Ihm, Oak Heui (2003) Transference and countertransference. In YeuSungMoon HwaYiRonYeunGooSo (ed.), *Feminism and Psychoanalysis.* Seoul, Korea: YeuYiYeun.

Jung, Kyungja (2003) Practicing feminism in South Korea: The issue of sexual violence and the women's movement. *Hecate, 29* (2), 261–284.

Kang, Hun (1997) HankukDaeJungUmAkRon (A theory of Korean popular music). *MinJokUmAkuiYiHae (Understanding of folk music),* Col. 4, 32–56.

Kang, Hyo Sun (2000) *A study on the music therapy function of "Kut".* Unpublished Masters Thesis, Seoul, Korea: Ewha Womans University.

Kawamoto, Judy Y. (1995) A Japanese American therapist discovers feminist therapy. In Jeanne Adleman & Gloria M. Enguidanos (eds.) *Racism in the Lives of Women: Testimony, Theory and Guide to Antiracist Practice.* New York: Harrington Park Press.

Kim, Elaine H. (1995) Home is where the han is. In Kate Mehuron & Gary Percesepe (eds.), *Free Spirits: Feminist Philosophers on Culture.* Englewood Cliffs, NJ: Prentice Hall.

Kim, Gab-Sook (2003) The impact of group art therapy on the psychological well-being of children who have experienced domestic violence. Hankuk Gahjungguanri Hakhae, *21*, 109–120.

Kim, Hye Eun (2003) *The effects of women's depression and stress coping on binge eating behavior.* Unpublished Masters Thesis, Korea: Seoul Woman's University.

Kim, Jung Mee & Chung, Choo Young (2005) *Feminism and militarism. Women and war, Retrieved* from http://www.womenandwar.net/bbs/index.php?tbl=M033&cat=&mode=V&id=7&SN=0&SK=&SW=

Kim, Jin-Sung (1994) A study on somatization in Korean women. *The Youngnam University Medicine Journal, 11*, 332–336.

Kim, Kwang-Soo, Jang, Giu-Ho, Chae, Jeong-Ho, Bahk, Won-Myong, Lee, Chung Tai, Lew, Tae-Yul, Paik, In-Ho, Bang, Seung Kyu, Lee, Sung-Pil, Jun, Tae-Youn, Han, Sang-Ick, Choi, Bo Moon & Go, Hyo Jin (1999) Results of 1998 Korean depression screening day and socio-demographic characteristics of participants. *Korean Neuropsychiatric Association, 38*, 1006–1015.

Kim, Won-Hong (2003) *Kaejong Chungbo Onul Ui Yosonghak.* Seoul, Korea: Konkuk University Press.

Kim, Y. C., (1976) *Women of Korea.* Seoul, Korea: Ewha Womans University Press: Kwang Myung Printing Co.

Kim, Young-Hwa (2002) Meaning of psychoanalysis for feminist practical method. *Bockjihaengjung, 12*, 167–187.

Kim, Young-Soon & Han, Myung-Hee (2000) Bridging the generation gap. *Inter-Asia Cultural Studies*, *1*, 503–511.

Korean Women's Development Institute. (2005) *Statistics.* http://www.kwdi.re.kr

Lee, Hyo-Jae (1989) *Women's Movement in Korea: Past and Present.* Seoul, Korea: Jungwoosa.

Lee, Janet (1997) Women re-authoring their lives through feminist narrative therapy. *Women & Therapy, 20*, 1–22.

Lee, Jae Kyung (1999) Modern transformation of Korean family: Feminist analysis. *Korean Women's Studies, 15*, 55–86.

Lee, Sung Hee. & Choi, Jin Ju (2005, March, 7) Today's woman in the view of a female journalist. *The Korea Times*, pp. B4–B5.

Lee, Young-Mee (1998) *HanKook DaeJung KaYoSa* (A History of Korean popular songs). Seoul, Korea: ShiGongSa.

Leigh, A. Leslie & Clossick, Michelle L (1992) Changing set: Teaching family therapy from a feminist perspective. *Family Relations, 41*, 256–263.

Mehuron, Kate. & Percesepe, Gary. (1995) *Free Spirits: Feminist Philosophers on Culture.* Englewood Cliffs, NJ: Prentice Hall.

Moreno, Joseph (1997) International perspectives. *Music Therapy Perspectives, 15*, 60–64.

Noh, Young-Hae (2001) Main themes of Korean popular songs in the last 30 years. *Music and Culture, 5,* 149–183.

Oh, Kyung Hee (2002) The examination of the issues of Ho-Ju system. *Women's Study, 13,* 1–13.

Paek, Hyun Mi (1998) Articles on popular music and drama: Duality of a view of womanhood revealed in drama of SP recordings. *HankukKoeumbanYenguhae, 10,* 287–297.

Park, Kyung (2002) The Cause of women's depression and psychotherapy. *Eclectic Psychotherapy, 2*, 31–44.

Park, Kyung (2003) Women's Mental Health and Feminist Therapy. *Journal of Korean Women's Studies, 19*, 215–244.

Park, Jong Sook (2000) Sex consciousness of female characters described mainly in Korean female writers' novels during 1920–1939 and during 1980-1999. *Journal of Korean Woman's Psychology, 5*, 89–104.

Priestley, Mary (1975) *Music Therapy in Action*. St. Louis, MO: Magnamusic-Baton.

Priestley, Mary (1994) *Essays on Analytical Music Therapy*. Phoenixville, PA: Barcelona Publishers.

Ro, Hea-Sook (1998) *Korean Women and Culture*. The Research Institute of Asian Women, Seoul, Korea: Sookmyung Women's University.

Scheiby, Benedikte B. (1999) Music as symbolic expression: An introduction to Analytical Music Therapy. In Wiener, Daniel J. (ed.), *Beyond Talk Therapy: Using Movement and Expressive Techniques in Clinical Practice*. APA Books: Washington, D.C.

Scheiby, Benedikte B. (2005) An intersubjective approach to music therapy: Identification and management of musical countertransference in a music psychotherapeutic context. *Music Therapy Perspectives*, *23*, 8–17.

Scheiby, Benedikte B. & Kim, Seung-A (2006) Analytical music therapy training: A Korean-American music therapist in American culture. In

Hyen-Ju Chong (ed.), *Music Therapy Techniques and Models.* Seoul, Korea: Hakjisa Publisher.

Skerrett, Karen (1996) From isolation to mutuality: A feminist collaborative model of couples therapy. *Women & Therapy, 19*, 93–107.

Spector, Rachel E. (2004) *Cultural Diversity in Health and Illness* (6th ed.). Upper Saddle River, NJ: Prentice Hall.

Stige, Brynjulf (2002) *Culture-Centered Music Therapy.* Gilsum, NH: Barcelona Publishers.

The Korea Times (2005, March 30) *Divorce, the Rate has Decreased by 16 Years,* p.1.

The Korea Times Media Research (2004, December 31) *The Way of Jungdo*, pp.B14–B17.

Wong, Yuk-Lin Renita & Tsang, A. Ka Tat (2004) When Asian immigrant women speak: From mental health to strategies of being. *American Journal of Orthopsychiatry. 74*, 456–466.

YeasungMoonhwaIronYeunguso (2003) *Feminism and Psychoanalysis.* Seoul, Korea: Yeuyiyeun Publisher.

Yoo, Gyesook (2004) Attachment relationships between Korean young adult daughters and their mothers. *Journal of Comparative Family Studies, 35*, 21–33.

Yu, Young Dal (2003) The difference of probability of mentally ill between men and women. *Women's Study, 14*, 127–160.

Chapter Six

WOMEN, POWER, MUSIC THERAPY: A FEMINIST PERSPECTIVE ON MUSIC THERAPY IN TAIWAN

ChihChen Sophia Lee

INTRODUCTION

Music therapy in Taiwan has recently moved into its second decade as an organized discipline. Although still far from maturity, the music therapy pioneers have accomplished several major tasks, including the establishment of a professional organization, clinical practices, and college-level preparatory curriculum. Music therapy techniques have also been adapted by medical and special education professionals for incorporation into their clinical practices as well as into their research designs. The public is now more aware that music therapy means more than passive music listening experiences or Music Prescription (Music Rx). Parents with children who have learning difficulties and developmental delays are very receptive to music therapy services for improving their child's functioning level. Indeed, the number of qualified music therapists in Taiwan does not seem to be sufficient to meet the growing demands.

Incorporating medical traditions from several cultures, music therapy in Taiwan has unique characteristics. As Taiwanese culture as a whole is made up of three cultural groups—indigenous, Chinese, and western—each cultural tradition offers challenges to, while also complimenting, the others. Inevitably, some of these cultural traditions support "masculine" norms that may have contributed to the dehumanization of healthcare in Taiwan: that is, emphasis on quantity of work, expectation for the instant treatment effect of symptoms, desire for aggressive/product-oriented work behaviors, just to list a few. Professions that place less emphasis on these norms seem to offer lower pay. For example, in terms of music therapy, those that conform to these norms, such as the commercialization of Music Rx and musical interventions emphasizing the magic of the "Mozart Effect," are in the spotlight and bring greater financial advantage.

The influence of patriarchal values on the operation of clinical practice and policy making would not seem compatible with a profession in which there is a predominance of female practitioners, such as music therapy. Not only do such values impact the potential of music therapy clinical practice and the depth of research, but they could also negatively impact client-therapist rapport, which tends to be qualitative in nature, and the therapist's personal life. Nevertheless, music therapists can benefit from the Taiwanese feminist movement in order to counteract the prevailing patriarchal values in the workplace.

Susan Hadley describes feminism as a "historical movement, a worldwide phenomenon enacted by women within their own specific cultural, social, and political matrixes, against political and economic male oppression, male discrimination, brutality and violence against women" (Hadley & Edwards, 2004). She also proposes that feminism is both reactive and active. As an active intervention it challenges male-centered definitions of what we believe and how the world is constructed. Feminism encourages us to view ourselves with an open mind and from a perspective other than that which has been heavily influenced by male norms. Music therapy practice that reflects these values, therefore, can be referred to as feminist music therapy.

Although it is not surprising to learn that music therapists in Taiwan have not begun to evaluate their theory and practice from a feminist perspective due to the demands of pioneering, the examination of the development of a feminist perspective of music therapy in Taiwan is crucial in promoting a healthier future for the profession. In this chapter, I will assesses the development of music therapy in Taiwan in terms of how the concept of music and healing, influenced by both the medical and musical cultures of the era, has evolved in terms of the integration of its various cultural traditions, and how these cultural traditions play a role in defining music therapy. I will also examine the historical roles of women in the healing process within these cultural traditions. This brief overview of both the feminist movement and music therapy in Taiwan will provide a context from which to better comprehend the challenges that music therapy in Taiwan currently faces from a feminist perspective. This chapter supports the need to develop music therapy practice that is meaningful to the community, culturally and socially as well as therapeutically. It also supports the need for more policies and administrative practices that address humanistic concerns.

CULTURAL TRADITIONS OF MUSIC AND HEALING IN TAIWAN

The use of musical experiences for healing purposes has existed long before music therapy as an organized profession in Taiwan and can be observed in the various cultural traditions that make up Taiwanese culture as a whole. As mentioned, the three major cultural traditions are the indigenous (aboriginal), Chinese, and western cultures. The functional use of music, in general and for healing purposes, was first documented in the field studies of the Japanese civil officers and ethnomusicologists in late 19th to mid-20th century (Hsu, 1994). According to aboriginal and folk medical practice, music facilitates healing because it enhances communications with the holy divine. Emphasis is placed on the importance of the patient's faith in the effectiveness of the intervention. Traditional Chinese medicine, as also seen in the ancient Greek culture, supports the prescription of music in a specific mode, instrumentation, and delivery method (e.g. listening or performing), for a designated therapeutic purpose. Health in traditional Chinese medicine refers to the state of balance and harmony within. The systematic and evidence-based principles of western medical culture encourage viewing in a scientific manner the use of music experience for therapeutic purposes.

As "music" and "therapy" are the two major components in defining music therapy, I will now discuss the ways in which medical care and music are delineated in each of the cultural traditions in Taiwan.

Indigenous (Aboriginal) Culture

Music has been significant in the healing rituals and the preservation of the orally based Taiwanese indigenous cultural legacy. Active on the island since 15,000 BC (Public Television Service Foundation [PTS], 2000a), the indigenous residents are the maternal ancestors of modern Polynesians—based on genetic evidence such as mitochondrial analysis (Chen, 2004; Yu, 2004). According to their geographical distribution, they were classified into 10 "plain-dwelling" and 11 "mountain-dwelling" aboriginal cultures. However, most plains aboriginal cultures became extinct as the residents integrated with Sino-Chinese immigrants from the 16th century on. Due to their more isolated residency, the cultures of mountain aborigines, which include Atayal, Saisiyat, Bunun, Tsou, Rukai, Paiwan, Puyuma, Amis, Yami, Thao and Truku (Wang, 2003), were better preserved.

The medical practice of the Taiwanese aborigines was shamanistic (Taiwan Medical History Digital Museum [TMHDM], n.d.a). The cause of illness in these cultures was mostly considered to be supernatural; religious ceremonies and herbal treatments were the medical interventions. For instance, according to the medical culture of the plains aborigines Ketangalan (TMHDM, n.d.b), the illness could be the result of a "call for mission" from the ancestors, conflict with the spirits of ancestors, or manipulation by the evil spirit. Designated ceremonies consisting of specific religious rituals, music, and dance were the ultimate medical treatment. Similar interpretations and treatments for illnesses were also observed in many other indigenous cultures in Taiwan. The culture of Bunun, on the other hand, believed that a human being (*Bunun*) consists of a physical body, a spirit (*Hanido*), and a consciousness (*Isang*) (TMHDM, n.d.c). Two types of hanido would lead a person to handle challenges in opposite directions; the spirit residing on the left shoulder promoted evil wrongdoing, and the spirit on the right shoulder promoted goodwill. When the strength of the evil and good spirits was equivalent, Isang could mediate the conflict. If a person accumulated a sufficient amount of good deeds before the spirit terminally departed from the physical body, Isang would become the good spirit; otherwise, it would turn into an evil spirit. Illness in the Bunun's medical interpretation, therefore, was the result of the evil spirit overtaking a person's balanced well-being. To heal the patient, a medical ritual in conjunction with herbal or botanical remedies was implemented to cast away the evil spirit. Music, in the form of singing, dancing, and/or instrumental performance, was indispensable for enhancing their religious, ceremonial, and healing rituals (Lu, 1982).

Females played a significant role in the healing processes of Taiwanese indigenous cultures, especially those that were female-dominant. For example, the most majestic healing ceremony of the female-dominant Ketangalan tribe, Kisaiiz, could only be performed by female shamans. Two other female-dominant societies, Amis and Puyuma, historically featured larger numbers of female shamans than the other cultures. In male-dominant societies such as Bunun, female community members would congregate to assist the male shaman by singing during the healing process (Lu, 1982).

Sino (Han) Chinese Culture

The use of music has also been identified in Chinese medical practice. Sino, or Han, Chinese culture was a new addition to Taiwanese culture when the first influx of Sino-Chinese immigration took place in the 17th century during the Dutch occupation. The wave of immigration was in response to the trading activities with the Dutch as well as the Dutch mass labor import from southeastern provinces of China such as Fujian and Canton (Wikipedia, 2005a & 2005b). The immigrants brought with them the practice of Chinese folk medicine. Folk medicine refers to "the healing approaches and procedures to body, mind, and spirit that have been evolved along with a culture or observed in folklore" (TMHDM, n.d.d). It includes the practice of religious healing, traditional healing from various ethnic cultures, and shamanism. These approaches provide alternatives to conventional medical practices and have a holistic emphasis. The trend of "self-healing" and the popularity of folk medicine is partially explained when conventional medical approaches are not available in a society, when there are conflicts of beliefs in the culture concerning the cause of illness, or when the conventional medical approaches do not deliver the expected effectiveness. The popularity of folk medicine also reflects people's perception of religion, the contemporary healthcare system, and concerns about the discrepancy between urban and rural medical resources. The practice of folk medicine does not intend to provide scientific evidence, although there are assumptions embedded within these practices. The effectiveness of folk medicine, however, is manifested by the faith of those who seek treatment. Music is applied in Chinese Folk Medicine through accom-panied chanting of sutras in healing ceremonies. This music is believed to strengthen or restore the balance of a person's psyche that is impaired by the evil spirit. Accompanied chanting is also implemented in funeral ceremonies to deliver the spirit of the dead to paradise. Otherwise it is believed that the spirit will stay around and harm the living.

A more systematic use of Chinese culture and medical practice was later introduced by Cheng Cheng-Gong (Koxinga) and his descendents in late 17th century (Wikipedia, 2005c; TMHDM, n.d.e), and other Chinese immigrants arriving in Taiwan during the Qing Dynasty and after 1949. Traditional Chinese medicine emphasizes the importance of both preventive and curative practices. The primary Chinese medical diagnostic process includes the thorough observation of physiological symptoms. In particular, the pulse reflects how the human circulation system is impaired by diseases or physical imbalance. Each physical malfunction is believed to cause a unique combination of pulses comprised of rhythms and accents. The wellness of a human being may be maintained or achieved by proper nutrition/dieting habits, individualized exercises, and meditation. All of these can be prescribed. The curative aspect of Chinese medical practice applies to herbal and synthetic (*Dan*) remedies, acupuncture, and surgeries (TMHDM, n.d.f).

According to traditional Chinese medical practice, both active and passive musical experiences can be prescribed for therapeutic purpose (Huang, 2001). In *Huang-Ti Ne-Chin*, one of the oldest Chinese medical texts, completed between 403-200 BC (Huang, n.d.), it indicates that each internal organ of a person corresponds with a specific emotion. If the "spirit" of the internal organs malfunctions due to an imbalance between emotions, it influences one's psychological and behavioral states. Analysis of the combination of rhythms and accents of the pulse (the "sound" from the organ) serves as the diagnostic tool. It also supports the view that the functioning of each component of the human physiological system should be in harmony with the regulation of the five elements (wood, fire, earth, metal, and water) in the environment. The healing process involves changing the external environment via the prescribed musical experiences such as vocal performance in a specific mode, utilizing a prescribed vocal method of singing, performance process, and breathing techniques (Table 1).

	Voice	***Approaches***	***Mode***	***Breathing Techniques***	***Targeted Organ***
Kidney	Longing	Humming	Yü	Circular breathing	Urinary Bladder
Heart	Speaking	Yelling Freely	Chih	Blowing	Small Intestine
Liver	Shouting	Satirizing	Chüeh	Exhaling	Gall Bladder
Lung	Crying	Lauding	Shang	Expelling	Large Intestine
Spleen	Singing	Singing	Kong	Hissing	Stomach
				Giggling	Gastroesophagus+ Pyloric + Urrthral Sphincters

Table 1 The Relationship between Human Organs and Voice. From *Tzi-Wo-Yi-Liao: Sheng-Yin Liao-Fa* [Self Healing: Sound Therapy], by Li-Tang Huang, 2001. http://www.geocities.com/Tokyo/Bridge/5282/medicine_01.htm. Adopted with permission.

The promotion of Confucian principles resulted in the denouncement of the power of religion and the "external spirits" in interpreting the function of music (Yen, 2004). Confucius emphasized the importance of music in education and civilization. According to him, aesthetic aspects of music could only be delivered by a performer with a cleansed mind; cleansed, "pure" music could alter the listener's behaviors for the good. However, Confucian philosophy discouraged the advanced education of women and eliminated the visibility of female practitioners in Chinese medical practice.

Examples of the therapeutic use of the process of musical performance can be seen in the practice of *Chiang-Hsiao Fa* (The Methodology of Long Bamboo Flute) and that of other wind instruments that were popular during the Wei, Chin during the Northern and Southern Dynasties (220-589 AD). The combination of wind instrument performance and breathing exercises was believed to prevent or improve many physical concerns such as hypertension, stomach ulcers, liver diseases, and cancers. In *Ju-Men Shih-Chin* by Chiang Tzi-Her, a renowned Chinese physician in the Yuen Dynasty, musical experiences were prescribed for the prevention and improvement of psychological and physical discomforts. According to Huang (2001), the *Yue-Fu Chuan-Sheng* by Hsu Ling-Tai, another distinguished doctor in the Qing Dynasty, should be considered as the bible of music therapy in Chinese medical history, as the theories included in the text were well examined. However, additional research concluded that the text was frequently cited instead for its contribution to vocal performance techniques and the applied aesthetics of Chinese vocal music. It should be noted that there was no documentation indicating the implementation of these therapeutic usages of music in Taiwan. In fact, Chinese medical practice in Taiwan has never been able to exceed western medical practice in significance. Even today it is considered as the "alternative" to western medicine, which is regarded as the "conventional approach."

Western Culture

The western practice of music and healing in Taiwan was closely associated with the Christian ministry until the systematic promotion of music therapy in the 1990s. Western culture, including music and medicine, first arrived in Taiwan as part of the colonial expansion from Europe as early as the mid 1500s (TAIWANDC.ORG, 2004; Wikipedia, 2005a). Around the same time that the Dutch controlled southwestern Taiwan (1624-1662), the Spanish claimed Northern Taiwan as its colony (1626-1642), until they was ousted by the Dutch (Wikipedia, 2005d & 2005e). Under colonialism, Taiwan became one of the most active trading centers in the region. To facilitate governmental affairs, commercial activities, and the Christian ministry, the missionaries learned and romanized the language of the plains tribe Siraya, known as Sinckan. They also founded the first educational institution in 1636 to teach western literature, religious doctrine, and church hymns in Sinckan (Wikipedia, 2005f). With the departure of the Dutch in 1662, the torch of westernization in Taiwan was temporarily extinguished.

The western influence to Taiwanese culture became significant again along with the second wave of Christian missionaries in the 19th century (TMHDM, n.d.g). Healthcare became more available to the public via medical missionaries. In addition, the prescribed use of imported medication to ease symptoms of diseases more efficiently than herbs and religious ceremonies directed Taiwanese medical culture toward a more scientific, evidence-based practice. Western medicine gradually became the trend of healthcare in Taiwan. The first western medical clinic in Taiwan was founded in Kaohsiung in 1865 by Dr. James Laidlow Maxwell, a missionary of the Presbyterian Church of England. The beginning of western medical education in Taiwan can be traced back to 1868 with Dr. Maxwell's acceptance of apprentices at another clinic he established in Tainan[1]. Other significant Christian medical missionaries in the 19th century who contributed to the modernization of the medical environment in Taiwan include Dr. Patrick Manson, Rev. George Leslie Mackay (dentistry), Dr. Gavin Russell, and Dr. David Landsborough. Along with their medical practices, these physicians conducted church services, Christian crusades, and bible studies; church hymns were incorporated to facilitate the process.

Systematic education in western music was resumed in the 19th century by Rev. David Smith of the Presbyterian church of England in 1876 (Hsu, 1994). He taught music at Presbyterian-affiliated educational institutions such as the Tainan Theological Seminary and the Presbyterian High Schools (now known as Chang-Jung Senior High School and Chang-Jung Girls Senior High School). The seminary became the cradle for Taiwanese church musicians as well as western music frontiers. In addition to the regular church functions, church choirs or smaller music ensembles comforted the sick or the needy at home or in institutions in order to spread the Christian gospel, known as *Yin-Yue-Yi-Liao* [music-medical mission] (Lo, 2003).

1895 marked the beginning of the Japanese era in Taiwanese medical history (TMHDM, n.d.h) after the Qing lost the second Sino-Japanese (also known as *Jiawu* or *Nisshin*) War in 1895 (Wikipedia, 2005g). In addition to the provision of medical care, the Japanese government introduced German-influenced medical education and placed emphasis on public health issues. Under the supervision of the first civil governor, Shimpei Goto, a German-trained physician and a member of the Public Health Bureau in Japan, the first medical and nursing training programs at the Taipei Hospital were founded in 1897. For many Taiwanese elites, medicine became a popular subject to pursue in higher education as they were politically suppressed, which somehow

[1] Tainan, which accommodated the earliest western, primarily Dutch, settlers in the early 17th century, was the first westernized city in Taiwan. Located by the shore of southwestern Taiwan, it was also referred in historical records as *Tayouan*, meaning "terrace bay," the peninsula/harbor where westerners were active in the 17th century (TAIWANDC.ORG, 2004; Wikipedia, 2005c). *Tayouan* is possibly a phonic alternation of *Tayan* in the language of plain aborigine Siraya (Ito, 1996), meaning "The Outsiders." It offers a possible interpretation for how the name *Taiwan* was originated.

discouraged the study of social sciences. For advanced studies in medicine, many Taiwanese went to Japan. Females who performed superiorly in subjects of applied sciences, with parents who were financially capable and believed in education despite their gender, were granted the same opportunity (Lin, 2004). For instance, Dr. Tsai A-Hsin graduated from Tokyo Women's Medical College and became the first Taiwanese female physician, specializing in Obstetric-Gynecology. Realizing the public's deficiency in obstetrical resources, she founded the first midwifery school in Taiwan in 1928 (Public Television Service Foundation, 2000).

Many medically trained Taiwanese were also active in social/political movements and cultural reforms. Drs. Lai Her and Chiang Wei-Shui were two significant figures. Graduating from the Government of Taiwan's Governor-General Medical School, they both emphasized the importance of culture on a person's well-being and urged the development of Taiwanese literature (TMHDM, n.d.i). One of the fruits of their labor was the establishment of the Taiwanese Culture Association in 1921 (Wikipedia, 2005e). They also helped found the Taiwanese People's Party in 1927 in order to organize a nonviolent anti-Japanese movement. Dr. Hsü Shih-Hsien was another remarkable political figure in Taiwanese history. In addition to her active political career, Dr. Hsü Shih-Hsien, the first Taiwanese female to receive a doctoral degree in medicine from Kyushu Imperial University in 1939 (Chu, 2000), became the first principal of Chia-Yi Girl's High School after the Japanese denounced their ownership of Taiwan in 1945. Dr. Hsü's political achievements include many terms as a municipal and providential representative, legislator, and as the Chia-Yi Mayor.

Japanese policies on public health included updates on the census, the implementation of immunizations, the installation of a sewer system and water processing plants, as well as the control of epidemic and infectious diseases. Residential facilities were built to care for the abandoned and the sick. In 1896, one year after its occupation of Taiwan, the Japanese government implemented laws and regulations in Taiwan concerning medical practices. The concept of rehabilitation for substance abuse was introduced in 1929; the first rehabilitation center for substance abuse (opium) began its operation in 1930.

Music education and music for healing by western missionaries continued during the Japanese colonial era, despite the additional restrictions from the policies of the new government. Music was mandated into the curricula. College became another higher educational institution that provided advanced western music education; western music and its theory were taught in high school and in post-secondary education. Students with outstanding achievement in music could receive scholarships for further music education in Japan. Concerts were featured for aesthetic purposes as well as for charity (Hsu, 1994). The development of western music education continued in a similar fashion after the Second World War.

Medical and Musical Culture in Taiwan after World War II

Being at a geographically crucial location for anti-communist efforts during the Cold War, Taiwan received substantial support from the US, including medicine. The North American medical system was adopted into Taiwanese medical education. Canada and the US became the preferred destinations for advanced medical training. For instance, Ms. Chen Tsue-Yu, a graduate of the University of Toronto and Boston University, implemented a North American nursing management system as the first chair of the nursing department at the National Taiwan University Hospital. The department became a model for nursing departments at other hospitals (Chu, 2000).

Taiwanese medical culture went through many devastating challenges after 1945. Due to the *February Twenty-Eighth Massacre* and *White Terror*, the majority of the Taiwanese Elite, including many physicians, were murdered, jailed, or forced to escape for their lives. The ones that survived the persecution either chose to be "behind the scenes," for example by doing research, or were not able to hold a position that had significant influence. Most of them, if still practicing, owned their own clinics. The influential or management positions in many disciplines, including in medicine and education, were reserved for the mainlanders who fled to Taiwan after 1949 with the Chinese Nationalist government, known as Kuomingtang or KMT, without regard for their training or competence to perform the job. Moreover, a good portion of the powerful did not practice with the expected ethical standard the Taiwanese were accustomed to back in the Japanese Era. To counteract these concerns, several policies and regulations were implemented. However, some of them were criticized as being implanted from other developed countries without proper adjustment to reflect the cultural uniqueness of Taiwan. The practice of medical specialties also resulted in criticism that physicians only care for human organs instead of being doctors of humans as a whole. The modernization of medical technology merely turned physicians more into skilled technicians rather than better doctors (Lin, 2004). From the physician's viewpoint, the decrease in a humanistic emphasis in the medical culture was a reflection of how the corporation owning the hospital measures "efficiency" as the quantity of patients being served instead of the quality of care provided, which is observed in the system today.

The lack of gender equality in the westernized healthcare system in Taiwan has also been disappointing. The healthcare culture in Taiwan has been criticized by women's organizations and the general public as being "not humanized, cold, authoritative," or that it operates on "the male-dominant traits"

(Chang, 2002). Female patients have expressed concerns about being "materialized"—treated as objects with malfunctioned parts instead of being cared for as human; doctors have also tended to disrespect female patients' rights by discussing their diagnoses with male family members first or only. As healthcare providers, female physicians were expected to "work like a man, behave like a woman" to survive in the male-dominant culture (Hsu, 2000); however, when it came time for promotion, the "glass ceiling" was frequently experienced as the result of gender-related misconceptions. Female doctors also had to confront prejudices such as "not being as aggressive (compared with their male counterparts) in terms of seeking promotion" or "having less desire to work overtime" due to the domestic obligation defined by the culture: childbirth, maternity leave, housework, and the education of their children. Without adequate social support, such as 24-hour childcare, in addition to gender-defined expectations at work and home, female doctors in general showed less desire to be in administrative positions even with superior professional experience. These concerns are still very realistic to female healthcare workers, although there have been improvements to some degree.

Although the music-medical mission continued through churches and Christian organizations, western music education evolved into a marker of social class. As primary and secondary education in Taiwan emphasized academic achievement, measured by the admission rate to prestigious high schools and colleges via examinations, classes that were not going to be tested, such as music, became compromised. Students showing interest and talent in music had to be supplemented with extracurricular music lessons; only families with above-average incomes were able to afford them. Traditionally, music was considered to be a "feminine" discipline and males were less encouraged to this as a profession, although there have also been a good number of outstanding male musicians. Many parents who provided music lessons for their daughters treated it as a dowry for marriage into another socially compatible family (e.g. marriage to a doctor) in addition to nurturing their love for music. With the culturally confined belief that "a good girl should not be publicly active," performing music for one's husband and members of his family or giving lessons at home not only served as an alternative yet legitimate physical restraint, but also reinforced the traditional image of the ideal wife. Some parents also viewed their daughters' music lessons as a springboard into a teaching position at public schools, which was considered to be another "feminine" profession because as compared with other career choices it allows females to more easily tend to traditional obligations as a wife, daughter-in-law, and a mother. The male-dominant operation overpowering the voice of female in both music and medical fields was about to be systematically challenged by a new wave of philosophy and movement—feminism.

A Brief History of the Feminist Movement in Taiwan

Considering the fact that the percentage of female politicians in Taiwan is the highest when compared to other Asian nations (Womenweb, 2004), women's status has improved in several aspects since World War II. The concept of feminism was formally introduced by Hsiu-lien Annette Lu, the current vice president of the nation, back in the 1970s. Although there were women's organizations operating between the 1950s and 1960s, their members were mostly the social elite, including the wives of politicians and officers. The major functions of these organizations were to support the government and its policy and to socialize with members of the same social class (Yum Women Web, 1997). These organizations were usually named as *Fu-Nü Hue* [Women's organizations]. Enlightened by the experience during the years of pursuing her Master's Degree in Law at the University of Illinois at Urbana-Champaign, Lu shifted her career focus from law to politics and feminism (Wikipedia, 2005h). She applied the term *Nü-Sin Chu-Yi* [Feminism] to refer to the concept of the feminist movement. Other terms in the Taiwanese feminist movement include *Fu-Nü Yün-Dong* or *Fu-Yün* [the Women's Movement], which describes the actions in response to women's concerns, and *Nü-Chuan/Fu-Chuan* [Women's Rights], the rights that women deserve in various circumstances. *Nü-Chuan Chu-Yi* [Women's Right-ism] is sometimes interchangeable with *Nü-Sin Chu-Yi* in Taiwan although the latter covers issues beyond women's rights.

After returning to Taiwan in 1971, Lu published books, *Sin Nü-Sin Chu-Yi* [The New Feminism] and *Shun-Chau Ning-Yi-San Tsuong* [Seeking Another Window], as well as establishing two telephone hotlines for women's rights, especially protecting victims of domestic violence (Wikipedia, 2005h). Her later involvement in challenging the KMT government, including being a part of the *Kaohsiung/Formosa Incidence* in 1979, resulted in a 12-year sentence for sedition. Lu's influence was considered to be the first wave of the feminist movement in Taiwan, although her political persecution briefly impaired the development. In 1982, the first organization emphasizing women's issues in a comprehensive manner, the *Awakening Magazine* (now known as the *Awakening Foundation*), was founded by Lee Yuen-Chen. Due to the fact that Taiwan was still ruled under Martial Law, issues that the organization felt comfortable addressing included child prostitution trafficking, awareness of sexual harassment, resources for homemakers, and promotion of gender dialogues. With the lifting of Martial Law in 1987, more organizations were established to advocate for women's rights and concerns. In addition to the traditional service- and rescue-oriented mission, these organizations also campaigned for the revision of the law as well as monitoring governmental policies for the promotion of women's status in the society.

Ellen Boneparth, cited by Yien-Ling Ku (n.d.), argued that to improve the status of women in a society, the political consciousness of women's rights advocates as an organization or as individuals should be activated so that the debate of women's issues can be elevated from a geographically limited level. Ku also summarizes Ethel Klein's construction of political consciousness into three stages: first, the participant should form an identity with women and concerns women have to face; second, the traditional image of women should be challenged—it should be redefined based on gender equality; third, the cause of gender/sexual discrimination, derived from the sociological structure, should be identified while simultaneously attempting to improve concerns via political avenues. Applying these principles to review issues supported and mobilized by feminist organizations between 1985 and 1995, the first concern to be addressed was child prostitution (1985). Other issues that were challenged included women's rights at work (1986), the materialization of women—pornography/sex industry and beauty pageants (1987), taxation methods (1987), Marital Law (1987), gender equality on campus (1988), implementation of Child Welfare Law (1988), political reform (equal representation of women in politics) (1989), Family Law (1990), feminist cultures (1991), (challenging) women's social obligation (1991), sexual harassment (1991), and women's right to their own body (1993). Analysis based on the frequency of actions in response to a specific issue shows that political reform has received the most attention. Women's rights in the workplace, sexual harassment, child prostitution, gender equality on campus, pornography/the sex industry, and the revision of Family Law are also issues that have resulted in more actions compared with the rest.

Learning from years of labor, Taiwanese feminist organizations have realized that educating the society to change male-centered attitudes is far more difficult to achieve than the "measurable" legal victories, such as increasing the percentage of female politicians and establishing a number of laws for women's rights. Socially, women still constantly battle with the gender-defined expectations that are rooted in the culture. Using education as an example, even though girls and boys were given equal opportunity for education; there were still fewer female graduate students (Womenweb, 2004). It seemed that girls tended to choose to give up advancing professionally and academically because of what they have been taught culturally. The challenge was especially obvious in the job searching and hiring process, which affected the economical status of women. Without jobs that secure financial stability, females were more vulnerable to poverty. As the society could not provide sufficient resources and welfare to support women's career advancement and still expected them to be primary caregivers of family, females were often involuntarily forced to remain single in order to be competitive at work or, instead, to forgo a career in order to take care of the family

Beginning in 1995, the Taiwanese feminist movement continued their mission to emphasize women's empowerment in various areas: know yourself and be who you are instead of placing emphasis on approval or disapproval by the culture. This concept was recently echoed in a study that found that women would choose not to compete with their male rivals even when they demonstrated the ability to make more money because they believe that there is more in life than competition and sums in a bank account (Tierney, 2005). The division of Women and Community of the Frontier Foundation has been focusing on communication and networking among women; websites with topics that matter to women have been created over recent years to educate the public. The Awakening Foundation's visions are being accomplished by hosting panel discussions and demanding the revisions of policies to protect women from violence and inequality at home and work. In 2005, its slogan was "Multifaceted Sisterhood," and the organization mobilized its members to be active legally, socially, culturally, educationally, and politically to ensure the rights of underprivileged females especially (e.g. aboriginal women and "foreign" brides), as well as to strengthen the confidence of other women on the decisions they have made (Awakening Foundation, 2005).

A Brief Overview of Music Therapy in Taiwan

The development of music therapy in Taiwan empowers female musicians to elevate their relationship to music from music as a marker of social status to music as a therapeutic tool. The development of music therapy in Taiwan as a discipline began in 1990s. Several music professionals, either receiving music therapy degrees or introduced to music therapy while studying abroad, returned home and advocated for this powerful educational/healthcare alternative; among them, Ms. Tsu-Sui Chang, a Certified Music Therapist (CMT) from the former American Association for Music Therapy, was a significant figure. In the following years, these Taiwanese music therapy pioneers invited numerous music therapy specialists from the United States, Japan, and Germany for intensive workshops (Tsai, 2002). On June 8, 1996, *Chung-Hua Min-Kuo Ying-Yung Yin-Yue Tui-Kuang Hsieh-Hue* [Association for the Promotion of Applied Music, Republic of China], known in English as the *Music Therapy Association of Taiwan* (MTAT), was officially founded. A primary function of the association was educating the public that music therapy is a profession. Its mission statement included: (1) to promote the application of music therapy for the psychological and physiological well being of an individual and the harmony of society; (2) to host (music therapy) related professional workshops; (3) to cultivate (music therapy) related professionals; and (4) to conduct research related to music therapy in education, counseling, rehabilitation, and medicine

(Music Therapy Association of Taiwan [MTAT], 1996). In 2003, the association proposed to officially change its Mandarin Chinese name to *Chung-Hua Min-Kuo Yin-Yue Chih-Liao Yen-Chiu Hsieh-Hue* [Association for Music Therapy Research, Republic of China], which is still in process; the English name and mission statement remained the same (MTAT, 2004). MTAT continues to invite music therapy practitioners around the world to promote regional, national, and international music therapy activities on a regular basis.

As in many other countries, female music therapists in Taiwan outnumber the male therapists. In fact, at present all music therapy practitioners in Taiwan are female. The gender-defined image of music therapy was observed in a recommendation by a staff agency, 104 Human Bank, that music therapy is one of the professions very suitable for women as a career choice since it emphasizes the need of "considerateness," a "feminine" characteristic, and goes along with the trend of promoting wellness, leisure, and stress reduction (Chen, 2005).

Currently, there are less than 20 qualified music therapy practitioners in Taiwan who have trained at accredited music therapy programs in the US, Europe, or Japan. This statistic remains similar to that in 2003 (Lee, 2003). Most of these music therapists hold full-time positions in hospital settings or at institutions for people with developmental delays (Chang, 2004). The largest populations receiving music therapy services in Taiwan are preschool to school-age children with developmental and/or learning concerns and people with mental health concerns. Music therapy interventions in Taiwan are most frequently applied as a part of early intervention programs, mental rehabilitation, and physical rehabilitation. Music therapy for older adults and in hospice settings is also practiced yet to a much smaller degree. Music therapy for victims of domestic violence is provided by invitation (Du, Wu & Chen, 2002). Some music therapy clinicians also teach introductory music therapy courses at various colleges and universities as adjunct faculty members; one of them is currently serving as a full-time instructor at the Early Childhood Education division of a college.

As public awareness of music therapy is increasing, the foremost concern of the profession in Taiwan is the insufficient number of qualified music therapists. The ratio of close-to-20 music therapists to more than 23 million residents indicates that a large number of prospective clients are not being served. Many qualified music therapists receive many more referrals than they can accept. The fact that the first and only 4-year baccalaureate music therapy curriculum was not available until 2004 may partially explain why the number of music therapists has not increased in the past 10 years along with the booming demand. In addition to the training workshops by MTAT, several institutions of higher education such as Fu-Jen Catholic University, Taipei

Medical University, and Soochow University have offered either an introductory course or curricular series in music therapy. With the support of its Continuing Education Department, Fu-Jen Catholic University and MTAT offered a series of music therapy courses in the school year of 2004-5, hoping that it will evolve into a certification program. In 2004, the Department of Applied Music of Tainan National University of Arts (TNNUA) was approved for a music therapy degree program. It is the first music therapy baccalaureate program in Taiwan. The music therapy curriculum of TNNUA, however, poses several immediate concerns. First, the curricular design and course objectives do not provide a clear definition of clinical competencies that reflect the economic, social and cultural uniqueness of Taiwan. The program proposal was initially submitted by an educator with little music therapy background; the music therapy professionals did not have a significant role in facilitating the process. Second, at the time that this chapter was written, there is no full-time faculty teaching the program. The university hired a US-trained music therapy practitioner, who received undergraduate equivalency training and Neurologic Music Therapy certification, to teach 1-2 courses per semester on an adjunct basis. Considering the intensive nature of music therapy education in other nations, such a lack of support for faculty is alarming and certainly not adequate to produce enough qualified music therapists to meet the demand for music therapy in Taiwan. The lack of music therapy preparatory programs that are needed to define the expected music therapy professional competencies for legislation also tempers the progress for developing a music therapy certification system.

Challenges to Taiwanese Music Therapists

The disadvantage of no legal endorsement is observed in many aspects. For instance, the professional organization was prohibited from legitimately publicizing itself as the "Music Therapy Association" in Mandarin Chinese, which creates a very confusing public image. Financially, music therapy services in Taiwan rely on private funding or research grants; unless they are administrated/endorsed by or co-treated with professionals with licensure such as physical therapists, occupational therapists, or speech pathologists, they are not eligible for either private or governmental insurance reimbursement. The salary of an entry-level music therapist is lower than that of other therapists with the exception of psychotherapists at the same level, although both music therapists and psychotherapists are more likely to hold master's degrees (Shu-Zen College of Medicine & Management, n.d.). The great level of involvement from professionals of other therapy disciplines in clinical operation also consequently leads to an over-inclusive definition on the qualification of music therapy service provider. According to a member on the executive committee of

MTAT who is an occupational therapist, music therapy in Taiwan currently should be defined as "the therapeutic use of music-related activities to promote or maintain both physical and psychological well-being by music therapists (professionals completing approved music therapy programs) or licensed health professionals" (Chuang, 2005). In other words, the implementation of music interventions by allied health professionals such as nurses, physical therapists, occupational therapist, psychiatrist, or counselors who have received music therapy-related training should be considered as music therapy, too. The autonomy of music therapy as a profession, thus, is seriously challenged.

As with other female professionals, music therapists in Taiwan have to juggle between the choice of family and career advancement. Already some "first generation" music therapists have either reduced their amount of clinical practice or quit their clinical practice due to this concern. There are also other factors hindering a healthier future of music therapy as a profession. Examining identified consequences such as the commercialization of "Music Rx" and the overwhelming demands for early childhood intervention/"Mozart Effect" classes (Lee, 2003), one realizes the degree to which patriarchy constructs Taiwanese economic, social, and cultural spheres. The popularity of Music Rx reflects a desire to define an instant and authoritative treatment to a specific symptom, which is welcomed in a male-dominant culture as an illustration of efficiency. The success of music therapy practice in early childhood intervention demonstrates not only parents' desire for more resources in special education, but also the significant influence of the attitude that "a child's needs/ achievements come first." The extent to which this attitude is observed in Taiwan, as well as in other Asian communities, is deeply rooted in patriarchy: The child in a male-dominant society was the property of parents, especially of the father's family, as he would be expected to secure the family's prosperity, which is considered to be an obligation to family honor. A recent survey concluded that at least 17% of Taiwanese parents still supported this belief (Chu, 2004). The parents, especially the mother as culturally defined as the primary caregiver of the family members, should do all they can to demonstrate their care in a measurable manner. This cultural burden often overshadows the sincere loving and caring nature of Asian parents. Spending time with their children in order to gain a more realistic understanding of their thoughts and capabilities, to some, is too luxurious especially when they feel bombarded by the stress of supporting the family. Music therapy treatments become therapeutic to some parents as well in that it brings a sense of relief that treatment was provided. When music therapists incorporate parents into the treatment process instead of only treating the child, it helps reverse the negative impact of this cultural characteristic by improving parent-child communication.

Feminist music therapy offers many qualities that can re-humanize the healthcare environment as well as the patriarchal tradition in Taiwan. The severity of dehumanization in medical care has intimidated female patients to the extent that some would rather seek healing from folk or shamanistic practice (Chang, 2002). With the attitude that they should behave in a "masculine" manner at work in order to be competitive (Hsu, 2000), female healthcare professionals, paradoxically, are rated as less empathetic than their male counterparts by female patients. A music therapist needs to be empowered in such a way that she can provide as well as advocate for the quality as well as or instead of the quantity of care for the patient, which at first may not be valued in a dehumanized healthcare system. A therapeutic model that emphasizes respect and equal contribution from the therapist and client challenges the authoritative hierarchy in medical culture. In this way, patients will learn to realize their own power and contribution to a personal experience of medical care, and that they have the right to acquire, interpret, and question given information and resources with a critical mind so that proper demands for desired healthcare may be executed. The practice of feminist music therapy emphasizes the importance of process and qualitative forms of measurement, alongside product/quantitative measurement, in the treatment process. All these characteristics, although serving as evidence of the operation of the medical system, would also hopefully restore the concept of healing a person as whole rather than that of the current focus of symptomatic treatment. These observations justify the need for Taiwanese feminist music therapy.

CONCLUSION

The Formation of Feminist Music Therapy Practice in Taiwan

The formation of feminist music therapy practice requires political, socioeconomic, and cultural resources from where it is rooted. As the construction of Taiwanese feminist music therapy moves forward, one may first realize the importance of being politically involved. Jane Edwards (2002) stated that "music therapy is always a socio-political work." Taiwanese music therapists do not have the luxury of being politically naive or "sterilized" especially dealing with feminist concerns in addition to healthcare policies. National feminist organizations such as Frontier Foundation and Awakening Foundation or municipal ones like Taipei's Women Rescue Foundation are wonderful allies for Taiwanese music therapists to stay current on socio-political issues before MTAT can afford designated personnel for government relations and policies related to feminist concerns. This also leads to the examination of social resources. Maria Hernandez shared the view at an international panel at the 2005 AMTA Conference that music therapy in "third-world" countries has been described as beneficial only to individuals who are "middle-class and above." People who cannot afford it are excluded from the service, despite its prospective benefits, unless it is paid for by social welfare or human rights advocacy agencies when third-party insurance reimbursement is not available. Similarly, in Taiwan, people who suffer from inequality in any form are most likely to be financially disadvantaged, too. Thus, victims of domestic violence, for example, are definitely underserved by music therapists in Taiwan; currently, only Taipei's Women Rescue Foundation offers regular group music therapy interventions to children traumatized by witnessing domestic violence. This program was initiated in March 2003 (Taipei's Women Rescue Foundation, n.d.). How to assist people in need on their journey of recovery without creating another unbearable financial burden is a genuine concern for feminist music therapists. Being in alliance with other healthcare associations, including those from creative arts disciplines, will also facilitate the professional growth of music therapy via recognition as a legitimate therapeutic approach both clinically and legally. Working proactively within the political and healthcare systems, while opposing their patriarchal norms, creates challenges for the feminist music therapist in Taiwan.

Meanwhile, Taiwanese music therapists need to begin reexamining their musical traditions from a therapeutic perspective. It is regretful to see the admission from Taiwanese music therapists that western music, administrated in Mandarin Chinese language, is what they are most comfortable with in terms of therapeutic implementation and interpretation (Chang, 2004). Propaganda in the past decades that systematically suppressed the value of traditional cultures in education, in addition to the fact that Taiwanese music therapy practitioners are currently more western-trained in terms of music therapy theories and techniques, may be the cause of this phenomenon. Nevertheless, meaningfully incorporating music from the aboriginal, Sino-Chinese, as well as the western cultures in the therapeutic procedure is the spirit of Taiwanese music therapy. It will be a personal as well as professional journey for Taiwanese music therapists to rediscover the musical treasures from various indigenous cultural traditions and be familiar with the possible musical resources. It will also be empowering in that it will validate the female role in the music healing process.

As the journey begins, one may be surprised to learn of discrepancies around the definition of "illness," "disease," "disability," "handicap," and other classifications that qualify an individual for therapeutic interventions among the nonwestern traditions compared with the western tradition. For instance, a person may be diagnosed as "imbalanced" or "inharmonious" internally, which causes a class of symptoms closer to (yet not the same as) the concept of "illness" in western interpretation that would be classified differently from "diseases," which emphasizes the "invasion" from an external origin. An "imbalanced" being is more vulnerable to disease. Therefore, cancer (if one does not consider radiation or excess toxins such as food additives as possible causes) is classified as an "illness," and bacterial or viral infections are considered as a "disease." In addition, a person with a "physical disability" is culturally considered to be "sick" while a person with a "psychiatric illness" is considered to be suffering from an imbalance or, according to the supernatural interpretation, suffering from demon possession. The perception of "therapy" is not quite the same as the western definition, either. Traditionally,there has not been a clear distinction between the concept of therapy and medical treatment in the Taiwanese culture; the definition of music therapy varies according to the population served. Music therapy is still somehow interpreted as the "medical use of music" and music therapists are "music doctors" especially in the healthcare system, as they are expected to perform curative or restorative procedures via musical experiences. The healing power is within the music itself; therefore, music prescription seems to be the way music therapy should be practiced. In special education/early intervention settings, on the other hand, music therapists are regarded as "teachers" (Lee, 2003) who implement music experiences differently from the "conventional music educator" for improving communication, cognitive, motor, and socio-emotional functioning. Although these concepts are constantly evolving, perhaps becoming more closely aligned with what is more familiar to the western culture, Taiwanese music therapists should still be aware of these traditional interpretations when evaluating and designing interventions. This would also result in a reexamination of the function of music that reflects the uniqueness of Taiwanese culture in both macro and micro scales.

Once the culturally unique function of music in Taiwan is systematically investigated and theorized, one would also realize the importance of revisiting the relationship between female practitioners and healing that was historical to the aboriginal Taiwanese culture. The feminine aspect of shamanism—holistically nurturing both the body and soul, being talented in more intuitive communication skills, providing supports in a more qualitative than quantitative orientation, etc.—may explain the popularity of female shamans in especially female-dominant cultures. Apart from its supernatural element, female shamanism holds the principles for feminist music therapy practice.

Last, yet not the least, Taiwanese music therapists need to be made aware of and motivated to implement feminist music therapy models in clinical settings—models that support equality, empowerment, and sociopolitical as well as cultural sensitivity. This means that music therapists need to be willing to step out from the professional comfort zone that a set therapeutic routine should be followed without being challenged. Another consequence of empowerment is that feminist therapy principles inherently promote the ongoing analysis and transformation of one's construct of the therapeutic procedure. The practice of Taiwanese feminist music therapy is more than the implementation of another therapeutic methodology; it redefines the art and science of therapy.

In summation, a working definition of Taiwanese feminist music therapy may be "the clinical (and evidenced-based) application of music interventions that incorporate elements from Taiwanese music cultures to accomplish individualized goals via the process of empowerment." The evidence of Taiwanese feminist music therapy should emphasize both quantitative and qualitative aspects, and the adaptation of Taiwanese musical elements into music interventions as well as the treatment approach should be therapeutically appropriate and honor the clients' cultural heritage. The voice of clients is heard in every stage of therapy; in fact, it is the key to the success of treatment. As the accomplishment of identified goals may require more than the transformation of clients via empowerment, music therapists should be socio-politically resourceful in order to challenge traditions and operations that hinder equality in any format.

Afterthought

If feminism is to object to inequality and violence, to embrace deserved respect and freedom of choice, and to strive for political participation and representation (Basu, 1995), then, Taiwan itself is a feminist concern.

As I was preparing to write this chapter, I came to realize that if the macrostructure of Taiwan as a political entity is still suffering from issues often raised in feminist discussions, every element within the macrostructure, including the development of Taiwanese feminist music therapy, also faces these same challenges. It was acknowledged that the dehumanization of the medical system in Taiwan is worse than in other nations (Huang, 2001). Huang identified a primary cause of this phenomenon to be that medical education is becoming excessively "vocational." To learn why medical education in Taiwan has failed to uphold the legacy of humanity and how the mentality of medical professionals has evolved over time, one should investigate this concern, again, from historical, sociological, and political perspectives. When the feeling of stability is constantly disrupted by political processes over the course of history, and the sense of security is persistently challenged by threats of attack from China and its intentional suppression of Taiwan from the international community, Taiwanese people first need to be healed and empowered, internally and externally, from a state of depressing mentality.

REFERENCES

Basu, Amrita (1995) Introduction. In Amrita Basu (ed.) *The Challenge Local Feminism—Women's Movements in Global Perspective*, 1–21. Boulder, CO: Westview.

Chang, Kue-Ying (2002) *Kao-hsiung Fü-nü Gi-ko Yi-chian Ling-Sho ti Fü-Nü Yi-Liao Sheng-ti Kuan-Tsa Chiau-Dian Tuan-Ti Chi-Hua Hue-Cheng Bau-Kau* [The Focus Group Project Report of Women's Healthcare Ecology by Leaders of Kaohsiung's Women Organizations] http://taiwan.yam.org.tw/nwc/nwc6/health/02.htm

Chang, Nai-Wen (2004) Yin-yue chi-liao shi ti yang-cheng yu Tai-wan yin-yue chi-liao fu-wu [The preparatory process of a music therapist and music therapy services in Taiwan], in Nai-Wen Chang, *Er-Tong Yi-Yue-Chi-Liao* [Pediatric Music Therapy], 296–315. Taipei, Taiwan: Hsin-Li

Chen, Chin-Fang (2004, August 28) Chue-che tzi-chu, Tai-wan yuen-chu-min shi Po-li-ni-si-ya-jin chu-sian [Researchers Support that Taiwan Aborigines are the Ancestor of Polynesians] *Epoch Times*. http://www.epochtimes.com/b5/4/8/28/n642898.htm

Chen, Yu-Chen (2005, March 8) Nü-sin tsuang-ye shua tsang-yi [Female entrepreneur is innovative] *Dajiyuan Times*. http://www.dajiyuan.com/b5/5/3/8/n841046.htm

Chu, Jen-Yi (2000) *Chau-Chi Chien-Yi Chao-Jen ti Yi-Che Niu-Che* [The persevering and superior females in the earlier Taiwanese medical history] http://home.i1.net/~alchu/medical/histor5.htm#cc

Chu, Ruo-Nan (2004, November 19) Liang-cheng chia-chang: Yiau-tsi-sha, chio-dai-hai-tsi yi-chi-she: Chia-fu wen-chiuan. . . [Twenty percent of parents: When pursuing suicide, bring your child along; Survey of CCF/Taiwan] *United Daily News*. http://www.libertytimes.com.tw/2004/new/nov/19/today-life6.htm

Chuang, Ya-Chin (2005, February 10) *Yi-Yue Chih-Liau Shu-Yao Ni-Wo Kung-Tong Tui-Kuang* [Music therapy relies on you and me for promotion] http://vita.fju.edu.tw/vita2/archives/000654.html

Du, Ying-Chio, Wu, Chi-Wei & Chen, Wei-Hsun (2002, January/February) *Long-Shan Fu-Nui Yuen-Hsun* [Long-Shan women's monthly report] http://www.goh.org.tw/chinese/lon/report_0102_2002.doc

Edwards, Jane (2002) Debating the winds of change in community music therapy, contribution #2, August 6, 2002. *Voices: A World Forum for Music Therapy*. http://www.voices.no/discussions/discm4_02.html.

Hadley, Susan & Edwards, Jane (2004) Sorry for the silence: A contribution from feminist theory to the discourse(s) within music therapy. *Voices: A World Forum for Music Therapy*. http://www.voices.no/mainissues/mi40004000152.html

Huang, Cheng (n.d.) Huang-ti ne-chin. *Huang-Ti.* http://hk.geocities.com/chinpcp/mecdical/yk.htm

Huang, Li-Tang (2001) *Tzi-Wo-Yi-Liao: Sheng-Yin Liao-Fa* [Self healing: Sound therapy] http://www.geocities.com/Tokyo/Bridge/5282/medicine_01.htm

Huang, Kung-Yien (2001) Fü-nü yü yi-liao shen-ti yian-tao hue ying-yien [Introduction at Women and Medical Ecology Conference] http://taiwan.yam.org.tw/nwc/nwc6/health/01.htm

Hsu, Pi-Chun (2000) [A research on the working status of female professionals: Using Taiwanese female doctors as an example] Unpublished Master Thesis. Taipei, Taiwan: National Cheng-Chi University.

Hsu, Tsang-Hue (1994) *Taiwan Yin-Yue Shih Tsu-Kau* [Taiwanese Music History, 1st ed.] Taipei, Taiwan: Chuan-Yin Music.

Ito, Kiyoshi (1996) Brief introduction of Taiwan. *Taiwan History.* http://members.shaw.ca/leksu/mainp1e.htm

Ku, Yien-Ling (n.d.) Fü-nü tsan-cheng: Ti-chih-wai te yün-tong [Women participating in politics: The movement external to the system] *Yam Women Web.* http://taiwan.yam.org.tw/womenweb/outmov_1.htm

Lee, ChihChen Sophia (2003) Music therapy in Taiwan [online] *Voices: A World Forum for Music Therapy.* http://www.voices.no/country/monthtaiwan_june2003.html

Lin, Chi-Yao (2004) *Yi-Hsue Yu-Tau Min-Su* [When Medicine Meets Folklore]. Taipei, Taiwan: Dacombooks.

Lo, Lian-Sheng (2003) *Ni-Man-Chu, Bing-Chu-Chuan* [Go and spread (the Gospel)] http://www.ccpct.org.tw/share/arthaw/1050635489241O6f4e0d.html

Lu, Ping-Chuan (1982) *Taiwan Tu-Chu-Tsu Yin-Yue* [Music of Taiwanese Aborigines] Taipei, Taiwan: Pai-Ker Cultural Inc.

Music Therapy Association of Taiwan (1996) *Di-Yi-Che Hue-Yuen Da-Hue Sho-Tse* [The Proceeding of First Assembly] Taipei, Taiwan: Author.

Music Therapy Association of Taiwan (2004) *Ju-Hue Shuo-Ming* [Explanation of Membership Requirement] http://www.musictherapy.org.tw/about.htm

Public Television Service Foundation (2000a) *Taiwan Yuen-Chu-Min Li-Shih Da-Shih Chi-Yuen Biau* [The chronology of Taiwanese Aborigines' historical landmarks] http://www.pts.org.tw/~abori/new_data/data05.htm

Public Television Service Foundation (2000b) *Taiwan Di-Yi-Wei Nu Yi-Shi—Tsai A-Hsin (1899-1990)* [The first Taiwanese female doctor—Tsai A-Hsin (1899-1990)] http://www.pts.org.tw/~web01/female/w2.htm

Shih, Yi-Nuo (2002) [Tone color of music and inappropriate behavior of the schizophrenic]. Unpublished master thesis. Taipei, Taiwan: Taipei Medical University.

Shu-Zen College of Medicine & Management (n.d.) *Sheng-Yai Kuei-Hua Chiang-Tso: Jang Jen-Sheng Do-Kai Chi-Shan Chuang* [Life planning series: Open up more windows to your life]. http://www.szmc.edu.tw/DeptJob/life.htm

Taipei's Women Rescue Foundation (2002) *Tian-Shi Fe-Hsian—Mu-tu Er-tong Yin-Yue-Chih-Liao Tuan-Ti* [Angels fly—Group music therapy for children witnessing domestic violence]. http://www.twrf.org.tw/chinese/programs_show.asp?kind_id=31&id=51

TAIWANDC.ORG (2004) *Taiwan's 400 years of history--Important milestones from the early 1600s to the present.* http://www.taiwandc.org/hst-1624.htm

Taiwan Medical History Digital Museum (n.d.a) *Yi-Liau Pe-Ching—Yuan-Chu-Min Yi-Liau She* [Background of medical treatments—Medical history of Aborigines]. http://203.65.117.106/project/abo/abo_main2.htm

Taiwan Medical History Digital Museum (n.d.b) *Ketangalan-Chu-ti-Tsu-Yi-Chi-Yi-Chien-Che* [A brief introduction to Ketangalan's healing ceremonies]. http://203.65.117.106/project/abo/abo_main5.htm

Taiwan Medical History Digital Museum (n.d.c) *Chu-Chiun-Sin-Yan-Chien-Che* [A brief introduction to tribal faith systems]. http://203.65.117.106/project/abo/abo_main3.htm

Taiwan Medical History Digital Museum (n.d.d) *Min-Su Yi-Liau Chien-Che* [A brief introduction to folk medicine]. http://203.65.117.106/project/abo/main4.htm

Taiwan Medical History Digital Museum (n.d.e) *Taiwan Yi-Liau Da-She Chi: Chu-Ti Yi* [The landmarks of Taiwanese medical history—Topic 1]. http://203.65.117.106/project/direct/main3_1.htm

Taiwan Medical History Digital Museum (n.d.f) *Chong-Kao Yi-Shue Li-Dai Zen-Wu Che-Shau* [The introduction to Chinese medical figures across history]. http://203.65.117.106/project/chinese/main3.htm

Taiwan Medical History Digital Museum (n.d.g) *Taiwan Yi-Liau Da-She Chi: Chu-Ti Er* [The landmarks of Taiwanese medical history—Topic 2]. http://203.65.117.106/project/direct/main3_2.htm

Taiwan Medical History Digital Museum (n.d.h) *Taiwan Yi-Liau Da-She Chi: Chu-Ti Shan* [The landmarks of Taiwanese medical history—Topic 3]. http://203.65.117.106/project/direct/main3_3.htm

Taiwan Medical History Digital Museum (n.d.i) *Taiwan Yi-Hse Dian-Fan Jen-Wu* [The role models in Taiwanese medical history]. http://203.65.117.106/project/people/main3.htm

Taiwan Medical History Digital Museum (n.d.j) *Taiwan Hu-Li Dian-Fan Jen-Wu* [The role models in Taiwanese nursing history].

http://203.65.117.106/project/nurse/main6.htm

Tsai, An-Ti (2002) Yin-yue chi-liao kuo-ne-wai fa-tsan sian-kuang [The current development of music therapy: National and international perspectives], in Yang Ching Wong, et, al., *Music Therapy*, 62-77. Taipei, Taiwan: Prophet.

Tsai, Tsu-Hsin (2005, June 25) Tai, Kong, Sin chin-chi kuan-si lian ching-shin [Alarms are flashing on the parent-child relationship in Taiwan, Hong Kong, and Singapore]. *Epoch Times*. http://www.epochtimes.com/b5/5/6/28/n968635.htm.

Tierney, John (2005, May 24) What women want. *New York Times*. Abstract http://query.nytimes.com/gst/abstract.html?res=F10E10F8395D0C778ED DAC0894DD404482&incamp=archive:search

Wikipedia (2005a, March 29) *Tai-Wan Her-Si Chih-Ming Shih-Chi* [Taiwan's Dutch-Spanish colony era]. http://zh.wikipedia.org/wiki/%E5%8F%B0%E7%81%A3%E8%8D%B7% E8%A5%BF%E6%AE%96%E6%B0%91%E6%99%82%E6%9C%9F

Wikipedia (2005b, April 13) *Taiwan under Dutch rule*. http://en.wikipedia.org/wiki/Taiwan_under_Dutch_rule

Wikipedia (2005c, May 18) *History of Taiwan,* last modified, 2005. http://en.wikipedia.org/wiki/History_of_Taiwan

Wikipedia (2005d, May 14) *Taiwanese Aborigine*. http://en.wikipedia.org/wiki/Taiwanese_aborigine

Wikipedia (2005e, April 13) *Timeline of Taiwanese history*. http://en.wikipedia.org/wiki/Timeline_of_Taiwanese_history

Wikipedia (2005f, April 30) *Sinckan manuscripts*. http://en.wikipedia.org/wiki/Sinckan_writing

Wikipedia (2005g, May 16) *Sino-Japanese War (1894-1895)*. http://en.wikipedia.org/wiki/Sino-Japanese_War

Wikipedia (2005h, August 9) *Lu, Hsiu-Lien*. http://zh.wikipedia.org/wiki/%E5%91%82%E7%A7%80%E8%93%AE

Womenweb (2004) *2004 Nian Tai-Wan Fu-Nü Zhu-Ching Bau-Kau* [Report of Taiwanese women's circumstances, 2004]. http://www.womenweb.org.tw/38/index.asp

Yam Women Web (1997) *Tai-Wan Fu-Nü Yün-Dong Fa-Tsang She* [History of the development of Taiwanese feminist movement]. http://taiwan.yam.org.tw/womenweb/action.htm

Yen, Hsiang-Jue (2004) *Yin-Yue Mei-Shue Shih-Hsiang Li-Shih* [History of music aesthetics: Chinese]. http://www3.ouk.edu.tw/culture/aesthetics/week5.htm

Yu, Chin-Fu (2004) Polyphonic improvisation and social restriction of Sedeq group in Tayal, *Yu-Shan Theological Seminary School Papers,* 11. http://www.yushanth.org.tw/publication/schoolpapers/011/11-8.htm

PART TWO

PART TWO

INTERLUDE II

The six chapters included in this section have clinical work as the central focus. In chapter seven, Terra Merrill reflects on her work as a Caucasian music therapist with a West Indian woman who was recovering from a cerebrovascular accident. Throughout the chapter, she integrates reflections from her journal which she then discusses using a feminist lens. Terra Merrill emphasizes the importance of being fully cognizant of her own direct experiences as a woman and as a music therapist who occupies multiple locations. She understands this to be integral to a feminist music therapy approach. Some of the more explicitly feminist features of her work that she explores in this chapter are reflexivity, power and influence, advocacy, activity, and voice.

The next three chapters are on music therapy with teenage girls and women who have been abused. In the eighth chapter, Colleen Purdon describes her clinical and community work in the area of violence against women. She begins by taking the reader on a journey through the various lenses which have shaped her understandings over her lifespan: the "normal childhood" lens, the "traditional music therapist" lens, and the "feminist" lens. Colleen Purdon not only works as a music therapist, but is a feminist counselor and community activist. In her chapter she reflects on issues of violence against women, our role as music therapists, and her clinical music therapy work with three abused teen girls. She uses a variety of music therapy techniques with these girls.

In the ninth chapter, Sandra Curtis describes the process she undertook in order to develop a feminist music therapy practice. She outlines major principles, goals, and techniques of a feminist therapy approach. She then outlines the steps necessary for a feminist transformation of music therapy. Following this, she provides descriptions of her work with two women with whom she worked at a battered women's shelter. The music therapy technique she uses with these two women is songwriting.

In the tenth chapter, Elizabeth York describes her clinical work and qualitative research protocol with women victims of domestic violence. This work is a representative sample of eight months of work with 40 women members of a support group run by a Community Abuse Prevention Services Agency in Utah. Creative arts techniques used include vocalizing, song discussions of women's music, creative writing, movement, imagery, drawing, and journal writing. These experiences culminated in the development of an ethnographic performance piece entitled, *Finding Voice.* For these survivors of intimate partner violence, finding the courage to speak out was a powerful aspect of the healing process.

In the eleventh chapter, Dorit Amir describes her work with Israeli women who have suffered trauma in their lives. She begins by describing feminism in

Israel and then briefly describes how her feminist values are woven into her work with women. She describes her work with three women who have suffered from traumas due to being Jewish and living in Israel: one who lost her lover when he was killed during the 1967 Six-Day War; one who was a hidden child during the holocaust, whose parents were killed by the Nazis while she survived and went to live in Israel; and one who lost her husband in the Yom Kippur War in 1973 and who later lost her daughter in a terrorist attack in 2001. The theme that runs through these stories is the loss of power due to traumas caused by human beings and the regaining of power while in music therapy.

Joke Bradt, in the twelfth chapter, describes her work with women suffering from chronic pain. She discusses socially constructed stereotypes related to chronic pain and the effect of these stereotypes and stigmas on her clients. Joke Bradt then describes the process she underwent working with these women and how she came to use vocal toning, breathing techniques, and vocal improvisation as techniques in order to help her clients to reconnect to their bodies and to their emotions. Through her work, these women have begun to feel empowered, to find their voices.

Chapter Seven

POWER AND VOICE IN THE INSTITUTIONAL SETTING: A JOURNEY TOWARD ACTIVATING A FEMINIST MUSIC THERAPY APPROACH

Theresa Merrill

Reflection

It is early morning on the Fraser River. One of Canada's largest and most important rivers, it winds its way through western British Columbia. Its waters are home to waterfowl, fish, and an extensive and fragile ecosystem; the power of this river turns the turbines that feed power-dependent residents in B.C. and much of California. I have always called her the Great Mother River: the Ganga of British Columbia. This morning, the river is working. Tugs with log booms move along its north fork toward the Straights of Georgia. At the river's edge, a small group of Chinese men and women practice Tai Chi as they do every morning, gracefully weaving together form, energy, strength, and art. Quicksilver and radiant beside them, the Fraser multi-tasks in ways that resonate with me as I write; my experience of and thoughts about feminism are like this river life: diverse, radiant, working, forward moving, artistic, energetic, and life sustaining. Feminism is, for me, about being myself, a woman within multiple contexts . . . situated and functional in diverse environments; and it is about being aware of those multiple contexts. The degree of adaptation required to negotiate these contexts is tiring. And it feels like a problem that women and music therapists share. There seems to be a different language for each context within which I function. And I feel tired of negotiating that in-between-ness. And so for me, the pain of being all things to all people releases into the comfort of a context to call my own . . . something with which to identify. So, I guess I see a feminist approach to music therapy as a home base where my many contexts are acknowledged and where my values are able to take centre stage.

INTRODUCTION

The overall purpose of this collection of women's voices is to explore what may be characteristics of a feminist-informed model of music therapy practice. The challenge for feminist-informed music therapists is that music therapy did not develop from within a blank theoretical slate, but in a time and within locations that were (are) reflective of male dominant paradigms. So for women (and men) who are so inclined, some of these paradigms feel foreign, artificial, and not resonant with her experience and worldview. In inviting dialogue, we can collectively tease out the meanings of a feminist-informed practice for us. Is it about working with women? Is it about doing women's work with women? Is it about the perspective and intention of the therapist? Can men do feminist work with women? Can women work within a feminist model with men? Is the essence of music therapy different in a feminist model than in other models? I am inclined to believe that a feminist-informed practice must really proceed from within a personal worldview that places women's values in a prominent position. To move toward a feminist theory of music therapy we must understand definitions of music and therapy that are uniquely feminist. These values may then be enacted from within a variety of service models or practices.

In this chapter, I reflect on my work with a woman recovering from a devastating cerebrovascular accident (CVA) and explore explicitly feminist features of that work: reflexivity, power and influence, advocacy, activity and voice. I structure this chapter in such a way that serves to develop a feminist understanding of ways of knowing, framing, and reflecting on our work. In Mary Brabeck and Laura Brown's (1997) exposition on feminist theory and psychological practice, they point out that feminist theory emerges from within direct experience and from within the relationships that develop between therapists, clients, and colleagues (p.24). I understand a feminist music therapy approach by being fully cognizant of my own direct experience as a woman and as a music therapist who occupies multiple locations. In my own words . . . when I tell the truth about what I do and the way I do it . . . it is inherently feminist—as I ask clients to explore their direct experience and as I explore my own relationship to client or student and to the music we make together as well as to the institution and environments that influence these relationships. I understand that from within these awarenesses, something broader can be understood about feminist approaches to music therapy.

Localizing the Subject—Who am I?

I am not a person who embraces labels easily. To embrace a label or to identify oneself to the world and to one's self as adhering to a particular set of values is an uncomfortable place for me. I seem to be much more comfortable moving between the lines, believing that as soon as a thing is defined, it seeks to break out of that definition. Claiming an identity, whatever that might be, is as empowering as it can be limiting; just as focusing energy within a form increases its potency. So for me, identifying as a feminist is about having some clarity about the particular human values I bring to my work. From an ethical point of view, it is also important for music therapists of all ideologies to have some kind of sense or articulation about the values they bring to their work. In this way, a client can be fully informed about the beliefs and approaches that ground the work.

Localizing the Context

My experience of being in health care is grounded in more personal history. As a young nursing student in the 1970s, I was deeply influenced by an unfolding feminism within nursing (Ashley, 1976). Nurse theorists challenged and ultimately rejected the pervading paternalism that had defined nursing practice up to that point. These voices helped create contemporary nursing theories that ultimately resulted in nurses finding a "room of their own"—indigenous theory that carved a spot for the nursing profession that was no longer dependently linked to medicine. It is not my purpose to reflect on these developments in nursing other than to say that my views of health, healing, and the provision of health services, and ultimately my music therapy practice within medical institutions, have been influenced by these important changes within my former profession. Within the past ten years, my music therapy practice has been influenced by Rosemarie Rizzo Parse's theory of Human Becoming (Parse, 1981, 1995, 1998). Parse's theory is not a feminist theory per se. Rather, it is a humanist theory. Parse herself rejects the notion that HBT is linked to feminism (personal conversation, 2003). Without entering into the specifics of that argument, or my response to it, suffice it to say that HBT has influenced my practice and I do not find that feminism contradicts that particular epistemology.

The feminist-informed work I present in this chapter was equally informed by HBT and third wave feminism. This is a story of how this feminism unfolded in my own practice of music therapy. In Jocelyn Chaplin's book *Feminist Counselling in Action* (1998), she identifies seven "stages" commonly experienced in feminist counselling. These are: Getting Started and Building Trust: the mothering phase; Identifying Themes: separating out the opposites; Exploring the Past: understanding the opposites and inner hierarchies; Dissolving the Inner Hierarchies and Facing Ambivalence: accepting the opposites; Making Changes: living with the opposites; Assertiveness Training:

expressing the opposites; and Standing Up on Both Feet: endings and new beginnings.

In my experience as a music therapist, I find many similarities with Chaplin's stages but am able to reliably identify only four from within my work. These I name: Developing Resonance; Finding a Voice: being an advocate; Being in the Music: holding the paradoxes; and The Solo Voice: on her own.

PART I: DEVELOPING RESONANCE

My practice, as I experience it, can be described as having distinct layers, levels or phases, frameworks, ways of understanding it. In each phase, the tasks are different. During the initial phases of music therapy, my task is to understand the therapeutic relationship and the potentials that may unfold in it through the music. I call this "developing resonance." This involves me coming to know the experience of my client in as many ways as possible. In my style, I use aesthetic replication as a means of cultivating resonance. I do that most easily and time-efficiently through the use of a reflexive journal. I present this case study to you through these reflections and through discussion of these reflections through a feminist lens.

Evelyn is a Black woman from a small Island near the Dominican Republic in the West Indies. I came to experience Evelyn in the environment of a long-term care area of a large multicultural hospital in Western Canada. I first became aware of her, as did most people not directly involved with her daily care, through the piteous sounds of her wailing. A middle-aged woman in her early 50s, aphasic and hemiplegic from a serious CVA, she cried out in anger and frustration (seemingly) at her inability to communicate with the world around her; and she wailed with an apparent grief so debilitating that it disturbed everyone within earshot. The wailing seemed unrelenting. Evelyn's physicians attempted to sedate her. She began to refuse that sedation. They began a trial of anti-depressants without effect. During a case conference, someone on the team suggested referring her to music therapy as a last resort before trying electroconvulsive therapy (ECT).

Reflection

Evelyn's wailing has a primal feeling to it. She is different than other residents of this continuing care unit. She is Black, she is younger than the predominately elderly demographic here, she has teenage children, she has a strength of will and purpose and uses that strength to say "no" to attempts to ameliorate or alienate her from her pain. Hearing her sounds pulls at something deep inside me. And it is uncomfortable. If I sit with that discomfort long enough, I know those sounds as my own and everywoman's. I see that one of my tasks as a therapist will be to walk a tenuous line in the countertransference, and I am reminded of the Shaman who walks between worlds. I see that I will need to be able to dip into and hold my own pain in order to be fully with Evelyn in the experience of hers and perhaps I can help her find a path through it to a different way of being with herself in this place.

Evelyn is already alienated from staff. In this very polite Canadian culture, dominated by a strongly English ethic, wailing, complaining, saying "no" and the expression of powerful emotions pushes buttons in this environment. I have worked here for eight years and Evelyn's wailing also makes me aware of just how incorrect it is to be too loud, too emotional, too visceral, not white.

Discussion

I had some apprehension about approaching Evelyn for individual music therapy based on a number of concerns not the least of which was being aware of my own whiteness, my own awareness that simply being with her in an authentic way would take me to uncomfortable places within myself and uncover uncomfortable positions of power within our otherwise homogenous setting (Mohamed and Smith, 1997). Another concern was that I did not have a pre-existing relationship with Evelyn and because her relationship with medical and nursing staff was conflicted at best, I had trouble imagining how I would obtain informed consent for individual therapy.

I began by extending an invitation to her to join an impromptu singing session with other residents. She agreed to come to that and I was surprised to see her move her body in expressive and evocative ways to the music. My impression at the time was that she experienced the music in a visceral way and that deprived of other methods of expression, she creatively used her body to make music with the rest of the group. I later came to understand these movements as an expression of an African aesthetic that was very intact in Evelyn (Epstein, 1983). Other examples of African aesthetics were evident in her musical preferences and the performance practices that emerged later in the music therapy. In retrospect, I could have moved more fully into this aesthetic with Evelyn had I more practical knowledge of her culture. That being said, in my style, I followed Evelyn's musical lead much of the time, and in this way became more culturally competent over time; though I am not sure I was as fully aware of that developing knowledge then as I am now. At the time, I believe I understood Evelyn's body play in the music to be unique and noteworthy, a positive response to what I was able to offer her.

This positive response to music encouraged me to offer Evelyn some private time with me in the music therapy studio at the piano and I was able to obtain her consent to experience music therapy in a general way; I also felt it was important to obtain her consent on a weekly basis. Unlike other individual clients in this setting, I did not have a regular weekly day and time with Evelyn; rather, I approached her at the beginning of the week with a calendar of my available session times from which she could choose. And unlike other clients, I gave her an appointment card every week. In the long-term care setting, this is a practice that is rare and empowering. I have maintained a belief that the practice of making weekly appointments with "regular" music therapy clients who live in institutions or communities is an empowering and normalizing practice. As a feminist, I have struggled a bit with the feeling that while it is normalizing and empowering in terms of enhancing personal power and choice, it could also perpetuate a hierarchical relationship. Upon reflection, I suppose that if a client had ever indicated to me that it would be easier for them to hold a regular time, I would support that too.

Reflection

In my intuition, I feel that this place takes too much for granted with Evelyn and that we have stopped treating her like a person with free will and power of her own. Moreso with Evelyn than with anyone else, I notice the horrible rigidity of the routines. Who are these for anyway? These routines are for us, not for the people who live here. Now I know very well that some of the residents here need and thrive in this kind of structure, but Evelyn . . . there is something about the flowing qualities of her body movements as she interacts with the music that lead me to want to provide as much creative input and openness in the therapy and within the therapeutic relationship as is possible for me to offer. This is one way that I feel I can resonate and mirror those movements in life outside the music therapy studio.

I am not quite sure of myself in these thoughts about race and colour. I have been trained as a cross-cultural music therapist. I am aware of my positions of power and of my whiteness, and I wonder if I am the right person to be working with Evelyn. Still I readily see and know very well that if asked to choose between working with this woman in all my straight-backed whiteness, even if I am a feminist, and leaving her to the physicians and the ECT, I will work with her and move along this path of empowerment as best as I am able.

Discussion

In the institutional setting, a feminist worldview holds a delicate paradox between the personal and the communal. In my early days as a music therapist, I remember feeling the pull between individual and group music therapy, and for years I have swung dualistically between these poles. A feminist music therapy practice can offer a balanced place between the two, and I feel that this balance is an important characteristic of feminist-informed music therapy as I practice it in institutions. Individuals can be empowered to hold a place and a unique role in the community of the institution.

Work in long-term care settings is also unique in that communal relationships challenge to a certain extent the traditional view of "dual relationships." In the previous reflection, I note that I am concerned with Evelyn's life "outside of the music therapy studio." Unlike private practice settings, the music therapist in an institution experiences many layers to her therapeutic relationships in that she may be able to experience her client in multiple situations. Once Evelyn identified herself as a "musician," she took part in any and every opportunity to be in music with others. Once she identified as a "healer," I made efforts to introduce her to residents in distress, thereby facilitating her role in the community. A private practice music therapist might not be in the position of influencing the environment to quite that extent. Further, when the music therapist is on staff full-time, informal access to the therapist on multiple levels exists for the client as well, and a community forms that, from a feminist perspective, has the potential to challenge traditional hierarchies. The challenge for the music therapist lies in holding the paradox of being in the community, as well as her position of power and influence within a code of ethical conduct. At the same time and from that vantage point, the feminist-informed music therapist will use that position to create awareness of rigid power structures and the values that lie beneath them. Experientially, this is a very real role that has emerged from within my feminist worldview and it is a scenario that is repeated regardless of the institution I happen to be affiliated with at a given time.

In terms of music, our first session revealed Evelyn's well-developed sense of harmony and melody as she picked her way through tunes on the keyboard. These tunes I began to recognize as spirituals. The first song she tapped out with the one finger of her good hand was "Old Black Joe." I played the song and sang the words while she closed her eyes and swayed along with the music. "Old Black Joe," composed by American composer Stephen Foster, is a very sad song of woe, separation and longing for death; themes common to the tradition of the music of enslaved Africans in the North American diasporas.

Old Black Joe

Gone are the days
When my heart was young and gay.
Gone are my friends
From the cotton fields away.
Gone from this place,
To a better land I know.
I hear their gentle voices calling:
Old Black Joe

Chorus:
I'm coming, I'm coming
For my head is bending low
I hear their gentle voices calling
Old Black Joe.

Why do I weep
When my heart should feel no pain
Why do I sigh
That my friends come not again
Grieving for forms
Now departed long ago
I hear their gentle voices calling:
Old Black Joe.

Chorus:

Where are the hearts
Once so happy and so free
The children so dear
That I held upon my knee
Gone to the shore
Where my soul has longed to go
I hear their gentle voices calling:
Old Black Joe.

Chorus:

She sighed deeply and her body seemed to rest, almost empty. After a time of silence, I asked Evelyn the question that I have come to believe is the most important part of treatment planning in music therapy:

> What is the most important thing for you right now?

"'ome." She wailed the word in the uncontrolled style of the severely dysarthric. She wanted to go home. 53 years old, two teenage children and a husband she loved dearly . . . I could understand her wailing in the context of not being able to see them again, of being confronted with the powerlessness of having been felled by a severe stroke, and then of being placed in a long-term care facility with residents much older than herself. I could only imagine her fears of losing her home, her status as mother and wife, fears of perhaps losing her husband. The full force of her grief moved across our shared field and I knew that the music therapy would need to move beyond expressivity to advocacy . . . the music therapy must have teeth and must seek to change the environment in which she was currently living.

PART II: FINDING A VOICE: BEING AN ADVOCATE

Brabeck and Brown (1997) note that feminist psychological practice has traditionally taken an action-oriented approach and has utilized forms of hands-on advocacy in the service of client needs. Further, they state that this advocacy is a prerequisite for a feminist theory of psychological practice. I would suggest that the same holds for the feminist-informed music therapist.

Reflection

I feel nervous about this work right now. I asked the questions, got the answers and now feel as though I need to deliver. Evelyn's care conference is coming up and I wonder how much courage I have in the face of the rest of the team to bring forward her hopes. I know very well that the Physiatrist[1] *has determined that she will not be able to go home. The physiotherapist tells me that there is*

[1] A physiatrist is a physician whose specialty is concerned with the diagnosis and treatment of musculoskeletal and pain syndromes, electrodiagnostic medicine and the rehabilitation of persons with severe impairments. In Canada, it is a Physiatrist who medically directs rehabilitation teams.

not enough time in the day to give Evelyn what she would need to be able to be at a functional stage where she could be discharged. And then, I am nervous about moving beyond the boundaries of my practice and expertise. The depression that I am expected to be addressing is directly linked to her physical status and to the powerlessness she feels in this environment . . . I know this in my bones. I know that my task in this meeting is to make this link explicit to the team. And then again, I am nervous about actually doing the work. I do not have expertise in the physical applications of music therapy. If I believe in supporting HER goals for her life, this is where it will lead, I know . . . to music-assisted mobilization. This is not where I have chosen to move in my practice and I notice tremendous resistance within myself to "going physical" with this client—yet if I value client-centeredness, I must act in truth with that value.

Discussion

The dilemma I found myself in was that in order to be fully client-centered, I needed to move into uncomfortable places within myself. I had to look at my own biases around models of practice. Up until this time, I had focused primarily on models of practice that led to depth and "insight work" in my work with wise elders. I maintained a fairly equitable balance between improvisational musicking and the use of pre-composed repertoire. I suppose that in general I hold to an "inter- and intrapersonal" imperative that pays less attention to the physical. Not that I exclude that entirely—one cannot work in a hospital setting and do that, but in general, I favour the psychological realms of experience.

During this time of the therapy, I found myself concerned with the larger aspects of Evelyn's life. I took on her issues and used my position of influence to advocate for her in order to obtain services that I was unable to provide through music therapy. Additionally, I spent time trying to create a team of people within the environment who would support her goals. I remember one team conference when I took a particularly assertive stance for Evelyn and her hopes. The medical director of gerontology suggested to me, and to the team, that I was supporting "false hope" with regard to Evelyn's desire to return home. There ensued a heated debate on the role of hope in the lives of humans and I pointed out to the team that I understood Evelyn's depression as an unrelenting hopelessness potentiated by an environment that would not hear her, not help her (from her perspective), and further, would prevent her from exerting her own power of will from even *trying* to work toward her own goals. I also remember saying "as for me, I would rather be guilty of supporting hope in patients than crushing it. All I am asking is that you allow Evelyn to pursue her hope. We do not have to guarantee that she will achieve that—but she needs to feel that she is working toward something." I followed that by asking "what would it take—what needs to happen for Evelyn to at least be able to visit her home?" Two treatments goals were identified and the staff in both nursing and physiotherapy agreed to begin programmes to address the issues they felt were realistic for Evelyn. She began a continence-training program and physiotherapy to increase strength and balance.

Reflection

Hope is neither true nor false—it simply exists or it does not. In some ways, I think that this is the essence of what we do when we are in music with clients. Those notes are truly life-giving. There is a hope for more beauty, more connection, more prana and people with even the smallest bit of will to live will hold onto that. If I am up to the challenge, and if I do it well, Evelyn will re-engage in her life and develop her own voice—so that she can create the kind of life that will be satisfying to her, in this environment or in another.

Discussion

In their edited volume *The Heart and Soul of Change* (2000), Mark Hubble, Scott Miller and Barry Duncan offer an understanding of therapeutic change. One of the factors they identify is hope, which they describe as how people think about the possibility of attaining their goals. They attribute 15% of therapeutic change to be due to hope, placebo effect, optimism, self-healing, and self-efficacy expectancy. They note that the opposite of placebo is 'nocebo' which can be defined as a lack of hope in a positive outcome. They also suggest that therapist expectancy and belief in the potential of the client to succeed is fundamental to the formation of therapeutic hope. Hope seems to me to be the outcome of unconditional positive regard and belief in the potential for wholeness for each person. Feminist-informed music therapy moves beyond the limitations of diagnostic criteria toward a broader belief in the inherent potential of a person to change.

It was also around this time that I came to terms with who I was and who I was not as a therapist. I stopped feeling guilty about not working in the physical domain and began feeling more fully embodied in the musical and psychotherapeutic context. I felt that Evelyn was having her physical needs met by others on the team, and that I was able to meet her emotional and expressive needs through music therapy. I decided to focus my work on what I knew.

PART III: BEING IN MUSIC

Reflection

There is a new sense of ease and comfort in the work with Evelyn. In some ways the hard, sloggy bits are over and we have eased into a way of being together that is music-centered—and we are also working on Evelyn's voice. She can really be understood when she sings—even though the pitch and quality of her voice is monotonous, the lyrics are clear. And she is generalizing this to the rest of her life—saying hello, asking for this or that, saying NO. She has been on home visits several times now and she seems to really "fluff up" when she has been at home. Her daughter tells me that Evelyn sits in her wheelchair in the kitchen and directs the cooking and cleaning, the re-arranging of decorations and "holds court" with the church ladies who come for tea on these days. There has not been an episode of wailing for 6 months and her affect is bright and positive. Her smile is broad and infectious. I feel that we are in a holding pattern—on a kind of plateau . . . and other clients have been drawing my strongest energy. Still we begin with a piano improvisation—I then ask Evelyn to decide the "most important thing" for today and that is what we do. She still chooses her appointment time and she often visits me in my office—checking in throughout the week. We have been working together for a year now and I am wondering if we need to identify a new direction. We do not hold to a tradition of solution-focused therapy here—but I am experiencing a bit of boredom and discomfort in spite of the "easiness" of our music and relationship. I have the sense that there is another place to go with Evelyn. I am just not sure what that place is.

Discussion

I find this entry so interesting in the sense of discomfort with which I experienced this phase of the work. This may be a characteristic of my personal myth, but I think it is also one of the paradoxes of feminist practice as I experience it: being vs. doing. As previously noted, feminist approaches to other forms of psychotherapy are characterized by the more active and activist aspects of the work. The more containing and space-holding aspects are lesser known and acknowledged (though often stereotypically attributed to a "Feminine" style) (Bruscia, 1995). Feminist studies seem to hold a distance between its more socio-political position and the archetypal one—often termed "The Feminine principle" (Zweig, 1990). The Feminine principle has, I think, been largely under-represented in second- and third-wave feminist literature because it provides a kind of psychospiritual context for what may have historically been used to perpetuate masculine hegemony, resulting in the oppression of women in diverse cultures and spheres of life. The misinterpretation of the differences between men and women from archetypal and spiritual perspectives has resulted in great suffering throughout history, and indeed reprehensible acts of persecution and exploitation of women and girls continue to occur in our own time.

In her extraordinary chapter titled *"The personal and cultural emergence of Yang-femininity"* (1990), Genia Pauli Haddon cracks open the being–doing paradox with a view of the Feminine archetype that is dynamically segmented into both Yin and Yang. Using body metaphors, she describes the Yin-Feminine as being tied to the gestating womb, the Yang–feminine to the birth-giving womb. To view the feminine experience as all containing and receptive or all active and productive is to miss the glorious point of the dynamic movement between the two. The notion of a Yin and Yang-Feminine holds the possibility for an explicit dynamic flow in the feminist-informed practice. It is a stance that listens, holds, contains, and receives and is also active, political, out-reaching, and assertive. These cycles are repeated in women's bodies and in the natural world. The discomfort I felt in this stage with Evelyn had to do with negotiating the in-between-ness of completing one cycle and beginning the next creative alliance: the move toward re-creating her role within the community of the long-term care setting.

PART IV: THE SOLO VOICE: ON HER OWN

Reflection

An interesting thing happened today in my session with Evelyn. A woman was crying and wailing in a nearby room, and Evelyn seemed to be preoccupied with it. Expressing deep concern with her face, she asked me to find out what was wrong with the woman. Across the hall, a very elderly East Indian woman sat in a wheelchair crying and reaching out. She had very long hair streaked with grey and a beautiful face without wrinkles. She spoke in a language I could not understand. Evelyn came out of the music therapy studio on my heels, wheeling with her one good arm and propelling with her one good leg. She wheeled herself close to the woman and made eye contact. She reached out and held the woman's hand in her own and in silence, they communicated. Evelyn held and kissed the woman's hand and the woman kissed Evelyn's in return. She continued to wail—this time with the full attention of a silent and compassionate witness . . . a witness who had known such grief herself. "Would you like to sit with her for awhile?" I asked. Evelyn nodded and I left them alone. I can only imagine what passed between these two women, but the wailing ceased and still Evelyn sat with her, until it was time to return to her unit.

Evelyn has long wished to go home. She has felt that her life's work was there, with her husband and children. I am seeing (and I wonder if she is seeing it too) a new possibility for Evelyn.

Discussion

In our next session, I brought up the seed of an idea that I had explored in my journal, and that was the possibility of reframing Evelyn's position about living in the institution. Up until the point of the wailing woman, Evelyn's position had never wavered: she did not wish to be here and wanted to go home. I still remember the look on her face as if a light went off in her head. "I wonder if one of the reasons you are here is to give comfort to others who are suffering?" Evelyn then disclosed something I never knew. Many years prior, Evelyn had been a practical nurse. Long before family and children, her life's work had been to help others. A new idea had formed—one of developing a new role in the very context she sought to escape—but a more assertive one, borne of her own pain and hard work. No longer alienated from staff, she became a comforter, a welcomer, part of the humanizing force that stubbornly continued to grow in the midst of a dehumanizing physical environment.

There were times I thought to regret that choice—as Evelyn showed up at my office door or to the music therapy studio with person after person in tow as if to say, "This woman will help you." I particularly remember a time when she declared in her dysarthric way to another resident: "If you sing, it will help."

Evelyn "solo" had developed into a person I could not have dreamed of initially. By following her flow, staying reflective and alert to the larger issues at play, by advocating and challenging the power structures, she was afforded the opportunity to re-claim her life and create it in a new way.

CLOSING THOUGHTS

To recap: This case presentation sought to uncover features and characteristics of a feminist-informed music therapy practice as I experience it. This practice can be described as occurring in stages or phases over time and include:

Developing Resonance
Finding a Voice: being an advocate
Being in Music: holding the paradoxes
The Solo Voice: on her own

This work calls something forth from the music therapist that seems unique and outside the acknowledged parameters of practice typically represented in the music therapy literature. Some of these features are:

Reflexivity

A feminist-informed music therapist will allow session events—music, impressions, and input from the entire environment—to impact her and then turn inward on herself to reflect. From those reflections, insights and active direction will occur.

Activity

A feature of a feminist-informed practice is activity. Not that a therapist will not present passive musical experiences, but rather that the process itself is an action-oriented one. Either the client is empowered to actively move forward in her life, or the therapy is environmentally based and the therapist is engaged in advocacy around the client's relationship with her direct environment. Another descriptor for this feature is "hopeful." Many times, my clients have lost the will to sustain hope for themselves and their life. By being in music, clients can sometimes begin to hear the stirrings of their own inner voice and can develop or rekindle a deeper sense of being—of identity—thereby having more complete and timely access to their preferences, hopes, and desires.

Advocacy

Within institutional and residential settings, there is no greater function than that of advocacy. In the case of Evelyn, I became a prosthesis for her voice, her wishes, and, having more power than she, I sought to influence the political and cultural forces that were working against her by making the players aware of the features of power inherent in our setting.

Environmental

Kenneth Bruscia (1995) and Brynjulf Stige (2002) eloquently describe music therapy approaches that actively address the environmental, cultural, and contextual conditions surrounding and impacting the client (also termed "ecological" by Bruscia 1998, p.229). The feminist-informed music therapist would have a heightened awareness of the entire environment as "client." In other words, the therapist would hold a worldview that understood that the environment: all that impacts a particular individual (in this case Evelyn) impacts us all (as an interdependent and shared system or field). Further, the feminist-informed therapist would have an awareness that the environment itself is one of the most powerful things we are working with and that the work can heal that environment to the extent to which some of the disabling sociopolitical, gender, racial, and power conditions that have been impairing the particular individual's ability to achieve the kind of wellness they are hoping for are ameliorated in the individual's (and presumably the system as a whole's) favour.

Creating community, and creating a reflective community that can agree on certain values that are generated from within it, is a function that could be extended to group music therapy. Another concept to consider is that of the feminist actively seeking to flatten or to equalize hierarchy. In this way, the music therapy can be described as holding a subversive position. One can view hierarchy as a symbol of the paternalism still pervasive in health care. In my practice this takes the form of creating opportunities for musicking that are inclusive of all. In our setting this includes "contracted out" staff, medical staff, nursing, housekeeping, management, families, volunteers, as well as patients/ residents. Tremendous effort is required to make this happen and it is a primary goal in my feminist practice with groups and environments.

Local

The work is localized within the socio-cultural context of the resident in past, present, and future terms. Not limited to healing past issues, or dealing with presenting concerns, a feminist practice is forward-moving, looking ahead and with a relevance to culture and race in an explicit way.

Political

The feminist-informed music therapist will explicitly consider the political factors that are influencing and impacting the client's situation, and then actively seek to influence the situation in the client's favour. In my discussions with Dr. Parse about a feminist interpretation of Human Becoming Theory, I came to understand that her reticence to acknowledge empowerment as a feature of her theory had to do with the dominance of the nursing profession in the political structures of hospitals. I think that music therapists, by virtue of their minority position in most hospital power structures, are potentially more resonant with the politics of the personal as we live such a unique reality in these settings.

Paradoxical

The feminist-informed music therapist holds the paradox of being and doing. This organic flow of taking in and bringing forth will be particularly evident in the inter-musical realms and in the 1-to-1 setting.

As I draw this chapter to a close, I need to note that the experience of writing for this volume was lengthy and laboured. I began my first draft while still a doctoral student in Michigan. I complete it from my desk in Portland, Oregon where I am beginning my second year as clinical coordinator in the music therapy program at Marylhurst University. Between beginning and end, I spent nearly a year back "home" in Vancouver, BC serving as professional practice leader for a team of music therapists in a large health care organization. I am now three times a grandmother. I conclude this experience with many of the same questions I began it with. What is a feminist-informed music therapy? The work with Evelyn, and the work I do currently with women, really does not feel in any way artificially adherent to any sort of external structure. It is informed, rather, by my own heart, which is inherently feminine and feminist. As I work with clients, my feminism provides the knowing that the clients experience their health and wellness through multiple layers and positions. Practicing in a feminist-informed way seems to open up broader areas that rather than feeling mutually exclusive, are intricately woven together. I believe that a feminist-informed music therapy addresses a fullness of being and experiencing beyond immediate health issues toward the environmental and especially the political. I also hold onto the concept of the Yin and Yang-Feminine—that which moves to action in a creative and nurturing way, both active and receptive . . . like music.

REFERENCES

Ashley, Jo Ann (1976) *Hospitals, Paternalism, and the Role of the Nurse.* New York: Teachers College Press.

Brabeck, Mary & Brown, Laura (1997) feminist theory and psychological practice. In Judith Worell & Norene G. Johnson (eds.) *Shaping the Future of Feminist Psychology: Education, Research, and Practice.* Washington, D.C.: American Psychological Association.

Bruscia, Kenneth E. (1998) *Defining Music Therapy. Second Edition.* Gilsum, NH: Barcelona Publishers.

Bruscia, Kenneth E. (1995) Modes of consciousness in guided imagery. In Carolyn Bereznak Kenny (ed.) *Listening, Playing, Creating: Essays on the Power of Sound.* Albany, NY: SUNY Press.

Chaplin, Jocelyn (1988) *Feminist Counselling in Action.* London: SAGE Publications.

Epstein, Dena J. (1983) A white origin for the black spiritual? An invalid theory and how it grew. *American Music, Summer,* 53–59.

Haddon, Genia Pauli (1990) The personal and cultural emergence of yang-femininity. In Connie Zweig (ed.) *To be a Woman—The Birth of the Conscious Feminine.* Los Angeles: Jeremy P. Tarcher, Inc.

Hubble, Mark A., Duncan, Barry L & Miller, Scott D. (2000). *The Heart and Soul of Change*. Washington, DC: American Psychological Association.

Mohamed, Carol & Smith, Ruthie (1997) Race in the therapy relationship. In Marilyn Lawrence & Marie Maguire (eds.) *Psychotherapy with Women—Feminist Perspectives.* New York: Routledge.

Parse, Rosemarie Rizzo (1981) *Man-living-health: A Theory of Nursing.* New York: Wiley.

Parse, Rosemarie Rizzo (1995) *Illuminations: The Human Becoming Theory in Practice and Research.* New York: National League for Nursing Press.

Parse, Rosemarie Rizzo (1998) *The Human Becoming School of Thought: A Perspective for Nurses and Other Health Professionals*. Thousand Oaks, CA: SAGE Publications.

Stige, Brynjulf (2002) *Culture–Centered Music Therapy.* Gilsum, NH: Barcelona Publishers.

Worell, Judith & Johnson, Norene G. (1997) *Shaping the Future of Feminist Psychology: Education, Research, and Practice.* Washington, D.C.: American Psychological Association.

Zweig, Connie (1990) *To be a Woman—The Birth of the Conscious Feminine.* Los Angeles: Jeremy P. Tarcher, Inc.

Chapter Eight

FEMINIST MUSIC THERAPY WITH ABUSED TEEN GIRLS

Colleen Purdon

INTRODUCTION

This chapter presents a personal perspective on music therapy and feminism as it has unfolded in my clinical and community work over many years. It examines the learning, values, and beliefs that have shaped my work as a music therapist since I began to work in the area of violence against women, and how this learning has impacted my clinical work with abused teen girls.

I have worked in my small, rural, Canadian community since 1986 as a feminist community organizer and advocate on issues of violence against women, and to a lesser extent, as a feminist music therapist in private practice. From 1975 to 1985 I worked exclusively as a music therapist and music therapy educator in Canada and Germany, in traditional institutional settings where feminist theory and practice were completely absent.

Throughout my formative years as a child, student, music therapist, feminist community worker, mother, and partner, I have developed "lenses" to help make sense of power and privilege within the family and the workplace, and to understand the role of women and men in the larger society. This has been a continuous process of shaping and challenging personal beliefs and values and ways of working over time. Over the past 20 years I have developed a feminist lens—a lens that informs the way I think and act on differences of power between women and men. It is this lens that informs my current work in community organizing and in music therapy practice.

Writing this chapter was not easy. My work as a feminist music therapist is something that grew out of necessity, not as the result of study or reflection. Once I began to work with abused women and children and became immersed in anti-violence work in our community, I was compelled to think and work differently as a music therapist. It was a challenge to meld these two worlds: the introspective and contained world of music therapy, and the world of feminist counselling and community activism directly linked to broad social change. To unravel the coming together of these two worlds, I will begin with some reflection on how I made sense of women's roles and equality over the years.

This refection acts as a backdrop for a wider discussion on the issue of violence against women and clinical music therapy with abused teen girls.

THE DEVELOPMENT OF LENSES FOR UNDERSTANDING

The "Normal Childhood" Lens

I was born in a tiny Canadian railroad village, the eldest of eight children in a white, working class, and Catholic family. The notion of normal that I was raised with was communicated clearly: my father was the wage earner, made all major decisions, and we deferred to his authority as "head of the household" while my mother, at home in charge of children and household, based her sense of self on her accomplishments as a housewife and the success of her children. The normal childhood lens of my childhood did not explain, or relegated to joke status, issues such as abuse, racial discrimination, gender inequality, sexuality, and sexual orientation. When I left home in 1970, I was equipped with a lens and a powerful set of beliefs about men, women, and power:

- Men are right, even when they are wrong
- Men have the right to power and decision making in families and in communities
- Women can be strong and influential, but they organize their power through the back door
- Women put the needs of their husbands and family first, and their own needs second, if at all
- Women's unpaid and paid work is rarely seen as important or valued, even when it is indispensable
- Leaders are male, except for the "exceptional" female

The "Traditional Music Therapist" Lens

The development of a music therapy lens began during my music studies in the early 1970's and after attending the founding meeting of the Canadian Association for Music Therapy as an undergraduate student. It continued while studying music therapy in England at the Guildhall School of Music and Drama with Juliette Alvin, and through the completion of Intertherap training in Analytical Music Therapy with Mary Priestley. My training with these extraordinary women sparked an intense passion and curiosity about music, music and psychotherapy, and the role of women in this new profession.

Clinical work in Canada and Germany provided a basis of experience in a broad range of treatment settings. In Canada I worked with dually diagnosed clients at a large institution for developmentally challenged adults. It was at this institution that I first became consciously aware of the phenomena of abuse. A colleague was fired when he complained to his supervisor when another staff member punched a female patient. Shortly after that, a patient I worked with came to his music therapy session with bruises on his neck, as a result of an assault by his counsellor. I felt helpless and decided not to report the assault, thereby joining the dominant culture of institutional secrecy and denial at the expense of safety and advocacy for victims.

I taught for two years at the first music therapy program in Germany and provided clinical training and supervision in inpatient and outpatient work with adults, youth, and children, then worked from 1980–1985 as a music therapist for alcohol- and drug-dependent clients at a residential psychotherapeutic clinic.

My experiences as a student, clinician, and mentor of music therapy contributed to a traditional music therapy lens:

- Music is a powerful language of feelings that can be used to empower or to control individuals.
- The music therapist (or therapeutic team) is "in charge" of the therapeutic process and usually "knows better" than the client when it comes to goals for the therapy.
- Healing work focuses on internal dynamics and early primary relationships, especially the relationship with the mother.
- Music therapy is rarely a primary therapy, but can be added or adapted to enhance or supplement a range of traditional treatment modalities.
- It is safer to protect yourself and your job than to stand up for the safety of abused patients in an institution.
- Women can be leaders in music therapy, but they face sexism and undervaluing in hierarchical systems dominated by men, and as practitioners of a profession deemed less valuable within the larger context of traditional treatment approaches.

The Development of a "Feminist" Lens

In 1986 I began work as the Executive Director of a shelter and counselling services for abused women and their children, a job I held for eight years. My work at the Women's Centre presented me some initially overwhelming questions:

- Why was I not aware of abuse and the impact of abuse on women, children, and families after more than 10 years of experience as a music therapist in mental health, addictions, and children's mental health?
- Why did I not know of the prevalence, seriousness, and impact of violence against women and children? Was the music therapy community part of the larger collective denial surrounding this issue?
- Was it possible to integrate a feminist analysis of violence against women and feminist counselling approaches with my previous training and experience as a music therapist?

Since 1995 I've worked as a music therapist in private practice and as a free-lance researcher and consultant on local, provincial, and national projects on women's issues and collaborative community responses to violence against women. The development of a feminist lens required acknowledging and understanding abuse, its impact on women, children, and the community, as well as training and research in feminist counselling approaches. It also required putting aside my traditional music therapy lens, and addressing my own deep-seated denial, shame, and victim blaming attitudes. This ongoing process has been shaped by many years of listening closely to the voices of abused and marginalized women in counselling, research, and community settings. I have been influenced by outstanding community service providers: police, social workers, attorneys, women's advocates, probation officers, and child welfare workers who work tirelessly as part of a collaborative community effort to address violence and abuse in families.

At the core of this ever-developing feminist lens is a focus on accountability to the safety and well-being of abused women and children in both clinical and community work. Our community has developed "Markers of Accountability" for the provision of services for abused women (Tettero, 2000). These markers guide my work as a music therapist and may be helpful for the reader:

- Work in a way that is truly helpful to women. This means taking the time to hear the whole story of the abuse and gaining a thorough understanding of the situation, history, and context of the abuse.
- Engage in teamwork with the victim in an egalitarian fashion: listen to the woman, ask about her wishes and fears, and respond to diverse and complex needs.
- Provide information about services, the therapy process, next steps, and options. Women need information about their options and how the therapy fits within the larger social service or justice system.
- Demonstrate an attitude of respect, understanding, patience, support, and empowerment. The attitude of the therapist is the most powerful predictor of the success of the intervention. This is also important in work with abusers who need to be held accountable for their abuse, while being treated respectfully.
- Ensure safety needs are met and work with women and children to develop safety plans that they can use.
- Hold the perpetrator of the abuse accountable for his actions. Work with the justice and social service system to hold perpetrators of abuse accountable and to support changing abusive behaviour.
- Level the playing field between the victim and the offender, and between service users and service providers. The therapist can advocate for women and intervene to address these power imbalances.
- Work to fill in cracks and close loopholes in the broad system response to victims of violence. Be part of a coordinated community response to violence and communicate effectively with other service sectors and providers.
- Prevent violence and abuse by engaging in prevention strategies and public education on violence in families.

UNDERSTANDING ABUSE AND OUR ROLE AS MUSIC THERAPISTS

Music therapists, like many therapists and workers in helping professions, have always worked with abused clients, often without identifying or acknowledging the abuse and without specific training or understanding of treatment and safety issues. When we consider that the majority of music therapists are women, we know many music therapists bring their personal experiences of abuse to the therapy setting as well.

The prevalence of abuse in all its forms in our society makes it essential for music therapists, regardless of their chosen area of practice, to be able to identify abuse and provide information and helpful supports for victims and perpetrators in a safe way.[1] Music therapists need to identify and respond to various forms of abuse: violence against women (woman abuse, sexual assault and harassment, date rape), child abuse (physical, sexual, emotional maltreatment and/or neglect, as well as children witnessing abuse in their family), elder abuse, and abuse of the disabled. We also need to understand how selected cultural, religious, ethnic, or economic groups are systematically abused by the dominant group in order to maintain forms of social order and control.

Abuse in all its forms is often hidden or denied. It can be found within intimate relationships and families, in institutions, and in the workplace. The victims of abuse are generally people in society with less power—women, children, the elderly and the disabled, the poor, and marginalized people in our society. Our understanding of abuse is closely connected to our social, historical, and cultural context as well as our own personal beliefs and values. Our response to victims and perpetrators is also influenced by social norms and our personal history or experience. For example, a woman who as a child watched her mother being beaten may believe that it is normal for men to physically abuse women (Purdon and Ostertag, 2000). Abusive and controlling behaviour is so prevalent that it is hard to imagine a music therapist who does not have firsthand experience as a witness to abusive behavior, as a victim or perpetrator, or as a helper.

> The home is the most violent place in America. In 1995, the FBI reported that 27% of all violent crime involves family on family violence, 48% involved acquaintances, with the violence often occurring in the home (National Incident-Based Reporting System, Uniform Crime Reporting Program 1999). The major context for violence in America is the family. Intra-familial abuse, neglect, and domestic battery account for the majority of physical and emotional violence suffered by children in this country . . . . Violent crime statistics, however, grossly underestimate the prevalence of violence in the home. It is likely that less that 5% of all domestic violence results in a criminal report. (Perry, 2004, p.3)

[1] For statistics and information on the prevalence of abuse check the following website: Fact Sheets from Status of Women Canada http://www.swc-cfc.gc.ca

Despite the prevalence of abuse in our society and the serious impact that abuse and trauma have on the physical and mental health of victims of all ages, the topic has not generated as much interest or research in the music therapy field as is warranted (Ostertag, 2002).[2] It appears that many music therapists do not have a good basis of knowledge or understanding of abuse-related issues. They may not recognize the impact of their own history, beliefs, and values on their work as clinicians, and they may be unprepared to respond to clients who voluntarily or involuntarily disclose current or past issues of abuse in the music therapy session. Music therapists may actually contribute to the revictimization of vulnerable people when they do not identify abuse or take appropriate action to meet the safety and treatment needs of their clients.

Music therapists need to recognize that there are personal and societal mechanisms and processes at work that may make the identification of abuse very difficult:

- Denial by the victim, perpetrator, and/or the therapist
- Minimizing the extent of the abuse or the harm caused
- Fear of reprisal by perpetrators, family, or the institution
- Reluctance to take "sides" or create a disruption in the family
- Fear of disclosure and involvement with agencies such as Child Welfare
- Pressure from clients, family members, or institution to keep secrets
- Believing the perpetrator's story or discrediting the victim's story
- Victims are compelled to protect the perpetrator or maintain silence
- Therapy focus is on symptoms and not on the experience of victims or perpetrators
- Discomfort with the issue or lack of training
- Personal experiences of abuse that have not been identified or processed

All music therapists need to have basic competencies to effectively screen for abuse with all clients, and then provide their clients with support and referrals, if

[2] Editor's note: It is important to note work in music therapy that has been done in the area of male violence against women (e.g. Cassity & Kaczor-Theobold, 1990; Rinker, 1991; Wallace, 1995; Whipple & Lindsey, 1999; Montello, 1999; Curtis, 2000; Austin, 2002; Amir, 2004; and, York & Hearns, 2005) with abused children/adolescents (e.g. Clendenon-Wallen, 1991; Lindberg, 1995; Rogers, 1992, 1995, 2003; Robarts, 2003; and, Edwards & McFerran, 2004) and with women abused in childhood who are pregnant or parents of young children (Day & Brudera, 2002).

they do not have the knowledge or expertise to deal with abuse issues (Purdon and Ostertag, 2001).

A feminist analysis of abuse, such as the theoretical model of the Power and Control Wheel (Pence and Paymar, 1990) which describes tactics that abusers use intentionally to exercise power and control over their victims, can help music therapists understand abuse and respond in a helpful way. The primary tactics used by abusers to establish and maintain control in their relationships are:

- Minimization of the abuse, denying, victim blaming
- Isolating the victim from family and supports
- Emotional abuse (put-downs, mind games, humiliation)
- Use of threats and coercion
- Intimidation
- Use of male privilege
- Using children (threatening to harm the child, using children as messengers)
- Economic abuse (controlling access to money, preventing the victim from working)

These tactics are used in woman abuse, sexual abuse, the abuse of children, and the abuse of the elderly and the disabled. In situations where one person has power over another, it is important to consider what tactics are used to keep power in balance. All music therapists are in positions of power over their clients. A feminist analysis of abuse helps us to analyze our use of power and recognize and take responsibility for overt or covert abusive tactics we use in our work with clients.

FEMINIST MUSIC THERAPY WITH ABUSED TEEN GIRLS

The feminist music therapy framework that guides my work with teen girls has three sources of influence:

1. A music therapy approach based on psychodynamic and cognitive principles reflected in musical improvisations, and other expressive activities (art, movement, storytelling, dance), and verbal processes in the music therapy session that originated in the models by Juliet Alvin (1975) and Mary Priestley (1975) modified to meet the needs of abused women and children (Purdon, 2002).

2. A feminist analysis of abuse that acknowledges the gender and power issues that lie at the root of abuse and how inequality between women and men, adults and children, the able and the disabled, contributes to abuse.

   This analysis recognizes:
   - the tendency to excuse the actions of perpetrators
   - the tendency to silence victims individually and collectively
   - the tendency to interpret abuse as a relationship problem or a problem with anger
   - the tendency to understand abuse as the personal failure of the victim or perpetrator, rather than a phenomena of a patriarchal society, and
   - a tendency to pathologize the survival methods of victims and to focus treatment on the symptoms rather than the cause
3. Participatory research with women of experience, training in group and individual feminist counseling techniques for victims and survivors of domestic violence and sexual abuse, the use of materials from *The Courage to Heal Workbook for Women and Men Survivors of Child Sexual Abuse* (Davis, 1990), and learning from the stories, experiences, and resources brought to sessions from abused women.

The Music Therapy Setting

The music therapy setting is structured to offer choice, confidentiality, and support for victims of violence. There is a wide range of instruments available, and various ways of sitting (chairs, cushions, a carpeted floor). There are art supplies and puppets, pictures on the walls and artwork from children and teens. The room is large enough to allow teens to have space away from the therapist, and space to dance. It has a workstation and computer, for writing, as well as a flip chart and lots of paper. In addition, we have access to tea, cookies, and drinks, which can be important when teens need a snack after school before starting the therapy, or when they need something concrete to help them settle and get ready to face the world after doing difficult work in the therapy.

Goals for the Work with Abused Teen Girls

The central goals for the therapy can be broadly described as:

- To identify safety issues with teen girls and engage them actively in planning for their safety and well-being.
- To explore with teen girls their understanding of abuse, why it happened, and who is responsible, and provide them with good information about abuse, the societal context of abuse, and the impact it has on victims and survivors.
- To mobilize hope and support teen girls in the development of self-confidence and realistic personal goals.
- To provide practical supports and strategies to help girls contain overwhelming feelings from the abuse and to work with them on new "survival skills" to help them cope with the effects of the trauma.
- To engage teen girls in decision making and control over their healing and recovery process.
- To communicate effectively with other professionals, family, and supports involved with the teen girl in order to coordinate services and enhance safety and opportunities for support and healing.
- To provide a "managed closure" to the therapy and engage teen girls in planning to recognize when they need support in the future and how to access help.

Structure for the Work

The music therapy process with teen girls is structured in three phases:

1. *Introduction and Assessment:* The first session is an opportunity for the music therapist, the young girl, and her support person (this may be a parent, foster parent, or social worker) to meet, share information, ask questions, see the music therapy room, and decide if music therapy is something they want to try out. The music therapist provides the teen with information about music therapy and her background working with abused women, including her understanding of abuse and trauma. We talk about documentation and how and what the music therapist communicates with parents and agencies. The music therapist makes it clear that it is not important for the girl to disclose abuse or talk about what happened to her, unless she

wishes to do that. The music therapist asks the teen about why she thinks she has been referred to music therapy, and what she thinks she would like to do in therapy. The music therapist asks the teen girl if she would like to come to two more sessions to try it out and to see if music therapy is helpful to her.

The next two sessions are a mutual assessment by the therapist and the teen. The focus is on an exploration of the music room, instruments, the teen's current issues and interests, and on building a supportive relationship through music and dialogue. The work rarely focuses on abuse, but the importance of safety is introduced and some safety planning for the session and for addressing any outside safety issues is done. At the end of the third session the music therapist and teen talk about what work needs to be done and what is important for the teen to accomplish. There is a commitment to a limited timeframe for the work (for example, ten sessions), with a date for a review.

2. *Working on Goals:* At the beginning of the fourth session, the music therapist and teen write down her goals for the therapy, and ways that the teen will know how she is doing. The therapist supports this process by providing information and feedback to ensure the goals are realistic. Over the course of the therapy, goals and progress are often discussed, and the therapist and teen collaborate on progress reports that are required by a referring agency.

   Every effort is made to involve the teen in ongoing documentation (writing, poetry, pictures, taping of music) of work done during the session. The therapist often writes what the teen says or has the teen make notes of her thoughts during the session. Some teens bring notes or poetry from home to sessions. Notes and pictures, as well as cassettes of music and songs developed in the sessions, are shared and often the teen takes these home, or they are glued in a scrap book provided by the music therapist (I keep a supply of attractive scrapbooks in the music room and offer all girls a choice). The therapist usually keeps the scrapbook in the music room, but teens often take their book home to put additional materials in it between sessions. It is important for young women to take charge of their information and have access to it during and following the therapy.

   During the sessions the music therapist and teen use music, improvisation, songwriting, art, story writing (with or without music), dance and movement, and dialogue to explore themes and problems that come from present-day issues or challenges, as well as issues from the past. The music therapist uses other tools as needed, for example a Trauma Assessment Tool (Hindman, 1989) has been a very helpful tool for a number of teen girls to assess how they experienced sexual abuse, the impact of the abuse, and how they made sense of it as children.

These tools are used to help teens express their feelings about the abuse, issues in their current life, or to explore coping and containing strategies to deal with the impact of trauma. The emotional and physical safety of teen girls is monitored through regular "check-ins" that are initiated by the therapist to discuss any emerging safety issues within the music therapy setting, from home, school, or in the teen girl's relationship with family and friends.

The music therapist respects the limitations and boundaries set by the teen, and helps her set safe boundaries for herself around the disclosure of abuse and painful memories and feelings. It is important in this work for the therapist to be an ally and model to help the teen deal safely with overwhelming feelings of shame, despair, and helplessness that come from sexual abuse. Improvised music needs to be used carefully, at the direction of the teen, to avoid landing her in emotional territory where she feels vulnerable and not able to cope. The music and the structure of the sessions are organized to help her feel in control, and to provide safe experiences where she can gather new insights, perspectives, and learning. This approach recognizes that girls can only do the work they need to do when the setting is safe and supportive, and when they have a relatively stable and abuse-free setting at home. It also recognizes that many abused girls are compliant and were trained to do what adults in their lives wanted and expected from them. The music therapist must consider this carefully to help the girl focus on her needs, not what she thinks the therapist needs or expects from her.

3. *Closure and Next Steps:* An important part of working with abused teens is careful preparation and attention to the closing of the therapy. Plans for the wrap-up of the therapy are made together with the teen and referring agencies to avoid sudden loss of control for the teen or revictimization. Even when the therapy is brief, a successful therapy closure can support future help seeking behaviour for teens. The impact of trauma and abuse will often resurface for victims at particular stages of their lives, for example when they become sexually active, start a serious relationship or marry, at the birth of a child, or the death of the perpetrator. A careful and supportive therapy closure can make it easier for survivors of trauma to access help from professionals, friends, and family when they need it. The closure includes a review of all the work that the teen has done over the

therapy process. This often takes the form of reviewing her scrapbook, listening to her tapes of music, and a review of session notes made by the therapist. The therapist and teen talk about her progress on goals and celebrate her achievements. Time is spent looking at what supports she needs now that the therapy is over and how she will know if she needs support in the future. If a final report for an agency is needed, the teen and the therapist work together on what is important to include. This provides teens with an opportunity for some input into the agency decision-making process and helps the music therapist accurately capture what was important, helpful, and unhelpful for the teen in the therapy. Each girl takes her scrapbook with her at the end of therapy. The scrapbook can be a helpful tool for the girls who access therapy or support at a later date and is a tangible way for teens to reclaim their history and hold on to positive experiences of growth and development from the therapy. It may also help when the girl is older to see what she believed, how she thought and felt at that time in her life, and what has changed or stayed the same for her since that time.

CASE EXAMPLES

The following case examples illustrate how three young women worked on goals to deal with the impact of abuse in their lives. The names and some identifying information have been altered to protect the identity of the young women.

Ann

Ann was a 14-year-old First Nations teen living on a small and isolated reserve with a member of her extended family. She was in permanent foster care with the local Child Protection agency as a result of her mother's alcoholism. The Children's Aid Society (CAS) knew very little about Ann but suspected that she was physically and perhaps sexually abused as a child. Ann was supposed to have regular visits with her mother, but her mother often cancelled when she was drinking. Ann was referred to music therapy because of concerns about depression that may be related to past abuse and because she liked music. Ann attended 12 music therapy sessions.

Therapy Goal: Mobilizing hope and supporting the development of self-confidence

The work with Ann centered on mobilizing hope to counter her deep unhappiness and her fear of the unknown. At the first session Ann agreed with her foster mother that she had many dark things weighing her down, but she was most interested in learning how to play the piano, something she always want to do but couldn't because there were no teachers on the reserve and no money. The music therapy sessions included structured instruction on piano and flute (exploring simple songs, duets, and some elementary work on learning notation) and improvisations between the therapist and Ann. The structured music clearly mobilized Ann's self-confidence and hope. She was surprised about her accomplishments at the keyboard, and took great delight in learning simple songs, especially the duets with the therapist. Although Ann was a shy and quiet girl, she gradually became more relaxed and talked freely about her love of the piano and the pleasure she experienced while playing. She was able to master tone production on the flute (with the hope of playing in the school band), and learned several folk songs, carols, and the melody from Beethoven's Für Elise (which we played as a duo) on the piano. She brought a fine sense of humour and fun to this work, becoming more confident in her playing and in her manner as the therapy progressed. Ann's success at the piano seemed to help her talk about her disappointment about her mother's ongoing drinking, missed visits, and lack of interest. These themes emerged as we sat together on the piano bench, providing a safe and supportive place for her to talk about painful experiences. The music also gave her something she could share with her grandparents at their home because they have an organ.

Ann's improvised music mobilized hope in a very different fashion. She played piano, gong, and metallophone with the therapist in a dreamy fashion that reminded me of water. There was little give and take or dynamic change in the music, and Ann seemed to disappear in a timeless, beautiful, and gentle river of sound. I found her music exquisite and timeless, but Ann was not impressed with it, and certainly did not want to talk about it. She reacted with surprise to my comments that the music was quite beautiful. Despite the lack of verbal processing, the music itself seemed to raise Ann's spirits and energy. At the end of music therapy Ann said that music therapy was helpful because she always felt tired when she came to music therapy and always felt better going home.

Therapy Goal: The music therapist communicates effectively with other professionals, family, and supports involved with the teen girl

Ann had great difficulty expressing herself verbally, especially around her wishes and feelings. She did not talk a great deal in the therapy, but did let me know that she was getting a keyboard for Christmas, something that she always wanted. Ann was distant, tired, and unhappy when she arrived at the first session after the holidays. She finally said that she didn't get a keyboard for Christmas, but was given a stereo instead. She said it was fine, and didn't matter. I was upset and told her that. I asked if she would like me to call her social worker about the keyboard, but she said it didn't matter. I called the social worker anyway and explained the importance of the keyboard for Ann, and the way it seemed to comfort her and help her express herself. It appeared that Ann's foster mother and the social worker did see the significance or the importance of this for Ann, and it was not a problem for them to arrange a keyboard. At the next session Ann came in very happy because she had a keyboard and had been up until 2:00 a.m. playing and showing her friends the music she learned in music therapy. We agreed that she would move on to take piano lessons, a positive and hopeful end to the therapy.

Tess

Tess was a 15-year-old Caucasian girl living in temporary foster care who was sexually abused at age 8 by a family friend. The family had a long history of CAS involvement. She was the oldest of 3 children, and her two younger brothers lived at home with their mother, while Tess was in foster care, after being abandoned by her father. The CAS reported that Tess was of low normal intelligence and experienced a chaotic life with many moves (she attended 15 different schools) as her mother changed partners and locations. The CAS referred her to music therapy because of concerns that she was sexually active at school and after she attacked her brother with a knife at a home visit. They planned for Tess to return to her mother's care in the near future. Tess attended 19 music therapy sessions.

Therapy Goal: Identifying safety issues and engaging teen girls actively in planning for their safety

Tess responded very positively to the music therapy setting, despite her reputation for defiant and oppositional behaviour. She used music therapy to identify and talk about safety concerns, and then worked with the therapist to plan for safety. Safety is a very relative concept for a young woman like Tess, and her ability to make safe choices was very limited. She was highly vulnerable because of her extensive experiences of abuse and poor self-image, and she lived in an unstable and confusing situation, caught between the Child Protection Agency, her foster mother, and her mother. Despite this, Tess identified many safety issues over the course of therapy:

- She was having unprotected sex and she was afraid she would get pregnant or get a disease
- She worried she couldn't control her use of drugs and alcohol
- She worried that the men she met used her for sex and didn't really care for her
- She ended up in some unsafe situations because she was drunk or out of it
- She didn't know how to protect herself from men
- She was worried about her anger and that she might really hurt someone, especially if she was drunk or out of it
- She was afraid to talk to her mom, her foster mom, or the social worker about any of these things, because she would be punished for doing bad things

Tess was successful in carrying out a safety plan to help her protect herself from a man who was using her. The plan involved talking to her friends about what they thought he was after, then making up her mind whether she would skip classes and visit him, or stay at school. In the therapy we used music to explore some of her worries about this relationship and how she felt. She proudly announced at the following session that she didn't skip class and had broken off with him.

We used a progress report for the Child Protection Agency as an opportunity to document some of Tess's safety concerns and bring them to the attention of her caregivers. Initially she was reluctant to have the CAS know that she used drugs or had sex, but in the end she agreed to report that she needed information and support so she could get sexual health counselling and help to deal with drugs and alcohol. We carefully documented what she needed, and her fears about possible punishment from the CAS or her mother in the report. It was very difficult for the adults in Tess's life to reach a consensus on how to support her safety needs. The CAS, the foster mother, and Tess's mother were locked in a battle with Tess in the middle, and the school did not seem to play any role in her safety. At the last music therapy session Tess reported that her mother was sending her to a religious residential program for girls and she would be moving once again.

Therapy Goal: Providing practical supports and strategies to help teen girls contain overwhelming feelings from the abuse and work with them on new "survival skills" to help them cope with the effects of the trauma.

Tess disclosed intense feelings of despair, hopelessness, and fear at many points in the therapy. At times she became overwhelmed when she talked about getting into trouble at school, her difficult and stressful relationship with her mother, or when she talked about the abuse she experienced. It was important to support Tess and deflect or stop her tendency to blame herself or put herself down. Tess talked about many traumatic incidents as a child, including witnessing her mother almost choked to death by her dad and her sexual abuse as a child. She said she was fucked up and her life stopped when she was eight years old after the sexual abuse. We used songwriting and improvised music to help Tess contain her fragmented thoughts and intense feelings. It also allowed her space to bring in dimensions other than the overwhelming negative feelings she was burdened with. When Tess cried in a session because she moved so many times and because she is a "dummy" and can't manage school, we created a rap song to pull the many pieces together and create "A Picture of Tess."

> A girl who likes making people laugh, being funny
> A girl who likes to pass her classes, but not a total brownie
> She knows where she is going in life, loves to act, sing and dance
> She likes to hang out with the guys; they let her be herself, not prissy
> She could care less what people think, but she has to fit in so she needs to care, kinda
> A girl who likes to rap
> I like to rap, when I was younger, I moved 18 times, or was it 25, lost track
> Some things about me I won't repeat
> I'm only 15 and I like to hang out with the guys, they're cool, they know who I am
> I like to rap
> I'm very sneaky, very sneaky.

One of Tess's goals for the therapy was to "have time to play and be a kid" She said she would really like to have her childhood over again so she could change the picture from feeling like an idiot. In each session we used music, dance, songwriting, art, and humour to support opportunities for play. This became even more important when Tess disclosed that as an 8-year-old her abuser invited her "to play" then sexually abused her. Tess blamed herself for going with him, and said she should have known better. Her ability to play as a normal child was cut off by the abuser and contaminated with self-blame and the painful memories of the abuse. Music, dance, drawing, and songwriting provided Tess with meaningful and safe ways to resume her play and allowed her to reclaim an important aspect of her childhood.

Eileen

Eileen was a 13-year-old Caucasian girl who was in CAS care for 5 years in permanent foster care. Eileen and her 4 younger siblings were removed from the family after Eileen disclosed sexual abuse by her father's cousins. The CAS believed there may have been other unreported sexual abuse as well. The family had a long involvement with CAS as a result of physical abuse by Eileen's father and extreme neglect by both parents.

Eileen was very involved in the care of her siblings when she lived at home, but following the apprehension they were all placed in permanent foster care or adopted out to different families. She was living with her third foster family in five years at the beginning of the music therapy and was placed in a fourth home during the therapy. The CAS referred Eileen to music therapy because of her difficulties with her foster mother and concerns about a placement breakdown, as well as her defiant and sexualized behaviour. She loved music and was a very intelligent young woman. Eileen attended 36 music therapy sessions over almost two years.

Therapy Goal: Engaging teen girls in decision making and control over their healing and recovery process

Eileen was initially quiet and reserved in the music therapy, but showed an early ability to set clear boundaries for herself. She had a history of defiant behavior in her foster care and school settings. I worked to engage her positively in making decisions about what was important for her in the therapy and how she would like to do this work. Making Eileen the person in charge of her therapy process countered her experiences of lack of control over the big decisions in her life, especially the devastating loss of contact with her siblings when they all became permanent wards of the state.

After three sessions Eileen set out three goals for her therapy:

- to talk about some of the things her foster mother and the CAS wanted her to talk about (her abuse)
- to have help with the things of despair or problems she faces

- not to have everything she does in life put on the computer and read by everyone at the CAS.

Eileen found ways to have positive control of her healing process. She agreed to complete a detailed Trauma Assessment process to talk about the sexual and physical abuse she experienced as a child. Over a four-month period she explored: Who was responsible for the abuse? Why was Eileen chosen? What happened when the abuse was disclosed? All of the detailed questions from the Trauma Assessment were glued into blank pages in Eileen's scrapbook. The scrapbook and the information in it belonged to Eileen and was not put on the therapist's computer. At each session she decided what work on the assessment she felt up to (she experienced anxiety, tiredness, and dissociated when she thought about the abuse) and then worked with the therapist on the questions. Eileen used improvisations with the therapist to help her deal with anxiety and dissociation, as a respite from the work, and to help her to explore her feelings about the abuse, while she worked on the Trauma Assessment. Eileen was very proud of her steadily increasing confidence and ability to talk about the impact of the abuse on her life. She completed all the pages and questions in the Trauma Assessment and continued to use the scrapbook for her songs and writing until the end of the therapy when she took it home. Eileen learned about why the abuse happened and who was responsible with the help of music and the trauma assessment tool. She acknowledged that she was not responsible for her sexual or physical abuse and that her parents failed to protect her. She had no wish to live with her parents, and (correctly) noted that they still were not able to care for their children. She did suffer from feeling responsible for the breakup of her family and the loss of her relationship with her siblings. During the therapy she said that her disclosure of sexual abuse to a school friend resulted in her losing her brothers and sisters, and she now regretted the disclosure. She wished that her parents could have gotten help to protect her and look after the children, so she could have a family of her own.

CLOSING REFLECTIONS

I believe that feminist-based music therapy offers abused teen girls a unique creative space where they can safely work on the impact of their abuse and build hope, self-confidence, and skills. A feminist approach empowers teens by believing them, focusing the work on their goals, and working with them in partnership. This includes involving teens in decision making, safeguarding their right to privacy, and advocating on their behalf within the larger system.

Improvised music has a very special role in the healing process of abused children and teens. My clinical work with abused teen girls supports research with abused children that found that music therapeutic improvisations relate to the life stories and trauma of abused children and offer children a safe experience of intimacy and nurturing (Ostertag, 2002, p.22). Music and music therapeutic improvisations can be a safe starting point for young women to explore and reclaim confidence in intimacy in their lives after surviving the trauma of abuse.

Music therapy is limited in what it can accomplish when children and teens girls are exposed to ongoing chaos, abuse, victim-blaming, and unsafe interventions outside of the music therapy room. Recently I listened to a young Canadian woman on the radio speak about her work with prostitutes. She spoke of being sexually assaulted as a child and how she began to use drugs as a young girl to deal with her shame and feelings of worthlessness. At the age of 12 she was kidnapped by a prostitution ring and spent the next 15 years of her life addicted to drugs and working as a prostitute. She spoke of her many attempts to get out of prostitution, and how she was beaten, raped, tortured, and moved to other communities when she ran away. She spoke of her experiences with the mental health system where she was diagnosed and treated for bipolar disorder, psychosis, and depression. The justice system, social service system, and the broader community clearly did not protect or support this woman as a child or as a teen. It was only as an adult that she was able to access supports, and was fortunate to find professionals who recognized her addiction and trauma issues and directed her to appropriate services. Her story did not elicit from the interviewer any sense of outrage about the injustices and appalling pain she experienced, or prompt any questions about how it was possible for the justice, medical, and social system to fail her so spectacularly. The story was framed as an example of how a young woman "turned her life around" and was now working to help other prostitutes get out of the sex trade. When I listened to this young woman, I thought of Tess and her vulnerability to sexual exploitation. I also thought about how very difficult it was for the adults in Tess's life to work together to address her safety needs, and protect her from perpetrators. I wondered about the longer-term consequences for Tess because of our inability to act collaboratively and decisively on her behalf at a time that she needed help.

A feminist analysis in music therapy is a good starting place for music therapists who wish to provide a helpful response to clients dealing with violence and abuse in their lives. The work is challenging and very rewarding. There is a much larger task for feminist music therapists and for the broader music therapy community. We do have an obligation to work together as a "community of adults" to protect children, teens, and the vulnerable and marginalized citizens in our society. Our music therapy community, and all music therapists, have an important role to play as individuals and collectively as part of a community response to violence and abuse that puts the safety of victims as its first priority.

REFERENCES

Alvin, Juliette (1975) *Music Therapy,* London: Hutchinson & Co., Ltd.

Amir, Dorit (2004) Giving trauma a voice: The role of improvisational music therapy in exposing, dealing with and healing a traumatic experience of sexual abuse. *Music Therapy Perspectives, 22*, 96–103.

Cassity, Michael David & Theobold, Kimberly A. Kaczor (1990) Domestic violence: Assessments and treatments employed by music therapists. *Journal of Music Therapy, 27,* 179–194.

Clendenon-Wallen, Joy (1991) The use of music therapy to influence the self-confidence of adolescents who are sexually abused. *Music Therapy Perspectives, 9*, 73–81.

Curtis, Sandra L. (2000) Singing subversion, singing soul: Women's voices in feminist music therapy. (Doctoral dissertation, Concordia University, 1997). *Dissertation Abstracts International, 60* (12-A), 4240.Montreal, Quebec.

Davis, Laura (1990) *The Courage to Heal Workbook for Women and Men Survivors of Child Sexual Abuse*. New York: Harper and Row Publishers.

Day, Toni & Bruderer, Helen (2002) *A Journey of Healing and Hope Through Song.* Brisbane: Queensland Government, Australia.

Edwards, Jane & McFerran, Katrina (2004) Educating music therapy students about working with clients who have been sexually abused. *The Arts in Psychotherapy*, *31*, 335–348.

Hindman, Jan (1989) *Sexual Victim Trauma Assessment.* Ontario, OR: AlexAndria Associates.

Lindberg, Katherine A. (1995) Songs of healing: Songwriting with an abused adolescent. *Music Therapy, 13*, 93–108.

Montello, Louise (1999) A psychoanalytic music therapy approach to treating adults traumatized as children. *Music Therapy Perspectives, 17*, 74–81.

Ostertag, Joachim (2002) Unspoken stories: Music therapy with abused children. *Canadian Journal of Music Therapy, IX*, 17–27.

Pence, Ellen and Paymar, Michael (1990) *Power and Control: Tactics of Men who Batter: An Educational Curriculum.* Duluth, MN: Minnesota Program Development, Inc.

Perry, Bruce (2004) *Understanding Traumatized and Maltreated Children: The Core Concepts*. Video Training: Series 1.

Priestley, Mary (1975) *Music Therapy in Action*. London: Constable.

Purdon, Colleen (2002) The role of music in analytical music therapy—Music as a carrier of stories. In Johannes Eschen (ed.) *Analytical Music Therapy*. London: Jessica Kingsley Publishers.

Purdon, Colleen and Ostertag, Joachim (2001) Music therapy and abuse: Training package for Wilfred Laurier Music Therapy Department, Waterloo, ON (unpublished).

Purdon, Colleen and Ostertag, Joachim (1999) Understanding abuse: Clinical and training implications for music therapists. *Canadian Journal of Music Therapy, VI*, 9–23.

Rinker, Rhonda Lineberg (1991) Guided Imagery and Music (GIM): Healing the wounded healer. In Kenneth Bruscia (ed.) *Case Studies in Music Therapy*. Gilsum, NH: Barcelona Publishers.

Robarts, Jacqueline (2003) The healing function of improvised songs in music therapy with a child survivor of early trauma and sexual abuse. In Susan Hadley (ed.) *Psychodynamic Music Therapy: Case Studies*. Gilsum, NH: Barcelona Publishers.

Rogers, Penny (2003) Working with Jenny: Stories of gender, power and abuse. In Susan Hadley (ed.) *Psychodynamic Music Therapy: Case Studies*. Gilsum, NH: Barcelona Publishers.

Rogers, Penny J. (1995). Childhood sexual abuse: Dilemmas in therapeutic practice. *Music Therapy Perspectives, 13*, 24–30.

Rogers, Penny J. (1992) Issues in working with sexually abused clients in music therapy. *British Journal of Music Therapy, 6,* 5–15.

Tettero, May (2000) Accountability to women (Appendix A). In Colleen Purdon, *The First Charge Intervention Process: A Model for a Coordinated Justice Response to Domestic Assault in Rural Areas*. Report to the Grey Bruce Court Coordination Committee, 13-31.

Wallace, Terra Eve (1995) The use of music therapy with a domestic violence support group in a women's prison. Unpublished Master's Thesis, The Florida State University, Tallahassee.

Whipple, Jennifer & Lindsey, Rebecca (1999) Music for the soul: A music therapy program for battered women. *Music Therapy Perspectives, 17,* 61–68.

York, Elizabeth & Hearns, Maureen (2005, July 20) *A music therapy research protocol with women victims of intimate partner violence.* Presentation at the 11th World Congress of Music Therapy, Brisbane, Australia.

Chapter Nine

FEMINIST MUSIC THERAPY: TRANSFORMING THEORY, TRANSFORMING LIVES

Sandra L. Curtis

It's revolutionary for women to sing the blues,
but it's even more so to sing all the songs of life.

—Gloria Steinem, *Revolution from Within*

The widespread impact of feminism is undeniable, with a diverse array of fields enriched by its contributions. Feminist therapy represents one of the most significant of these contributions in the area of women's wellness. Developing in response to the second wave of feminism and feminist critique of traditional therapy, feminist therapy has now established a rich tradition of theory, practice, and research (Bricker-Jenkins, Hooyman, & Gottlieb, 1991; Brown & Root, 1990; Burstow, 1992; Worell & Remer, 2003). This tradition has influenced those working in such fields as psychotherapy, counseling, and social work—whether in choosing to practice feminist therapy directly or to use it to inform their own practice. With its roots in the 1970's, feminist therapy is still greatly needed today: to address unique issues facing women; to provide a more complete understanding of women in the sociopolitical context of ongoing patriarchy and institutionalized oppression; to fill gaps in current theory and research; and to provide creative therapeutic approaches which better meet women's needs (Worell & Remer, 2003).

At the same time as feminist therapy has been developing, music therapy has been developing its own rich tradition of theory, research, and practice. This tradition has, however, been relatively untouched by feminist therapy. While some music therapists' lives and practice may have felt the impact of feminist therapy, until now this has been little reflected in music therapy writing, theory, or research (Baines, 1992; Curtis, 2000; Hadley & Edwards, 2004). Yet each has much to offer the other. Feminist therapy brings with it an understanding of the silencing of women's voices in the current sociopolitical context. Music therapy brings with it a creative approach which provides women a powerful and real counterpart to the metaphor of voice. Both recognize women's affinity for the creative arts, particularly music (Curtis & Harrison, 2006; Herman, 1997). Combined, they provide a dynamic new approach for empowerment—feminist music therapy.

In this chapter I will look at the development of feminist music therapy—as both a specific practice and as a process others may adopt should they be interested in starting their own journey towards feminist music therapy practice. Focusing initially on feminist therapy, I will outline its definition, principles, goals, and techniques. A process for the feminist transformation of music therapy will then follow. I will conclude the chapter with women's own voices, using examples from their individual experiences in feminist music therapy to illustrate its theory and practice—to demonstrate the power of transforming theory to transform women's lives.

Feminist Therapy

Feminist therapy is a philosophy of treatment which is based on a feminist belief system and which has as its purpose both personal and sociopolitical transformation (Rosewater & Walker, 1985; Worell & Remer, 2003). As such, it has many different definitions, just as feminism itself has many different definitions (Hadley & Edwards, 2004; Lerman & Porter, 1990). There are also many different types, such as liberal, womanist, cultural, and radical feminist therapy (Brown & Root, 1990; Burstow, 1992; Johnson, 1983; Worell & Remer, 2003). Yet despite these differences, there is a strong consensus concerning the basic principles of feminist therapy (Brown, 1994; Rosewater & Walker, 1985). There are essentially three major and overarching principles from which all others derive: 1) the personal is political; 2) interpersonal relationships are to be egalitarian; and 3) women's perspectives are to be valued (Bricker-Jenkins et al, 1991; Worell & Remer, 2003).

The principle that *the personal is political* is rooted in a feminist analysis of women as an oppressed group in our culture and of the psychological effects of such oppression, as well as its interaction with other forms of oppression such as classism, racism, ageism, ableism, and heterosexism (Laidlaw & Malmo, 1990; Ballou & Brown, 2002). As a result, the focus of feminist therapy is both internal and external. Its purpose is not to enable women to adjust to a dysfunctional culture, but to seek social change for all women in order to improve the situation, while at the same time seeking personal change for individual women who have been harmed by the current situation (Laidlaw & Malmo, 1990; Lerman & Porter, 1990; Worell & Remer, 2003). Feminist therapy must be practiced not only as a healing art for individuals, but also as an "intentional act of radical social change" (Brown, 1994, p.30).

The feminist therapy principle which stipulates that *interpersonal relationships are to be egalitarian* applies to the client-therapist relationship, as well as to the personal relationships of both client and therapist. Thus, clients must be empowered within therapy and within their own individual lives. Feminist therapists must not only empower their clients, but be empowered themselves in their own lives. To be and to practice are one and the same in feminist therapy (Bricker-Jenkins et al, 1991; Worell & Remer, 2003).

Similarly, the third overarching principle, that *women's perspectives are to be valued*, applies within the client's life, the client-therapist relationship, and the therapist's life. Feminist therapists are to enable their clients to understand and value women's perspectives; they must also enable their clients to value themselves. In order to do so, feminist therapists must also value themselves, their clients, and other women, both in attitude and action (Burstow, 1992).

The goals common to all feminist therapy practice stem directly from these overarching principles. As such, they include both personal and sociopolitical transformation (Bricker-Jenkins et al, 1991). The focus of these goals is threefold: to eliminate the oppression of women; to enable women to recover from the specific harm of oppression; and to enable women to deal with the internalization of this oppression.

Some of the specific goals within this focus are:

1) to empower women and increase their independence, developing their personal and social power
2) to increase understanding of the sociopolitical context of women's lives and problems; to increase understanding of the interaction of multiple oppressions (e.g. sexism, racism, classism, heterosexism, etc.)
3) to achieve optimal functioning as defined by each individual woman, rather than by the therapist or society; and
4) to initiate necessary social change (Burstow, 1992; Worell & Remer, 2003)

To accomplish these goals, a number of feminist therapy techniques have evolved. Although small in number, they are essential, distinguishing features of feminist practice. The core techniques include: demystification, feminist analysis of power, and feminist gender-role analysis (Laidlaw & Malmo, 1990; Worell & Remer, 2003). *Demystification*, although not unique to feminist therapy, is essential—only by providing clients with information about therapy and in actively involving them in all its aspects, is it possible to establish the necessary egalitarian client-therapist relationship. The feminist therapy technique of *power analysis* is unique and is used to increase clients' understanding of the relative societal powerlessness of women and the role that this plays in their lives. This feminist analysis of power is not used to identify women as helpless victims of society or as entirely powerless. Rather, it is used to enable women to see both the personal and societal sources of their problems, to see both their sources of powerlessness and of power, and to see both societal and personal solutions to the situation (Hall, 1992; Laidlaw & Malmo, 1990; Lerman & Porter, 1990). The feminist therapy technique of *gender-role analysis* is used to identify and critically examine women's and men's socialization process—the shared messages received by women and men (regardless of race, class, culture, etc.) and the impact these have. These reflect institutionalized, integrated, and internalized sexism and, while shared, they intersect with and are mediated by other societal oppressions such as racism, classism, heterosexism, etc. As with power analysis, feminist analysis of gender-role socialization identifies the sources of strength as well as harm and involves personal and societal change (Laidlaw & Malmo, 1990; Worell & Remer, 2003). With these core techniques, stemming from the core goals and principles, it is clear that feminist therapy is far more than a non-sexist approach; it involves a radical transformation of the therapy process, with feminist analysis engaged in by client and therapist to accomplish both personal and political change.

Transforming Music Therapy

Feminist therapists generally receive training within a traditional therapeutic approach and only later undergo an individual process of feminist transformation of their practice. It is this process, as it pertains to music therapy, which will be outlined next. Judith Worell and Pamela Remer (2003) identify five steps in this feminist transformation: 1) to identify sources of bias in the theory; 2) to modify or eliminate any biased components; 3) to assess the theory's viability; 4) to determine its compatibility with feminist criteria; and 5) to highlight its unique contributions to feminist therapy. In developing my own practice of feminist music therapy (Curtis, 2000), these steps were most helpful and will be briefly outlined here.

A search for specific sources of bias reveals music therapy's history to be a source of strength. Music therapy has been informed by a variety of other theories concerning such issues as personality development, source of client problems, and the client-therapist relationship. If we strip away these other theories, their inherent biases can be eliminated, leaving a generally neutral music therapy theory about the human response to music. The focus of this neutral theory is on the capacity of music to evoke physiological, affective, and cognitive responses, making it a unique and effective treatment medium. By stimulating brain functions involved in memory, in learning, in motivation, and in emotional states, music has considerable potential for use in therapy to influence human personality and behavior, and to activate healthy thinking (Thaut, 1990; Thaut & Smeltekop, 1990). This potential to elicit change is put into action by means of the unique relationship established between client, therapist, and music

In light of this neutral focus, music therapy proves to be especially available for feminist transformation (Curtis, 2000). Music therapy meets, or can be readily adapted to meet, feminist criteria. There is nothing specific in this neutral music therapy theory which precludes it from being: gender-balanced (as opposed to androcentric or gendercentric), multicultural (as opposed to ethnocentric or heterosexist), interactionist (as opposed to intrapsychic), and life-span oriented (as opposed to deterministic). While music therapy theory has not traditionally included a specific focus on women in general or on women of diverse races, cultures, classes, abilities, and sexual orientation, it is certainly sufficiently flexible to be modified to include these. The neutral music therapy theory does not address the issue of the source of the individual's problems and so, while it is not specifically interactionist or life-span oriented, it too can be modified to become so. Finally, while this music therapy theory does not necessarily or specifically adhere to feminist principles, neither does it contradict them. To go further and embrace feminist criteria fully in the development of a truly feminist music therapy requires transformation of the client-therapist relationship, of the music therapist's personal life, and of music therapy principles, goals, and techniques.

The neutral music therapy theory, while acknowledging the importance of the client-therapist relationship within the framework of music experience, makes no specific stipulations concerning the nature of that relationship. Thus, it must be transformed to incorporate the very important and specific stipulations of feminist therapy for an egalitarian relationship—as much as is possible given the inherent power differential in any therapeutic relationship. This issue of power has been problematic for feminist therapists who increasingly accept that power exists in all interpersonal relationships and that the eradication of all power differentials, even in feminist therapy, is impossible (Lerman & Porter, 1990; Smith & Dutton, 1990). Feminist therapists, however, see the power inequity in therapy as temporary—it is their task to make the therapeutic relationship as egalitarian as possible and at least equal in respect and value, if not in actual power. They must strive continually towards a greater balance of power through their work with their clients within the therapeutic process and through simultaneously working for social change (Lerman & Rigby, 1990; Smith & Dutton, 1990)

To place such importance on the nature of the client-therapist relationship highlights the importance of therapist attitudes. As a result, personal transformation is required such that the personal relationships of feminist music therapists themselves are characterized by equality and ongoing feminist analysis. Furthermore, they must spend a portion of their personal lives in actively advocating for social change in order to better the external world for all women.

In the area of principles and goals, music therapy's transformation is readily accomplished through the straightforward adoption of all feminist therapy principles and goals. This is not unreasonable to assume given music therapy's long tradition of adopting those of other theories. Feminist transformation of music therapy techniques involves the integration of feminist techniques within a music therapy context. The techniques of feminist analysis of gender-role socialization and power are hallmarks of feminist therapy used to accomplish a number of its major goals. Two music therapy techniques which involve a combination of music and verbal processing are particularly well suited for this: lyric analysis and songwriting. Music performance, composition, and recording can also be used to accomplish the feminist goals of empowerment and of reclaiming voices which have been silenced in patriarchy. As well, the valuing of women and of women's self-nurturance can be accomplished through the music therapy techniques of music-centered relaxation, music and meditation, and music and imagery.

The final step in feminist transformation is the identification of the unique contributions music therapy can make to feminist therapy. These lie in the dramatic power of music to change lives, in the unique medium music therapy offers with its particular appeal to women, and in the rich resource of women's music well suited for feminist analysis of women's lives in the current socio-political context. Perhaps the greatest contribution lies in the opportunity it provides for women to write and record their own songs. In listening to and singing the words of women songwriters, women can explore the subversion of the patriarchal message. In writing and singing their own songs, they can tell their own stories and lay claim to their own unique voices.

Personal Contexts

In discussing the development of a new practice of feminist music therapy, it is important to understand that this practice will reflect great diversity. While each therapist will strive to incorporate an understanding of the complex interaction of oppressions in our lives, we all view the world through our own lenses. Our clinical practice and our writings are informed by our personal frame of reference. Therefore, I would like to be transparent about my own perspective by sharing a little about my personal background.

My personal context is characterized by the contrast of experiences of privilege and of oppression. I am a white, middle-class, educated, able-bodied, heterosexual woman born in the mid 1950's. As such, I have experienced certain privileges of dominant group membership, such as access to privileged places, people and resources, including higher education. As a heterosexual woman, I have been free to love whom I choose without fear of discrimination or hatred. I have also, however, had the experience of being the "other," of living on the margins, and of being oppressed as a woman living in a patriarchal culture. The nature and extent of such marginalization has been the topic of considerable feminist literature (Anzaldúa, 1990; Brown & Gilligan, 1992; Chesler, 1990; Gilligan, 1982; hooks, 2000). For me, it has run the gamut from feeling constrained by gendered career stereotypes to being unable to find myself in any of my readings which only made reference to men and mankind. Indeed it was these readings which led to my initial interest in feminist literature during my teenage years. It is, however, my personal experience of violence which has been the most profound.

Violence in Women's Lives

Violence is central to the lives of women living in a patriarchal culture (Burstow, 1992). This violence can be both emotional and physical: Women are violently reduced to bodies, bodies for men as seen in the widespread objectification of women; these bodies themselves can then be violated. This violence can be either actual violence itself or simply the fear of violence which shapes our lives in a myriad of ways—from the way we dress and talk to the times and places in which we walk. In whatever shape it takes, violence is integral to women's lives regardless of any differences such as race, class, etc. (Curtis, 2000 & 1994).

In addition to the general experiences of any woman living in a patriarchal culture, my personal experiences of violence have also played a part in creating the lens through which I view the world. I have an on-going struggle with issues of weight, body-image, and self-esteem; I believe this struggle to be partly a direct result of a culture which violently reduces women to bodies and then enforces increasingly unrealistic standards of beauty for those bodies. As well, I have had personal childhood experiences of emotional and sexual abuse. The insidious nature of some of the emotional abuse was such that it served to leave me questioning the actual existence of the sexual abuse: Was it really *"that bad"* that it should be called sexual abuse? It is only as an adult that I have come to see it for what it truly was—sexual abuse prefaced by the ultimate betrayal by a male adult authority figure.

Transforming Lives

Having examined the feminist transformation of music therapy and having outlined my personal contexts, I will turn next to the actual experiences of women in feminist music therapy. From the large number of women with whom I have had the honor of working, I have chosen to focus on two here so that their stories can be fully heard in all their contextualized richness and complexity. While unique, the stories of these two women—Julie and Roslyn[1]—are representative of the many women I have worked with in Canada and the United States. Their experiences truly reflect the marvelous transformation I have witnessed.

Julie and Roslyn participated in a feminist music therapy group with me at a battered women's shelter. Prior to working with these women, I had to do some preparatory work—to ensure I had an in-depth feminist understanding of the nature of male violence against women and to develop cultural competence for working with diverse women. Feminist analysis of woman abuse within intimate relationships identifies it as a gendered phenomenon deeply rooted in a patriarchal culture which not only perpetuates the violence, but is in turn perpetuated by it. This abuse is related to all types of male violence against women (e.g. rape, incest, sexual harassment, etc.), each one being a manifestation of male control of women and each one being condoned and encouraged by patriarchy (Curtis, 2000; Marshall & Vaillancourt, 1993). While women abuse survivors share much in common, their experiences also differ because of the diversity of their backgrounds (Burstow, 1992). Subsequently, I began a self-directed process of developing cultural competence for working with the diverse women in my practice. This is a life-long process recommended for any therapist working with clients of differing sex, race, class, sexual orientation, etc. It involves an examination of one's own cultural background and attitudes, followed by the development of cultural literacy and skills (Curtis, 2004).[2]

[1] For confidentiality purposes, the names used here are fictitious.

[2] An excellent introduction to this important topic can be found in *This Bridge Called My Back* by Cherríe Moraga and Gloria Anzaldúa (1983) and in Gloria Anzaldúa's (1990) *Making Face, Making Soul: Hacienda Caras*).

Julie

Julie's Story

Julie, an African American woman, was 25 years old when she joined the music therapy group. She was single, with a 6-month-old daughter. She came to the women's shelter seeking safety from an abusive boyfriend.

In describing her experience of abuse, Julie indicated that the abuse had started in the first year of her 4-year relationship, escalating as time passed, becoming particularly bad at the time she became pregnant. This is not uncommon for abused women. Julie mentioned that the abuse included all types, with control being an important part of it all:

> "He would come home and he would bad-mouth me, call me fat, um, bitch . . . and other words, you know, I'd rather not say . . . But you know he controlled me so much to the point where I was really scared to leave. He would threaten me, tell me that he would kill me if I left him. And I really thought he would, so I wouldn't."

Julie's Songs

Julie was involved in a feminist music therapy group with me twice weekly for 10 sessions. Because of the demands of infants present in the group on their mothers, Julie was not able to do any relaxation to music. Her time in therapy was spent doing feminist analysis of power and gender role socialization through lyric analysis, singing, and songwriting. For purposes of lyric analysis, Julie received a songbook and recording of a wide variety of songs written and performed by women on a great diversity of themes such as love, romance, violence, gender role socialization, healing, and empowerment. From Alanis Morissette to the Dixie Chicks, from Tracy Chapman to Alisha Keyes, women singer-songwriters are singing eloquently about women's lives.[3] Julie was very articulate and participated enthusiastically in the discussions during lyric analysis. She readily drew connections between issues addressed in other women's songs and her own experience. She also suggested some song titles—R&B—which she thought would be good for the group to listen to and discuss. These songs by Jody Watley, Mary J. Blige, and Chantay Savage, as well as songs from the "Waiting to Exhale" movie soundtrack (1995), were particularly

[3] A thematic listing of songs and a description of their use in feminist analysis can be found in "*Empowering Women through the Healing Arts: A Manual for Workers with Survivors of Violence*" (Curtis, 2003) and in *Singing Subversion, Singing Soul: Women's Voices in Feminist Music Therapy*. (Curtis, 2000).

effective for Julie and the other women in the group—they mirrored their experiences as women of color.

In songwriting, Julie was much more hesitant initially. Her first song was a genuine struggle for her. Yet by the next song, her progress in recovering from the abuse began to become apparent. Written with the piggy-back technique to the melody of "Hand in My Pocket" by Alanis Morissette (1995), it sings of hope and resistance: "And what it all comes down to is I've finally got peace of mind / I've got one hand in my pocket and the other's thanking the Lord . . . / What it all comes down to is the road's not so rough anymore / I got one hand in my pocket and the other's shooting the bird." Julie's final song—her first with original lyrics and music—clearly illustrates the changes in her thinking about women's and men's relationships in general, and about her own relationship in particular. "Not Anymore" provides a strong message of resistance and of self-valuing.

Not Anymore

There comes a time in a woman's life when she doesn't want to be alone
She wants that peace of mind, the need to be touched
By a strong man with strong hands, the kind that turns her on
But not anymore

I thought I found that man of my dreams
But roses turned blue and milk got sour, the grass wasn't green
Not anymore

Who do you think you're calling bitch?
I was good to you from day one, and never stopped
I should have recognized the signs, but I was blinded by love, you see
But guess what baby?
Not anymore

You see I realized the day I left you
That roses are red, only violets are blue
So you can kiss my ass and the baby's too

I don't have to take your shit
I am Black, I am beautiful, I am strong, I am proud
And we don't need you
No, not anymore.

Julie chose to do this song in the style of Jody Watley's "When a Man Loves a Woman" (1996)—spoken, with background music. Julie also chose to perform it herself for the final recording—a very self-affirming experience for her.

Julie's Transformation

Julie's progress in feminist music therapy was notable. This was reflected both in standardized measures and in Julie's own words. Her self-esteem increased from the 60th to the 80th percentile on the Tennessee Self Concept Scale (Roid & Fitts, 1991). When asked in an exit interview about her efforts to recover from the harm of abuse, Julie replied:

> "You were one of them. Yeah. Because I love music and it helps for me to get it out because [in a whisper] I never talked to anybody about my problems . . . So I kept everything inside and it was killing me . . . Just being here, talking to the girls, talking with you . . . It really helped me out."

Julie described her experience in music therapy saying:

> "It was, uh, more emotional therapy, you know, because some part was putting your feelings into music. It was just, it was the way I expressed myself that made it good. And that really helped me out emotionally. Made me sit down every Monday and every Wednesday and just think a little more. You know, and uh, and [she starts clapping as she sings:] "I don't have to take this shit." You know, you know [laughter]."

In summarizing what she would take with her from her experiences in music therapy, Julie commented:

> "I won't leave here and get involved with a man and go through the same changes I been through before. It will never happen again. And I know a lot of women say that and don't follow up behind it. But I think even if I didn't have a child to live for . . . It's not just because of her, but it's because of me . . . so I meant, "No. Not Anymore."

Roslyn

Roslyn's Story

Roslyn, a European American woman, was 45 years old when she started music therapy. She was single, with grown children no longer living at home. Roslyn came to the shelter seeking safety from an abusive boyfriend.

In describing her experiences of abuse, Roslyn indicated that her last two relationships had been abusive. Roslyn described the abuse in her most recent relationship as involving both physical and emotional abuse:

> "It was 2 weeks ago he took me with a rope . . . I was asleep . . . I woke up with a noose around my neck. And he was hollering, "Say you want to live." And he said, "If you want to die, I'll kill you." And what's sad is I never did ask him to stop . . . because he had me convinced I was just an idiot, just totally stupid."

Roslyn's Songs

Roslyn was involved in feminist music therapy with me twice weekly for 8 sessions. Being in the same group as Julie, Roslyn's time in music therapy was spent doing lyric analysis and songwriting using the same collection of women's songs.

Although she was somewhat quieter than the other women in the group (particularly in the earlier sessions), Roslyn listened attentively and then later participated eagerly in the discussions during lyric analysis. For Roslyn, it seemed that hearing women songwriters sing about abuse and hearing the other women in the therapy group discuss their experiences helped break the isolation and gave her permission to discuss her experiences. Initially she expressed her feelings of fear and shame. When faced with a song which had women's righteous anger as a theme, Roslyn stated simply that she was not at a point where she could express anger at her abusers, nor could she visualize herself ever reaching such a point. Yet 2 weeks later, she eagerly and with much laughter recounted to me in therapy how she had puzzled her counselor earlier that day; to his question about what she hoped to become, she had replied, "a bitch with a bad attitude," making reference to the song of that title (Adegabalola, n.d.). Roslyn finally felt that she had the right to be angry, to express that anger, and to refuse to be abused or to be blamed for the abuse any longer. As in one of her favorite lines from that song, "It's better to be pissed off than pissed on."

This remarkable progress for Roslyn from victim to strong survivor is clearly evidenced in the songs she wrote in music therapy. Roslyn took to songwriting immediately. For her, the written word seemed a safe way to express herself. In songwriting, Roslyn had no difficulty finding the right words and those words clearly reflected her progress.

In a song with original lyrics written to the melody of "Hand in My Pocket" (Morissette, 1995), Roslyn expressed some of her conflicting emotions at that time—the harm she suffered, yet her hope for a new life, one with peace of mind and serenity. Roslyn felt strongly about her repeated line, "I've closed my mouth and opened up my ears," commenting that it reflected her desire to listen and learn from her mistakes. I believe it also reflects the stage Roslyn was at during the time she wrote it—a time when she still felt considerable self-blame for the abuse and a time when her voice was still silenced. This was also reflected in one of her song's lines—"And what it all comes down to is I'm looking for me." Her final song reflects a remarkable difference. In "Here Comes Roslyn," with its original music, no longer is Roslyn a silenced woman. In good-humored fashion, Roslyn gives voice to her anger, holding the abuser responsible for the violence. But "Here Comes Roslyn" is not just a song of anger and resistance. It is a song celebrating her new found life and her new found ability to value herself—"Watch out world 'cause here comes Roslyn / I'm claiming my spot, gonna have me some fun."

Here Comes Roslyn

I prayed to God and got away
Now son of a bitch you're gonna pay
I'm signing your card and
putting it in the mail
Happy Mother's Day babe,
I hope you rot in jail
I've got your name on the soul of my shoe
Watch out now,
you don't know what I'll do

Chorus:
Watch out world 'cause here comes Roslyn
I'm claiming my spot,
gonna have me some fun
Watch out world 'cause here comes Roslyn
I'm claiming my spot,
gonna have me some fun

Home, family, & friends are back so far
Hopefully soon I'll come up with a car
My psyche is strong,
another human won't break
The burden on my heart is
no longer an ache
You controlled my life
like a cancerous mole
Now I have my life,
but you're still an asshole

I'm happy, happy, having fun
I'm happy, happy, having fun

You say you teach tough love
with every hit
I learned loser you're full of shit
I'm out on my own and lovin' Roslyn
If I were a big man
you'd be totin' a bruisin'
Your bridges you are burning out fast
I pray for all victims
that I was your last

Chorus
I'm happy, happy, having fun
I'm happy, happy, having fun

In discussing the recording of her song, Roslyn had been adamant that I record it for her, saying that she had no voice for it. At the very last minute, having heard Julie record her own song, Roslyn asked if she might also record hers. Although she had thought she would recite it as Julie had done with her song, I suggested she try singing it in the blues style in which it had originally been composed. With microphone in hand and with some initial trepidation, Roslyn started to sing her song, surprising both of us with her deep and strong voice. Roslyn had truly found her own genuine voice.

Roslyn's Transformation

As remarkable as Julie's progress was, Roslyn's eclipsed it—both on the standardized self-esteem test (with an increase from the 8th to the 46th percentile) and as reflected in her final interview. In response to a request to describe herself, she commented:

> "Like I told you, I'm fixin' to be [a moment of silence]. What the, the [Interviewer: You can say it on tape], the bitch with an attitude. I'm talking about . . . I, I have found so much of myself that I like and I have found out that I have a lot of good in me."

Discussing the experience of songwriting, Roslyn stated:

> "Oh, you saw me glowing in there like a light bulb! I'm still lit up now. I'm so excited I can't stand it and it looks so professional. I think if people heard it, they'd love my song! I do. Now you can see I'm well . . . I'm strong."

Finally in summing up what she would take with her from the music therapy experience, Roslyn said:

> "I really do feel nobody will ever be able to break my spirit again . . . I've gotten it back a lot through this music."

CONCLUSION

In this chapter, the transformation of theory has been examined, with an opportunity to hear the voices of individual women and their own particular experiences in feminist music therapy. In working with these women, I have learned much—about their experiences, about the fragility of the human spirit on the one hand and its resilience, when nurtured, on the other hand, and about the transformative powers of music. I have seen women move from unfamiliarity with feminist music therapy, uncertainty as to what it might offer them, and even, for some, initial reluctance to participate in such a thing when they were hurting so much, to eager anticipation and surprised delight in themselves and their music. There were times when they were no more surprised than I was at this transformation and at the power of music in their lives.

In exploring this new thing called feminist music therapy, the importance of group work should not be overlooked. Some have argued that women do not need therapy; they simply need to talk with other women friends about their experiences. One therapist, Laura Brown (1994), agrees but goes further to say that women of today rarely have the opportunity just to chat with other women and so, rather than supplanting woman talk, feminist music therapy provides a much-needed opportunity for it. Thus, it was when the women in my feminist music therapy sessions perceived their experiences as simply time spent chatting with good friends, that I believe they were most empowered. In feminist music therapy, the women were able to participate as members in group song discussions, as individuals within a group in writing and recording their individual songs, and as a group in listening to each other's original compositions—providing both validation and inspiration to each other in finding their own voices.

When looking back at the women's experiences in feminist music therapy—their self-esteem, their songs, and their voices in interview, the transformational power of music becomes clear. The testimony of these women is compelling. They have moved in feminist music therapy from finding their own voices and stories in the songs of other women, to finding the value of their own voices such that they were able to write and record songs themselves. Their experience has genuinely been one of finding their own true spirit. Since such a great debt is owed to these women for their lessons to us about the power of music to transform lives, it is only fitting that the final words belong to their voices of subversion and of soul.

> "My soul wasn't gone, but my spirit was totally crushed. And I've gotten a lot back through this music . . . I'm fixin' to be a bitch with an attitude . . . And nobody's gonna take my spirit from me."
>
> —Roslyn

REFERENCES

Adegabalola, Gaye (n.d.) Bitch with a bad attitude [Recorded by Saffire Uppity Blues Women]. On *Old, New, Borrowed, Blue* [CD]. Chicago: Alligator Records.

Anzaldúa, Gloria (1990) *Making Face, Making Soul. Haciendo Caras: Creative and Critical Perspectives by Women of Color*. San Francisco: Aunt Lute Books.

Baines, Susan (1992) *The sociocultural and political contexts of music therapy: A question of ethics*. Unpublished master's thesis, New York University, New York.

Ballou, Mary B. & Brown, Laura S. (2002) *Rethinking Mental Health and Disorder: Feminist Perspectives.* New York: Guilford Press.

Bricker-Jenkins, Mary, Hooyman, Nancy R., & Gottlieb, Naomi (1991) *Feminist Social Work Practice in Clinical Settings*. Newbury Park, CA: Sage.

Brown, Laura S. (1994) *Subversive Dialogues: Theory in Feminist Therapy.* New York: Basic Books.

Brown, Laura S. & Root, Maria P. (1990) *Diversity and Complexity in Feminist Therapy*. New York: Harrington Press.

Brown, Lyn M. & Gilligan, Carol (1992) *Meeting at the Crossroads: Women's Psychology and Girls' Development*. Cambridge, MA: Harvard University Press.

Burstow, Bonnie (1992) *Radical Feminist Therapy: Working in the Context of Violence*. Newbury Park, CA: Sage.

Chesler, Phyllis (1990) Twenty years since "women and madness": Towards a feminist institute of mental health and healing. *Journal of Mind and Behavior, 11*, 313–322.

Curtis, Sandra L. (2006) *A Diversity of Voices: Cultural Competence for Music Therapists*. Manuscript submitted for publication.

Curtis, Sandra L. (2003) *Empowering Women Through the Healing Arts: A Manual for Workers with Survivors of Violence*. Manuscript in preparation.

Curtis, Sandra L. (1994) Killing us softly: Male inner violence against women. In Stanley G. French (ed.), *Interpersonal Violence, Health, and Gender Politics* (2nd ed.). Dubuque, IA: W. C. Brown.

Curtis, Sandra L. (2000) Singing subversion, singing soul: Women's voices in feminist music therapy. (Doctoral dissertation, Concordia University, 1997). *Dissertation Abstracts International*, 60(12-A), 4240.

Curtis, Sandra L. & Harrison, Gisele C. T. (2006) Empowering women survivors of childhood sexual abuse: A collaborative music therapy – social work approach. In Stephanie Brooke (ed.), *Creative Modalities for*

Therapy with Children and Adults. Springfield, IL: Charles C. Thomas Publishers.

Gilligan, Carol (1982) *In a Different Voice: Psychological Theories and Women's Development*. Cambridge, MA: Harvard University Press.

Hadley, Susan & Edwards, Jane (2004) Sorry for the silence: A contribution from feminist theory to the discourse(s) within music therapy. *Voices: A World Forum for Music Therapy*. http://www.voices.no/mainissues/mi40004000152.html

Hall, C. Margaret (1992) *Women and Empowerment: Strategies for Increasing Autonomy*. Washington, DC: Hemisphere Publishing Corporation.

Herman, Judith (1997) *Trauma and Recovery: The Aftermath of Violence—From Domestic Abuse to Political Terror*. New York: Basic Books.

hooks, bell (2000) *Feminist Theory: From Margin to Center*. Boston: Southend Press.

Johnson, Eleanor (1983) Reflections on Black feminist therapy. In Barbara Smith (ed.), *Home Girls: A Black Feminist Anthology*. New York: Kitchen Table Women of Color Press.

Laidlaw, Toni A., Malmo, Cheryl, & Associates (1990) *Healing Voices: Feminist Approaches to Therapy with Women*. San Francisco: Jossey-Bass.

Lerman, Hannah & Porter, Natalie (1990) *Feminist Ethics in Psychotherapy*. New York: Springer.

Lerman, Hannah & Rigby, Dorothy N. (1990) Boundary violations: Misuse of the power of the therapist. In Hannah Lerman & Natalie Porter (eds.), *Feminist Ethics in Psychotherapy*. New York: Springer.

Marshall, Pat F. & Vaillancourt, Marthe A. (1993) *Changing the Landscape: Ending Violence—Achieving Equality. Final Report of the Canadian Panel on Violence Against Women*. Ottawa, Canada: Minister of Supply and Services Canada.

Moraga, Cherríe & Anzaldúa, Gloria (1990) *This Bridge Called My Back: Writings by Radical Women of Color*. New York: Kitchen Table: Women of Color Press.

Morissette, Alanis (1995) Hand in my pocket. On *Jagged Little Pill* [CD]. Los Angeles: Maverick Recording Company.

Roid, Gale H. & Fitts, William H. (1991) *Tennessee Self-Concept Scale (TSCS): Revised Manual*. Los Angeles, CA: Western Psychological Services.

Rosewater, Lynne B., & Walker, Lenore E. (1985) *Handbook of Feminist Therapy: Women's Issues in Psychotherapy*. New York: Springer.

Smith, Adrienne J. & Dutton, Mary A. (1990) Empowerment as an ethical imperative. In Hannah Lerman & Natalie Porter (eds.), *Feminist Ethics in Psychotherapy*. New York: Springer.

Steinem, Gloria (1992) *Revolution from Within: A Book of Self-esteem*. Boston: Little, Brown & Company.

Thaut, Michael H. (1990) Neuropsychological processes in music perception and their relevance in music therapy. In Robert K. Unkefer (ed.), *Music Therapy in the Treatment of Adults with Mental Disorders: Theoretical Bases and Clinical Intervention*. New York: MacMillan.

Thaut, Michael H. & Smeltekopf, Roger A. (1990) Psychosocial and neurophysiological aspects of music therapy interventions. In Robert K. Unkefer (ed.), *Music Therapy in the Treatment of Adults with Mental Disorders: Theoretical Bases and Clinical Intervention*. New York: MacMillan.

Waiting to Exhale [CD] (1995) New York: Arista Records.

Watley, Jody & Campbell, Larry (1996) When a man loves a woman [Recorded by Jody Watley]. On *Jody Watley: Greatest Hits* [CD]. Universal City, CA: MCA Records.

Worell, Judith & Remer, Pamela (2003) *Feminist Perspectives in Therapy: Empowering Diverse Women*. New York: Wiley.

Chapter Ten

FINDING VOICE: FEMINIST MUSIC THERAPY AND RESEARCH WITH WOMEN SURVIVORS OF DOMESTIC VIOLENCE

Elizabeth York

PRELUDE

This chapter tells the story of a clinical and qualitative research protocol with women victims of domestic violence, informed by feminist therapy, grounded theory, and creative arts approaches to music therapy. The author and research assistant conducted music therapy and creative arts sessions with forty women over an eight-month period. All were members of an ongoing women's support group provided by the Community Abuse Prevention Services Agency (CAPSA) in a small university town in Utah. The purpose of the research was to explore the efficacy of music therapy and creative arts interventions on the self-esteem and empowerment of the female victims. A secondary purpose of the research was to examine the levels at which the women "entered in" to the project. Research questions related to the creative and therapeutic process were developed. Could levels of self-disclosure be determined? Were the women willing to explore their creative selves, embrace new forms of therapy, and to articulate meaning derived from these experiences? Could participation in this form of therapy create meaningful changes in their lives? How did their experiences with abuse translate into creative materials and to what degree might those materials be shared with others?

The result of this work was the development of a book of poetry, an ethnographic performance piece entitled "Finding Voice," performed at nine venues across the state of Utah, and a compact disc of the entire production. Increases in self-esteem, in positive interactions with family members, in risk taking, in rediscovery of musical and creative impulses, and decreases in anxiety, were all cited as positive outcomes.

Intimate Partner Violence

The issue of domestic violence, also referred to as intimate partner violence, remains a pervasive social problem in this country. One out of four women in the United States reports having been raped and/or physically assaulted by a current or former spouse, live-in partner, or date at some time in her life (National Violence Against Women Survey, 2000). According to the National Women's Health Information Center (a project of the US Department of Health and Human Services, Office on Women's Health), women from the US are between five and eight times more likely than men to be victimized by an intimate partner, even though men are more likely to be victims of violent crime. An estimated four million women in the United States are physically abused by their spouses or live-in partners each year. One out of every six women in the US has experienced some form of sexual assault or abuse during her lifetime. Of these women, 76% of them over the age of eighteen report that they have been raped by someone they know.

According to Evan Stark and Anne Flitcraft (1998), battering is the major cause of injury to women, resulting in more injuries than auto accidents, muggings, and rapes combined. Every year, domestic violence results in almost 100,000 days of hospitalizations, almost 30,000 emergency department visits, and almost 40,000 visits to a physician (American Medical Association, 1991). A survey on the extent, nature, and consequences of intimate partner violence (National Violence Against Women Survey, 2000) conducted by the National Institute of Justice-Centers for Disease Control found that 41.5 % of women who were physically assaulted by an intimate partner were injured during their most recent assault. The survey also found that women whose partners were jealous, controlling or verbally abusive were significantly more likely to report being raped, physically assaulted, and/or stalked by their partners, even when other socio-demographic and relationship characteristics were controlled.

Female victims of domestic violence also experience psychological abuse, which is often overlooked and/or trivialized. Abused women have reported psychological abuse to be as damaging as physical battering because of its impact on the self-image and self-esteem of the victim. Emotional abuse may consist of verbal attacks and humiliations, including repeated verbal attacks against the victim's worth as an individual, or role as a parent. Verbal attacks often emphasize the victim's vulnerabilities; threats to personal safety can increase fear responses. Isolation may occur when abusers attempt to control victims' time, activities, and contact with others. Abusers accomplish this by interfering with supportive relationships, creating barriers to normal activity, and lying or distorting what is real in order to gain psychological control

(National Women's Health Information Center, US Department of Health and Human Services, Office on Women's Health).

Intimate Partner Violence in Utah

According to a recent report by the Utah Commission on Criminal and Juvenile Justice (Hadden & Christenson, 2005), "Rape is a curious and outstanding anomaly within the confines of violent crime in Utah. Since 1991, Utah's rape rate has consistently been higher than the national rate" (p.1). Victims of rape were predominately female (98.3%) and, although one in five women in Utah is a victim of forcible rape during her lifetime, only one in six of these crimes was reported. In another study, reported in the Salt Lake Tribune (November 19, 2003), 144 out of 360 (40%) women polled reported having been abused during their lifetime. Ten percent of patients seen in Utah hospital emergency rooms are victims of domestic violence (Allen, 2003). Between July 1, 1999 and June 30, 2000, domestic violence shelters in the state received a total of 45,929 crisis calls. The total clients sheltered that year was 4976, and clients served but not sheltered totaled 12,426. The total number of sheltered nights during this period was 40,998 (Domestic Violence: 2000 Annual Report, Utah State Domestic Violence Cabinet Council).

The Community Abuse Prevention Services Agency (CAPSA) (where this research took place) was formed in the late 1970s after a group of women under the sponsorship of the local university Women's Center met to discuss the plight of rape victims. CAPSA grew into an organization that provided shelter to 212 women and children, answered 4,692 crisis telephone calls, counseled more than 1,800 individuals, and provided 479 public education presentations in 2002 alone (CAPSA history, brochure, 2003). Services include crisis intervention, victim advocacy, case management, and facilitated support groups for female victims and their children. Between July, 2002 and June, 2003, CAPSA received a total of 5882 crisis calls, sheltered 96 women, and served a total of 102 women in Latina and Anglo support groups. Eighty-one children were served in the children's group during the same period (K. Monson, personal communication, November 12, 2003).

Music Therapy with Victims of Domestic Violence

There has been scant published literature on music therapy with adult female victims of domestic violence (e.g. Whipple and Lindsay, 1995; Rinker, 1991; Curtis, 1997; Austin, 2002). More of the literature has focused on music therapy with abused children and adolescents (Lindberg, 1995; Rogers, 1992, 1995; Clendenon-Wallen, 1991). Other music therapy case studies have focused on particular diagnoses of women who have been abused: eating disorders (Ventre, 1994); posttraumatic stress disorder (Montello, 1999); and major depression. Michael Cassity and Kimberly Kaczor Theobold (1990) surveyed music therapists to ascertain "whether a practice of music therapy exists for assessing and treating clients involved in domestic violence" (p.181). Responses to that survey identified 80 music therapists who had treated victims of domestic violence. Of that number, 45 worked with women victims, 61 with children, and 28 worked with male perpetrators. Respondents indicated a range of between 2 and more than 10 years of experience with victims of domestic violence. Respondents were employed in private residential facilities (20%), mental health centers (17%), and public residential facilities (13%). The remaining 50% were employed in a wide variety of settings (Cassity & Theobold, 1990).

In the same survey, Cassity and Theobold (1990) also elicited information about areas of assessment and treatment of victims of domestic abuse. Respondents reported that they typically assessed a variety of areas, dependent on gender and developmental level of the client. Lack of assertiveness, cognitive distortions ("learned helplessness"), denial, and isolating behaviors were identified as problem areas for battered women, as were blunted emotional expression, and poor body image (Cassity & Theobold, 1990). Music therapy treatment with battered women, according to this survey, often consisted of composing, singing, performing instruments and instrumental instruction, and listening to music, as well as the analysis of song lyrics, drawing to music, and physical movement to music.

Rhonda Lineberg Rinker (1991) reported on a case study using Guided Imagery and Music (GIM) techniques with an adult woman client suffering from physical and emotional abuse. GIM is a music therapy technique in which clients image in an altered state of consciousness while listening to recordings of classical music selected by the therapist. According to Rinker, after twelve GIM sessions the client reported significant gains in body image, self-confidence and a "healthier, more positive outlook on her life" (1991, p.318).

Jennifer Whipple and Rebecca Lindsey (1995) reported on a music therapy program for fifteen battered women temporarily residing in a shelter. Specific music interventions were developed that were deemed appropriate to the short-term treatment provided by a shelter. Interventions addressed goal setting and improving communication, mood, and self-esteem. Plans for each of the eight group sessions revealed the use of songs with affirming lyrics such as "I Believe I Can Fly" (R. Kelly), "The Rose" (McBroom, 1977), and "Takes a Little Time" (Grant & Kirkpatrick, 1997) to be used for 1) lyric analysis and discussion, 2) prompting other therapeutic activities such as writing something "good" about every woman in the group to the tune of "With a Little Help from my Friends" (Lennon and McCartney, 1967), and singing "The Greatest Love of All" (Creed and Masser, 1977).

A Rationale for Feminist-Informed Music Therapy

Women's issues have rarely been addressed in the music therapy literature although approximately 85% of music therapists are women (American Music Therapy Association, 2004). One landmark survey addressing women's issues in music therapy revealed bias against feminist psychotherapy models (Curtis, 1990). Eighty-four percent of the women surveyed (N=836) were unfamiliar with feminist models of therapy. Of those women, 37% were opposed to feminist psychotherapy in principle, or at least to the term "feminist." Since the shelter movement emerged from social action undertaken by feminists in the 1970s (CAPSA brochure, 2003), and given the attitudes revealed in Sandra Curtis' survey, it is perhaps not surprising that music therapists may have had little exposure to a feminist model of practice. In the introduction to her landmark book on trauma and recovery of domestic violence victims, Judith Herman (1992) noted that "the ordinary response to atrocities is to banish them from consciousness. Certain violations of the social compact are too terrible to utter aloud: this is the meaning of the word *unspeakable*" (p.1). Perhaps music therapists have been reluctant to acknowledge the reality of domestic abuse and enter into this area of clinical practice and research. Perhaps, given the burgeoning undergraduate curriculum, they have been academically unprepared both in course content and in practicum opportunities.

A subsequent dissertation by Curtis (1997) described a model of feminist music therapy to increase the self-esteem of thirty-five women victims of domestic violence in a Georgia shelter using a casc study approach. Curtis defined feminist music therapy as using innovative techniques to integrate principles and practices of feminist therapy with those of music therapy. She hypothesized, for example, that lyric analysis and songwriting could be used to explore the feminist analysis of power and gender-role socialization.

Six women met the criteria for inclusion in the data-collection part of Curtis's study (completion of at least eight feminist music therapy sessions and a final evaluation and interview). Results indicated a marked increase in self-esteem for four of the six women and a modest increase for one on the Tennessee Self-Concept Scale (TSCS). Curtis concluded that feminist music therapy may be an effective approach for use with women recovering from abuse.

Personal Grounding

> *How do I enter into your world? I come to you as a fellow survivor, as a feminist, as a woman who loves and respects women, as a woman who has been touched by the power of women's music—who knows the strength of lyrics that have affirmed me, given me the courage to be myself, to speak from my heart, to be authentic. I want to share what I have learned in hopes that you might also experience a reawakening to your true selves. (Personal log, October, 2002)*

Reflecting on the empowering effects of feminism and feminist therapy on my own life experience, and as a composer, singer-songwriter/performer in women's music festivals and concerts, I intentionally undertook a feminist research standpoint and a feminist approach to music therapy with the women participants in the current study. Susan Hekman (1997b) identified a feminist research standpoint as "women speaking their truth" (p.401). Caroline Ramazanoglu (2002) summarized Hekman's key characteristics of a feminist standpoint as including the following:

> A feminist standpoint assumes the inseparability of politics, theory and epistemology. It problematizes the nature of relationships between ideas, experience and social reality. Women "speaking their truth" are situated in relation to forms of power: that shape their lives; that they can (variably) exercise; that constitute what counts as knowledge; that determine whose voice can be heard . . . taking a feminist standpoint entails women voicing their experience. (p.65)

I was first exposed to feminism during my music therapy internship at Porterville St. Developmental Center (then Porterville State Hospital) in 1972-3. Female interns from a variety of disciplines organized a weekly consciousness-raising group that became a touchstone and a life-changing experience for me. I became aware of how I had devalued myself as a woman as well as my relationships with other women. The experience was empowering, causing me to examine myself, my relationships with men, and to question my sexual identity. It also led me to value the work I had done as a singer-songwriter and composer, and in 1981, I began to perform at local, regional, and national women's music festivals and concerts, most notably with flautist/composer Kay Gardner. My own recording of instrumental music entitled "Transformations" was produced by Ladyslipper Records (www.ladyslipper.org), a woman-owned record and distribution company in Durham, NC, and was marketed in their catalogue. The compositions on that recording paralleled and reflected my own healing journey, and I subsequently began therapy with a feminist therapist.

Feminist goals in therapy defined by Judith Worell and Pamela Remer (1992) include: 1) helping clients to trust their own experience and their intuition; 2) enabling clients to appreciate female-related values; 3) assisting women in taking care of themselves; 4) helping women accept and like their own bodies; and 5) helping women define and act in accordance with their own sexual needs. The course of my own therapy assumed this route and a feminist consciousness continues to guide my decision making and shape my value system. The empowerment of young women is always an underlying theme as I work with music therapy students who are overwhelmingly female in our large undergraduate program. I have begun to successfully integrate discussions of feminist therapy into my senior classes entitled "Music Therapy with Adult Populations" and "Clinical and Professional Issues in Music Therapy," especially as we discuss posttraumatic stress disorder, other anxiety disorders, gendered personality disorders, and depression.

FINDING VOICE

"Finding Voice" is a qualitative research initiative initially funded by the American Association of University Women (American Fellow) during my sabbatical year from April, 2002 through October, 2003. I conducted music therapy and creative arts sessions with a total of forty women over an eight-month period, members of a support group served by the Community Abuse Prevention Services Agency (CAPSA) in a small university town. The purpose of the research was to explore the efficacy of a feminist approach to music therapy and creative arts interventions on the self-esteem and empowerment of female survivors. A secondary purpose of the research was to examine the levels at which women "entered in" to the project. Research questions related to the creative and therapeutic process were developed. Were the women willing to explore their creative selves, embrace new forms of therapy, and become empowered through these experiences? Could participation in music therapy create meaningful changes in their lives?

My unique feminist approach to music therapy involved the use of "women's music" throughout the eight months of sessions. Western Classical and "ethnic" music composed by women, and songs with affirming lyrics by female singer-songwriters were used throughout the sessions. "Women's music" is defined by Margie Adam as "music that affirms and empowers women" (www.margieadam.com/info/thoughts.htm). The genre is a cultural arm of the women's movement that began in the 1970s and has continued to be nurtured through women's music festivals and concerts throughout the country. I hypothesized that using selections from this repertoire of songs and instrumental music might facilitate changes in the psychological abuse described by women victims of domestic violence including low self-esteem, cognitive distortions, poor body image, "learned helplessness," and depressive symptoms. I further hypothesized that these musicians and their music might serve as healthy role models for creative expression and give permission for women victims to tell their own stories using music and the creative arts. According to Herman (1992), "Remembering and telling the truth about terrible events are prerequisites both for the restoration of the social order and for the healing of individual victims" (p.1).

Method

"Finding Voice" was originally designed to analyze the therapeutic, thematic, and creative components of the sessions. Research methodology, clinical protocol, and consent forms were approved by the university's Institutional Review Board (IRB). Case managers and the facilitator of the support group informed potential participants about the research opportunity and obtained written consent from women interested in entering into the project. Participants were subsequently referred into the support group.

Participants

A total of forty women consented to participate in the project, ranging in age from 18–58. All were Anglo-American. All were concurrently receiving case management services provided by CAPSA because they were victims of domestic violence. Many presented symptoms related to posttraumatic stress disorder, major depression, dependent personality and/or substance abuse. Most common were: 1) low self esteem, 2) poor body image, 3) hyperarousal/anxiety, and 4) depressive symptoms. Some expressed difficulties with boundaries and enmeshment with the perpetrator. Others related the perpetrator's suppression of creative outlets including playing music and writing. One woman characterized this phenomenon as "soul theft."

Protocol, Data Collection and Analysis

All sessions were audio recorded and transcribed by research assistant Maureen Hearns, MA, MT-BC. Transcriptions of a total of thirty sessions were systematically analyzed each week for thematic content via a coding procedure and followed a grounded theory approach. According to Dorit Amir (1996), grounded theory "entails the creation of theory by systematically and intensively analyzing the data—often sentence by sentence or phrase by phrase—contained in field notes, interviews, or other documents" (p.111). The goal of this analysis is not simply to collect or order this data, but also to uncover/discover the themes and broader ideas which inevitably emerge (Glaser & Strauss, 1967, cited in Langenberg, Aigen & Frommer, 1996). According to Amir, thematic materials may then be synthesized to assist in theory building. "The search for grounded theory leads to the generation of new theory based on comprehensive description, analysis and interpretation of data" (Amir, 1996, p.111).

The Support Group

How did you get here; where did you come from
How did this happen to you?
Tell me the reason; tell me the story
As it comes clearer to you.

York, Finding Voice, 2005

The support group was structured as a drop-in group that had been an ongoing service provided by CAPSA for many years. Consequently, women entered into the music therapy project at different stages of treatment and recovery. Some were already divorced from their spouses and were beginning to see themselves as "survivors." Others were in the process of divorce proceedings, including negotiating custody of minor children. Still others were in crisis, responding to recent abusive incidents, and were in the process of making safety plans and/or obtaining shelter, and securing protective restraining orders.

There were also differences in the length of time women had been involved in the support group and in their connections to one another. Some women had been members of the group for up to ten years or more, and had made friendships with one another outside the group. Others joined more recently and committed to the group because of the music therapy project. Others were more transient, fleeing perpetrators from other states. Several of these women attended only one or two sessions. However, the average attendance in the weekly two-hour groups was eighteen women.

The Sessions

I play the recording of the second movement of "Transformations" and ask the women to write what they hear in the music. Some hear my pain, others, my strength; others comment that they feel relaxed and safe within the music. They feel the connection and relate to me. I

> *ask if I may be a part of their support group and they unanimously say "yes." One says, "You are one of us." (Personal log, June 18, 2002)*

Barbara Scott, the support group facilitator, was an equal collaborator in the project, and contributed her own creative energy and willingness to add a music therapy component to the group. We shared in leading the sessions. We agreed that during the initial assessment phase, the music/creative arts component would serve an adjunctive role, with arts interventions gradually being integrated into weekly themes taken from a psycho-educational curriculum (*Journey Beyond Abuse: A Step by Step Guide to Facilitating Women's Domestic Abuse Groups*, Fischer & McGrane, 1997). Planning and debriefing sessions with Barbara and with my research assistant Maureen Hearns occurred on a weekly basis throughout the eight-month period. These debriefing sessions became increasingly important as a means of self-care while we processed the difficult stories and situations that were related during the therapy sessions. In addition, a music therapist based in the UK and a qualitative researcher from another university also served as guides and sounding boards during the course of this project; all of us kept journals and shared our writings with each other throughout the eight-month period.

During the first hour of each session, Barbara checked in with each group member and presented relevant curriculum materials and themes. This allowed me to interact as a "participant observer" in the group, building trust and confidence between me and the group members. I facilitated music therapy and creative arts interventions during the second hour that were directly related to weekly themes presented in the curriculum. Gradually, Maureen entered into the sessions as an additional co-therapist. After three months, music therapy interventions were conducted by both of us.

During the eight-month period, the women were invited to participate in a variety of creative arts and music therapy experiences that enhanced the themes of the sessions. These included: 1) vocal warm-up exercises and instruction in choral techniques; 2) writing to and analysis of vocal and instrumental music composed by women (both non-Western and Western) and songs from the American "women's music" repertoire; 3) therapeutic drumming and percussion-based interventions; 4) music and movement interventions; and 5) music and visual arts projects, including music imaging with mandala drawings to music and constructing a frame drum. Women were also invited to share poetry and other creative materials generated outside of the sessions. Journal writing had already been encouraged as a means of creative expression and had become incorporated as part of the therapeutic process within the group.

In addition to the analysis and coding of transcribed sessions, a procedure was developed whereby the women gave me permission to work with contributed materials every week by placing them in a large wicker basket placed in a prominent position within the circle. Placing materials in the basket gave me permission to "work with" the materials in a variety of creative ways between sessions: I edited, compiled, reconfigured and reformatted many of the submissions, while concurrently analyzing and coding the thematic content of each work. During follow-up sessions, the materials were presented back to the women, as choral readings, songs, and poetry.

Working with the revised materials in the group engendered an egalitarian, collaborative, creative process as the women contributed their own ideas and feedback on each "new" work as they read, sang, and/or performed pieces for each other. During this period, I acknowledged and encouraged a redefinition of our roles. As I claimed and modeled my own creative process and laid myself open for critique, the women took more risks as well; power sharing became the norm. Consensual decision making was easily woven into the group process, even as I facilitated and guided composition and the shaping of creative materials. We all took on the roles of "creators," acknowledging multiple talents, multiple contributions, multiple perspectives.

Women who felt comfortable using dance and movement shared their ideas. Women who had previous music skills were encouraged and guided to improvise music that supported readings and movement interventions with flute, recorder, and guitar accompaniment. Maureen and I offered specific percussion techniques to contain and give permission for difficult feelings of anger and frustration to be expressed. This creative sharing was followed by verbally processing how it felt for each woman to hear or read her own words, to witness the creative movement of her peers, and to hear the unique quality of each woman's voice, as feelings, stories, poems, and music were shared. An idea to configure the mandala drawings into a quilt was realized by a woman who possessed this unique skill. All of the forty women who participated in the project contributed creative materials during sessions, including personal stories transcribed from the sessions, choreography, artwork, original songs, and poems based on their lives as survivors of abuse.

> *They lovingly spread out [the mandalas] before me. There are tears as the women claim their images. I hear strength and power in their voices. A rose representing integrity; a fiery ball glowing in colors of black and blue transmuting to brilliant yellows and oranges—the movement from abuse to healing; images of women with muscular arms, of strong trees, of dark balloons rising into the air, some still*

> *weighted down in darkness, but rising nevertheless. (Personal log, January 7, 2003)*

The Development of an Ethnographic Performance Piece

> *We move to how the images [in the mandalas] might be transformed. Into a quilt, one says. Into a backdrop for a stage, a warm coverlet to be caressed in, to be danced with. There is excitement as each woman contributes her ideas: how it will be constructed, what shape it will take (most OVERWHELMINGLY see a CIRCLE), how it will be displayed. This exchange is filled with delight, with new ideas. Transformation of pain into art. I am moved by their joy, by the power of creative intention. I am honored to witness this healing. (Personal log, January 7, 2003)*

During the course of the sessions, several women brought up the possibility of creating a performance piece from the materials generated during the sessions. A subsequent review of the literature that I conducted resulted in the discovery of a creative means of configuring and representing the collected data known as "ethnographic drama" or "ethnographic theater" (Atkinson, 1990, 1992; Mienczakowski, 1992, 1994, 1995; Coffey & Atkinson, 1996). In this genre, data (including transcriptions and dialogue), are transformed into theatrical scripts and performance pieces. The discovery of this alternative qualitative means of data representation provided further validation for the project and complemented the women's desire to share their work with others.

> Theatre provides a way of perhaps more accurately giving voice to those who may consider themselves without power. Similarly, reconstructing an event as lived experience with multiple perspectives can give voice to what may be unspoken but nevertheless present. (Coffey & Atkinson, 1996, p.126)

The women's wish to share their personal experiences of domestic violence via performance was a breakthrough in the work, indicating a level of ownership, trust, and empowerment that was unanticipated at the beginning of the project. It was during this phase of the research that I, along with Barbara and Maureen, began to re-vision the intention, format, and content of the sessions. All of us were in agreement that sessions should continue to be driven by the women's willingness to explore their own creative potential and to value that work as an integral part of their personal and therapeutic growth. Clinical and administrative staff members were informed of this change, and they began to attend sessions on an informal basis. They supported, recognized, and valued the changes that had become apparent as the women became more assertive, autonomous, and committed to the creative aspects of the support group sessions.

As I began to edit and work with the numerous themes that emerged from the transcriptions and creative materials, my creative representation of the data slowly evolved into a loosely scripted performance piece. The "scenes" were collapsed and synthesized from the identified themes that had emerged during the course of the sessions. We all agreed to the naming of these themes: 1) First Contact (stories that described their initial contact with CAPSA); 2) Common Ground (identification of common themes shared in the support group; and 3) Healing (how each woman defined her healing process). Stories, poetry, and songs were arranged within those broad categories. Dialogue, monologue, and choral readings derived from creative submissions and session transcriptions served as connecting devices, from song to poem. This creative process reflected the development of an ethnographic drama: a dynamic means of organizing raw data in a creative, experimental new form. According to Amanda Jane Coffey and Paul Atkinson (1996):

> It is common to base reconstructed dialogue very closely on actual words uttered in interviews or in naturally occurring interactions. The resulting work is crafted by the analyst insofar as he or she selects, edits, transposes, and juxtaposes in order to convey particular effects. In other words, these exercises are not based on purely fictional invention; rather, they take real data and apply certain sorts of editorial license in the construction of textual representations. (p.124)

Transition

When a draft of the script was completed, a first "read through" was held with the participants to validate, from the women's perspective, whether the script was an authentic representation of their experiences. Revisions were made to the draft, and discussions began as to who might become cast members. A second consent/release form was developed and signed to further protect the women in situations/artistic endeavors that could potentially arise from the project including: 1) having their names printed in performance programs, or other printed materials; 2) video/audio-recordings, 3) inclusion of submissions in a book of poetry derived from creative writings, and 4) articles that might be generated for professional journals or books. Issues of confidentiality and personal safety continued to be addressed. The use of pseudonyms, masks, and other costumes to protect participants' identities during performances was suggested and discussed.

This was a critical period for the women who had originally agreed to participate in the research. The shift from "therapy group" to "performance group" caused them to reflect on their level of comfort, prior commitments, and life circumstances that might necessitate changes in their level of participation. An ongoing discussion ensued regarding "informed consent" and their continued participation. Some women elected to leave the project at this time, although they still consented to have their creative materials remain in the script and included in an anonymous book of poetry. Some decided to become "technical support staff" and took on the roles of prop manager, set designer, and artistic director. These decisions were compatible with their own perceived levels of safety. Some continued to receive case management services at CAPSA. For others, a decision to leave the group was based on the realization that they no longer required CAPSA services and they moved onto more long-term, individual counseling. Several left for unrelated reasons (moving to another locale, for example). Another contributing factor was the impending end of this particular support group based on an administrative decision to adopt a different service delivery model.

Outcomes

The twelve women who agreed to continue in the project—to become "cast members"—did so for many reasons. Some recognized that they were feeling differently about themselves, transforming from victim to advocate, from client to singer, dancer, and creative artist. One woman wrote, *"Finding Voice" has helped me become more aware of the "child within" that needs healing and acceptance from ME so that I no longer will become a victim* (Carra, 2003). Some recognized the need for the "voice of the child" to be included in the production, and an additional woman, a victim of child abuse, was invited into the group as stage manager after sharing her own healing song from the child's point of view. Her stage management, professionalism, and participation in the performance increased the women's empowerment by urging them to reach within themselves for strength and courage to tell their stories authentically and with conviction.

Simultaneously, many of the cast members were making changes in other aspects of their lives both inside and outside of the group. Several women made plans to return to college, applied for scholarships, and were accepted into the local university. Others procured gainful employment. One woman ceased her dependency on anti-anxiety medication. As of this writing, all but two had divorced abusive spouses.

Others rediscovered musical skills and creative skills that had been "stolen" while they had been abused. Two bought their own guitars and began writing and sharing their own songs. A woman who had been a singer-songwriter (and whose singing had been silenced by her spouse) offered to sing an original jazz song in the performance. Another offered to play her flute in the production. Songs emerged from the poetic contributions: eight original songs were composed and arranged for the performance either as solo or choral works, including the song from the "voice of the child."

The twelve cast members continued to discuss the potential for educating the public with the developing performance. Time and again, they insisted on using their own names in the production, both in the program, and in the performance itself. They discussed their desire to demonstrate the positive effects of music therapy and the creative arts on their personal empowerment, as well as to break through misconceptions and stereotypes about domestic violence and its victims. Since committing to the project, all recognized changes in themselves related to self-expression, confidence, feelings of self-worth, and in their ability to form healthier relationships outside of the support group. These changes were expressed in writing as another means of validating the work. *"I've discovered hidden talents, dreams, and aspirations. I am experiencing an increasing ability to try new things—-the courage to take risks"* (Ginny, 2003).

As the women began to rehearse the script, noticeable changes began to take place in body language, assertiveness, and expressed emotion, paralleling the demands placed on them as "musicians, actors, and dancers." Posture and coordination began to improve as the women worked on blocking and choreography. Imagined connections to a potential "audience" (as they rehearsed spoken and sung lines) improved vocal projection, emotional expression and eye contact. *"Having an opportunity to express myself and hear how others feel has been beneficial"* (Martha, 2003). Carra wrote:

> *I found changes happening from within that gave me permission to shine a little. I'm beginning to believe I'm worth it. That is a miracle in itself. The confidence I'd hoped for wasn't coming overnight, but it was coming. Focusing on the music and the production has helped me get on with MY life. I'm finding it easier to let my "ex" have his life and be okay when our lives have to meet once in a while* (2003).

Some women began to articulate that they had found a creative means of channeling their repressed anger, fear, and shame. *"The 'therapeutic benefits' came with finding myself being able to express and feel my feelings through [the] different [creative] outlets"* (Jan, 2003). Other women expressed the need for their voices to be heard and for the message of their work to be shared with a larger audience. One wrote: *I want to be part of the solution so that other women's lives will be blessed—that women down the road will be better off because of how I dealt with my experience* (*Finding Voice*, p.20). Another agreed: *"It is an honor to work on this project—wonderful to be a part of something that can help people who assist domestic violence victims as well as the victims themselves."*

As weekly sessions began to take on the appearance of "rehearsal" rather than "support group," women began to find their places in the script, to claim their "parts." They also began to discuss venues where they wanted to perform. Who would be invited? How many performances, and where? The consensual decision-making process continued and reflected the women's perceived levels of safety/comfort, self-confidence, and trust in the inherent value of the message contained in the performance piece. The control the women exerted in decision making built confidence and more egalitarian relationships. We continued to acknowledge changing roles and began to shift from therapist/facilitator to musician/director/artistic director/collaborator.

The Performances

> *These women deserve credit for standing up and expressing what they have gone through. I realized that it [Finding Voice] was a healing process. Power to these women.*
>
> *(audience member, Utah State University, October, 2003)*

> *I applaud these women for sharing such a difficult part of their lives with strangers. I was touched by their healing; I was angered by their anger, and I appreciate that they are so willing to share what the world needs to know . . . these women have a voice.*
>
> *(audience member, University of Utah, October, 2003)*

> *It was our pleasure to witness "Finding Voice" in Moab. Thank you for your work. It was an outstanding, emotional, familiar performance for us.*
>
> *(audience member, Utah Shelter Conference, June, 2003)*

The first performance of "Finding Voice" was a gift to CAPSA staff, and was held in the same building where the support group had met. The space provided a safe, nonthreatening environment whereby the women felt supported by the staff members who were closest to their life situations. A question-and-answer session following that first performance became a part of each subsequent performance and provided validation for their courageous work. Interacting with the audience enabled the women to express what being a part of "Finding Voice" meant to them and how it had affected their lives. Performance anxiety gave over to excitement and pride. To provide additional self-care for the cast members, we added relaxation exercises, meditation, and Reiki into our pre-performance routine as well as post-performance time to process any feelings that may have arisen during or after each performance.

Given the positive feedback generated by the first performance, gradual expansion of the project into the community was inevitable. As the women took more ownership of their creative work, word spread, and more opportunities arose to perform. Cast members began to ask friends and family members to attend rehearsals which were subsequently moved to a stage in a local church social hall. Additional interaction with those audiences reinforced the powerful messages embedded in the performance, and the confidence of cast members continued to increase. Consensual decision making (and ongoing informed consent) as to whether or not a particular performance request felt "safe" continued, as the women took more and more control over their creative work. In all, nine performances were presented, gradually expanding the audiences into the wider community. Venues included meetings of the state Domestic Violence Coalition, the Utah Shelter Conference, and the Utah Victims Assistance Training Academy, a training program for advocates of women survivors. Two performances were sponsored by the Women's Resource Centers of two state universities as a part of Domestic Violence Awareness Month and were attended by hundreds of students, faculty, and community members. Radio interviews and articles in three local newspapers reinforced our success.

POSTLUDE

The final phase of "Finding Voice" was the compilation of the entire body of creative materials into products that might be shared with an even wider community. An anonymous book of poetry was produced containing materials from all forty participants. Thanks to a generous donation of studio time and sound engineering, a recording of the entire play on compact disc was completed by the cast members using their given names and photographs on the jacket insert. This was the last and clearest indication of the degree to which these women felt empowered by their own creative processes. They demonstrated the courage to "go public" with their journeys, to break the silence, and to become community advocates and mentors to other women experiencing domestic violence. The women of "Finding Voice" continue to network, and some continue to express a desire to share this experience with others. Their last public performance was called "Sacred Journeys": five songs from "Finding Voice" presented as part of an Arts and Lecture Series at the local Tabernacle.

It has been two years since sessions ended, and the healing continues. In the spring of 2005, a CD signing party was held as a final tribute to the women's accomplishments. Their success stories continue to inspire. The one thousand donated copies of "Finding Voice" will be used to raise funds for CAPSA and continue music therapy services at the shelter. I remain humbled by the degree of trust bestowed upon me, the degree to which each woman entered into the creative process, and inspired by the personal gains made. Notes that I receive continue to validate the power of this creative, musical, therapeutic process.

> *[Finding Voice] took my life to far reaches I had no idea I could go. Till the day I die I will be eternally grateful for the dear friends of "Finding Voice" and all the life lessons I have learned through this experience. . . . I love you all.*

And . . .

> *The writing expressed my thoughts; the music gave my thoughts feeling. It occurred to me that the spirit of this script would endure past our participation. It's about my heart reaching out to other people's hearts and giving them a message of hope. What an honor. It will take a book to come near to expressing what it has all meant.*

Finally . . .

> *I have an opinion, a voice. What I think and feel is important. I can make decisions and take a stand. I can defend my beliefs and values. I do not have to "just listen" anymore. I can participate. I am not afraid anymore.*

The experience with the women of "Finding Voice" has reinforced my conviction that a feminist approach to music therapy, when used to empower women survivors of domestic violence, holds great potential as change agent, as consciousness raiser, as confidence builder and life changer. During the course of the research, qualitative data collection methods utilized in grounded theory assisted us in organizing and identifying relevant themes posed during the course of sessions. And data representation using alternative means such as ethnographic drama are compatible with the creative processes inherent in music therapy treatment.

The metaphor of "Finding Voice" is a powerful one. Finding the courage to speak out, to be heard, to tell one's story, is a potent part of the healing process for survivors of intimate partner violence. As Bonnie Morris (1999) has stated: "Women's voices are a moral template, the narrative of survival. And all who listen are changed forever" (p.xi). We, as music therapists, take this a step further when we set our clients' stories to music.

I am rooted in the power of song as confessional,
As cathartic self expression, as lament.
It is one thing to tell a story
It is another thing to sing it.
Listen as melody and harmony flesh out feelings,
Listen as we sing through pain.
When the song is shared, we affirm our truths.
We sigh together, breathe together, feel together, heal together.
(Personal log, October 30, 2002)

REFERENCES

American Medical Association (2000) Report 7 of the Council on Scientific Affairs. Violence Between Intimates. http://www.ama-assn.org/ama/pub/category/13577.html#intimate_partner_violence

American Music Therapy Association (2005) *Resource Directory*. Springville, MD: American Music Therapy Association.

Amir, Dorit (1996) Experiencing music therapy: Meaningful moments in the music therapy process. In Mechtild Langenberg, Kenneth Aigen, & Jörg Frommer (eds.), *Qualitative Music Therapy Research: Beginning Dialogues*. Gilsum, NH: Barcelona Publishers.

Atkinson, Paul A. (1990) *The Ethnographic Imagination: Textual Constructions of Reality.* London: Routledge.

Atkinson, Paul A. (1992) *Understanding Ethnographic Texts.* Newbury Park, CA: Sage.

Bruscia, Kenneth E. (1991) *Case Studies in Music Therapy.* Gilsum, NH: Barcelona Publishers.

Cassity, Michael D. & Theobold, Kimberly Kaczor (1990) Domestic violence: Assessments and treatments employed by music therapists. *Journal of Music Therapy*, *27*, 179–194.

Clendenon-Wallen, Joy (1991) The use of music therapy to influence the self-confidence of adolescents who are sexually abused. *Music Therapy Perspectives, 9*, 73–81.

Community Abuse Prevention Services Agency (2005) CAPSA History. CAPSA Volunteer Training Manual.

Coffey, Amanda Jane & Atkinson, Paul A. (1996) *Making Sense of Qualitative Data.* Thousand Oaks, CA: Sage.

Corey, Gerald (2001) *Theory and Practice of Counseling and Psychotherapy.* Stamford, CT: Brooks/Cole.

Curtis, Sandra L. (1990) Women's issues in music therapy. *Music Therapy Perspectives*, *8,* 61–66.

Curtis, Sandra L. (2000) Singing Subversion, Singing Soul: Women's Voices in Feminist Music Therapy. (Doctoral dissertation, Concordia University, 1997) *Dissertation Abstracts International*, 60(12-A), 4240.

Domestic Violence: 2000 Annual Report, Utah State Domestic Violence Cabinet Council.

Fischer, Kay-Laurel & McGrane, Michael F. (1997) *Journey Beyond Abuse: A Step by Step Guide to Facilitating Women's Domestic Abuse Groups.* Amherst H. Wilder Foundation: St. Paul, MN.

Glaser, Barney & Strauss, Anselm (1967) *The Discovery of Grounded Theory.* Chicago: Aldine.

Hekman, Susan J. (1997a) Truth and method: Feminist standpoint theory revisited. *Signs, 22*, 341–365.

Hekman, Susan J. (1997b) Reply to Hartsock, Collins, Harding and Smith. *Signs, 22*, 399–402.

Herman, Judith L. (1992) *Trauma and Recovery: The Aftermath of Violence—From Domestic Abuse to Political Terror*. New York: Basic Books.

Langenberg, Mechtild, Aigen, Kenneth, & Frommer, Jörg (1996) *Qualitative Music Therapy Research: Beginning Dialogues.* Gilsum, NH: Barcelona Publishers.

Lindberg, Katherine A. (1995) Songs of healing: Songwriting with an abused adolescent. *Music Therapy, 13*, 93–108.

Mienczakowski, Jim E. (1992) *Syncing Out Loud: A Journey into Illness.* Brisbane, Australia: Griffith University Repregraphics.

Mienczakowski, Jim E. (1994) Theatrical and theoretical experimentation in ethnography and dramatic form. *Journal of National Drama, 2*, 16–23.

Mienczakowski, Jim E. (1995) The theatre of ethnography: The reconstruction of ethnography into theatre with emancipatory potiential. *Qualitative Inquiry, 3*, 360–375.

Montello, Louise (1999) A psychoanalytic music therapy approach to treating adults traumatized as children. *Music Therapy Perspectives, 2*, 74–81.

Morris, Bonnie J. (1999) *Eden Built by Eves: The Culture of Women's Music Festivals.* Los Angeles: Alyson Books.

National Women's Health Information Center (March, 2003) http://www.4woman.gov/violence/

Paget, Derek (1987) Verbatim theatre: Oral history and documentary techniques. *New Theatre Quarterly, 12,* 317–336.

Ramazanoglu, Caroline with Janet Holland (2002) *Feminist Methodology: Challenges and Choices.* London: Sage Publications.

Richardson, Laurel & Lockridge, Ernest (1991) The sea monster: An ethnographic drama. *Symbolic Interaction, 14,* 335–340.

Rinker, Rhonda Lineberg (1991) Guided Imagery and Music (GIM): Healing the wounded healer. In Kenneth Bruscia (ed.), *Case Studies in Music Therapy.* Gilsum, NH: Barcelona Publishers.

Rogers, Penny J. (1992) Issues in working with sexually abused clients in music therapy. *British Journal of Music Therapy, 6,* 5–15.

Rogers, Penny J. (1995) Childhood sexual abuse: Dilemmas in therapeutic practice. *Music Therapy Perspectives, 13*, 24–30.

Stark, Evan & Flitcraft, Anne (1988) Violence among intimates: An epidemiological review. In Vincent B. Van Hasselt, Randall L. Morrison, Alan S Bellack, & Michel Hersen (eds.), *Handbook of Family Violence.* New York: Plenum.

Tjaden, Patricia & Thoennes, Nancy (July, 2000) Extent, Nature & Consequences of Intimate Partner Violence: Findings from the National Violence Against Women Survey. National Institute of Justice, Center for Disease Control. http://www.ojp.usdoj.gov/nij

Ventre, Madelaine E. (1994) Healing the wounds of childhood abuse: A Guided Imagery and Music case study. *Music Therapy Perspectives, 2,* 98–103.

Whipple, Jennifer & Lindsey, Rebecca S. (1999) Music for the soul: A music therapy program for battered women. *Music Therapy Perspectives, 17,* 61–68.

Worell, Judith & Remer, Pamela (1992) *Feminist Perspectives in Therapy: An Empowerment Model for Women.* New York: John Wiley & Sons.

For information on how to order the "Finding Voice" CD, contact Maureen Hearns, MT-BC, at Utah State University: mhearns@cc.usu.edu. Proceeds from sales will benefit CAPSA and ensure the continuation of music therapy services to women and children served by the agency.

Chapter Eleven

AWAKENING THE "WILD WOMAN": FEMINIST MUSIC THERAPY WITH ISRAELI WOMEN WHO SUFFERED TRAUMA IN THEIR LIVES

Dorit Amir

This chapter examines my music therapy practice from a feminist perspective. I first describe feminism in Israel, briefly delineate my feminist values, and explain how these are interwoven into my work with women. I then present the stories of three women who have suffered from traumas due to being Jewish and living in Israel. The first story is Suzi's, a woman who lost her lover who was killed during the 1967 Six Days War. The second one is Michaela's, a woman who was a hidden child during the holocaust, who lost her parents who were killed by the Nazis while she herself survived and came to live in Israel. The last story is Sonia's, a woman who lost her husband in the Yom Kippur War in 1973 and later lost her daughter in a terrorist attack in 2001. The theme that runs like a thread through these stories is the loss of power due to traumas caused by human beings, and the regaining of power while being in music therapy. Music, in its various implementations, played a central role in these women's therapy and lives. Being a powerful, creative force, music empowered these women and gave them the courage to go on with their lives.

Feminism in Israel

In general, the Israeli feminist movement has had quite a long journey and has resulted in many achievements. The empowerment of women, in general, is being felt in all areas of cultural and public life in Israel. More women go into political life and more women reach top positions in the business world. It is interesting to notice that even in the Israeli army[1] there is a huge change in the

[1]The service in the Israeli army is mandatory for both men and women. Women are required to serve for 20 months.

perception of the place and task of women soldiers. Lately, women are being accepted into the most prestigious and "masculine" pilot courses, and join officers' courses that were open to men only until a few years ago. There is obviously more awareness about the subject of gender—most universities now offer courses in gender studies, in which women's needs and contributions are being learned about and discussed. However, women still do not have equal rights. Only 10% of executive directors are women, 8% of associate professor ranks in the universities are inhabited by women, and there are only 5 Israeli women ambassadors among 100 representatives in the world. Also, there is still widespread discrimination in salaries based on gender (Gera, 2004).

In spite of the solidarity that exists among Israeli feminists in creating and achieving change in the patriarchal agenda, a multi-cultural feminism has emerged. This has happened because the feminist agenda was until recently the agenda of white "straight" women from a high socio-economic class. The problems of such women are not the same problems of women from a low socio-economic class. Multi-cultural feminism claims that room should be allowed for many female voices in feminist dialogues. As a result, lesbians, black women, Sephardic women, and women from lower socio-economic classes stood up and started to develop their own theories and to develop separate agendas that cover their own unique needs. Multi-cultural feminism has identified a phenomenon of suppression of women by women (Banush, 2002). Out of Israeli feminism the Sephardic feminist movement was created—Sephardic women felt that they have been suppressed not only by men and by patriarchal approaches in general, but also by Ashkenazi women within the feminist movement. This movement within a movement is very similar to the Black feminist perspective in the United States.

My Own Perspective of Feminism

Most of my clients, students, and supervisees are women. I enjoy working with them. In her book *Women who Run with the Wolves* Clarissa Pinkola Estes (1992) writes about healthy women who show a keen sensing and playful spirit, "possessed of great endurance and strength . . . they are deeply intuitive . . . they are experienced in adapting to constantly changing circumstances, they are fiercely stalwart and very brave" (p.4). Estes's book made a big impression on me and influenced my understanding of feminism. Even though the creative place of wisdom within human beings has been introduced by many writers using various terms—the music child (Nordoff & Robbins, 1977), the unconditional awake presence (Welwood, 1990), the embryonic wisdom (Welwood, 1990), the child within (Whitfield, 1989), the true self (Miller, 1996; Winnicott,

1971), the transcendent self (Jung, 1972) and others—I have always felt that these terms do not capture this essence fully and accurately and therefore diminish its power. When I came across Estes's term *the wild woman* (Estes, 1992), it immediately rang true to me. I feel that this term captures all dimensions of this phenomenon and depicts its nature. I feel that Estes created a new language and terminology for describing the female psyche in its truest sense. Estes uses musical terms when explaining and describing the wild woman: it comes to us through sound, "through music which vibrates the sternum, excites the heart. It comes through the drum, the whistle, the call, and the cry" (Estes, 1992, p.7).

Estes is a wonderful storyteller. Through telling the stories of various women, she brings this concept of the wild woman to life. The theme that runs through her stories is about teaching women how to reconnect with their healthy, instinctual, intuitive place of wisdom. It is my belief that women need to tell their stories in order for them to be heard and understood. Sharing our journeys results in many possibilities to regain power in our societies and revitalize the feminine side of human beings. This is what I try to do in my practice. There are special moments in my music therapy practice when my client and I experience our female psyches vibrating and radiating while playing or listening to music. Estes's stories are full of compassion, heart, love, and respect. This is the way I view feminism. It is my commitment to finding, re-discovering and strengthening human characteristics such as the ability to feel, to express, to share, to support, to care, to nurture, to hold, to contain, to intuit, to understand with, without, and between words. As a woman therapist, feminism is my duty—to try to remove barriers that limit my clients' personal, social, political, economic, creative, sexual, and spiritual potential. It is about improving, fulfilling, and empowering both women's and men's lives.

Power is one of the central issues that is constantly being raised and dealt with in my practice. Most if not all women who come to me for music therapy have experienced power in negative ways—loss of power, misused power, false and negative power. My women clients have been raised in cultures where women are being dominated by men. They come from patriarchal families where fathers and even older brothers consider themselves to be more important than women; families where they were raised up with men's specific stereotyped expectations of wives, mothers, and daughters concerning rights, duties, household tasks, and certain behaviors (in regard to how to dress, how to talk, and how to behave, etc.). All these usually result in women's low self-esteem, poor self-image, confusion in regard to who they are and what their values, needs, and wants are, and denial of their right to live their lives according to their beliefs and what they stand for.

My feminist consciousness has been developed together with my spiritual consciousness; my own personal and professional journeys have served as a firm foundation for awakening both. Growing up with a very dominant father who died rather suddenly when I was 14 years old and left me feeling alone and confused; watching and experiencing my mother trying to take upon herself the role of the father in addition to being a mother, a very difficult task that left its scars on me; having two younger brothers and no sisters; knowing that almost all of my father's family and some of my mother's family were killed by the Nazis during the holocaust—all forced me, later on, to explore and start being who I am. I made a commitment to continue to nourish my psychological and spiritual growth. Throughout my life, music connected me to my father, not in the way he intended it to, but in the way that better suited who I am. My own professional and personal journey paved the way to the awakening of my spiritual self as well as my feminine psyche.

Traumas caused by the holocaust, wars, and terrorist attacks add a new dimension and meaning to the feeling of powerlessness. The three stories in this chapter are about women whose traumas—the loss of their loved ones and their unique and painful life circumstances—were created by violent acts of specific cultures, societies, and political events. These violent acts were created by human beings who misused power. "The personal is the political" is one of feminism's key concepts (Russell & Carey, 2002). This phrase represents a commitment to understand people's personal experiences as influenced by broader relations of power. In this way, a woman's personal experiences are not solely her own, but are linked to other women's experiences and to a broader politics.

Another important aspect of feminism is the determination to create space for the telling of women's "unstoried" experiences (Russell & Carey, 2002). This resonates with the way I see my practice. My work with women is about reconstructing narratives which are based on woman-centered descriptions and interpretations. By deeply listening to their stories, respecting their wisdom and intuition, acknowledging and valuing their stories, I become a witness to their journeys and help them regain power and confidence. Women who regain power in their individual therapy change not only themselves but their families, their immediate surroundings and communities.

Some of these women become more active in community life and contribute to the cultural life in their area.[2] The publishing of women's stories by feminist therapists and therapeutic journeys by women clients has already

[2] See the example of Tamara, in Dorit Amir (2004) Community music therapy and the challenge of multiculturalism. In Mercedes Pavlicevic & Gary Ansdell, (eds.) *Community Music Therapy*. London: JKP, pp.249–266.

made a difference in our society. The more these stories are published, the more powerfully the feminine voice is being heard, which helps to revitalize the feminine side of human beings. A society with strong women who voice their opinions in regard to various matters is a better and healthier one.

Narrative approaches to identity and therapy are informed by post-structuralist understandings of identity and particularly the idea that our identities are not fixed but multi-storied (Thomas, 2002). Our identities are dynamic and constantly constructed (Russell & Carey, 2002). Understanding our identities as multi-storied is very helpful to me in my work with women. Working with women who had traumatic experiences in their lives, the goal of therapy is to slowly change the narrative (and the identity) of being a victim of men, society, politics, and life circumstances to one of empowerment—finding a new power in re-constructing one's identity, in finding one's voice, music, and creativity. I perceive the wild woman as an essence in each woman waiting to be released. My intentions as a feminist music therapist are to bring back the playful spirit, to remind the "wild woman" to come back, to regain power by awakening sounds and music and to try to excite the heart.

Here are the stories of three women with whom I worked in music therapy.[3] The stories are being told in the first person, very much the same way they were being told to me, and in the present tense in order to bring you, the reader, more deeply into the experience.

Suzi

The first time I see Suzi, a 40-year-old woman, I am struck by how much her face looks old and tired. She says:

> *During the last two years I have not been feeling well, suffering from headaches, chronic fatigue and loss of energy. All physiological-medical checks were negative and there was no pathology found. I am very tense and afraid that my marriage is over. Maybe this is a mid-life crisis.*

I think to myself that she is too young for that, and wonder what brings her to me, a music therapist. She talks about dissatisfaction in her personal and professional life and I notice that she talks in a very quiet, weak voice. When I ask her what brings her to me she says:

[3] All names have been changed in order to protect privacy and anonymity.

> *My body speaks to me, screams things that are beyond words, and I want to experience the rhythms and music of my body and mind, to understand what is going on within me. This is why I decided to go to an unconventional, creative psychotherapy. I love music. I used to play the flute when I was young, and therefore thought that I want to go to music therapy.*

I immediately notice a change in her rhythm and tone of talking. It is more alert, more alive. The "wild woman" is there, I think to myself.

Suzi is married and has two children—a 10-year-old daughter and a 6-year-old son. They live in the city and both husband and wife work as architects. Suzi was born in the USA, and her family immigrated to Israel when she was 5 years old. She has two older brothers, married with children, who also live in Israel. Her father, who was also an architect, died a short time before she started music therapy. Her mother is a housekeeper who now lives by herself in the same city.

She recalls her childhood as a very happy one:

> *I got a lot of attention from my parents and brothers. I was a very good student and had many friends. During adolescence, I became a little fat and did not like my body and the way I looked. In the army I served in the air force and liked my job. During that time I had a couple of boyfriends. After serving in the army I studied architecture and met a man who was 4 years older than me who also studied architecture. We started dating and 8 years later we got married when I was 31.*

To my question of why they waited such a long time until they got married, she said:

> *I was the one who hesitated. I simply wasn't sure that he was the right man for me. Finally I decided to marry him since he was a nice man and took good care of me.*

After one year, their daughter was born and four years later she gave birth to her son.

> *My husband and I had a good connection throughout the years, but lately I have been feeling that we are drifting apart from each other.*

> *My husband works long hours in his office and we hardly spend time together.*

It is interesting for me to notice that she does not mention the word "love" in her descriptions. Maybe she does not let herself experience feelings and sensations in a full manner. I am wondering if she is afraid of emotions, if she ever experienced love.

> *I used to love dancing and going out, but during the last two years I haven't been going out so much, due to lack of energy.*

When I ask her about music in her life, she says:

> *I love classical music. I used to go to concerts and loved it. My favorite composer is Beethoven, since there are real storms in his music that are being expressed in such aesthetic, beautiful forms. I also love Schubert, Brahms, and Chopin since he is so romantic!*

I notice that Suzi does not talk about music in her past and ask her if she remembers music from her childhood. She hardly does.

> *I played the flute for 8 years. I started when I was 10 until I went to the army. Over the years I tried to pick up the flute and play it, but it did not sound good and I gave it up.*

I ask Suzi to bring her flute with her, and during the first sessions we play a few Israeli songs. Her playing improves and she manages to make a fuller sound.

> *It is strange for me to play the flute here: I have a love-hate relationship with it. On one hand, I love it since it reminds me of my happy childhood. On the other hand, I haven't played it for such a long time and don't feel that I am good at it. I also never liked playing in front of others, and I actually suffered a great deal when I played in front of an audience.*

I ask her how does it feel playing in front of me and she says: *"O.K."* She remembers that in her childhood her parents asked her to play the flute for their friends.

> *I used to have stomach aches and diarrhea before playing, but I did not dare to say no to my parents.*

I notice that even then her body reacted to the emotional pressure and wonder if there is a connection to Suzi's painful body today. I have a feeling that her body screams her distress, but does not release it.

After a few sessions we start improvising together. She plays the flute, I am at the piano. I feel that I have a tendency to play loud and cover her. I wonder if I do it in order to protect her so that she won't be exposed in her playing like she used to be in her childhood. I wonder if I should play less loud and let her be in the center, but decide to continue playing naturally even if I cover her. At one point, she stops playing and says:

> *I cannot hear myself since the piano is too loud.*

Even though she says it in a very quiet voice, I encourage her to see how she feels about it via the instruments. She takes the bongos and beats in a harsh, loud manner. We talk about anger and she says that nobody in her family has ever expressed anger. She is surprised to find that out. We talk about her family of origin. She talks about her father, who was a very dominant figure. Even though he gave her attention, it was according to his values. He did not really see her or listen to her. He was the one who decided where and what she would study and told her more or less how to live her life. We talk about her painful body and she says that now, like in the past, her body stores harsh memories and feelings inside it and does not release them.

Suzi experiments with various musical instruments in the room. At the end of each session she looks and feels tired and asks me to play a Chopin waltz for her.

> *It brings me to the dance hall. I imagine myself dancing in the arms of a man of my dreams. It makes me feel sad.*

Suzi starts crying and says:

> *I do not feel loved or able to love. I feel uncreative, unproductive and closed. I feel stuck.*

She plays the wind chimes in order to calm herself.

I am thinking to myself that Suzi's "wild woman" is probably hidden inside her, covered up with lots of painful, blocked memories.

At the beginning of one particular session I ask her how she feels today and she says: *"not good."* I ask her to close her eyes and try and connect to that feeling.

> *I feel very tired. I imagine my inner self as a transparent balloon, full of air, and all of a sudden it blows and all the air goes out. The balloon becomes tiny, empty, and sad—with no air.*

She improvises on the wind chimes.

> *This balloon is very tired. At first it is full of air but the air is locked inside. Maybe it is a good thing that it blew—the air that was blocked inside got released.*

She starts improvising the image of the balloon on her flute. She plays a melody in A minor, soft and slow, going up and down to the tonic. I think to myself that she chooses to play her flute, the instrument that symbolizes her past, her childhood, in order to play the wounded balloon. The melody turns out to be of a Hasidic character.[4] I listen and all of a sudden remember my own father, who died many years ago. Maybe her balloon is empty also because her father died? During her playing I feel that the balloon starts to fill up again—it becomes filled with sounds. Suzi puts the flute aside and continues with her voice. She is humming the melody and I join her. We sit closely together, on the carpet. There is a feeling of intimacy and sisterhood between us. She tells me about her father who died last year, how much she misses him. Suzi looks fragile to me.

During the next few months she mourns her father's death, but also allows herself to express anger towards him. We try to process her feelings towards her mother as well and I encourage her to give herself permission to feel and express verbally, musically, and emotionally all that was forbidden to express in the past. She is ambivalent about what's happening to her—she is glad that she allows herself to feel, but at the same time she feels distress. Even though she gains insight and better understands her inner life, she still feels tired, angry, and frustrated. At one of the sessions she tells me that she feels an inner chaos and I ask her to try and express it musically. She gathers many instruments and starts beating several drums, wind chimes, and cymbal, playing loud and chaotic rhythms. At the same time she puts a whistle in her mouth and plays it like a siren. I feel as if I am in a war. Fear enters me, and I find myself humming a

[4] Hasidic songs are considered to be the richest among all Jewish folksongs. The Hasidim are a mystic Jewish sect which flourished in Eastern Europe, originally in the Eastern Carpathians, in the middle of the 18th century. The Hasidic songs are unique in character and form. Niggun is the Hasidic term for a tune. "Most niggunim are sung without any words, with the frequent use of carrier syllables such as Ah, Ay, Oy, Hey, Ya-ba-bam, etc." (Hajdu & Mazor 1972, p.1423). The tunes are mystical in character, and usually have a prayerful mood.

song that my father used to sing to me when I was young. When she finishes playing, she starts crying and thanks me for soothing her with this particular song I hummed.

Later, when I was thinking about this session, it took me back to two personal painful experiences. One was during the 1967 Six Days War, to the first moment when we heard that the war started. I started feeling very frightened and found myself humming this song. The song soothed me and made me less scared. The second memory was connected to a specific moment that I experienced during the 1973 (Yom Kippur) War. I was sitting in the shelter, listening to the horrifying radio reports from the battlefields that reported thousands of killed soldiers. I had many friends who were in the army and I was very worried, feeling helpless and fearful. I remember singing the same song to myself in order to calm myself and regain power.

In the next session, we talk about the previous one and I share with her my image of being in a war and the need to protect myself while she was playing. We listen to the recording and I notice that her body is trembling. All of a sudden she starts crying. After a while she stops and remembers that during the Six Days War she lost a very good friend of hers.

> *"In fact,"* she says, *"this was the man I really loved. The man I wanted to marry. He got killed in the war."*

Both of us are totally speechless. This is the first time that she mentions it. She totally blocked this experience from her memory.

At that time Suzi decides to take a break. It is too much for her to handle. She returns after three weeks and says that her headaches have disappeared almost completely. We continue the process and she allows herself to express her feelings via music, songs, silences, and words. While listening to classical music she is able to acknowledge and process the blocked memory and to mourn the loss of the man she really loved. This is a powerful experience that gives Suzi the power to let other losses in her life surface and we talk about them. Feeling the pain and mourning the losses slowly make room for a new feeling of renewal and empowerment.

> *"I still feel tired,"* she says, *"but it has a different quality. It is no longer the result of blocked trauma, but of the opposite—I allow myself to express the trauma, to give it voice, and I am tired since this is a new experience for me. My body is heavy, since it is not used to releasing the blocked energy."*

Suzi gradually gives herself permission to experience, to express, and to share her feelings in an authentic and full manner. At this time Suzi is more capable of sharing her feelings with her husband and they both agree to go to couples therapy.

At the end of our journey together Suzi feels that she rediscovered her inner creativity and strength, and is capable of renewing her life. She starts playing the flute again and takes a movement and dancing class. The "wild woman" is not hiding anymore.

Michaela

Michaela, a 60-year-old holocaust survivor is a mother of 3 grown-up children and has 5 grandchildren. She suffers from anxiety attacks, nightmares, depression, headaches, and digestion problems. She is in the middle of a marital crisis that worsened after the children moved out.

> *I love to listen to classical music. However, there are compositions, such as Ravel's "Bolero," that while listening to I get a panic attack, and, in fact, this is the reason why I am here—I want us to listen together to Ravel's "Bolero" and try to understand what's going on within me.*

Michaela was born in Poland, in Ghetto Warsaw, the only child to her parents. In November 1940 when she was 5 years old the ghetto's gates closed. In 1942 her parents were sent to Treblinka by the Nazis and they were murdered at the gas chambers. Before her parents were taken by the Germans her mother brought her secretly to Polish friends who lived close to the ghetto and they promised to hide her in their home until the war was over. In 1945 she was taken to an orphan's camp in Italy where she stayed a whole year with many other orphans who later were brought to Israel. In Israel she stayed with relatives who adopted and raised her. When she was 20 years old she married and had three children—two daughters and one son.

All three children have married. Both daughters have children and the son is divorced, with no children.

> *I enjoy being with my grandchildren, but after a while I lose my patience and start experiencing worries, tension, restlessness, anxiety, and panic. When I was a young mother I consciously tried to avoid any painful memories and I blocked them completely. I avoided meeting people who were holocaust survivors like me and never*

talked about the subject. Every year, when the Holocaust Memorial Day comes, it brings up an enormous amount of pain but I don't talk about it with anyone.

When I ask her if she told her children about her childhood she says:

I tried as much as I could not to talk about this period in my life with my family. I totally blocked it and in fact I referred to it as non-existing. Only in the last few years, I feel that pictures and memories from my childhood come back to me in a very confused and chaotic way.

The idea of working with Michaela is rather difficult for me. Most of my father's family and some of my mother's family were killed by the Nazis. It has always been a tough subject for me to touch. I am afraid and wonder if I will be able to be there for her, if I have the strength to accompany her in her journey. After much thought and hesitation I decide to work with her. As part of my preparation, I read books on the holocaust and survivors' testimonies concerning the physical and emotional symptoms and their influences on the survivors and their families.

Michaela suffers from what is known as "concentration camp syndrome" (Elizur, Tiano, Munitz, & Neumann, 1987). The main symptoms include: anxiety, tension, restlessness, panic responses, overexcitement, low tolerance for stimulation, little patience, nightmares, sleepless nights, and recurring associations that are connected to traumatic experiences and amplify them. There is a tendency to experience psychosomatic symptoms such as headaches, tiredness and feeling weak, and digestion problems. Menopause and aging come at an earlier age than usual. Many survivors are preoccupied with thoughts and memories that are related to their holocaust experiences and have a tendency to idealize their lives prior to the holocaust (Elizur et al, 1987).

Michaela was 5 years old when the ghetto gates closed and 7 when her parent disappeared. Garland (1993) found that survivors who were children at the time of the holocaust and experienced loss, separation, and death of their parents and other family members report somatic pains, difficulties in expressing anger, and a general anxiety concerning themselves or their children. They also suffer from developmental delay or distorted development due to the early separation from their parents and the horrendous traumas during that time. In this age group severe personality disorders and psychoses developed at a more frequent rate than in any other age group that survived the holocaust (Elizur et al, 1987).

Michaela comes to music therapy due to anxiety, somatic symptoms, and marital crisis, but she does not relate them directly to the holocaust. During therapy it becomes clear that these symptoms are connected to blocked memories from her childhood.

After a few conversations, Michaela wants to listen to Ravel's "Bolero" in a safe space. I do guided relaxation with her, and at the end I ask her to see herself in a place where she feels comfortable. She sees herself on her home balcony, sitting in a recliner and looking over the garden. During the first few months she prefers to sit on a chair while listening to the "Bolero." Later she agrees to lie on a mattress. At the beginning, I play "Bolero" for only 3-5 minutes, and when Michaela starts to experience anxiety I stop the music so she can breathe and relax. I gradually play it for longer periods of time until we can listen to the whole composition. Michaela sits or lies and slowly starts seeing images and blurred pictures. I accompany her journey, witnessing her experience, serving as a midwife who helps her to get out her horrific life story.

From Michaela's Journal:

During our sessions, Michaela sits or lies, listens to the music with her eyes closed, and tells her story. I sit next to her and write what she says.

> *We lived in Warsaw in a nice apartment—Dad, Mom, and me. Dad had a clothing store and Mom helped him in the store. I went to a kindergarten and in the afternoons I would play outside our home. We had a piano and I started taking piano lessons at a very young age. I can see myself sitting next to the piano and playing. I play a minuet, and Dad looks at me with a smile on his face—I think he is proud of me. I love playing the piano.*
>
> *I see Mom and Dad whispering to each other and they look worried. I don't understand what is happening. I only remember them whispering. I feel scared . . . confused. . . . I am not sure what's happening. . . . I am next to the piano; I somehow feel that the piano gives me confidence.*

Things start coming out in a confused and cut manner:

> *I see myself as a little girl in a dark place. I shout Mom! Dad! But they don't come. I cry but no one is coming to get me. I am alone in the dark, crying and screaming till I fall asleep. . . . I can see my mother takes me in the dark and brings me to a strange home and*

leaves me there. I scream and cry: Mommy! Mommy! I am left with two strangers, who try to calm me down, but I continue to cry and scream and they put me inside a closet and close the door.

I remember my parents taking me with them to a coffee shop in Warsaw, in the ghetto, where live music was played. I loved listening to it. I thought that when I become a grown up person, maybe I will be a pianist and perform in front of an audience.

I see myself full of scabies, scratching my head, my body, my clothes . . . there is a very sharp, terrible smell. . . . I can smell it. . . . I see naked bodies that are partially covered with newspapers on the sidewalks. . . . I was very thin, and my Mom sent me to stand at the wall and try to beg strangers who passed there for a piece of bread or potato. . . .

I am scared. . . . I hear footsteps. . . screams . . . shooting. . . .
I see myself with my girlfriends Esther and Frieda. We are playing outside—it is snowing and we throw snowballs at each other and laugh . . . what fun we had together! After two years they both were taken together with their families and I never saw them again. Later on I heard that they were both murdered.

I hear the airplanes bombing the city. . . . I am scared . . . the sound of the bombs is heard everywhere . . . the floor and the ceiling of the house are shaking . . . the sirens of the ambulances in the streets. . . . Mom and Dad tell me that I have nothing to be afraid of, but I am petrified. I am screaming and crying, I don't want to leave Mom and Dad. "Mom, please don't leave me, I will be a good girl, I promise!"

Michaela sits down and cries. I put my hand over her shoulder in order to support her.

Many times during therapy Michaela covers her ears with her hands and her forehead is covered with sweat. She asks me to stop the tape. She cannot go on. I am horrified and have goose bumps all over my body. I give her a glass of water and we sit quietly for a few minutes. These moments are most difficult. I end these sessions with playing something quiet and relaxing.

After 6 months of therapy pictures from her past continue to surface. During this time, every time the "Bolero" gets louder it brings pictures of German soldiers walking in the streets, shouting, shooting, hitting, and humiliating. She remembers one time when she saw a German soldier hit her father and finally in a miraculous way, let him go. Her father came home bitten and crying, and her mother puts him on the bed, cleaned the blood from his face, took care of him, and cried. . . .

> *I remember that my mother used to cry a lot, especially during the nights. I would come to their bed and would feel the pillow that was wet from tears. I rolled up in my mother's arms and fell asleep like that . . . .*

Time after time, images, pictures, and memories from her childhood keep coming up, both from the Ghetto and from the Christian family where she was hidden. She starts to recognize faces from the Ghetto. She remembers neighbors, friends of the family, adults, children, and tells me about each one. She remembers how she went to church with her new father and mother. She met a girl her age and became friends with her.

For three years Michaela lived with her new family. Her "new parents" and her friendship with the new girl helped her to block the trauma and continue with her life. The war ended when she was about 12 years old. Warsaw was being released from the Germans and one day a stranger knocked on the door. He explained that he was a relative of Michaela who survived the camps and came to take her. He said that her real parents were killed and he made a promise to them that he would find her and take her with him. These Christian people saw Michaela as their own child and did not want to give her up, but eventually he managed to take her and brought her to an orphanage. Again, she found herself totally alone in the world, without any familiar face, lonely and scared. These memories usually come up as the "Bolero" reaches its peak moments; when the melody is very loud. She then experiences anxiety again. Then we need to take a break and relax.

Michaela, like many other children who were hidden by Christian families, could not understand why her real parents left her and never came back to take her. Later on, when she was taken to the orphanage, she could not understand the same exact thing: why was she taken away from her "parents" and kept asking when would she return to them.

Like many holocaust survivors, Michaela went through excruciating physical and emotional suffering and lost the people who were the closest to her. The way she rehabilitated herself is amazing. She came to Israel, got married, raised children, and became an active woman in the community. However, like many others, she had mental scars that caused her and the people around her great distress.

Listening to the "Bolero" in the therapy room allowed the stories and pictures to surface after years of being deeply blocked in her mind (exactly like

Michaela, who was hidden in a closet for long periods of time). My task was to help Michaela organize these stories and pictures and recreate a past that she could mourn. I am with her while she listens to quiet music in order to relax and to organize herself. Michaela finds songs that tell her story and reads them out loud while there is music in the background. With my help, she writes songs that tell her story and contain the images that were brought out in therapy. Each song has a title and we arrange them in a chronological order: "Playing the piano," "me and my parents," "hiding in the closet," "the visit," "the new home," "Olga" (her Christian friend), etc. Throughout therapy Michaela creates a song book that contains 30 songs that tell her personal history. Some of the songs I compose according to the mood the words create, and she sings them while I accompany her on the piano. I encourage her to share the songs with her family and occasionally she reads them some of the songs. With her permission, I record some of the songs we perform on a cassette that Michaela takes with her and plays at home.

Our therapy sessions continued for two years. The "Bolero" flooded her with anxiety, but in the way we worked—desensitization (the gradual reduction of anxiety together with the stimulus that activates it)—the anxiety was brought under control while traumatic memories from the past were being released. I cut the music whenever it was too much to handle, and in this way Michaela was able to take it slowly and gradually. She stopped in order to relax, to digest, to then move again, and to continue the journey. Quiet music ended each session and helped to sooth, relax, support, organize, and protect. A new narrative was created that reconstructed her past.

Michaela ended therapy with a feeling of empowerment and some relief in regard to her physical symptoms. The headaches and digestion problems were gone. She was less tired and felt more energy. Michaela continued to feel some anxiety, but she could better control it. She realized that she could not change the past, but she could change the present. Michaela could now listen to Ravel's "Bolero" with a feeling of control. The images came back again and again, but she did not feel the same amount of anxiety and panic attack. She still suffered from nightmares, occasionally waking up covered with cold sweat. She felt that her relationships with her children improved—she started being more open with them. The terrible, mysterious secret that was an integral part of the children's lives was gone.

Sonia

Sonia was 45 when she came to music therapy. Her parents were born in Poland. They met each other before the Second World War, survived the war, came to Israel, married and gave birth to their only child, Sonia. Most of their relatives were killed by the Nazis. Sonia grew up in a kibbutz, met her husband in high school, married when she was 20 and raised two children. Sonia was 28 years old when her husband was killed in a battle on the second day of the 1973 Yom Kippur War. She was left with a 5-year-old daughter and a 3-year-old son. Sonia raised her children by herself and never remarried. In the initial interview, she told me that she had been quite lonely and depressed over the years and could not make any meaningful changes in her life. She wanted to meet new people, but lacked the energy to socialize.

At that time, I started a women's group that consisted of women who had lost their husbands or children. Sonia joined the group, and usually remained quiet. The group started with singing a song that was brought by one of the members. Each member had to bring a song that represented something about her. Sonia sang some of the songs that were brought by other group members in a very quiet voice and only occasionally participated in group discussions. When her turn came, she brought two songs. The first song is called "Shuva Elai"[5]—"return to me." The melody is written in A minor, in a ballad style. "The lights went out again and the voice of my horse lost in the sand is still ringing. Return to me from the desert and together we shall gallop away." The second song is called "Halicha Le'Caysaria"—"going to Caesarea."[6] The song is also written in a minor key. A prayer to God, the song expresses the wish that the sand, the sea, the rush of the waters, the crash of the heavens, and the prayers of man will endure for eternity. Hanna Senesh, who wrote the song, was a Jewish paratrooper who was killed by the Nazis in World War II.

The group felt sadness and longing while singing these songs. In the discussion, some members felt that Sonia lived in the past. She was still waiting for her husband to come back and refused to go on with her life. The group felt that both songs conveyed a powerful message concerning Sonia's attitude: "I want things to stay the way they used to be, to stay as they were, to never change." The first song made Sonia realize that she refused to acknowledge reality. Sonia told the group:

[5] The song is written by A. Etinger and J. Hadar.

[6] The song is written by H. Senesh and D. Zehavi

> *Even though so many years had passed since my husband's death, I still retain his clothes and keep his personal things the way he left them.*

Sonia realized that by keeping him so "alive" in her life, she could not end the grieving. She therefore was unable to go on with her life.

The second song, "Halicha Le'Caysaria," brought Sonia back to her original family. She told the group that her parents never talked about the holocaust. Her father died when she was 15 years old and her mother died shortly after. She remembered them as being very loving, caring, and overprotective parents. Her father was very dominant and there were many things he did not allow her to do. Both her parents had a thing with food. She had to eat everything even if she didn't like it because "food is not to be thrown away." She also remembered that music played an important role in family gatherings. At every Sabbath dinner they used to sit around the table and sing Sabbath and other Israeli and Yiddish songs. Only after their death, Sonia gathered some information about her parents' existence during World War II from a relative who was with them at that time. Other group members shared their own personal stories concerning the holocaust.

At the end of the session, I asked Sonia to sing "Halicha Le'Caysaria" again, this time as a prayer, and to ask for the courage to be able to change the things she can in her life. Sonia transformed the song into a song of hope. She sang the song with new energy and strength. The whole group joined her. It was a very moving experience for all participants.[7]

The group sessions end and I don't see or hear from Sonia for two years. One day I receive a phone call from her. She says that she needs to see me right away. She comes and tells me that her daughter was recently murdered in a suicide bomb while traveling on the bus. Her daughter, married with a child, was on the bus on her way to work. The suicide bomber was standing a few meters away from her when he exploded. Sonia's daughter was killed on the spot. Sonia had to go with her daughter's husband to identify the body that was in the worst shape. Sonia's whole world fell apart. For three months, she could not get out of bed. Later she started going to work, but told me that she lost her appetite and her will to live.

She is back in therapy. I accompany her in her unbearable mourning. The loss is bigger than life. During the first year, I mainly stand by her and support her. The pain is enormous. She is very fragile and I feel that all I can do is to contain her with my presence and music. I play and sing for her, try to ease the pain. I do most of the playing while she lies on the carpet in a fetal position,

[7] More about this group can be read in: Amir (1997) and Amir (1998).

crying. Flashbacks from the time when her husband was killed come back and wake up old feelings. There are days when Sonia sits on the chair but does not have any energy to do anything—not even talk or play.

Slowly she starts eating more properly and regaining some strength. She feels that again, like before, she is the victim of circumstances and cannot understand why she deserves such a destiny.

> *Isn't it enough that I lost my husband in the war, now I lose my daughter in a terrorist attack?! Why me? What did I do wrong? Why? My parents survived the holocaust and came to live in Israel so that I, their only child, will lose my husband and daughter in other violent acts that occurred because I live here, in this country, which is constantly at war? Isn't it enough that my parents' families and relatives got killed by the Nazis because they were Jews? Now we live in our own country and cannot live peacefully, and get killed and murdered all the time?*

Sonia's narrative is a victim's narrative. During this entire narrative I experience an excruciating feeling of helplessness. What can one say to a mother who just lost her child? What can be said in this kind of a situation? Being a mother myself, I couldn't really deal with it. We both feel powerless, due to the misused power by human beings, political leaders.

We work together for two years. What brings back the will to live is Sonia's granddaughter, who is only 3 years old and who needs a lot of care and nurturing. Sonia realizes that now she has to live for her granddaughter. This realization gives her energy and she slowly starts to come back to life. A clear sign of that is when she starts to sing and play music in the room. She sings Israeli songs again, like we did in our women's group. The big and varied song repertoire enables Sonia to express feelings of pain, rage, anger, frustration, and helplessness. At the same time it gives her power. I encourage her to get in touch with some of the other women who were in the women's music therapy group and ask them if they would like to meet every once in a while, sing songs, and share a feeling of sisterhood. Sonia picks up the challenge and forms a women's group. She calls it "my creative women's group." This group, together with her music therapy sessions and another support group of people who lost their children in terrorist attacks, helps Sonia to strengthen her will to live. Her granddaughter forces her to get in touch with her creative and playful self. Her narrative changes from a victimized one to a more holistic one. The "why" transforms to "how"—how can I give meaning to my life now, having suffered so much? How can I heal myself in spite of my broken heart?

DISCUSSION

What do these Three Women have in Common?

These are Jewish women who live in Israel, which is a small state in the Middle East, surrounded by Arab countries. Most Arab states (except two, Egypt and Jordan, with which Israel has a peace agreement) that surround the country are in war terms with Israel. The life in this small country, which throughout its inception in 1948 has been fighting for its existence and has suffered from wars and terrorism, has caused huge distress to its inhabitants. The price has been heavy: thousands of killed and wounded people, thousands of families who have lost their loved ones, traumatized people and people with posttraumatic stress disorders. The holocaust with its horror, terror, and influence on holocaust survivors as well as on second and even third generations has had its impact on the emotional, mental, spiritual, and physical lives of many. These traumatic factors are in addition to other traumatic events in people's lives (such as car accidents, crime, violence, and abuse both inside and outside the family), which happen anywhere in the world.

Suzi, Michaela, and Sonia suffered from traumas due to the holocaust, war, and terrorism. These women's spirits were broken and their weak bodies screamed. All three women were raised in a patriarchal culture, in families where men were considered to be the dominant ones; homes in which negative emotions were not allowed to be expressed. They became victims of un-controlled horrible life circumstances, therefore they could not grow up to become who they really were and fulfill their dreams and potentials. Suzi grew up in a family where her father was a very dominant figure and the children had to obey him, no matter how they felt. She did not dare to say "no" to her father or reject his wishes. In addition, she was not allowed to express negative feelings. The family's hidden agenda, which was unconsciously dictated by the father, was that they were not to deal with harsh feelings. The most important thing was to obey your parents and to pretend that everything was fine. Due to political circumstances, Michaela said that from a very early age she had had very limited opportunities to feel that she had a say in her life. She had been unable to shape her life in the directions of her own choosing. When she left Germany, the unconscious memories from her childhood, together with physical discomfort, stepped in and continued to dictate the direction of her life. She continued to feel powerless and she could not live her life according to her own preferred ways. Sonia, as a second-generation holocaust survivor who lost her husband and her daughter, was also a victim of horrible life circumstances over which she did not have any control; she had lost her drive to live.

What was the Role of Music in their Lives?

Music empowered these women. All three women loved and appreciated music and led active musical lives, whether in their childhood, adolescence, or adulthood. Suzi and Michaela played an instrument and all three of them went to concerts and listened to music at home. Music played an important role in Suzi's childhood, and her relationship to music brought her later to music therapy. Suzi used to play the flute in front of her parents' friends and relatives. Although Suzi hated these concerts, she obeyed her parents and therefore created a love-hate relationship with her flute. Michaela was a music lover. She used to play the piano when she was a small girl and loved it. She dreamed of being a pianist, but these dreams vanished due to her horrible life circumstances. Later on, she loved to listen to music and go to concerts. A certain piece of music—Ravel's "Bolero"—triggered strong bodily reactions and caused her to come to music therapy. In Sonia's case, music was very much present in her parents' home. Singing was an integral part of family rituals and gatherings and Sonia inherited the love of singing from her parents.

What was the Role of Music Therapy?

Music therapy allowed these women to explore their experiences that had been shaped by the abuse of power. Over time, they were able to begin to notice moments when they were able to reclaim their lives and be released to some extent from its destructive influences. The ways in which they regained power—resuming playing and dancing (Suzi), writing, reading, and singing songs (Michaela), playing music and singing (Sonia)—can be viewed as attempts to maintain health and well-being. Therapy provided the opportunity to "deconstruct" the powerful and damaging relationships that existed within the context of abuse and violence, to recognize unhelpful beliefs and behaviors that belonged to past contexts that constructed them, and to understand that these unhelpful beliefs and behaviors are not the total of who they are as human beings. Therapy helped to create alternative life stories where creativity became more acknowledged. In this process, Suzi's, Michaela's and Sonia's identities have transformed from an emphasis on bodies that ache and scream, minds that feel helpless with absolutely no power, to acknowledging the fact that in spite of the horrifying circumstances, they are not helpless women. They lost their playful spirit, but in therapy, managed to regain their strength, and to show how brave they are in adapting to changing circumstances (Estes, 1992).

Music therapy helped to awaken the "wild woman," the creative place of wisdom that comes through sound and music which excites the heart (Estes,

1992). Music, in therapy, played an important role in exposing, dealing with, and healing the traumas. At the beginning stage of therapy, in Suzi's and Michaela's cases, the music triggered the exposure of traumatic memories and brought them from the unconscious to the conscious mind. In Sonia's case, the music helped her to deal with all the losses she suffered throughout her life: the loss of her husband, the loss of family members due to the holocaust, the loss of her parents, and the loss of her daughter. At a later stage, the music helped these women to get in touch with their creative selves and regain their power.

Suzi remembered, processed, and expressed her feelings concerning death and loss in her life via music, songs, silences, and words. Bringing and playing her flute, the instrument that symbolized her childhood, brought insights concerning her parents and her relationship with the flute. The Hasidic melody that she played on the flute and hummed brought a feeling of intimacy and sisterhood between us. It also allowed sadness to surface and gave her permission to deal with her relationships to her father and his death. The chaotic improvisation that she played during one session made me feel scared, and sharing my image and feeling with her brought back a hidden memory of the man she wanted to marry who was killed during the 1973 war. Listening to classical music helped her to acknowledge and process the blocked memory and to mourn the loss of the man she loved. This was a powerful experience that gave Suzi the strength to talk about and deal with other losses in her life. Feeling the pain and mourning the losses slowly made room for a feeling of renewal and empowerment. Suzi gave herself permission to experience, to express and to share her feelings in an authentic and full manner. The tiredness she still felt was of a different quality. At the end of therapy she resumed playing the flute and started dancing again. She rediscovered the "wild woman" within her.

In Michaela's case, listening to Ravel's "Bolero" within the therapeutic context brought images and memories to the surface and proved to be very effective in reaching her past. The "Bolero" enabled Michaela to express feelings of pain, rage, anger, frustration, helplessness, and anxiety. Quiet music that was played at the end of each session helped to organize, support, protect, and soothe her. It enabled her to feel compassion towards herself, and also hope. Songwriting, poetry reading, and singing helped her to reconstruct her past and enabled the mourning process to take place. The creation of a song book helped her to share her horrible secret with her family in a less threatening and more controlled, creative way. Musicking gave Michaela strength by connecting her to her creative part. It empowered her, and also compensated for what was lost (piano playing and dreams that accompanied it). It helped Michaela to create a new narrative, to maintain a more organized flow of events, and to achieve an integration of identities. She got in touch with, and hopefully rediscovered, her "wild woman" to some extent.

In Sonia's case, the music in the women's group allowed her to deal with the loss of her husband and other losses concerning the holocaust. In her individual therapy, after her daughter was killed, the music soothed her, contained her, supported her and later on screamed her screams, allowed her to feel the pain, and helped her to stay alive. She had moments when the "wild woman" was touched—unfortunately, not enough, in my opinion.

SUMMARY

This article is about rediscovering the "wild woman" within each one of us, re-finding the creative place of wisdom and bravery. In presenting these stories I give voice to my feminist beliefs. I believe that the way we dealt with, looked into, and processed these women's lives resulted in reconstructed stories that contained messages of hope and empowerment instead of guilt, helplessness, depression, and despair. In this way, music therapy with these women can be viewed as a feminist approach to music therapy. The music, songs, and stories created by these women clearly demonstrate the power of music therapy to empower and to give hope.

Out of many years of experience, I have found that my women clients are not afraid of showing their emotions. They listen to their hearts and each one knows the right way for her. They have the courage to dive, explore, and contain the unknown within themselves. I have seen that women who come to therapy believe that the journey to the stormy water of the inner self has its healing power even if it goes through huge, rough waves, and even if the light at the end of the tunnel is not in view. They know, intuitively, that the light is there, waiting for the right moment to show itself.

While the evolution of feminism continues to invite me to question my practice as a therapist, the work with these particular women forced me to get into a dialogue with myself, to question my perceptions, and to understand more deeply what my feminist values are and how they are interwoven in and contribute to my life, my work, and to the field of music therapy. This article is a result of this dialogue.

REFERENCES

Amir, Dorit (1997) Understanding the role of folk songs in Jewish-Israeli culture: Implications for music therapy. *The World of Music, 39*, 111–127.

Amir, Dorit (1998) The use of Israeli folksongs in dealing with women's bereavement and loss in music therapy. In Ditty Dokter (ed.), *Arts therapies, Refugees and Migrants—Reaching Across Borders*. London: Jessica Kingsley Publishers.

Banush, Noa (2002) Multi-Cultural feminism. http://www.tapuz.co.il/tapuzforum/main

Estes, Clarissa Pinkola (1992) *Women who Run with the Wolves*. New York: Ballantine Books.

Elizur, Avner, Tiano, Shmuel, Munitz, Hanan, & Neumann, Michah (1987) *Selected Chapters in Psychiatry*. Tel Aviv: Papirus Publishing (in Hebrew).

Gera, Ela (2004) What is feminism? http://cms.education.gov.il/EducationCMS/Units/Shivion/ShivionMigdari/

Hajdu, Andre & Mazor, Yaacov (1971) The musical tradition of Hasidism. In *Encyclopedia Judaica, Vol. 7*. Jerusalem: Keter Publishing Company, 1421–1432.

Jung, Carl G. (1972) *Collected Works, vol. 8*, 2nd edition. Princeton, NJ: Princeton University Press.

Miller, Alice (1996) *The Drama of the Gifted Child. The Search for True Self.* New York: Harpercollins, 3rd edition.

Nordoff, Paul & Robbins, Clive (1977). *Creative Music Therapy.* NY: John Day Company

Russell, Shona & Carey, Maggie (2002) Re-membering: Responding to commonly asked questions. *International Journal of Narrative Therapy and Community Work, 3*. http://www.dulwichcentre.com.au/intjournal.html

Thomas, Leonie (2002) Poststructuralism and therapy—What's it all about? *International Journal of Narrative Therapy and Community Work, 2.* http://www.dulwichcentre.com.au/intjournal.html

Welwood, John (1990) *Journey of the Heart*. New York: Harper Collins Publishers.

Whitfield, Charles (1989) *The Child Within*. Deerfield Beach, FA: Health Communications.

Winnicott, Donald (1971) *Playing and Reality*. London: Routledge.

Chapter Twelve

THE VOICES OF WOMEN SUFFERING FROM CHRONIC PAIN

Joke Bradt

INTRODUCTION

As you begin to read this chapter, I would like to engage you in a moment of reflection. I will assume that you have met people who suffer from chronic pain or chronic illness. I would like for you to recall the times when these people have shared their pain or illness stories with you, have complained about their symptoms, or have even canceled a dinner or luncheon at the last minute. Now revisit, without censoring, your reactions to them as well as how you share these reactions with others. Have you found yourself getting bored or annoyed when listening to their pain stories or complaints? Have you wondered why they are telling the same story over and over again? Have you had doubts about the veracity of their complaints? Have you labeled the person's complaints as attention-seeking or hypochondria? These questions probably cause some uneasiness as affirmative answers may reflect some judgmental and unempathetic characteristics in you. However, the truth is that people with chronic pain repeatedly find themselves being questioned, judged, and devalued.

In 2003, I began to work with college students suffering from chronic pain. Although the music therapy services are advertised to the campus community at large, so far only women have been seeking the services. As these women's stories unfolded in the sessions, themes of power struggle, stigmatization, humiliation, rejection, loss, and limitation dominated their narratives. However, despite their weak physical appearance, I was struck by their inner strength. This apparent paradox intrigued me. As I was listening to their stories, I was wondering if I was projecting strength onto them. Why did I perceive them as strong while all of these women reported that people viewed them as weak and whining? "*People only see my limitations . . . they think I am weak*"; "*People only see my ice packs, they don't see me.*" In addition, they felt that they were not taken seriously: *"I am not being heard"*; *"I feel as if nobody wants to listen to what I have to say"*; *"No matter how hard I scream, nobody seems to hear me."*

It was after a music therapy conference, during which I had shared with Sue Hadley my experiences in working with women with chronic pain, that I received an invitation to contribute a chapter to this book. I was excited to share my work, but, at the same time, I was not sure whether I "belonged." Was I feminist enough to contribute to this important book? Although I recognized that my work was characterized by feminist values, I had read only a handful of feminist articles and book chapters. I do not view myself as a feminist scholar. Because of the invitation to write a chapter, I felt pressured to get up to date with recent feminist publications related to (psycho)therapy and counseling. I began to wonder how so many of the feminist principles, issues, and values had entered my worldview before becoming "educated" about them through the literature. We are who we are because of and in spite of our past experiences and encounters. So which of these experiences had a significant impact on my worldview as a woman and as a therapist?

As a child I continuously witnessed and experienced excessive patriarchy at home. I only recall negative interactions between my parents in which my father treated my mother in an extremely demeaning manner. His constant threats were meant to "keep her down," silence her, and confine her to the role of "housewife." However, my mother found the strength, over and over again, to stand up to him. I remember vividly how much fear this caused in me as this infuriated my father even more. I recall screaming at her to be quiet . . . not to speak. But as I grew older, I learned that it was her voice and her strength that had protected us and given us opportunities in life that we would have never had.

Another influential event was my confrontation with the "American culture" when I came to the US to study music therapy. As a Belgian, I was (and still am) appalled at the "dating language" used by men in this country (e.g. going to a bar to *pick up women*). I was shocked by the genderization of girls and boys (e.g. boys wear blue and girls wear pink). I was stunned by the objectification of women's bodies and the "dress code" of women (long hair, high heels, dresses or skirts, and push-up bras). And I was sickened to see how young girls are dressed. Although I had already become an independent and strong young woman, it was the encounter with the extreme sexism in this culture that strengthened my feminist voice.

I realize that witnessing my mother suffer and having my own voice silenced by my father has been a driving force in my desire to empower women and strengthen their voices. The culture shock upon my arrival in this country evoked in me a critical mindset related to genderization, objectification, and power inequality of women.

In this chapter, I first discuss several socially constructed stereotypes related to chronic pain. These are stereotypes and stigmas that my clients are struggling with on a daily basis. This is followed by a description of our musical journey on the road to empowerment, acceptance, and new beginnings.

Women on Trial: Fighting the Stereotypes

Pain is a person's private experience to which no one else has direct access. Because of the subjective nature of pain, people with chronic pain repeatedly find themselves being questioned and judged about the veracity of their pain (Werner, Widding Isaksen, & Materud, 2004). Women, especially, find themselves being accused of malingering. One of my clients, suffering from fibromyalgia[1], shared: "*I feel as if I am constantly on trial. I am constantly trying to defend myself, trying to convince others that I am in a lot of pain . . . but most of them have already made up their mind: She looks fine . . . she must be faking it . . . I can see that they think I am crazy.*" In the narratives of my clients, there is an abundance of societal, often stigmatizing, stereotypes about chronic pain.

"It's in your head!"

What is pain? How can you verify the intensity of somebody's pain? The answers to these questions will vary greatly according the social and cultural context in which they are placed. For many years, the medical community defined pain solely in terms of tissue damage, namely as a transmission of impulses from the nerve receptors at the site of injury to the part of the brain responsible for pain perception with the intensity of the pain proportional to the extent of the tissue damage (Chapman, 1995). However, the fact that people with similar bodily injuries report very different levels of pain and the fact that pain is frequently reported in the absence of tissue damage, led researchers to believe that pain perception is more complex than a neural transmission of noxious stimuli. As a result, pain became defined as a subjective experience. Margo McCaffery (1968), for example, developed the following definition: "Pain is whatever the experiencing person says it is, and happens whenever the experiencing person says it does" (p.95). Commenting on this definition, Sherry Jimenez (1996) points out that "the subjective and unverifiable nature of pain necessitates such a subjective and unverifiable definition" (p.53). Important in

[1] Fibromyalgia Syndrome (FMS) is a chronic musculoskeletal pain disorder predominantly experienced by women and characterized by pain, fatigue, sleep disturbance, and multiple tender points at distinct locations on the body.

McCaffery's definition is that it gives power to the person who is experiencing pain by giving her control over the assessment of the presence, the description, and the intensity of the pain.

Judging by the fact that the literature has increasingly recognized the subjective nature of the pain experience, one could conclude that the medical community has taken some major strides in the assessment and management of pain. The stories of my clients, however, reveal a stark contrast between the construction of pain in the literature and its conceptualization in clinical practice. Their narratives indicate that in most traditional medical encounters—and in most societal encounters, I would add—they find themselves in an arbitration-of-truth situation. Even though the medical literature claims that pain is widely accepted as a complex and subjective phenomenon, they are continuously confronted with a reductionist and medico-centric construction of pain as "a symptom in need of corroborating [physical] evidence" (Eccleston, Williams, & Stainton Rogers, 1997, p.700). In other words, it is still common for pain to be put in a Cartesian discourse where one needs to rule out organic disease or *judge* whether or not there is *sufficient* tissue damage to explain the pain.

Chronic pain,[2] in particular, challenges the basic assertions of medical epistemology, which are based on the concept of objectivity and observable facts and which regards the subjective as obscure. Because the medical community is in the business of determining diagnoses that are firmly based on physical and visible observations, it is often at a loss with chronic pain that cannot be "medically" explained. Of course, the androcentric belief system, with its need for hard evidence, is not exclusive to the medical community. Our Western society is, at large, biased towards positivism: our need for *evidence* in our pursuit of the "truth" has imparted a judgmental stance towards others. This statement may raise objection in feminist readers as feminism accepts the subjective. However, I would like to take you back to the questions at the beginning of the chapter. How many of us have questioned the pain reports or complaints of others? How many of us have tried to detect evidence to legitimize the complaints? The fact that pain is invisible and escapes our senses naturally leads to a questioning, and often judgmental, attitude.

Unfortunately, when no physiopathological evidence can be found for a medical condition, including chronic pain, psychiatric explanations abound, especially when the sufferers are women. In the absence of evidence, chronic pain sufferers have been accused of fabricating pain for secondary gain, or of

[2] Chronic pain is clinically defined as pain that persists longer than the usual course of a disease or beyond a reasonable time required for injury to heal (Brena & Chapman, 1984).

merely manifesting psychological problems, and are left with the isolating message that it *must be in their heads* (Kendall-Tackett, Marshall, & Ness, 2003). The intensity of the pain is often devastating and dehumanizing, but I have seen in my clients that the "social verdict" and the psychosomatization is equally, if not more, detrimental.

"Be a man!"

Women in chronic pain often find themselves in a vulnerable position due to societal stereotypes related to women and pain. Several studies have provided evidence for a genderization of pain, potentially leading to discriminatory health care practices. A study by Stephen Colameco, Lorne Becker, and Michael Simpson (1983), for example, found that physicians attributed a component of emotionality *only* to the somatic complaints of women. Other studies have shown that women receive less pain medication and more sedative agents compared to men, suggesting that physicians perceive women as more emotional and therefore in need of sedatives rather than pain-relieving medication (Calderone, 1990). Women may find themselves being *muted* by sedatives instead of treated for their pain. It has also been reported in the literature that health care professionals frequently "downsize" women's pain reports and "upsize" men's pain reports (e.g. *he is just trying to be tough; I am sure his pain is more severe than what he says it is).* It is, of course, fair to ask if there are no true sex differences in pain. Several studies have indeed found evidence for such differences. However, it needs to be pointed out that for nearly every study reporting a sex difference in pain, one can find another reporting none (Kupers, 1997).

So where is this bias against women coming from? Despite the progress that has been made during the last decades, we are still plagued with strong stereotypes of how boys and girls should behave and what they should feel or not feel. It could be hypothesized that men and women respond differently to painful stimuli based on adherence to cultural norms. Boys are expected to be heroic and manly and not complain too much after minor injuries. The masculine gender role emphasizes tolerance for pain in order to avoid appearing unmasculine. Boys are often encouraged to suppress their pain complaints, whereas girls may receive subtle reinforcement for verbal expression of their pain. Boys, furthermore, are encouraged to use active pain coping strategies (i.e. physical activity), whereas girls may be encouraged to rely on more passive methods such as rest and taking medicine (McGrath, 1993). Studies have shown that even young children have already internalized these gender expectations related to pain (Robinson, Riley, & Myers, 2000). Look around at how parents react differently to pain reports of boys versus girls; the observations will be quite astonishing. How do you react to pain complaints by a male versus a female friend or family member? Does their gender influence your assessment of the severity of their pain and of the impact of the pain on their functioning?

The genderization of pain has made women more expressive of their pain symptoms than men. Our Western society, however, has little patience and tolerance for complaints. Rather than trying to understand the pain experience, women with chronic pain are written off and are said to be exaggerating their pain or dramatizing their pain. This is not a new concept. Many centuries BCE, the Egyptians and the Greeks already made an association between female pains and *hysteria,* which is Greek for "wandering womb." Still today, the assumption that women with pain are manifesting classical "hysteria" or conversion reactions is frequently used to "explain" unexplained pain in women. Moreover, women in pain are construed as evading responsibility, being psychologically weak, and unable to meet the cultural expectations of their gender (Feldman & Tegart, 2003; White, Lemkau, & Clasen, 2001). The women in my practice often speak of their frustration with the image of weakness and fragility that is being projected onto them. At times, they blame themselves for being weak, for giving into the pain, and for not being able to carry out a task.

A feminist interpretation of chronic pain may, of course, lead to another level of bias. While there is a valid concern that emphasis on psychological issues as contributing factors to chronic pain may lead to negative gender stereotyping, ignoring the role of psychological factors would be equally damaging. Instead of trying to find causal explanations for the presence of the pain, it is essential to be open-minded and explore a wide range of biomedical and psychosocial factors without stigmatizing women in the process (White et al, 2001).

"You look fine!"

A third stereotype that my clients are confronted with is the idea that people in pain should *look* like they are in pain. Several of my clients have told me that when they look healthy, it increases the risk of being dismissed or inappropriately treated. Although many women in severe pain may not have the energy to put on make-up, style their hair and dress up, others do make an extra effort to "look good." It makes them feel better about themselves and they hope it will enhance opportunities for social interactions. However, if a person looks healthy it is difficult to believe that she is sick or in pain. If we cannot see evidence of the disease or the pain, we are suspicious and reach the conclusion that the person is malingering. One client told me that she feels stuck in a vicious circle: *"The other day, I attended a neighborhood event and I tried to look nice. My neighbor, the one that drives me to places, told me I looked great. The next day she told me that she couldn't drive me to my doctor's appointment . . . she had already made other plans because she thought I would be fine driving myself after she saw me at the party. I don't know what I am supposed to do anymore! If I try to look nice, they think I don't need help. If I complain and walk around in my sweat pants, they tell me I need to be stronger. Whatever I do, it always backfires! I feel like I am always losing . . . ."*

"Fight the pain!"

Finally, I would like to point to the construction of pain as an enemy that needs to be driven out. Nobody wants to suffer from pain. When we experience pain, we try to "get rid" of the pain by taking medication, by changing our posture, by rubbing the painful site, by relaxation, or distraction. The media continuously broadcasts the message that pain can be "expelled" if only we take the right medication. In the event of chronic pain, the person experiencing the pain is often viewed as the only one who can truly combat the pain. However, for chronic pain patients, the awareness and acceptance of the fact that the pain is here to stay will often be more beneficial in reducing the suffering than trying to desperately escape from the pain.

Empowering the Muted Self

Although pain is the experience of the sufferer, the voice of the person is often lost. If patients complain of pain and fatigue for which physicians can find no pathophysiological cause or evidence, whose discourse is authoritative—that of the physician or the patient? In our Western society, we ascribe authority to those who have developed expertise through years of scientific and objective study. Personal experience and intuition appear second-hand. The never-ending power struggle with others gradually mutes the patient's voice. Continuous attempts to escape from the pain leaves behind a disconnected body. Finally, the separation of the self from the body results, in turn, in muted emotions.

Strengthening the Muted Voice

The marginalization and tabooing of illnesses and pain complaints that cannot be explained medically makes talking about the pain and discomfort a forbidden subject for most chronic pain sufferers (Werner et al, 2004). As stated before, the experiences of chronic pain sufferers are often trivialized by doctors as well as family and friends who doubt the reality of their pain. This disbelief of the medical community and the social environment discounts these patients' ability to "tell their story." And so, slowly but surely, the voice of the storyteller is silenced, especially when the storyteller is a woman.

As I listen to the stories of my clients during initial sessions, I am often struck by the quality of their voices. Although I sense an enormous inner strength, their voices sound weak and even distorted. I cannot help wondering whether they have internalized the voice that society has projected onto them, voices of weak "distorted" women. Their stories about their power struggles with not only the medical community, but also friends and family as well as institutions of authority (e.g. Social Security, Worker's Compensation) suggest that their voices have been muted by skepticism and mistrust. My clients are tired, exhausted and drained physically as well as emotionally.

Diane Austin (2001), in an article on the use of vocal holding techniques with adults traumatized as children, wrote: *"In essence, traumatized individuals survive by forfeiting their own voice."* Many of my women clients have indeed forfeited their own voices in order to survive the emotional turmoil caused by their chronic pain and society's insensitive reactions to their condition.

One day, Rosa, suffering from severe pelvic pain, entered a group session completely mute. She signed to me that she couldn't talk. As she had arrived late, the group had already started with a vocal improvisation. I was supporting the vocalizations with simple chord progressions on the piano. I asked Rosa if she wanted to join in with an instrument but she gestured that she wanted to be left alone. I respected her request, although I suspected that she came to the group because she did not want to be "alone." However, I was not sure if she wanted to be heard or if she was just looking for a comforting, supportive environment. After a couple of minutes, I asked her to focus on her breathing while we continued to vocalize. She sat up more straight and closed her eyes. As soon as she had taken a couple of deep breaths, she began to cry softly. Her soft cries soon developed in uncontrollable sobbing. The group stopped singing and began to offer verbal comfort. As the group was still new to music therapy, I could feel that they were unsure about how to offer support in this new medium. However, as Rosa could not talk (and therefore did not answer the questions posed by the group members), she gestured to please continue to play and sing. I suggested to the group to softly hum along or just listen to the music. I began to play in a lullaby style, softly vocalizing a melody above the accompaniment. I was hoping that the music could provide a holding environment to Rosa and comfort her in her sadness. We continued like this for a while. I slowly simplified the melody until I was vocalizing elongated tones. Some group members joined me softly. To their surprise, Rosa started to softly hum along. Her humming was alternated by soft crying. When I stopped playing, we sat in silence for several minutes. We were all deeply affected by the extreme sadness that had filled the room. I felt extremely heavy . . . as if somebody was pulling my body down to the ground. Was this how she was feeling? Rosa began to talk softly. Apparently, she had woken up with no voice at all that morning, without any signs of illness. She had tried to talk, but had been unable to produce a sound. I asked her how she has been feeling lately. She explained that she has been feeling very depressed during the past week. She told the group that she just can't continue to live like this, that she is so tired of fighting and struggling. On top of that, she had discovered that her boyfriend was drinking which had resulted in a big fight the evening before. We explored her feelings of powerlessness and I suggested that losing her voice was a physical manifestation of not wanting to fight any more and of longing for inner peace. As I continued to work with these women, it became very clear that many had given up their voice. Disconnecting from one's voice facilitates a detachment from one's emotions and one's inner self.

Besides the weakened voices, I was also struck by their intense need to tell their stories. Many of the initial sessions passed with little use of music. Instead, stories were told over and over again. At times, I became frustrated about the minimal use of music in the sessions. I felt that the part of me that would be best able to offer support and explore their struggles was not being given a chance. Were they resisting music out of fear for the emotional power of music? Or was it me who was avoiding the use of music out of fear that the music would not be able to contain their physical and emotional pain? Did I need to be more explicit about how music could help them? Did I need to structure the sessions more so that the clients knew what to expect in terms of musical engagement? The latter was suggested to me in a supervision session but, no matter what I did, each time the clients' need to tell their stories surfaced. One day, I told Lucy, a woman with severe upper extremity pain, that I was feeling frustrated about the lack of music in our sessions. I explained to her that I felt limited in what I could offer her if I could not use music. Lucy looked surprised. She told me that each week she was looking forward to our session. She felt that our music making had been helping her a great deal as it had enabled her to refocus on her body and to work with the pain, rather than fight the pain. Moreover, this was the only place where she felt comfortable telling her story without fear of judgment. After several months, music became a more important and equal partner in the sessions with Lucy. I realized that it had been my need for validation of my expertise in the use of music for pain management that had caused my impatience. Lucy's statements also led me to decide not to assess or evaluate my clients' pain with a formal pain assessment tool. I felt that asking them to rate their pain would portray a need in me to verify and even judge their pain. Instead, I ask my clients what they are experiencing in their bodies and what is happening with the pain. Rather than obtaining quantitative indicators of their pain, I ask them for detailed descriptions about their pain.

Before I started to work with women with chronic pain my work was mainly based on the use of instrumental improvisations. However, the apparent disconnect from their inner voices and body led me to the use of toning and vocal improvisations. I believe that strengthening their voices, giving them the experience of having their voices be heard, and enabling their voices to impact on the relationships that surrounded them would be beneficial.

Reconnecting to the Divorced Body

A woman with chronic pain will try anything to escape from her painful body. It is important, however, that a chronic pain sufferer forms a relationship with her pain, rather than runs away from it. Entering the pain and working *with* the pain is a more effective pain management approach than working against the pain. When people experience that they can actually interact with their pain, the power of the pain is greatly diminished. Instead of feeling invaded and victimized by the pain, they feel an increased level of control.

By engaging in the technique of toning, a client can begin to connect with the pain on a physical and emotional level. Toning is the singing of extended vowel sounds. Singing prolonged vowels produces vibrations that can be felt in our bodies with different vowels and different tones resonating with different areas. In Eastern meditation and healing practices, toning is used to access the different chakras. Try singing a high pitched ee-sound (as in "meet") for several seconds. Now sing a low oo-sound (as in "wood"). Most of you will have felt the ee-sound vibrating in the skull and the oo-sound in the area of the solar plexus. Continue to explore your body with different vowels. Now, try changing the frequency or pitch of the sound. Did you feel the vibrations moving up and down with higher and lower frequencies? A high-pitched ee-sound will be felt in the middle to the top of the skull whereas a lower ee-sound will be felt at the base of the skull or even the throat. By manipulating the vowel and the frequency you can direct the vibrations to specific places in the body.

I usually start by asking a client to sing different vowels with me in unison. After each vowel, we discuss where the vibrations were felt in the body. Once we have identified the vowel that targets the painful part of the body, I encourage the client to slide her voice up and down until a pitch is found that resonates most intensely with the pain. At first, clients are apprehensive about using their voices freely. Therefore, I initially give step-by-step instructions for the vocal bodily journey until the client becomes more comfortable taking charge. After exploring different vowels and frequencies, I also encourage the client to experiment with volume. Ideally, the vibrations should be strong enough to be able to embrace the pain rather than just approaching it. However, when the sound is too loud, the client may not be able to tolerate the strong resonance with the pain.

Once the client has been able to reach the pain vocally, I may engage the client in two different toning interventions. First, the client enters the pain area with a specific vowel and then imagines smoothing out the pain with sustained vowels. I sometimes use the image of the pain being a crunched up piece of paper or fabric and the sound being the hands or iron that can smooth it out. Usually, the muscles in the painful part of the body are very tense, exacerbating the pain. The "smoothing out" practice helps clients to relax the muscles. Moreover, the vibrations produced by the toning feel like an inner body massage. Second, the client can "grab" the pain with a sound and, with a forceful "slide," move it to a different part of the body. For example, in case of a headache, one can use a high-pitched ee-sound to grab the pain and then let the sound slide down to a much lower pitch and a rounder vowel, bringing the pain to a lower part of the body. In my experience, I have noticed that some people like to bring their headaches to their solar plexus area. Last week, Lucy wanted to move her pain from her shoulders up to the base of her skull. I suggested that she used the oo-sound to grab the pain and change to an a-vowel with a wide open mouth to let the tension exit the body through her mouth. Being able to move the pain is a powerful experience when the pain has been "stuck" for months and even years.

Finally, toning promotes deep breathing. Deep breathing slows down our physiological responses, inducing a state of relaxation. Reduction of stress is a significant need of my clients. Their stress is caused by their pain, social demands, job loss, loss of friends, and academic demands. Many of these issues will, of course, not be resolved by stress reduction techniques. However, it is of crucial importance to their emotional survival and their physical comfort to find temporary stress relief. Toning is a technique that can be easily taught and that the client can take with her anywhere, any time. After a toning experience, one of my clients shared: *"I felt so at peace. . . . I really was in the music. I felt that I could just be and that nobody was questioning the existence of my pain . . . nobody was judging me. . . . I was allowed to just be me."* Just allowing her *to be* became a major theme in the sessions.

Reviving the Muted Emotions

We control the awareness and expression of our feelings partly by our breath. When trying to repress our emotions we physically close off our throat. Take notice of your body when you are trying to hold back your tears. Where can you feel the most tension? Many of you will feel pain in your throat. In addition, you may start breathing more shallowly. A shallow breath indeed helps to keep the emotion repressed in the body. Notice what happens to your breathing when you are trying to hold back sudden anger at somebody. We even hold our breath when we get shocked, scared, or excited. While we are instinctively and unconsciously accustomed to modulating our emotions through changing our breathing patterns, we can become more adept at emotional self-regulation through manipulating the breath consciously. Singing facilitates deep breathing and helps release blockages of energy (Austin, 2001).

Toning and breathing exercises will often open the *emotional gateway*. Therefore, toning should never be used without appropriate training. Intense emotions that have been stored away for a long time may be brought into existence rather abruptly. Many of my clients have intense anger towards the person who they believe is at the cause of their pain (e.g. surgeon, drunk driver, employer, etc.). The magnitude of their anger makes it unacceptable for expression. They tell their story, they cry, they try to understand but seldom do they get a chance to truly express the anger to its fullest extent. In music therapy, intense feelings can be expressed without fear of judgment for their "ugliness." We are all born with primal instincts to scream when we are angry, to scream when we experience pain and to hold our breath when we get very scared. Most of my clients are extremely angry, are in extreme pain and are extremely scared. For many of us from Western cultures, societal norms do not allow us to scream out our anger and pain, but encourage us to be stoic, reasonable, and quiet. Toning and vocal improvisations often allow that primal scream to be born into a world where it can be *held* and nurtured. The feelings, no matter how intense, are given permission to exist. Only then can we truly begin to process them.

Creating a New Self

Often, people with chronic pain are catapulted from a period in life characterized by strength, well-being, and independence to a period of immobility, dependence, and chaos. Their pain condition changes their role in the world from *doing* to just *being*. The inability to function in those areas that previously had given their lives meaning and purpose results in a dramatic loss in self-esteem and identity.

> With a "traditional illness," the self adopts a transitional identity as a person whose body is temporarily not functioning well—this places

> the person in a medically legitimated place. However, the lack of a clear and accepted diagnosis [often the case in chronic pain], leaves the self without the legitimating discourse from the powerful medical profession. In addition, because of loss of jobs and friends, these women also lack the legitimacy offered by a place in the economic and social structural orders. In absence of legitimate discourses from the medical, social and labor force structures, individuals create alternative selves. (Clarke & James, 2003)

Many of my clients are desperately hanging on to the past. Mary, for example, used to mountain climb and run. Because of a medical error, she is left with severe neuropathic pain. Still, she hopes that she will get better and will be able to do the things she used to do. Of course, Mary needs hope to be able to cope with the hardship of her condition. However, it is very likely that Mary will suffer from pain for a very long time, if not the rest of her life. Holding on to past roles and abilities will not help Mary to move forward. In adapting to her chronic pain condition, Mary must face the reality that she can no longer count on being who she once was or who she imagined herself to be. The losses of both bodily integrity and a secure and predictable future are inevitably accompanied by frustration, anger, and grief. The continuous confrontation with her limitations has rendered Mary depressed, helpless, and scared:

> *"I used to like myself. . . . I was pretty, I was in good shape. . . . I used to be very active and I liked to have fun. How can I like myself now? I have gained so much weight. I can't do a thing without getting exhausted. I don't have energy and I certainly don't have any fun. How can I keep on living like this?"*

In addition to the loss of identity, people with chronic pain often become isolated. Friends and family members have grown tired of the complaints and may feel that they have done enough for them. Rather than receiving more support in this difficult time, many of my clients find themselves alone. This only adds to their identity crisis.

Finally, the senselessness of the suffering in chronic pain offers a fundamental threat to meaning and to identity, creating the urge and desire for meaning to be found (Jackson, 1992). The construction of pain as a sign of physical damage is often the dominant mindset of people with chronic pain. Most people *want* the pain to be explained as symptomatic so that it has a utility above suffering. Once the cause is found, meaning can be ascribed and hope can be restored. However, "once the pain becomes chronic and medical tests do not provide evidence for a 'cause,' the patient becomes 'the lost cause'" (Eccleston, et al, 1997, p.700).

Before meaning can be found and a new self can be created, it is important that the client is given the opportunity to mourn the losses she has suffered and continues to suffer. The use of vocal holding techniques, developed by Austin, has been effective in allowing my clients to express feelings of deep sadness, anger, and despair. The predictability of two or three alternating chords provides the client with a safe and caring environment to explore those feelings. During the vocal holding, the client is encouraged to stay with her feelings and to allow them to develop.

As blocked energy is released, the process of creating new beginnings can begin. Through the creation of music, the client can begin to discover new parts of herself, including her inner strength and her motivation to live. Austin (2001) writes that

> [The] act of singing is empowering: sensing the life force flowing through the body: feeling one's strength in the ability to produce strong and prolonged tones, experiencing one's creativity in the process of making something beautiful; having the ability to move oneself and others; and hearing one's voice mirroring back the undeniable confirmation of existence. Owning one's voice is owning one's authority and ending a cycle of victimization. (p.24)

Although she wrote this in regard to her work with traumatized clients, it is very relevant for women suffering from chronic pain.

For most of the women I have been working with, the process of creating a new self is only beginning as I am writing this. It will not be an easy process as the theme of loss and limitations accompanies them like a musical ostinato on their journey. New beginnings are often fragile and may not always be able to withstand new losses, confrontations, and limitations. But the music remains hopeful and has the power to nurture their inner strength and empower their voices. In music therapy, their being is not judged or questioned; they are accepted as women in pain whose voices need to be heard.

REFERENCES

Austin, Diane (2001) In search of the self: The use of vocal holding techniques with adults traumatized as children. *Music Therapy Perspectives, 19*, 22–30.

Bradt, Joke (2001) *The effects of music entrainment on postoperative pain perception in pediatric patients*. Unpublished Dissertation, Temple University, Philadelphia.

Brena, Stanley F. & Chapman, Stephen L. (1984) Chronic pain states and compensatible disability: An algorithmic approach. In Constantino Benedetti, C. Richard Chapman, & Guido Moricca (eds.) *Advances in Pain Research and Therapy: Recent Advances in the Management of Pain, vol. 17,* 131–145. New York: Raven Press.

Calderone, Karen L. (1990) The influence of gender on the frequency of pain and sedative medication administered to postoperative patients. *Sex Roles, 23*, 713–725.

Chapman, C. Richard (1995). The affective dimension of pain: A model. In Burkhart Bromm & John E. Desmedt (eds.) *Advances in Pain Research and Therapy: Pain and the Brain: From Nociception to Cognition, vol. 22,* 283–301. New York: Raven Press.

Clarke, Juanne N. & James, Susan (2003) The radicalized self: The impact on the self of the contested nature of the diagnosis of chronic fatigue syndrome. *Social Science & Medicine, 57*, 1387–1395.

Colameco, Stephen, Becker, Lorne A., & Simpson, Michael (1983) Sex bias in assessment of patient complaints. *Journal of Family Practice, 16,* 1117–1121.

Eccleston, Chris, Williams, Amanda, & Stainton Rogers, Wendy (1997) Patients' and professionals' understanding of the causes of chronic pain: Blame, responsibility and identity protection. *Social Science & Medicine, 45,* 699–709.

Feldman, Scott & Tegart, Georgina (2003) Keep moving: Conceptions of illness and disability of middle-aged African-American women with arthritis. *Women & Therapy, 26*, 127–143.

Jackson, Jean E. (1992) "After a while no one believes you": Real and unreal pain. In Mary Jo Delvecchio Good, Paul E. Brodwin, Byron J. Good and Arthur Kleinman (eds.), *Pain as Human Experience: An Anthropological Perspective,* 138–168. Berkeley: University of California Press.

Jimenez, Sherry (1996) Pain & comfort: Establishing a common vocabulary for exploring issues of pain and comfort. *Journal of Perinatal Education, 5,* 53–57.

Johansson, Eva E., Hamberg, Katarina, Westman, Goran, & Lindgren, Gerd (1999) The meanings of pain: An exploration of women's descriptions of symptoms. *Social Science & Medicine, 48,* 1791–1802.

Kendall-Tackett, Kathleen, Marshall, Roberta, & Ness, Kenneth (2003) Chronic pain syndromes and violence against women. *Women & Therapy, 26*, 45–56.

Kupers, Ron (1997) Sex differences in pain: And now for something completely different [commentary]. *Behavioral and Brain Sciences, 20*, 455–456.

McCaffery, Margo (1968). *Nursing Practice Theories Related to Cognition, Bodily Pain, and Man-Environment Interactions*. Los Angeles: University of California at Los Angeles Students' Store.

McGrath, Patrick A. (1993) Psychological aspects of pain perception. In Neil L. Schechter, Charles B. Berder & Myron Yaster (eds.) *Pain in Infants, Children, and Adolescents*. Baltimore, MD: Williams & Wilkins.

Robinson, Michael E., Reily, Joseph L. III, & Meyers, Cynthia (2000) Psychosocial contributions to sex-related differences in pain responses. In Roger B. Fillinghim (ed.), *Sex, Gender, and Pain. Progress in Pain Research and Management, 17,* 41–68. Seattle, WA: International Association for the Study of Pain.

Werner, Anne, Widding Isaksen, Lise, & Materud, Kirsti (2004) "I am not the kind of woman who complains of everything": Illness stories on self and shame in women with chronic pain. *Social Science & Medicine, 59*, 1035–1045.

White, Mary Terrel, Lemkau, Jeanne Parr, & Clasen, Mark (2001) Fibromyalgia: A feminist biopsychosocial perspective. In Ellyn Kascak (ed.) *Minding the Body: Psychotherapy in Cases of Chronic and Life-Threatening Illness,* 45–58. New York: The Haworth Press.

PART THREE

PART THREE

INTERLUDE III

The four chapters included in this section critically reflect on significant aspects of music therapy: discourse, music, music therapy techniques/approaches, and issues of representation. Randi Rolvsjord, in chapter thirteen, examines the use and functions of the language we use in music therapy—how we talk and write about music, clients, pathology, the therapeutic relationship, gender, or relationships. She believes that the way we use discourse in music therapy has political implications. Her work is inspired by postmodernist and poststructuralist feminist traditions, specifically the French feminist tradition, which focuses on language and power-relations in language. Using a destabilizing discourse analysis, she discusses the use of "mother" concepts in music therapy literature and how these contribute to the conservation of traditional expectations of gender roles.

In chapter fourteen, Laurie Jones examines song selection for women's empowerment in music therapy. She suggests that it is crucial that we not only consider client preference, and the relevance of lyric content to client issues and treatment needs, but that we consider the significant impact of the larger environment/society on the welfare of our clients. She suggests that it is our responsibility as music therapists to become aware of the sexist subtext found in much of the popular music we use in music therapy sessions—both the overt and covert messages which contribute to the ways clients view themselves and/or their attitudes about and behaviors toward women. She provides the process by which she analyzes the music and lyric content of songs for use in therapy, and provides several examples of songs that can empower women.

In chapter fifteen, Elaine Streeter explores the idea that the rise of capitalism has lead to competitiveness which ultimately has lead to the branding of various marketable products, including music therapy. She notes that we have now defined many separate approaches to music therapy, within which we separate out and name distinct techniques. This branding allows groups of practitioners access to a specific theoretical and therapeutic marketplace and allows students to shop around for a brand they like before starting a training course. However, it can also lead to protection of the brand and may lead to a fundamentalism arising from the branding.

Finally, in chapter sixteen, Jane Edwards explores ways we can improve as music therapists in terms of issues of representation. She proposes that we can do this through greater acknowledgement of the achievements of women music therapists, by examining our discourse of health and illness and how this discourse is formed and framed by patriarchy, through our understandings of gender and sexuality, and by examining the ways women are represented in music. She also stresses how critical it is to hear the voices of, and advocate for, our clients.

Chapter Thirteen

GENDER POLITICS IN MUSIC THERAPY DISCOURSE

Randi Rolvsjord

INTRODUCTION

As this book clearly demonstrates, feminism is not one unified political movement or a unified approach to research. It is a label used to describe a multiplicity of approaches, perspectives, and theoretical traditions. However, some common themes or family resemblances might be identified such as 1) the high valuing of women, positing women as worthy of study in their own right, and 2) the recognition of the need for social change which must be understood as having a political agenda related to gaining equal rights for women and men, and defeating oppressions and inequalities. These two themes, it could be argued, are common to most feminist theory and research (Wilkinson, 1997). But these two themes, along with the postmodernist and constructivist third wave of feminism, which focuses upon language and discourse, might also be related to a historical progression, or used to identify different theoretical stands (Baxter, 2003).

In this chapter, I will focus on music therapy discourse, the way we talk and write about music therapy, inspired by postmodernist and poststructuralist feminist traditions. The focus upon language and discourse, and the power-relations intrinsic in language and discourse, are central in a postmodernist feminist tradition. My aim is to ask critical questions about the gender politics in music therapy discourse. To study discourse means putting a strong focus upon the uses and functions of language, which is integral to postmodernist perspectives and poststructuralism. My own introduction and source of inspiration to this tradition comes from the French feminist tradition, specifically Julia Kristeva, who does not call herself feminist, but whose work has become very significant in feminist approaches (Rolvsjord, 2004).

A feminist critique of music therapy research, theory, and practice has been virtually absent from the discourse of music therapy to date. In a way, this is surprising due to the large number of female music therapists (Hadley &

Edwards, 2004), but it is perhaps also understandable for a small and young discipline in development. But as meta-perspectives and critical reflexivity evolve in music therapy, feminist critique should inform such critical reflexivity and meta-perspectives. This chapter represents my effort toward a feminine beginning of a feminist meta-perspective in music therapy discourse.

Political aspects of music therapy have been discussed previously by Even Ruud (1996), who claims that music therapy has contributed to important changes in Norwegian cultural politics. In addition, the elaborations of community music therapy practice and theory (Ansdell, 2002; Stige, 2003; Pavlicevic & Ansdell, 2004) raise questions about the role of music therapy vis-à-vis change in communities. Furthermore, issues of gender politics have been discussed by Sandra Curtis (1996), Dag Körlin and Björn Wrangsjö (2001), Anthony Meadows (2002), and Susan Hadley and Jane Edwards (2004).

The basic assumption underlying the argument in this chapter is that music therapy discourse is an arena for politics. How we talk and write about music, how we talk and write about clients, pathology, gender, or relationships has political implications. Music therapy is not an arena assured of political neutrality (Rolvsjord, 2004b), not even from gender politics. I will start with an all-too-brief introduction to the postmodernist and poststructuralist feminist tradition, emphasizing particularly the focus upon language and of power-relations in language. Then I will turn to the discourse of music therapy and, inspired by the methodology of destabilizing discourse analyses, I will specifically discuss the use of "mother" concepts in music therapy literature.

GENDER POLITICS IN DISCOURSE

One of the key themes in postmodernism is the centrality of discourse (Alvesson, 2002). The postmodernist philosophical stand gives primacy to discourse in terms of its constitutional power to structure not only the experience of the world, but also the person's social identity and subjectivity. The specific locus of interest in poststructuralism, which could be understood as a branch of postmodernism (Baxter, 2003), is in language as an arena for the construction of social meaning. Languages and discourses are understood as systems that provide particular unities, divisions, and distinctions. It is through this system of distinctions that discourse has a constitutional effect (Alvesson, 2002). This comprises a strong critique of materialistic (Marxist) or essentialist under-standing that emphasizes the biological differences between men and women (Henessy, 1993).

Discourse is a concept used in a variety of ways. It can refer to language in use. However, as I have already pointed to the centrality of discourse, the use of the term in this context must also imply elements of a context and of constructive power. Discourse is often used, according to Michel Foucault, to denote "practices that systematically form the object of which they speak" (Baxter, 2003, p.7). A discourse then is more than a corpus of texts, it is a use of language and practices that not only represent, but also form, reality. Thus, there is a strong constructivist implication in this definition, which implies an understanding of reality not as an unmediated given, but as a process of constructions and co-constructions. The notion of co-constructions impels us not to neglect the material world totally. Such a neglect of the material world would be, as Mats Alvesson puts it, an "'essentialistic position' against essentialism" (Alvesson, 2002, p.51). This would be a contradiction to the postmodern project which emphasizes the fragmented identities and multiplicity of identities. The notion of co-constructions must be related to the discursive context and to intertextuality. It is important to note that the constitutive power of discourse, the constructive force so to speak, lies in the way different texts are related and interact, the transpositions or intertextuality (Kristeva, 1984; Fornäs, 1995) of discourses. The constitutive, and thereby political, power is indeed not a possession in somebody's hand, but rather a net-like organisation (Baxter, 2003).

In poststructuralist and postmodern feminism this net-like organization of political power has led into a discussion of power relations and constitutions of positionality of gender, and especially of the feminine, in language. According to Foucault, power resides in the discursive formation itself, and is related to the power to define others (Alvesson, 2002; Foucault, 2001). The understanding of discourse as a political arena is connected to the power of defining people and values through distinctions and divisions in language. The constitutive element in language is seen as binary oppositions (Kristeva, 1984; Irigaray, 1985) and this inevitably implies the possibilities for dominant discourses to privilege one pole of opposites over the other—objectivity over subjectivity in scientific discourse or masculinity over femininity in patriarchal discourse (Baxter, 2003; Pringle & Watson, 1992), for example. The constitution of language based upon binary oppositions is said to conserve traditional (patriarchal) power structures, due to the highlighting and construction of differences and oppositions between the female and male sex (Kristeva, 1984; Moi, 1986; Alvesson, 2003). Thus, in poststructuralist feminist research, the very basis of an oppositional relationship in language is questioned, to a degree that calls into question our basic understanding of a division between men and women, outlining the diversity and multiplicity of gender identities (Gatens, 1992; Wilkinson, 1997; Baxter, 2003; Alvesson, 2002).

Thus, the focus is moved from the discussion of sexual differences and similarities, to the cultural expressions of gender. The basic idea is to call into question the binary oppositions that seem to form the basis of our language and cultural thinking in western societies, and even question the notion of difference itself, arguing that it is possible to be both different and alike (Barret & Phillips, 1992). This perspective then represents a critique of feminist as well as patriarchal research that emphasizes or takes gender differences for granted. Although some biological differences between men and women are acknowledged, the use of "men" and "women" as research categories in social science, as well as in music therapy research (although not yet explicitly criticised), is questioned—which means that the "woman-man" distinction as a grand narrative in research is challenged (Gatens, 1992; Alvesson, 2002; Haavind, 1998). Instead, local, fragmented, and multiple identities are emphasized and researched. For this reason, it has been argued that postmodernist thinking is contradictory to feminism, which advocates for social and political change (Baxter, 2002; Barret & Phillips, 1992). However, *destabilizing theory* is a concept that describes feminist aspirations from feminist postmodern and poststructuralist works from the 1990s, and it points to the political dimensions of feminist ideas. When the binary oppositions of our language are revealed and questioned, this threatens the assumptions that are taken for granted in a culture and that contribute to processes of change (Pringle & Watson, 1992; Kristeva, 1984).

How can Gender Politics Possibly be Part of Music Therapy Discourse?

Let me now turn to the discourse of music therapy, and I admit to the reader at this point that I suspect that we tend to think about music therapy as politically neutral. Moreover, we are probably more likely to think about gender politics in relation to music therapy in terms of salary for our female-dominated profession or in terms of the femalization of music therapy just like other professions concerned with "care," than to think about gender politics related to music therapy discourse. I must also stress that I do not think that the discourse of music therapy is generally a patriarchal discourse. There is probably no need for revolution, but for more feminist, as well as political, reflexivity in general.

The discourse of music therapy involves not only the music therapy literature but also the stories and images about music therapy, the way we talk about music and music therapy to colleagues, clients, and others. This discourse not only reflects a practice, but music therapy discourse may even constitute music therapy (Ansdell, 2003). Furthermore, music therapy discourse is influenced by other academic, political and cultural discourses. The need for meta-reflections and cultural awareness is obvious even if our own stories are true. This must also include, as Gary Ansdell (2003) reminds us, reflexivity in terms of a larger body of academic and political discourses. It is primarily in such an intertextual relationship and interaction within a historical and cultural context that music therapy is part of the co-constructions of our reality and thus our political power.

Judith Baxter (2003) defines feminist poststructuralist discourse analysis as "an approach to analysing the ways in which speakers negotiate their identities, relationship and position in their world according to the ways in which they are located by competing and intervowen discourses" (Baxter, 2003, p.1). The following discussion is inspired from a methodology based on poststructuralist ideas of destabilizing theories, the destabilization analysis of discourses (Søndergaard, 2000), and the unpacking of dominant categories and notions (Alvesson, 2002). In this analysis of discourses, the task is to reveal ideas that are taken for granted in the culture and then question their value. The process of such an analysis is to identify the processes that constitute the categories, in our case the constitution of gendered categories, that is, the characteristics that we attribute to humans who are gendered male or female. Dorte Marie Søndergaard (2000) uses the concept "storyline" as a more concrete expression of the cultural narratives or assumptions that are taken for granted.

Texts and practices, or discourses, can be regarded as stabilizing or destabilizing in relation to such storylines. Any text or practice that is in coherence with such a storyline will stabilize or conserve the idea, whereas any text or practice that is contradictory to or questions the storyline will contribute to destabilization and change. The clinical practices and theoretical perspectives of music therapy are constantly in interaction with our culture. As part of the culture, music therapy practice, research, and theory, can either be regarded as conserving cultural values or reforming or even revolutionizing the cultural values of a society. This cultural influence will also include gender issues.

Music therapy practices and texts about music therapy can either be conserving in terms of stabilizing existing "storylines" of gender or gender stereotypes, or they can destabilize and reform such storylines. Gender politics in music therapy discourse might occur at different levels of the discourse. It might be connected to the practice of music therapy in general, to the therapeutic process and the communication between therapist and client, in presentations and literature, theory, or in research methodology. I will give a few examples of how music therapy discourse might be an arena for gender politics. These are potential areas for feminist critique, defined only through the connections to feminist critique upon other disciplines. I will briefly outline four different domains:

1. *Choice and use of musical instruments, musical genres and musical roles*

It is pointed out by several researchers in musicology that rock music as well as the use of electric instruments has been dominated by male musicians, and that female musicians' practice in this genre is often devalued. Instead, women's roles are conservatively understood as pop singers, pin-ups, groupies, or sex objects (Bayton, 1997; Cohen, 1997; Coates, 1997). To what degree is music therapy discourse conserving traditional gender roles and distinctions related to use of musical instruments, musical genres, and roles in musical performances?

2. *In clinical practice and literature connected to sexual oppression, sexual violence, and trauma*

The traditional medical and psychological focus upon psychopathology as problems residing in the individual is questioned by feminists. Such individualisation of problems and pathology sweeps important political issues concerning oppression and sexual violence under the carpet (Ballou & Brown, 2002; Worell & Remer, 1996/2003; Goldstein 1997; Jordan, 1997). To what degrees are the discourse(s) in music therapy conserving political and social systems that revictimize survivors of sexual oppression and sexual violence?

3. *Research methodology and actual research*

Postmodern feminism questions the very notion of "woman" and "man" and emphasizes the multiplicity and fragmentation of gender identities rather than differentiations. A strong critique is waged against the enormous amount of research designed to reveal differences between "women" and "men," and the use of such studies to generalize about gender (Haavind, 2000; Alvesson, 2002). In much of music therapy research we find the grand narratives "man" and "woman" as unquestioned categories, even if the biological sex of the informants seems unimportant according to the issue of the research. To what degree is music therapy research concerned with generalisations about gender, or to what degree is music therapy research open in terms of the multiplicity of gender?

4. *Use of gendered conceptualisations and metaphors*

The use of gendered conceptualisations in descriptions of music is pointed out by Susan McClary (1991), who claims that music is not politically neutral, but even constitutive of gender politics. In her thought-provoking and controversial book *Feminine Endings* (1991), she discusses how music has been described and analysed in gendered terms, built upon binary oppositions. The masculine is connected to the strong, the aggressive, the dominant, whereas the feminine is attributed to the more lyrical, gentle, romantic, weak. One example that she cites is the schema of the sonata–allegro movement that is the traditional opening movement in the classical symphony. According to this schema, the second, weak, feminine theme will conform and adapt to the first, strong, and masculine theme during the exposition part of the movement. According to McClary, we tend to attribute gendered meanings to music in a way that conserve traditional gender stereotypes based upon the binary oppositions in language. The problem is the use of categories that automatically lead to the making of essential connections between the body, specific processes of social construction, and a set of characteristics (Alvesson, 2002). To what degree are gendered metaphors used in music therapy discourse(s)? And to what degree are such gendered metaphors consistent with a reconstitution of the binary oppositions between "man" and "woman," between "female" and "masculine" traits?

A DESTABILIZING ANALYSIS OF "MOTHER" CONCEPTS IN MUSIC THERAPY DISCOURSE

In the second part of this chapter, I will discuss how feminine and masculine gender categories are represented in music therapy discourses through the use of the "mother" concept. This gendered metaphor is widely used in music therapy discourse, but here I will only put forward a few examples from the literature. My critique of the "mother" concept in music therapy is aimed at the use of the concept in situations that are not related to actual situations including primary caretakers of the female biological sex. As I have already emphasized that the political power of discourse must be related to intertextuality and context and history, it is important that we look at how Mothering and Motherhood are understood in a wider cultural and historical context.

The Mother—In Western History and Culture

Marriage and motherhood have, throughout modern western history, been social contracts in which the woman's desires and wants did not figure at all. Marriage has been a regulation of man's desires and a consolidation of the family's economic situation and wealth. In much of the philosophical literature, gender is described in terms of polarities. For example, Jean Jacques Rousseau, describing Emile and Julie and their living together, describes Emile as the active, independent, educated, social person, and Julie as the passive, dependent, unknowing and withdrawn person. Emile goes to work; Julie takes care of the children, making a home base for her husband and their children. The polarities are even clearer in the description of their sexual life: They contribute to the same goal, but he is active and strong and she just adds a bit of resistance. According to Rousseau, masculine love is Eros, which is connected to the desire for the other, but female love is Agape, the servile and self-sacrificing love (Forna, 1998; Viestad, 1989). Julie's task is to create a nurturing atmosphere for her husband and her children.

This type of depiction is also evident in literature and films, and in other media presentations where mothers who sacrifice (sometimes even their own lives) for their children are seen as "good" mothers, whereas those who are selfish, meaning the mothers who do not sacrifice their lives or careers, are "bad" mothers. This is just another version of the story of the Whore and the Madonna. Good mothers stay home and sacrifice their work and their own private interests. Good mothers keep the house clean and make healthy food. Good mothers remember all the birthdays and organize the day for the whole family. Susan Walzer (1998) argues that women experience expectations toward motherhood as a pressure that makes them feel guilty. It seems that culturally, in western societies, mothers are thought of as having nesting instincts, whereas fathers are thought of as having breadwinner instincts (Fornäs 1998, Walzer, 1998; Henessy, 1993).

The "Holding Mother"

In recent music therapy literature, the *mother-infant dyad* has been widely used to describe qualities in the musical interplay between music therapist and client. Research on early communication and inborn capacities for communication have influenced our clinical thinking, as well as our concepts of music and musical communication. The research of Colwyn Trevarthen, Ellen Dissanayake, Steven Malloch, Daniel Stern, and Metchild Papousek, among others, has, in this way, contributed to music therapy theory and our understanding of the musical interplay, supplying useful and nuanced concepts (Rolvsjord, 2002).

Furthermore, the *mother* concept has been used by several music therapists during the last decade to describe the holding, supporting, and nurturing qualities of music therapists, and the holding, nurturing, and supporting qualities of music. Some of these draw on Donald W. Winnicott's theories on early development and his concept of the "good enough mother" (Summer, 1995; Wärja, 1999). Similarly, in Carolyn Kenny's book *The Field of Play* (1989), the musical space is said to be similar to the space created between mother and child. She identifies this space as a "home base," a safe as well as a sacred space. Further, this "home base" is identified as a contained space, private and intimate:

> *The musical space is a contained space. It is an intimate and private field created in the relationship between the therapist and client. It is a sacred space, which becomes identified as "home base," a territory which is well known and secure. In early childhood development, it is similar to the space created between mother and child.* (Kenny, 1989 p.79)

A somewhat different perspective is explored by Kenneth Bruscia (1995). In his article "Modes of consciousness in GIM," he discusses the therapist's modes of consciousness and the therapist's ways of "being there" with the client. Bruscia is taking a gender-oriented approach, discussing how archetypal differences between female and male represent tendencies to "be there" for the client in different ways. He emphasizes that these female and male ways of "being there" are not solely connected to biological sex. But nevertheless, the qualities connected to the female are that of the container, to be holding and creating a nest, whereas, the male therapist is more likely to be a penetrator. Again, the female qualities are connected to reproduction, body, and more implicitly to mothering:

> *It occurred to me that if there are archetypal differences between female and male with regard to space, and if these differences center around tendencies to be container versus contained, and penetrator versus penetrated, then the idea of moving into and out of different worlds may make quite different demands on male and female therapists.* (Bruscia, 1995, p.194)

These holding, nurturing, supporting, and containing qualities are pointed to as significant aspects of the therapist's role and the music's role in the music therapeutic process by these authors. And I agree! Holding, supporting, and nurturing as well as containing are important aspects of the therapist's role, as they are for the mother. However, I do not think that describing these as "mother" qualities is useful. The mother in western culture is traditionally a self-sacrificing figure with no desire, which makes her unable to create a relationship based on equality and mutuality. When focusing on the holding, supporting, and nurturing abilities as "mother" qualities, or when relating these to the female gender in general, we tend to conserve the traditional mother and woman, ignoring the universal aspects of these abilities (that is, as they apply to men as well), and making indistinct other qualities of the female gender. First, the "holding mother" concept contributes to the conservation of traditional expectations of gender roles. Second, the mother qualities in these examples are explicitly connected to the "home base," which is another strong connection to the traditional mother and woman based in the domestic sphere.

The Holding, Nesting, and Nurturing Mother Represents a Re-establishment of Gender Stereotypes

Mother, described as holding, providing a home base, nurturing, and containing, is consistent with a woman's role in life as defined in terms of reproduction: giving birth and raising children. And let me emphasize, these are important things to do, they are good and wonderful—I have four children. But why are these qualities and characteristics predominantly connected to the female sex? The question of sexual difference is, of course, in this discussion, most interesting in terms of motherhood. Motherhood is often related to nature, the "mother" concept is even used to express nature itself. However, although reproduction is a biological phenomenon, we must also admit that motherhood is a construction and that it is the result of cultural shaping and technologies. Adoption, surrogacy, lesbian mothers, and "test-tube-mothers" are the concrete evidence of such cultural and technological aspects of motherhood (Ragonè & Twine, 2000). In spite of such technologies, the significant "mother" is difficult to escape regarding pregnancy, childbirth, and breastfeeding, but nature does not tell us to divide primary caregivers into "mothers" and "fathers" (Alvesson, 2002).

Although what is often called "the traditional family," one in which the mother is the primary caregiver and housewife, and the father earns the money, is not the only model of family structure, it is still influential on how new mothers and fathers transition into parenthood (Walzer, 1998). In Daniel Stern's (1995) book *Motherhood Constellation,* he stresses the importance of the parenting models that we have experienced as educative to our own practice as mothers and fathers. He claims that parents need support from other parents from the same sex, usually their own mothers and fathers. In this way, he argues, patterns of mothering and fathering are socially inherited. Stern's argument is similar to that of Nancy Chodorow (1978) who argues that parenting styles are created through children's identification with their own parents. Perhaps having a more feminist agenda, she claims that boys who have experienced a father who does not play an important part in caretaking, will devalue caretaking behaviour because this is associated with femaleness.

Furthermore, it seems that in "equal families," families where the mother and father share the responsibility and the daily care for the children, fathers communicate with their children in the same ways as mothers. In Daniel Stern's and Nadia Bruschwiler-Stern's more popular book *The Birth of a Mother* (1998), the authors state that in traditional families the father, when he comes home in the evening, will interact with the baby more playfully and less sensitively than the mother. He will throw the baby in the air and show less sensibility towards the regulation of the baby. It is likely that the mother will tell him to slow down so that the baby will go to sleep in the evening. But this difference is not gender-linked or innate, say the authors, because when the father stays at home with the children, and the mother comes home late after work, she is the one that will be more playful and less sensitive.

Colwyn Trevarthen (1997) makes a similar point in his article entitled "What infants' imitations communicate with mothers, with fathers and with peers." In this article, he reviews a great deal of research on how fathers communicate with their children. He emphasizes that in traditional families, the infants seem to imitate and tune into their mothers more than their fathers. On the contrary, in studies where fathers are primary caregivers, it was found that the infants equally imitated and tuned into their mothers and fathers. This indicates that familiarity more than biological sex is a significant factor.

There are many institutions in society that conserve or stabilize the traditional mother role. Let me just give a few examples. First, I find it difficult not to mention the toy stores and the toy commercials directed toward parents and children. Toys intended for girls are toys that emphasize being beautiful (and let me add: for whom?) and toys that emphasize domestic life and tasks, such as ironing, making food, and dolls. Even the Danish trademark Lego has a special series for boys and one for girls—for girls, with houses, dolls, and horses, and for boys, with fishing, firemen, police, spacemen, etc. Second, I would like to mention the large number of popular books about pregnancy and childcare. I read one written by Sheila Kitszinger (1992). In that book, it is suggested that the pregnant wife should arrange for a friend to help her husband shop for the groceries if this domestic task is too heavy for her to carry out late in the pregnancy! Such conserving of traditional patterns of mothering and fathering are still keeping mothers from their careers and are keeping fathers from more contact with their children. It is also providing mothers with what Walzer (1998) calls *mental mother labour and guilt*. This mental mother labour and guilt involves an expectation of her having primary responsibility for the children as well as for the domestic work. Walzer argues that there is both a relational and an institutional context for gendered transitions into parenthood. Institutional reinforcement exists, related to the labour market, birth and childhood education during pregnancy and early childhood, in media, film, and literature.

The images of motherhood that I have explored here can be understood as *storylines*, more or less conscious images that seem to be conserved or even constantly constitute our understanding of and interaction as mothers and fathers, and our relationship as parents. The music therapy discourse that continually describes these holding and nurturing and nest-building motherly therapists, or motherly music, will stabilize such storylines about parents' engendered roles and sexual differences. Some authors in music therapy as well as in psychoanalytical writing, for example, try to escape the gendered meaning of the "mother" concept by explaining that people of both sexes could have mother qualities, or by stating that when using concepts like "mother-infant interaction" they really mean "primary caretaker-infant interaction." However, I think the concept of mother is so closely related to the female sex that our associations will conjure up a female person, and then exclude the holding father as well as the holding and nurturing male music therapist. The challenge for the feminist music therapist must be to find non-gendered concepts to describe general human abilities.

Rethinking the Therapeutic Relationship—Do We Need the "Holding Mother"?

It needs to be emphasized that mothers are not self-sacrificing, desireless, abjects (to use Kristeva's terminology). Many mothers are not oppressed, but equal to men in domestic life as well as in professional and other domains of life. Other mothers are happy as traditionalists, and are even fighting in the name of feminism to increase the value of the traditional mother role (Hennessy, 1993). But the position and representation of "mother" in language and discourse is problematic independent of the actual situation of some or even most mothers. If the gender stereotypes such as the nesting, nurturing, and holding mother are preserved in language, the language might be used in a way that normalizes inequality, and thereby restrains some women as well as some men from important life experiences and possibilities. However, this is not solely a question about gender politics, although this has been the main concern in this chapter. It is equally important to ask whether the "holding mother" is a good metaphor for the therapist's role in the therapeutic setting.

If the "holding mother" metaphor is functioning as a model for the therapist's role, this might restrain the therapist from becoming a visibly authentic person for the client. Such a distanced and unauthentic therapist role is not consistent with the philosophy of feminist therapy that emphasizes egalitarian relationships (Worell & Remer, 2003; Jordan, 1997). This is a question about roles and relationships. Judith Jordan and Linda M. Hartling (2002) argue that growth fostering relationships are characterized by mutual empathy and mutual empowerment. They explain this mutuality stating that:

> *When individuals are engaged in mutually empathic and mutually empowering relationships, both people are becoming more responsive in fostering the well-being of the other and of the relationship itself; both people are growing through connection.* (Jordan & Hartling, 2002, p.51)

Moreover, they argue that the outcome of such a mutual relationship is also a desire for relationships that go beyond that particular relationship. Hence, growth is not a development towards separation and individual autonomy, but a development towards greater mutuality and empathic possibilities. In order to be empowered in the relationship, people need to contribute to, as well as to benefit from, relationships (Sprague & Hayes, 2001, p.683).

To actively strive to establish such a mutually empathetic, mutually empowering relationship with the client is, however, not to disclose anything and everything. It does not mean to abandon the asymmetry of the therapeutic relationship in terms of the legal constraints or the economic and professional basis. It does not imply that the client is going to take care of the therapist (Surrey, 1997). Nor does such a mutual relationship represent a withdrawal from professional competency and professional skills. Mutuality does not imply that we are alike (identical) (Sprague & Hayes, 2001). Mutuality refers to a way of being in the relationship, empathically attuned, emotionally responsive, authentically present, and open to change, and is something that can also be constructed between people with very different abilities (Surrey 1997; Sprague & Hayes, 2001; Rolvsjord, 2004b).

CONCLUSION

In this chapter, I have argued that the discourse of music therapy is political. The use of the "mother" concept that I have criticized is obviously not intended to conserve the traditional gender roles and the patriarchal power structure that is implicit in the female-male dichotomy. However, in ignorance of such conservation of traditional and patriarchal (sexist) values and politics, music therapists might reconstitute the traditional storyline of the self-sacrificing, caring woman situated in the domestic sphere. This "mother" concept is even more problematic because it is the use of a gendered concept to describe general human capacities and characteristics. Furthermore, the "holding mother" is also questionable as a model for the therapist's role in the relationship between therapist and client, because it is believed that "she" is unable to go into equal and mutually empowering relationships.

The political power in music therapy can be related to what is called defining powers. This power makes music therapy discourse(s) constitutive of music therapy and even influences the client's experiences in therapy and the outcome of the therapeutic processes. But it also urges us to be more reflexive about larger political, academic, and cultural contexts and discourses and to be aware of the intertextuality of discourses of which music therapy is a part.

The other day my daughter asked me if women can ride motorbikes. And people question whether there is still need for feminism!

REFERENCES

Alvesson, Mats (2002) *Postmodernism and Social Research.* Buckingham, UK: Open University Press.

Ansdell, Gary (2002) Community Music Therapy and the winds of change. In Carolyn Kenny & Brynjulf Stige (eds.) *Contemporary Voices in Music Therapy.* Oslo: Unipub Forlag.

Ansdell, Gary (2003) The stories we tell. Some meta-theoretical reflections on music therapy. *Nordic Journal of Music Therapy 12*, 152–159.

Ballou, Mary & Brown, Laura S. (2002) *Rethinking Mental Health. Feminist Perspectives.* New York: Guildford Press.

Barrett, Michèle & Phillips, Anne (1992) *Destabilizing Theory. Contemporary Feminist Debates.* Cambridge: Polity Press.

Baxter, Judith (2003) *Positioning Gender in Discourse. A Feminist Methodology.* New York: Palgrave Macmillan.

Bayton, Mavis (1997) Women and the electric guitar. In Shiela Whitely (ed.) *Sexing the Groove: Popular Music and Gender.* London: Routledge

Bruscia, Kenneth (1995) Modes of consciousness in Guided Imagery and Music: A therapist's experience of the guiding process. In Carolyn Kenny (ed.) *Listening, Playing, Creating. Essays on the Power of Sound.* New York: SUNY Press.

Chodorow, Nancy (1978) *The Reproduction of Mothering.* Berkley: University of California Press.

Coates, Norma (1997) (R)evolution now? Rock and the political potential of gender. In Shiela Whitely (ed.) *Sexing the Groove: Popular Music and Gender.* London: Routledge.

Cohen, Sara (1997) Men making a scene. Rock music and the production of gender. In Shiela Whitely (ed.) *Sexing the Groove: Popular Music and Gender.* London: Routledge.

Curtis, Sandra L. (2000) Singing Subversion, Singing Soul: Women's Voices in Feminist Music Therapy. (Doctoral dissertation, Concordia University, 1997). *Dissertation Abstracts International*, *60*(12-A), 4240.

Foucault, Michel (2001) Power/Knowledge. In Steven Seidman and Jeffrey C. Alexander (eds.) *The New Social Theory Reader*. London: Routledge.

Forna, Aminatta (1998) *Mothers of All Myths. How Society Moulds and Constrains Mothers*. London: Harper Collins Publishers.

Fornäs, Johan (1995) *Cultural Theory and Late Modernity*. London: Sage Publications.

Gatens, Moira (1992) Power, bodies and difference. In Michèle Barrett & Anne Phillips (eds.) *Destabilizing Theory. Contemporary Feminist Debates*. Cambridge: Polity Press.

Goldstein, Howard (1997) Victors or victims? In Dennis Saleeney (ed.) *The Strengths Perspective in Social Work Practice*. New York: Longman.

Haavind, Hanne (1998) Understanding women in the psychological mode: The challenge from the experiences of Nordic women. In Drude Von der Fehr, Anna Jònasdòttir & Bente Rosenbeck (eds.) *Is There a Nordic Feminism?(Gender, Change & Society)* London: UCL Press.

Hadley, Susan & Edwards, Jane (2004) Sorry for the silence: A contribution from feminist theory to the discourse(s) within music therapy. *Voices: A World Forum for Music Therapy*.
http://www.voices.no/mainissues/mi40004000152.html

Henessy, Rosemary (1993) *Materialist Feminism and the Politics of Discourse*. New York: Routledge.

Irigaray, Luce (1985) *This Sex which is Not One*. N.Y: Cornell University Press.

Jordan, Judith & Linda M. Hartling (2002) New developments in relational cultural theory. In Ballou, Mary and Laura S. Brown (eds.) *Rethinking Mental Health & Disorder. Feminist Perspectives.* London: The Guilford Press.

Jordan, Judith V. (1997) *Women's Growth in Diversity. More Writings from the Stone Center.* New York: The Guilford Press.

Kenny, Carolyn B. (1989) *The Field of Play*. Atascadero: Ridgeview Publishing Company.

Kitzinger, Sheila (1992) *Boken om svangerskap og fødsel*. Oslo: Teknologisk Forlag.

Kristeva, Julia (1984) *Revolution in Poetic Language*. New York: Columbia University Press.

Körlin, Dag & Wrangsjö, Björn (2001) Gender differences in outcome of Guided Imagery and Music (GIM) therapy. *Nordic Journal of Music Therapy* 10, 132-143.

McClary, Susan (1991) *Feminine Endings. Music, Gender and Sexuality*. Minnesota: University of Minnesota Press.

Meadows, Anthony (2002) Gender implications in Guided Imagery and Music therapists' constructs of their clients. Doctoral Dissertation, Philadelphia, PA: Temple University.

Moi, Toril (1986) *The Kristeva Reader*. Oxford: Blackwell.

Pavlicevic, Mercedes & Gary Ansdell (2004) *Community Music Therapy*. London: Jessica Kingsley Publishers.

Pringle, Rosemary & Sophie Watson (1992) 'women's interests' and the post-structuralist state. In Michèle Barrett & Anne Phillips (eds.) *Destabilizing Theory. Contemporary Feminist Debates*. Cambridge: Polity Press.

Rolvsjord, Randi (2002) *Når Musikken blir Språk*. Oslo: Unipub Forlag.

Rolvsjord, Randi (2004a) Music as a poetic language. *Voices: A World Forum for Music Therapy*. http://www.voices.no/mainissues/mi40004000138.html

Rolvsjord, Randi (2004b) Therapy as empowerment. Clinical and political implications of empowerment philosophy in mental health practices of music therapy. *Nordic Journal of Music Therapy, 13*, 99–111.

Ragonè, Helena & Twine, France W. (2000) *Ideologies and Technologies of Motherhood.* New York: Routledge.

Ruud, Even (1996) Musikkterapi som Reformpedagogikk. *Musikk og Verdier*. Oslo: Universitetsforlaget.

Sprague, Joey & Jeanne Hayes (2000) Self-determination and empowerment: A feminist standpoint analyses of talk about disability. *American Journal of Community Psychology, 28*, 671–695.

Stern Daniel N. & Bruschweiler-Stern, N. (1998) *The Birth of a Mother. How the Motherhood Experiences Changes you Forever*. New York: Basic Books.

Stern, Daniel N. (1995) *The Motherhood Constellation*. New York: Basic Books. Harper Collins Publishers.

Stige, Brynjulf (2003) Elaborations toward a Notion of Community Music Therapy. Oslo: Unipub forlag.

Summer, Lisa (1995) Melding musical and psychological processes: The therapeutic musical space. *Journal of the Association for Music and Imagery*; 01/31.

Surrey, Janet L. (1997) What do you mean by mutuality in therapy? In Judith Hartling (ed.) *Women's Growth in Diversity. More Writings from the Stone Center*. London: The Guilford Press.

Søndergaard, Dorte M. (2000) Destabiliseriende Diskusranalyse: veje ind I en poststrukturalistisk inspireret empirisk forskning. Haavind, H. Ed. (2000): *Kjønn og Fortolkende Metode*. Oslo: Gyldendal Akademisk.

Trevarthen, Colwyn (1997) What infants' imitation communicates: With mothers, with fathers and with peers. In Jacqueline Nadel & George Butterworth (eds.) *Imitations in Infancy*. Cambridge: Cambridge University Press.

Viestad, Else (1989) *Kjønn og Ideologi. En studie av kvinnesynet hos Locke, Hume, Rosseau og Kant.* Oslo: Solum Forlag.

Walzer, Susan (1998) *Thinking About the Baby. Gender and Transitions into Parenthood.* Philadelphia: Temple University Press.

Wärja, Margareta (1999) Music as mother. The mothering function of music through expressive and receptive avenues. In Stephen K. Levine & Ellen G. Levine (eds.) *Foundations of Expressive Arts Therapy*. London: Jessica Kingsley Publishers.

Wilkinson, Sue (1997) Feminist psychology. In Isaac Prilletensky (ed.) *Critical Psychology. An Introduction.* London: Sage.

Worell, Judith & Remer, Pamela (1996/2003) *Feminist Perspectives in Therapy. Empowering Diverse Women.* New York: John Wiley and Sons.

Chapter Fourteen

CRITICAL REFLECTIONS ON SONG SELECTION FOR WOMEN'S EMPOWERMENT IN MUSIC THERAPY

Laurie Jones

Song communication, lyrics analysis, sing-along, music reminiscence—whatever the label—many techniques of music therapy incorporate the use of popular music. As part of the musical selection process, we consider client preference, as well as lyric content and its relevance to client issues and treatment needs. This client-centered approach compels us to view our clients' functionality within their immediate environment, addressing barriers to growth. However, the significant impact of the larger environment (i.e. society) on the welfare of our clients may also need to be addressed, in order to treat the "whole person."

A research program at the University of Connecticut on gender role provides an operational definition for the resultant negative impact society can have on an individual. While their study is focused on males, the definition of "Gender Role Conflict" could just as easily be used to describe woman's discordant experience of daily life:

> Gender Role Conflict is a psychological state in which socialized gender roles have negative consequences on the person or others. Gender Role Conflict occurs when rigid, sexist, or restrictive gender roles result in personal restrictions, devaluation or violation of others or self. The ultimate outcome of this kind of conflict is the restriction of the human potential of the person. (O'Neil, 1997, p.10)

If society indeed contributes to the uplifting and/or detriment of an individual's life, we have an obligation to identify and address pertinent factors which contribute to this dichotomy; in our work, that is music.

The framework of society since its inception has been built on the tenets that the strong shall survive, and thus rule. The establishment/promotion of men as the stronger sex has led to oppressive regimes in virtually all areas of society. In man's quest to perpetuate the unequal power relations inherent in these regimes, music has been an unwitting accomplice. Part of our responsibility as music therapists, then, is to become aware of the sexist subtext found in much of the popular music we allow to take center stage within the music therapy session. By screening the music we use in therapy for messages, both overt and covert, which seek to divide us through gender role socialization, we can contribute to reframing our clients' views of themselves and their attitudes about and behaviors toward women.

Throughout history, music has served society by bringing together groups of people who share cultural and religious heritage, geographic and economic backgrounds, ideological and political persuasions, and gender. Women's music, defined by feminist singer-songwriter Margie Adams as "music that affirms and empowers women . . . made by women . . . for anyone but especially women and pro-feminist men" (Adams, 2002, p.1), has experienced an upsurge of sorts in this, the third wave of the feminist movement. Hereafter in this chapter, the term "women's music" will refer to popular music (folk, rock, adult contemporary, R&B, country) with lyrics that adhere to the above definition. It is important to note that there are many forms of "women's music," each of which is influenced by a complex interaction of factors including race, class, sexual orientation, ability, religion, etc. As such, different forms of women's music speak to different experiences of being a woman. All of these factors are important to consider when analyzing music for use with a particular client or group of clients in therapy. Without taking these factors into consideration, we could be selecting women's music that reinforces white, heterosexual, middle class ideas about life and love.

"Music is a symbolic system that allows us the ability to think not only of what is, but of what was and what can be, even of what can never be" (Kohl, 1997, p.3). Therefore, in order to understand the current climate of women's music, we must not only reflect on its rich historical roots, but also project the future growth of this genre and its subsequent implications for music therapy.

In this chapter I will: 1) provide a brief summary of the representation of women (where we've been, where we are, and where we're headed) in the world of popular music; 2) provide an overview of the lyric content of selections of popular music, in terms of gender representation; 3) suggest guidelines for lyric and music analysis of individual songs to determine appropriateness for use in therapy; and 4) discuss the role of women's music in therapy and our responsibilities towards that aim. It is perhaps worthwhile to note at this point that songs included in this chapter were chosen first and foremost on the basis that they were written by women, and second on the basis that their lyric and musical content supported the idea of empowering and affirming women. In addition, due to space limitations, artists and songs chosen for more in-depth analysis were limited to solo artists (though at times, some of these women were part of a group) whose music falls within the category of "rock and roll," the one genre of music where women are still considered outsiders.

Feminist traditions exist both in oral and written form, and thus lend themselves to be viewed through the lens of popular music. As a political vehicle, "movement music" serves the purpose of "spirit maintenance and/or reaffirmation" (Rosenthal, 2001, p.11) and does so through the symbiotic relationship of words and music. When these two entities are in one accord, "movement music": 1) serves the committed through expressing and thus reinforcing the basic tenets that define a particular group; 2) educates persons on new approaches to society and does so by drawing the listener into a "safe mental space" where these thoughts can be birthed; 3) recruits like-minded individuals to move from "sympathizer" to "supporter" through inspirational lyrics and motivating rhythms and melodies; and 4) mobilizes supporters to action (Rosenthal, 2001, pp.11–13), for even through the simple act of singing songs of empowerment, women can take an active role in spreading a strong message of women's right "to be and to do."

Popular music, defined here in general terms as "musical styles, with the exception of the classical genre, that are accessible to the general public and are distributed commercially" (Hargreaves & North, 1997, p.142), is a vibrant cord/chord woven into the tapestry of our individual and collective lives. This has been true throughout the history of popular music, and as such, a basic overview of women in music from the wake of the first wave of the feminist movement to present day is warranted.

The lineage of today's popular music can be traced back to "The Blues," whose form birthed "rock and roll" and whose lyrics were considered a "life-sustaining vehicle" (Davis, 1998, p.xix) for artists and consumers of the day. During the 1920s, African American women reigned supreme in the recording industry, thus amassing a "vast body of music" (Davis, 1998, p.xii). Due to the early success of "women's blues," record companies assumed that only women could be successful recording artists. Wanting to capitalize on the "black market," record executives hurried to sign contracts with these artists, only to abandon them in favor of their African American male counterparts who subsequently arrived on the scene. Nothing, however, could silence these women who had experienced lifetimes of hardship and yet emerged on the other side stronger and more capable than ever.

A discussion about the unsung heroines of women's music would be incomplete without the mention of the contribution of early blues artists, such as Gertrude "Ma" Rainey and Bessie Smith. These courageous African-American musical foremothers laid the foundation that has allowed women to "play against type" in the music industry. Through their unconventional vocal stylings, they paved the way for female artists to explore the gamut of their musicality.

This resulted in women utilizing non-traditional and heretofore "unconventional" instruments, such as the guitar, previously dominated by their male counterparts. Further, female blues artists' bold use of lyrics liberated the voice of present-day female singer-songwriters, enabling them to write "music of conscience" (Davis, 1998, p.2).

Blues music has been chronicled by music therapist Joseph Moreno (1987) as lending itself readily to the full range of expression of feelings (p.339). In listening to the blues, one identifies with the problems expressed by the singer, and thus feels less alone. The sharing of feelings between singer and listener is a form of healing ritual (Moreno, 1987, p.335). Within the context of music therapy, blues music can function as a transitional object which helps to ready the client for personal exploration. The music therapist can then "assist the client in clarifying, discussing, and better understanding the feelings or issues that may come to light" (Moreno, 1987, p.339).

Blues lyrics were intellectually independent and representationally free compared to other music of that era. The themes of sexuality, ideology, and domesticity challenged the mainstream ideals of the day, and thus were progressive and even perilous in nature (Davis, 1998, p.3). With songs such as "Poor Man's Blues" and "Backwater Blues," Bessie Smith proved a force to be reckoned with, speaking out on racism and class relations. Her "Safety Mama" is considered a "song of advice that counsels [Black/poor] women to take strong stands" with the men in their lives (Davis, 1998, p.58). Following suit was Gertrude "Ma" Rainey with "Rough and Tumble Blues," which "presents a powerful, fighting, rough and tumble woman who boasts about her assertiveness" (Davis, 1998, p.47). Gertrude "Ma" Rainey's lyrics are indicative of what Alice Walker defines as a womanist (a term that African American women have deployed in order to distinguish themselves from white middle-class feminists). The term womanist came from the term "womanish" (like a woman), a term given to female children signifying the opposite of being girlish (frivolous, irresponsible, not serious). Womanish also referred to "outrageous, audacious, courageous or 'willful' behavior . . . . Acting grown up . . . [As in] 'You trying to be grown.' Responsible. In charge. 'Serious'" (Walker, 1967/1983, p.xi).[1] These "womanist" blues songs are significant in that they voice beliefs and values relevant to Black working class women.

While the first wave of the feminist movement, which occurred roughly between the years 1835–1920, is associated with "women's suffrage," the second wave, which emerged during the mid-1960s, is often termed the "Women's Liberation Movement." From protesting the Miss America Pageant to converging on the offices of *Ladies' Home Journal*, demanding the hiring of

[1] I would like to thank Sue Hadley for bringing this similarity to my awareness.

more women to positions of influence, women of the '60s began to break free from the oppressive stereotypes and gender roles assigned by a patriarchal society (Gaar, 1992, p.116–7).

The rise of Motown coincided with the rise of the civil rights movement, and independent artists such as Aretha Franklin and female groups like The Supremes made strides toward redefining media's portrayal of women (Gaar, 1992, p.70). However, prior to and during this period, the portrayal of women in popular music lyrics generally continued to fall into two categories, "vamp" and "dumb blonde," despite the fact that Blues music had already deconstructed that notion. Perhaps this is indicative of an area where we have won battles but have yet to win the war. Media representations of women, created by men, portrayed (and still portray) women as inferior, capable only of serving men's needs, whether they be domestic or sexual in nature (Maruszak, 2003, p.1). Through songs such as "It's A Man's, Man's, Man's World" by James Brown and "Under My Thumb" by The Rolling Stones, male artists perpetrated the myth that women were less intelligent and less strong than their male counterparts. And songs such as "Backstreet Girl" by The Rolling Stones and "Build Me A Woman" by The Doors encouraged society to view women as "sex objects," existing only to be viewed and used for men's sexual pleasure.

With the emergence of singer-songwriters such as Joni Mitchell and Janis Joplin, society was once again faced with a vision of women in music, and thus, women, in general, who did not fit the media mold. As was the case with African-American female Blues artists, Mitchell and Joplin exuded a naturalistic, somewhat rough appearance, delivering daring performances with gritty vocals and expressing bold desires.

One of Joplin's more well-known songs, "Piece of My Heart," plays as almost a defiant dare to a male love interest challenging him to just try again to mistreat her. This sentiment was echoed (in meaning, if not musically) in Joni Mitchell's "Woman of Mind and Heart," in which she explores and expresses her expectations for a healthy love relationship. And while Black women have historically had strong female role models to look up to, these musical assertions by Joplin and Mitchell appealed to a generation of white middle-class women who were hungry for strong female role models of their own. They got this and more from some "all-girl" bands which surfaced during this time period when the Chicago Women's Liberation Rock Band, Fanny, and Isis arrived on the scene in the 1970s. [2]

[2] It is interesting to note that at this time, during the '70s and '80s, Olivia Records hired only women—ONLY women. Every employee of the legendary Olivia label—administrative, creative, those involved with production, promotion, janitorial, or whatever—was a woman.

Many of the female musicians who were members of these bands had already been acculturated into the music scene through the process of playing in male-dominated bands. After having experienced firsthand the sexism which exists in the world of music, these female musical pioneers determined that their music would seek to unite rather than divide and build up rather than tear down. This effort proved to be somewhat difficult, in that not only did they essentially have to create a new type of music, they also had to acquire new instrumental skills, master sound systems, fix equipment problems, and monitor and control their stage production (Gaar, 1992, p.146).

Early "girl bands" faced discrimination in that they were always referred to as "the all-girl band such and such," which had the effect of making a distinction between them and the all-male rock acts of this era (which were never referred to as "the all-male band such and such"). These distinctions "worked to perpetuate a difference, a product of lesser value" (Gaar, 1992, p.127). Fanny was a trailblazing band, and their first album release was groundbreaking, as every note was written, sung, and played by women. However, Fanny and bands like them were viewed as an anomaly and became known as "novelty acts" (Gaar, 1992, pp.134–139). Of course, describing them as different and marginal has the effect of undercutting their force/power. This view of all-female bands as novelty acts was carried into the decades that followed.

In the 1980s, "girl bands" continued to try and make their mark, and in 1982, the Go-Go's were the first all-girl band, not under the control of male producers, that wrote, played, and recorded their own music, to chart a number one album in the history of Rock & Roll. Other girl bands of this era included The Bangles and Bananarama. But while girl bands of past decades sought to rely on their music rather than their sexuality, it is my opinion that girl bands of the '80s seemed to regress back into the stereotype of women as sex symbols that our musical foremothers worked so hard to destroy.[3] Solo female artists, such as Suzanne Vega, whose music brought social issues to light ("Luka"), as well as troubadours like Tracy Chapman, with her poetry-driven music, were considered controversial because they did not fit the MTV "fun-oriented" style (Maruszak, 2003, p.2).

This brings us to the 1990s, which begins the third wave of the feminist movement. Leslie Heywood and Jennifer Drake, editors of *Third Wave Agenda:*

[3] Some third wave feminists, such as Jennifer Baumgardner, Amy Richards, and Karen McNaughton, criticize sexist language while at the same time using mimicry and subversion in terms of exaggerating stereotypes that have traditionally been used against them. As such, some female musicians believe that flaunting their sexuality is empowering and contrary to the view that women should adhere to norms that portray "good" girls as virginal.

Being Feminist, Doing Feminism, explain third wave feminism as "a movement that contains elements of second wave critique of beauty culture, sexual abuse, and power structures while it also acknowledges and makes use of the pleasure, danger and defining power of these structures" (Maruszak, 2003, p.3). Throughout the '90s and into today, women have had more opportunities and rights than ever, and yet in many respects we are still tethered to the roots of a patriarchal society, particularly in the world of rock. All-female bands and women singer-songwriters are still the exception rather than the norm, lacking the media support necessary to make them a household name and mainstay (Westmoreland, 2001, p.207). However, the efforts of Chrissie Hynde, Joan Armatrading, Melissa Etheridge, Tracy Chapman, and others who stake their musical claim as guitarists is of great significance to the cause of feminism. "For women to play and sing through the same forms dominated by men is inherently a form of resistance" (Westmoreland, 2001, p.209), and so we celebrate this female presence on the rock scene.

The diversity of musical styles in the past decade or so has opened channels for women singer-songwriters to establish an independent artistic identity, as well as develop a fan base. Women's music of the present day embraces the multifaceted representations of what it means to be a woman and makes no apologies for what sometimes results in a contradiction in terms. Take, for instance, the song "Bitch" by Meredith Brooks. While the term has historically taken on a negative connotation, Ms. Brooks "reclaims the sexist term and uses it to criticize sexism" (Westmoreland, 2001, p.205). Janet Jackson's "Nasty" also takes a negative stereotype (woman as aggressive sexual being) and demonstrates that women have the right, if they so choose, to turn the tables on men, using them for sexual gratification. If we, as music therapists, are to draw upon the wealth of musical resources now available, it is important for us to be able to discern the therapeutic potential of such songs.

As has already been mentioned, much of popular music perpetuates a negative message to and about women. Blatant examples of such songs include "Hot Legs" by Rod Stewart, "Take It Off" by Kiss and "Balls in Your Mouth" by Kid Rock to name but a few. As the titles alone suggest, their view of women is clearly derogatory, and it is reasonable to expect that the lyrics would follow suit. Female artists are often no friend to women when their songs, whether written by them or not, portray women in a negative light. Examples include "Material Girl" by Madonna, and "Stupid Girl" by Garbage.

Other songs may be less obviously sexist, and so care should be given to ferret out any hint of sexism in the popular music we utilize; however, that is not to imply that these songs don't have purpose in therapy. In fact, they could be used in a positive way to encourage debate and provide a safe outlet for challenging such stereotypes and debunking myths. But again, this requires awareness and expertise on our part.

More important for the building up of our female clients is to provide them with an abundance of music which seeks to portray women in a positive manner. In ascertaining whether or not lyrics are affirming and empowering for women, it is necessary to determine the qualities and characteristics of an affirmed, empowered woman. In order to do this, I looked to the words of well-known, successful, empowered women (some of them musicians). From the following, I have developed a description of an empowered woman.

> Woman must not accept; she must *challenge.*
> She must not be awed by that which has been built up around her;
> she must reverence that woman in her which *struggles for expression.*
> *Margaret Sanger*
> Themes: accepting challenges and challenging opinions, truths; self-acceptance; self-love; self-worth; ability for self-expression

> The most common way people give up their *power*
> is by thinking they don't have any.
> *Alice Walker*
> Themes: self-knowledge; confidence; innate power

> *Courage* is like a muscle.
> We *strengthen* it with use.
> *Ruth Gordon*
> Themes: courage; strength; growth

> If we don't change, we don't grow.
> If we don't grow, we are not really *living.*
> *Growth* demands a temporary *surrender of security.*
> *Gail Sheehy*
> Themes: growth; fearless living; risk-taking

> Just don't give up trying to *do what you really want* to do.
> Where there is love and inspiration, I don't think you can go wrong.
> *Ella Fitzgerald*
> Themes: risk-taking; confidence; self-knowledge

When we speak we are afraid our words will not be heard or welcomed.
But when we are silent, we are still afraid.
So it is *better to speak.*
Audre Lorde
Themes: self-expression; fearless living; confidence

If you do not tell the *truth* about your*self*
you cannot tell it about other people.
Virginia Woolf
Themes: fearless living; self-knowledge; self-acceptance

The beauty of a woman
isn't in the clothes she wears,
The figure that she carries,
or the way she combs her hair[4]

The *beauty of a woman*
must be *seen from in her eyes*;
Because that's the doorway to her heart,
the place where love resides.

The beauty of a woman
isn't in a facial mole;
But *true beauty* in a woman,
is *reflected by her soul.*
Maya Angelou
Themes: inner beauty; self-knowledge; self-love; innate power

[4] Some of these issues are particularly significant for African-American women in terms of how their bodies and hair have been seen as the antithesis of beauty as defined by white men. It is important that we don't always speak of generic women, but that we understand that the experiences of women are different given their race, sexuality, class, ability, etc.

The Empowered Woman, she moves through the world with a sense of *confidence* and *grace.*
Her once reckless spirit now tempered by *wisdom.*
Quietly, yet firmly, she *speaks her truth* without doubt or hesitation and the life she leads is of her own creation.
She now understands what it means to *live and let live.*
How much *to ask* for herself and how much *to give.*
She has a *strong,* yet *generous heart* and the *inner beauty* she emanates truly sets her apart.
Like the mythical Phoenix, she has risen from the ashes and *soared* to a new plane of existence, *unfettered* by the things that once posed such resistance.
Her senses now heightened, she sees everything so clearly.
She hears the wind rustling through the trees; beckoning her to *live the dreams* she holds so dearly.
She feels the *softness* of her hands and muses at the *strength* that they possess.
Her *needs and desires* she has learned to *express.*
She has *tasted the bitter and savored the sweet* fruits of life, *overcome adversity* and pushed past heartache and strife.
And the one thing she never understood, she now knows to be true, it all begins and ends with you.
Copyright © 2003 Sonny Carroll All Rights Reserved
Themes: confidence, grace, wisdom, self-expression, fearless living, self-knowledge, innate power, strength, perseverance.

In summary, an empowered woman:

Knows her value extends beyond physical attributes
Comes in all shapes, sizes, and colors and knows she is beautiful
Is strong and perseveres through adversity
Engages her mind in pursuit of her life's ambition/calling and problem-solves ways of attaining it
Has one arm reaching toward her future and one arm reaching back to assist others in their journey
Has a sense of self-worth that comes from being principled, independent, intelligent, fearless, and extends to others in a straightforward, confident manner with a sense of justice distributed to all
Is a courageous survivor and fearless liver of life
Possesses the courage of her convictions
Tolerates nothing "less than" from self, others or her environment

Subsequently, music-assisted empowerment must reflect these characteristics and/or convey messages that encourage and support women's right "to be" and "to do."

As I reflected personally on the music I use most often in therapy, I discovered that the majority of songs were written and performed by men. I can rationalize that this is the music popular of my era, the '60s and '70s, and thus is the music with which I am most intimately acquainted. I can also argue that this is also the music most preferred by my clientele. However, I must recognize that it is possible that the predominant use of music by male songwriters conveys an unspoken message that we accept the media "status quo," in which the only voice worthy of being heard is that of a man.

Rather than an admonishment, this is an encouragement to be like the empowered women mentioned previously, in terms of being self-aware, with a sense of justice for our clients and channeling all of that into choosing "women's music" for use in therapy. In fact, the very process of critical reflection about our song choices has the effect of empowering us, and in turn, our clients. In researching this topic, I discovered an abundance of websites dedicated to the support and promotion of female singer-songwriters. Whether or not these artists identify themselves as "feminists" is not significant. What *is* significant is that the lyrics are "pro-women," and as such can be useful in supporting our female clients to be emboldened in their pursuits, as well as educate our male clients on the true value and role(s) of women in society.

Given the vast array of popular music, a comprehensive analysis of "pro-women" songs would be beyond the scope of this chapter. Representative songs to be examined here have been chosen according to the guidelines already set forth, as well as my own knowledge of and experience with this music in therapy. For sake of clarity, songs will be framed within their corresponding messages of empowerment identified in the previous section.

Problem-solving—defined here as "facing and dealing with problems head on; making decisions; working things through"

Self-knowledge/awareness/acceptance—defined here as "questioning and searching for answer within; peace and tolerance; honesty with self and others; seeing complexity and ambiguity in situations that are often seen in either/or terms"

Strength/Innate Power—defined here as "realization that they have the resources and the strength to survive; stability; inner beauty; wholeness"

Perseverance—defined here as “staying the course; making strides towards achieving goals”

Intolerance of “less than”—defined here as “striving for the best from self and others; being willing to confront and walk away if need be”

Courage/Confidence—defined here as “trust in self and others; balance between vulnerability and strength; voicing concerns”

Growth/Risk-taking—defined here as “leap of faith which propels self forward”

Independence—defined here as “autonomy, speaking for one’s self without being unhealthily dependent on others; being okay with being alone; personal responsibility”

Because popular music is generally “text-intensive” (Fornas, 2003, p.37), our first area of focus is to interpret lyric content. “Interpretation is an active creation of meaning, resulting from the contextualized encounter between human subjects and texts” (Fornas, 2003, p.39). Our initial encounters with music often give us the clearest interpretation of meaning because we have yet to develop an association with it. Our previous associations can complicate our interpretations due to the difficulty involved in disentangling our personal meanings of the song from other possible interpretations. Therefore, it would be beneficial to scout out music that we might not normally gravitate towards and respond to it on a personal level based on manifest issues. When analyzing lyrics for use in therapy, I find it helpful to listen to a song several times, each time from a different position; i.e., from the positions of “singer,” “sung to,” and “sung about.” Another strategy when analyzing lyrics is to allow yourself to take portions of lyrics out of context to procure yet another point of view. This is often how our client’s project onto the lyrics, for they key into whatever resonates with their personal “here and now” experience, regardless of whether or not the song in its entirety reflects that issue or theme. We facilitate that simply by guiding clients to that section of the song we feel would be beneficial to focus on. Finally, I explore the latent issues, which is a subjective experience of reading between the lines, expressed in the lyrics. Even our old favorites can take on new meanings through a fresh perspective born out of analysis.

Analyzing lyrics for relevancy to woman’s empowerment is a necessary first step; however, our expertise as music therapists extends beyond words. “Music underpins the whole performance and can provide the emotional intensity so crucial for the reception of the popular song message" (Maruszak, 2003, p.208). When I analyze popular music for use in therapy from a musical standpoint, I get an overall impression to see if certain expectations (cadences, form, harmonic progressions) can be found within the song. Basic music psychology teaches that music preference is in large part a result of meeting expectations we have become accustomed to in Western popular music. I then listen for levels of complexity (texture, modulations, instrumentation, syncopations, dynamics), for this becomes important in terms of depth perception, depending on clientele. In other words, some clients can handle a more complex song structure, and this can actually deepen the experience for the client, but other clients will require a more simplistic structure so they are not overwhelmed. And then I determine how clearly the lyrics are conveyed, for it is my bias that we should model clear self-expression for our clients. Even if we utilize lyric sheets at times, I believe we want to engage our clients in the music and/or lyrics, and we can't do that if the music and/or lyrics are obscured in some way. Personally, I am constantly questioning "what is music therapy?," and when many helping professions (nursing, psychology, etc.) utilize popular songs in their own practice, I am faced with "what do I, as a music therapist, bring to this technique, that is more specialized than what they're doing over there?" And what I always come back to is that because of my music background, I know the ins and outs of the music I choose to utilize and through training in music therapy techniques, I have mastered the art of engaging my clients in connecting with the music, which is where I believe the true healing power of music resides. This constant questioning, while infuriating at times, is what spurs me on to continue honing these analytic skills, and is the rationale for explaining my process, in the hopes that we all continue to be invested in our modality, music therapy.

Beyond what has already been mentioned in terms of analyzing music, in "Lyric Analysis for Song Communication" (1995), I looked at the importance of congruency between lyrics and music. As I researched 500+ popular songs and chose approximately 100 for musical analysis, I discovered that from reading the lyrics, I would develop an idea of how the music would go before I listened to it. And while most songs compared with my ideal, there were many that didn't seem to "go" with what was being conveyed in the lyrics. For instance, in Simon and Garfunkel's "I Am a Rock," the lyrics are poignant, sad, angry, defensive and yet the music, including the manner in which it is sung, is for the most part buoyant and pleasant. And so I began to think about the implications of this in therapy. What I discovered is that this incongruence sometimes has the effect of dividing a group, rather than unifying it towards a main theme. While there is no inherent danger of this—for the music therapist can easily work through the discrepancies with their clients—if your aim is to unify your group, you will need to know whether a song is congruent. In determining congruency, we consider whether musical elements, including meter, tempo, voice, and texture, are compatible with the conveyed messages found in the lyrics.

The following are guidelines for listening to these elements, with further suggestion of ways they contribute to or detract from lyric content.

1) Meter—most songs are in common time (4/4), but for those in 3/4, 6/8, 7/8 and the like, the meter can throw off the stability and structure of a piece, which can bring the piece into incongruence, especially if there are numerous and abrupt changes, particularly if the lyrics suggest "steadiness."
2) Tempo—slow, moderate, upbeat, fast; changing or steady; all will impact congruency; also, some song tempos are difficult to distinguish because the beat is one tempo and the manner of playing makes it seem another.
3) Voice—Part: whether soprano, alto, tenor, bass; Timbre: rich, think, full, hollow, bright, mellow; Voice Placement: chest, throat, nasal, head, falsetto or any combination of these; Clarity: how easily lyrics can be understood.
4) Texture—What instruments are used; salience of instruments; in other words, what instrument captures the ear in the most prevalent way; whether or not there are counter-melodies.
5) Points of Interest—backup singers; subjective response to the song-writer's use of space; syncopation or lack thereof.

Society and the media often convey mixed messages about and to women. For instance, a woman is supposed to seek out opportunities but not be an opportunist; she is to be independent but function as part of a couple; she should take steps in achieving her dreams, so long as she ruffles no feathers along the way. Therefore, I think we want our song choices to be as clear and straightforward as possible, which means that musical elements need to reflect, support, and propel the pro-woman message onward/forward in a non-duplicitous manner.

What follows is an example of women's music of the latter part of the second wave and into the third wave of the feminist movement; that is, women's music from the 1980s to present day. Due to space limitations and copyright issues, portions of lyrics will be highlighted and expounded upon in terms of themes and possible interpretations, and analysis of musical elements will serve to illustrate congruency. For ease of reference, artists are listed in alphabetical order.

Tori Amos

"Girl" (1991) from the album *Little Earthquakes* (Atlantic)

"From in the shadow she calls, and in the shadow she finds a way, finds a way; and in the shadow she crawls . . . . she's been everybody else's girl maybe one day she'll be her own"

Themes	Music/Congruence
Perseverance—pressing on to find the light Courage—shadows suggests she's in a precarious situation, and yet she continues	Rhythm, chords and chord progression, instrumentation in the verse gives a suspenseful vibe (precarious situation), as in "there's something around the corner"; chorus musically resolves a bit and gives the listener, if identifying with "sung about" some relief, which results in giving space to reflect on whether or not this is an accurate depiction of her life, as well as to identify with the pain of keeping true self in the shadows; bridge gets more insistent while uplifting through the addition of many voices and contrasts in dynamics, as in a support network literally lifting the listener from those shadows.

India Arie

"Strength Courage and Wisdom" (2001) from the album *Acoustic Soul* (Motown)

"It's time to step out in faith . . . . I found strength, courage, and wisdom and it's been inside of me all along"

Themes	Music/Congruence
Truly, I feel that all themes are evident in this song, however: Strength/Innate Power—this is an overt theme Growth/Risk-taking—taking a chance	Soulful; nicely pulsating rhythms in the percussion (which is often a protest instrument); gives listener a sense of calm energy, easily engaging auditory and kinetic senses, which has the result of internalizing the music, and thus the message; voice is strong and "chesty"—gets the listener into their own heart.

Pat Benatar

"Treat Me Right" (1981) from the album *Crimes of Passion* (Capitol)

"You want me to leave, you want me to stay; you ask me to come back, you turn and walk away; you wanna be lovers, you wanna be friends; I'm losing my patience, you're nearing the end"

Themes	Music/Congruence
Courage—telling him how she feels Strength/Innate power—realizes that she deserves more Problem-solving—trying to work it through by talking it through	Voice is salient element—strong, forward-focused, loud—gives listener feeling that singer has thought this through and is unafraid and confident in expressing self—a good role model; driving bass and drums spurring the listener on—gets the listener "revved up"; melody in chorus moves upward and is sung in such a way that it sounds like an exasperated release, as in "listen to me!"; there's a musical "question and answer" melodically and rhythmically that matches the dichotomy of lyrical phrases.

Meredith Brooks

"Shine" (2002) from the album *Bad Bad One* (Gold Circle Records)

"That's where you shine—when you're sinking you swim, when you see your way out instead of in . . . like a diamond in the rough, you're always so resilient"

Themes	Music/Congruence
Problem-solving—evidence of working through problems Strength/Innate Power—resiliency	Upbeat and forward movement in harmonic progressions plays as a celebration of self; chorus of female voices on "that's when you shine" has the effect of having your own personal cheering section; melody utilizes many repeated notes (otherwise, it is stepwise), as if the message is "matter-of-fact"; the upward motion of bass line gives listener a sense of inspiration.

Tracy Chapman

"All That You Have Is Your Soul" (1989) from the album *Crossroads* (Elektra/Asylum)

"My mama told me . . . don't be tempted by the shiny apple, don't you eat of a bitter fruit; hunger only for a taste of justice, hunger only for a world of truth 'cause all that you have is your soul"

Themes	Music/Congruence
Intolerance of "less than"—don't settle for the bitter, pursue the sweet Strength/Innate Power—your soul is all that you have which can't be taken away, so nurture the inner	Bare texture—predominantly voice and guitar—singer wants to be clear; this simplistic texture and structure (basic blues progression) gives listener a sense of intimacy with singer, which co-ordinates with the idea that she is conveying lessons she has learned from things her mother has told her—an intimate exchange; music is slow, but the words move fast—could be seen as a bit incongruent, but you may look at it as the singer having a lot to say and keeping the listener "slowed down" so they can absorb it all.

Shawn Colvin

"Nothin' On Me" (1996) from the album *A Few Small Repairs* (Sony)

"So in case you hadn't noticed, I'm alright—not like I was before; things used to be so hopeless, but not tonight—tonight I'm walkin' out that door"

Themes	Music/Congruence
Problem-Solving—making strong decisions Strength/innate power—realization that she can leave Intolerance of "less than"—she discovers she deserves more Growth—the singer has changed	A return to the '50s style—"happy-go-lucky" sound; simple, stepwise melody, steady beat, basic rhythm section accompaniment with bass line being somewhat "bluesy"; gives listener sense that you can be happy even after making some tough decisions— happiness after hopelessness.

Des'Ree

"You Gotta Be" (1994) from the album *I Ain't Movin'* (Sony)

"challenge what your future holds . . . go ahead release your fears . . . stand up and be counted. . . ; you gotta be bad, you gotta be bold, you gotta be wiser . . ."

Themes	Music/Congruence
Strength/Innate Power—the listener has it within herself to be bold, etc. Perseverance—keep on movin Courage/Confidence and Growth/Risk-taking—have trust and take that leap	Steady—moves, but not too fast; melody is simple, especially in chorus—chant-like—easy for clients to remember and replicate, as in "positive affirmations"; singer exudes positive attitude and confidence—can hear the "smile" in her voice—makes the listener smile, as well.

Ani DiFranco

"32 Flavors" (1995) from the album *Not A Pretty Girl* (Righteous Babe Records)

"squint your eyes and look closer—I'm not between you and your ambition . . . I am 32 flavors and then some . . . and I'm beyond your peripheral vision, so you might wanna turn your head . . . some day you are gonna get hungry and eat all of the words you just said"

Themes	Music/Congruence
Self-awareness, self-acceptance—has embraced her complexity (32 flavors) Strength/Innate Power—a sense of "I've got what I need to make it, and I want you to feel the same about yourself" Courage/Confidence—dares those around her to not look at her in narrow terms; kind of a "ha-you thought you knew me, and you tried to tell me what I could and couldn't be, but I proved you wrong—now eat your words" Independence—marches to the beat of her own drummer	Rhythm of melody and accompaniment salient; melody "chant-like," as if singer doesn't want a fancy melody to obscure words, which is the deepest aspect for the listener; syncopation in words add to a sense of extreme confidence that at the same time is not overbearing due to the voice timbre and exchange of frontal and breathy sounds; strong rhythms support the "in-your-face" lyrics and compliment the inner strength of the singer; voice sails above the accompaniment (not embedded) exuding independence.

Melissa Etheridge

"Truth of the Heart" (1999) from the album *Breakdown* (Polygram)

"We all begin this race at the start; But I have come this far with a truth of the heart"

Themes	Music/Congruence
Self-knowledge—knows and accepts herself Perseverance—she has come far	Slow-moving song—holds listener, as in an embrace, as chord changes take longer to happen than anticipated at times; guitar strums keep the song moving rhythmically, as in assisting the song to persevere to its conclusion; voice is strong, resilient, but at the same time, warm; singer takes great care to connect with her listener, as if really wanting them to "get it."

Macy Gray

"A Moment to Myself" (1999) from the album *On How Life Is* (Epic)

"Deep in the struggle I have found the beauty of me; God is watchin' and the devil finally let me be . . . . There is a conversation I need to have with me; It's just a moment to myself"

Themes	Music/Congruence
Self-knowledge—the introspection of conversing with self Strength/Innate Power—realization that beauty is from within	Vocal timbre most salient—gritty, tough, speak-singing, gives the listener the feeling that the singer is thinking out loud; accompaniment supports the strong vocals with a "bluesy" progression and feel, with moderate to upbeat tempi; results in positive vibe.

Lauryn Hill

"Everything Is Everything" (1999) from the album *The Mis-Education of Lauryn Hill* (Sony)

"Sometimes it seems we'll touch that dream, but things come slow or not at all; and the ones on top won't make it stop . . . let's love ourselves then we can't fail to make a better situation; tomorrow, our seeds will grow—all we need is dedication"

Themes	Music/Congruence
Self-knowledge—awareness of what we want from life Problem-Solving—taking steps to reach dream Courage—trust in self and others	Most salient are the spaces within the accompaniment, which allow the listener to reflect and be patient, as well as to trust the process—for when the bottom falls out (i.e. the accompaniment), we must continue on (i.e. the vocals); also of note is the stepwise movement of the melody, as in "taking steps to reach dream."

Annie Lennox

"Sisters Are Doin' It for Themselves" (1985) from the album *Be Yourself Tonight* (Eurhythmics) (RCA)

"Sisters are doin' it for themselves; standin' on their own two feet and ringin' on their own bells"

Themes	Music/Congruence
Independence—self-explanatory Strength/Innate Power—expression of wholeness; we can do for ourselves and don't need anyone else to toot our horns for us!	Most salient are the many voices that are utilized in the chorus (all female, I believe, but with some low contraltos like Annie, which have the effect of being in touch with both female and male parts of ourselves); these voices convey the message of the title itself; music is upbeat and driving, dance-like, celebration.

Alanis Morissette

"You Learn" (1995) from the album *Jagged Little Pill* (Maverick)

"You live you learn, you love you learn, you cry you learn, you lose you learn, you bleed you learn, you scream you learn"

Themes	Music/Congruence
Self-knowledge and Growth—no matter what the experience, the singer learns about herself and grows through it	Quality of voice is salient—Alanis's signature vocal style (almost a yodel-type vocalization at ends of phrases) gives a sense of authenticity to lyric content—it's easy for listener to identify because it sounds raw and thus, real; simple texture and rhythm keeps listener on basic level of insight—a good "starter song" for self-awareness.

Stevie Nicks

"Landslide" (1975) from the album *Fleetwood Mac* (Warner Brothers)

"Can I sail through the changing ocean tides; can I handle the seasons of my life. . . . I've been afraid of changing 'cause I built my life around you; but time makes you bolder"

Themes	Music/Congruence
Self-knowledge—questioning and searching; insight into how fear holds her back Courage—voices concern about taking risks	The constant movement (fingerpicking, often downwards melodic progression) of guitar lends itself to the feeling of "landslide" and has potential effect of taking listener deeper each time the cycle returns, getting listener more in touch with their own "landslide"; Stevie's signature vocal styling is always authentic—never contrived—this is the sound of experience, and the listener can easily believe that the singer has "walked the talk"—this has effect of creating trust; melodic range is small, melody uses repeated notes with some leaps—gives feeling of "talking to yourself," helping the listener to be introspective.

Suzanne Vega

"Ironbound/Fancy Poultry" (1987) from the album *Solitude Standing* (A&M)

"Fancy poultry parts sold here—breasts and thighs and hearts; backs are cheap and wings are nearly free"

Themes	Music/Congruence
Strength/Innate Power—"backs are cheap" gives the sense that the person is working hard for little pay, and yet . . . Perseverance—persevere through great odds because they have hope for a better future Growth—enduring hardship often leads to growth	Folksy-rock, guitar-driven music plods along as the lyrics describe a bleak existence; however, when it gets to the part about "wings are nearly free," the upward use of the voice and harmonic progression gives the listener an image of something/someone soaring toward the skies.

While a few of these artists might be considered R&B rather than Rock (India Arie, Des'Ree, etc.), these women rock harder and have more to say than most, and so they have been included in this section. Also, the analysis here gives only a bird's-eye view of what's encapsulated in each song. Themes discussed are manifest themes only. To look at latent themes would require a full printing of the lyrics, which is not feasible for this chapter. There is much more to these songs than meets the eye, and hopefully your interest is piqued enough to explore these songs for use in therapy.

Another aspect to consider is whether you use the recorded version of popular music or present them "live." I have always held to the belief that in "live" presentation, we must keep as closely to the style of the original artist as possible, choosing songs that can be satisfyingly replicated with just guitar and voice or piano and voice. My rationale for this has been that our clients will have certain expectations, and if they prefer Pat Benatar, they don't want to hear Beverly Sills doing Pat Benatar. While I still believe this is important, I now see there is additional reasoning for being true to style. In looking over how important the voice is in conveying congruence, if we can't convey "rawness" when it is called for, or "warmth" when it is needed, we will not only be doing a disservice to the artists and in turn disappointing our clients, but more importantly, we may end up preventing our clients from fully engaging with the music and the meaning therein.

Gerri Gribi (on creativefolk.com) has compiled similar lists of "women's music." Accessing this work would be a step in the right direction in growing your repertoire and music library.

So far, I have considered the voices of female singer-songwriters in mainstream music. But what of our client's voices? How much more meaningful/empowering is it for our clients to create their own music? Again, as music therapists, we have the expertise necessary to assist them in this endeavor, and yet, how often do we involve our clients in the cathartic experience of songwriting?[5] To do so would additionally provide us with the opportunity to model the behaviors and attitudes indicative of an empowered person.[6]

And then, what of our own voices? What better way to demonstrate the tenets of empowerment than in our original songs as therapists? Throughout my career, when I haven't been able to find a song that adequately conveys (through lyrics and music) the essence of the issue at hand, I have had the pleasure of creating original compositions to meet those various needs. It has been a "freeing" experience for me, because I actually find that it is quite simple to compose with a specific focus in mind, and the results are satisfying, both to me and, seemingly, my clientele. One such experience involved a support group for women who had lost a child, either to miscarriage or still birth. They determined there needed to be a memorial for their deceased children, and the idea for "Precious Treasures" was born. I was asked to sing at the dedication of this memorial, and was then faced with the task of finding a song. I wanted something poignant but not too sad, and there was just nothing to be found. I decided to write my own, hoping that I would convey in an empathetic way, the thoughts and feelings of those the song was meant to touch. With the title already established by the memorial, I was quickly on my way, and the song, "Precious Treasures," was finished in just two hours. At the memorial dedication, many women from the support group were in attendance, and I prayed it would be a healing song for them. Afterwards, several women came to me with tears in their eyes and asked me "how did you know?" and I could only say that I just tried to put myself in their shoes and hoped I was walking on the right path. There seems to be a mindset in our society that if a child dies before, at, or soon after birth, there is no need for grieving. I would like to believe that "Precious Treasures" helped empower some of those women to claim the right to their feelings about the loss of their child.

[5] Recently, more has been written on the use of songwriting in music therapy. See Felicity Baker and Tony Wigram (eds.) *Songwriting: Methods, Techniques and Clinical Applications for Music Therapy Clinicians, Educators and Students* (London: Jessica Kingsley *Publishers*, 2005).

[6] For examples of this see the chapters by Sandra Curtis and Elizabeth York in this book.

CONCLUSION

In conclusion, it appears as though there is an underground movement afoot which serves to bolster these female artists to take the music scene by storm. "Whenever and wherever (women's music) is played, it continues to stand as a direct challenge to women-hating culture" (Adams, 2002, p.5). Covering such diverse styles as punk, heavy metal, R&B, adult contemporary, women are relishing in their voice and spirit, and it is only a matter of time until they are heard. Which raises the question "why haven't they been heard more thus far?" The answer to that may be more complex than can be addressed here, but it seems that these artists' songs and persona are not marketable to mainstream media. In the music business, historically a male-dominated profession, producers, agents, and managers draw a salary from promoting artists and music that serve to keep alive the age-old stereotypes and oppressive views of woman's societal stature. Why? Because these views have become familiar and even comfortable in our (Western) society (culture) today. The danger of this is that young girls absorb and internalize these views and subsequently accept that they are to exist in society only as passive observers, which makes the following all the more heartening.

In the predominantly African-American Dorchester neighborhood of Boston, three teenage girls, fed up with the negative images of women found in much of today's Rap and Hip-Hop music, came up with an idea for a local radio station. They would, under the tutelage of the staff, provide an alternative to radio stations that played "endless rap and hip-hop music that depicted women as sex objects and fashion accessories" (Austin, 2004, p.14). So, from 4p.m.-7p.m. each Monday, the girls would write and deliver public-service announcements, "conduct interviews and chat sessions, and play music that sends positive messages to girls" (Austin, 2004, p.14). This initial endeavor has expanded to include 12 teenage girls, as well as incorporate a course which provides students with the tools necessary for dissecting media messages. The results have been positive and advisor Pat Younger states that she has seen "an immediate rise in her students' self-esteem" (Austin, 2004, p.15). This anecdotal evidence of the use of woman-affirming music as a vehicle to improved sense of self and reduction of barriers to wholeness provides further argument for analysis and implementation of such songs in therapy.

While my focus in this chapter has been music, it bears mentioning that much of music's appeal lies in the accompanying videos, which have conveyed the unattainable (for most of us!) or at least unrealistic examples of beauty, always from a male perspective. That, in and of itself, is damaging to a woman's sense of personal beauty and worth. This is why it would be premature to think that the work of "women's music" is complete, despite the positive influence of such artists as Mary Chapin Carpenter and Ani DiFranco in mainstream music (Adams, 2002, p.2). An ongoing challenge will be to "support women's culture, nurture the women who create it and pass this feminist vision on to the world who desperately need it in order to save itself" (Adams, 2002, p.5).

Music that implores and causes us to rethink our belief systems, many of which have been passed down from generation to generation, is unpopular because it's uncomfortable for us to "question" what we have always taken as a "given." And so promoting songs called "I Get Out" (Lauryn Hill) and "In the Eye" (Suzanne Vega), tackling messages of "deliverance from abuse and/or addiction" and "defiant opposition to injustice" is considered a risk. We can be thankful that someone took a risk on Tori Amos, Tracy Chapman, and Sarah McLachlan, to name just a few. They have spoken for us, relaying ideas we dare not indulge; they have spoken to us relaying messages of self-worth and self-determination. Their struggle is our struggle, for the personal is political, and by utilizing music written by and for women, we can take a proactive role in helping ourselves and our clients, both women and men, to redefine the terms "women," "female," "feminine" and "feminist."

REFERENCES

Adams, Margie (2002) Thoughts on women's music. www.MargieAdams.com

Amos, Tori (1991) Girl. On *Little Earthquakes* [CD] New York: Atlantic Records.

Arie, India (2001) Strength Courage and Wisdom. On *Acoustic Soul* [CD] Los Angeles: Motown Records.

Austin, April (2004) Teenage girls spin the dial toward positive lyrics. *Christian Science Monitor,* 14–15.

Benatar, Pat (1981) Treat Me Right. On *Crimes of Passion* [CD] Hollywood, CA: Capitol Records.

Brooks, Meredith (2002) Shine. On *Bad Bad One* [CD] Santa Monica, CA: Gold Circle Records.

Chapman, Tracy (1989) All That You Have Is Your Soul. On *Crossroads* [CD] New York: Elektra/Asylum.

Davis, Angela Y. (1998) *Blues Legacies and Black Feminism.* New York: Random House.

DiFranco, Ani (1995) 32 Flavors. On *Not A Pretty Girl* [CD] Buffalo, NY: Righteous Babe Records.

Etheridge, Melissa (1999) Truth of the Heart. On *Breakdown* [CD] Los Angeles: Polygram Records.

Fornas, Johan (2003) The Words of Music. *Popular Music and Society, 26*, 37–52.

Fox, Laurie B. (1995) Lyrics Analysis for Song Communication. Temple University Independent Project.

Gaar, Gillian (1992) *She's A Rebel.* Seattle, WA: Seal Press.

Gray, Macy (1999) A Moment to Myself. On *On How Life Is* [CD] New York: Epic Records.

Hargreaves, David & North, Adrian (1997) *The Social Psychology of Music.* New York: Oxford University Press.

Hill, Lauryn (1999) Everything Is Everything. On *The Mis-Education of Lauryn Hill* [CD] New York: Sony Records.

Kohl, Paul R. (1997) Reading between the lines: Music and noise in hegemony and resistance. *Popular Music and Society,* 21, 3–18.

Lennox, Annie (1985) Sisters Are Doin' It for Themselves. On *Be Yourself Tonight* (Eurhythmics) Los Angeles: RCA Records.

Maruszak, Beata (2003) Women's quest for empowerment in the pop-music culture of the 1990's. In Irmina Wawrzyczek and Zbigniew Mazur (eds.) *Studying "New" Britain: Popular Culture and Ideology*. Warsaw: UMCS Lublin.

Moreno, Joseph (1987) The therapeutic role of the blues singer and considerations for the clinical applications of the blues form. In *The Arts in Psychotherapy*, *4,* 333–340.

Morissette, Alanis (1995) You Learn. On *Jagged Little Pill* [CD] Los Angeles: Maverick Records.

Nicks, Stevie (1975) Landslide. On *Fleetwood Mac* [CD] Burbank, CA: Warner Brothers.

O'Neil, James and Good, Glenn (1997) Men's gender role conflict: Personal reflections and overview of recent research (1994-1997). *Society for the Psychological Study of Men and Masculinity (SPSMM) Bulletin*, *2*, 10–15.

Rosenthal, Rob (2001) Serving the movement: The role of music. *Popular Music and Society, 25*, 11–24.

Vega, Suzanne (1987) Ironbound/Fancy Poultry. On *Solitude Standing* [CD] Santa Monica, CA: A&M Records.

Walker, Alice (1967/1983) *In Search of Our Mothers' Gardens: Womanist Prose*. NY: A Harvest Book, Harcourt Brace & Company.

Westmoreland, Kalene (2001) "Bitch" and "Lilith Fair": Resisting anger, celebrating contradictions. *Popular Music and Society*, *25*, 205–220.

Chapter Fifteen

WHAT ARE WE DOING TO OURSELVES? THE BRANDING OF MUSIC THERAPY IN ACADEMIA

Elaine Streeter

> *Draw near woman, and hear what I have to say. Turn your curiosity for once towards useful objects, and consider the advantages which nature gave you and society ravished away. Come and learn how you were born the companion of man and became his slave; how you grew to like the condition and think it natural; and finally how the long habituation of slavery so degraded you that you preferred its sapping but convenient vices to the more difficult virtues of freedom and repute.*
>
> —Choderlos de Laclos, 'On the Education of Women' (1783)

PERSONAL PROLOGUE

Writing in 2005 on feminism and music therapy has drawn me back to the late sixties and early seventies, a time when feminism was on the hot wash cycle and Donald W. Winnicott and Ronald D. Laing were writing some of their most radical works.

For me, feminism then was not so much an academic subject as a series of interpersonal acts that led to decisions that changed my life. Music therapy and feminism came together for me at a particular point in my life.

By the spring of 1969, I had finished my first two terms of music studies at the Guildhall School of Music and Drama where I was the only female studying composition. During the Easter break I got married and moved into a flat in central London with my new name and my new husband, marvelling at my good luck, as in those days it was not easy to escape the family home unless married.

The week after I graduated, in 1971, my husband decided that rather than work as a film editor for the BBC, he wanted to move to Norfolk to study philosophy at the University of East Anglia. The university was 200 miles from London on the edge of a provincial town where I knew nobody. My first reaction was to burst into tears.

By mid-September, before any motorway ran up into East Anglia, we made the then-five-hour trip across country in our V.W. Beetle. Our destination: a remote cottage that my husband had arranged for us to live in, 15 miles north of the university town. There was no telephone, no transport, and no shop. A phone box at the end of an ancient green lane was our only connection to the outside world.

On Mondays, I used to watch, through the condensation of the kitchen window, as the tiny red lights on the back of my husband's car turned the corner of the disused airfield and disappeared into the mist. A terrifying quiet descended on the washing up.[1]

Some months later I came across two books that changed my life, one by Germaine Greer entitled *The Female Eunuch* (1970) and one by Paul Nordoff and Clive Robbins entitled *Therapy in Music for Handicapped Children* (1971).

By 1974, I had left my husband, returned to London, was sharing a flat with a friend and had started my music therapy training.

THE RISE OF EDUCATIONAL BRANDING

> *The babies did not go towards the things which it was supposed would have pleased them, like for example, toys; neither were they interested in fairy stories. Above all they sought to render themselves independent of adults in all the actions which they could manage on their own; manifesting clearly the desire not to be helped, except in cases of absolute necessity. And they were seen to be tranquil, absorbed and concentrating on their work, acquiring a surprising calm and serenity.*
>
> —Maria Montessori, 1956

With the fall of socialism, capitalism has become the major driving force of the developed and developing world. Competition has infiltrated all areas of society and all levels of activity, including education. A recent study from the Institute of Education (Ball & Vincent, 2005) reveals that middle class parents strive to pack in as many separate skill-based activities as early as possible in order to prepare their children for the race ahead. Children as young as three are in

[1] "Washing up" is an English term for 'doing the dishes'

competition with one another: "For middle class parents, giving your preschool child a head start, which after all means over other children, is commonly understood as 'good parenting'" (Beck & Beck-Gernsheim, 1995).

Anxious that without "enrichment" activities such as music, drama, art, or sport, children are in danger of falling behind, parents use time, previously available to their children for free play, to buy into pre-set activities. The researchers concluded that "Enrichment activities are one response to the anxiety and sense of responsibility experienced by middle class parents as they attempt to resist 'fears of falling' (Ehrenreich, 1989)" (Ball & Vincent, 2005).

It is interesting to note that throughout the 1960s and 1970s, during which time the women's movement was influential on child care policy, the established view was that the ability of a child to form relationships went hand in hand with free play. Who would have guessed that teachers in the 21st century would have to restate what Maria Montessori, Friedrich Froebel, and Jean Piaget had argued decades before; that young children learn best through spontaneous exploration. The head teacher of a London nursery school recently had to clarify, as if it were a forgotten concept, that children who have free time to make mud pies or construct games react more freely with other children and seem to be more independent because they have been allowed to develop their own set of skills.

Educational competition now starts at the cradle and pervades all levels of education, right up and throughout university education. Whether teaching or learning, we are all affected; academics are now ranked on their individual research contributions, rather than on their ability to work as a team.

Productivity and Marketing

It is ironic that the one female prime minister we have had in the UK has largely been responsible for much of this change towards an individualistic ethos. Under Margaret Thatcher, non-manufacturing activities, from which one was able to derive any kind of income, began to be termed industrial: The music industry, the film industry, the tourist industry, to name but a few. Creative potential began to be considered as productive potential; productivity led to growth and growth has indeed brought about economic prosperity—for some. (The difference between rich and poor in the UK is reportedly greater now than it has been since Victorian times.)

It is argued that the spin-off from competition (advantages of one product over another fought for, innovations emerging as a result) lead to a "healthier" economy. What benefit these new technologies have for the wider society that we live in seems of relatively little interest overall. It is growth that has for so long now been the driving force. As Thatcher herself famously said, "There is no such thing as society" (Thatcher 1987).

Companies, inevitably in competition with one another, hunker down and compete, working their employees long, blinkered hours. It is not difficult to understand how the resulting technological spin-offs have led to our sending a small probe, about the size of a fridge, via Venus, Earth, Jupiter, to the rings of Saturn, through the rings of Saturn to land on the surface of Titan, Saturn's moon, whilst back here on earth, climate change is about to run out of control. We are not functioning as a balanced society, in which notions of care are equal to notions of competition, but as a marketplace.

Productivity feeds on growth and products require marketing. With marketing comes branding. A known brand is easier to market than an unknown brand. Thus an image of the MacDonald's "arches" is now as powerful as the US flag.

So academic subjects, separate in their enquiry, must compete for survival with one another. If students don't want to study physics, then a physics department is no longer viable. Some departments bask in their research productivity, those less "productive," such as music, fight to keep up. As for a discipline as small and therefore potentially uncompetitive as music therapy, we are lucky if we can keep hold of the tiny crevices of the educational "market" that we have painstakingly acquired.

Clearly we no longer inhabit the same world as we did forty years ago when feminist writers were busy influencing education. Back then, it was still possible to learn for learning's sake in educational establishments that would largely have admonished any demand for accountability as to the monetary value of one subject as opposed to another. Selling a subject because it might attract students was incompatible with academic reputation.

In her chapter "Baby," Greer (1970/1971) discusses the importance of Montessori's work in establishing open classrooms in which children could spontaneously learn together. From our "post-feminist" perspective here in 2006, it is interesting to note how Greer railed against the fact that Montessori's methods had not yet reached the universities, as if that were an entirely possible project: "Even at university level I have found it impossible so far to run a research laboratory which would be a similarly cooperative effort" (Greer, 1970/1971, p.73).

The words "so far" capture the spirit of the age—these were revolutionary times, chaotic yes, but alive and inspirational. It is not difficult to imagine what the modern day university administrator would make of such a project, or how the modern day health service manager would react to Winnicott's view:

> It is only in playing that the individual child [*or adult*] is able to be creative and to use the whole personality, and it is only in being creative that the individual discovers the self. (Winnicott 1971, p.63)

Is capitalism destroying feminism and with it the ability to play? From my experience, back in the 1970s, little children used to be out on the streets with mud on their shoes. Now they are glimpsed, staring blankly out of car windows between assignments.

The Branding of Music Therapy

By the late seventies, alongside Thatcherism with the second wave of feminism in decline, a need arose to define separate approaches to music therapy. Within each approach attempts were made to separate out distinct techniques and to name them.

Women are known to be skilled at multitasking, managing a number of muddled situations all at once—like feeding a baby whilst attending to a toddler. I do not intend to make any assumptions about this, in terms of whether it was men or women who took a more active approach in separating off defined music therapy approaches. I limit myself here to thinking about the effects of this process on the profession, keeping in mind a symbolic muddle capacity[2] and a symbolic aim capacity that both women and men utilise at different times. Capacities that feminism suggests need to be kept in balance.

I will briefly outline how I experienced some definitions emerging from a UK perspective. This is not a historical account. Others have already usefully mapped this out (Bunt & Hoskyns, 2002). Originally, Receptive Music Therapy and Active Music Therapy were the two most-used definitions in the UK at least, registering the difference between a method of playing music to patients as opposed to patients being invited to create music with therapists.

Mary Priestley's model which integrated concepts from Sigmund Freud, Carl Jung, and Melanie Klein, was then defined as Analytical Music Therapy,

[2] 'Muddle capacity': By this I do not mean muddle-headed but the means by which multistranded, unpredictable interactions are engaged in and valued for what they are—indistinct. The muddle capacity is useful because it allows muddled situations to be contained and responded to without the need to distinguish between discrete elements. Perhaps without it, maternal preoccupation would not be possible, for how would you manage to think about yourself and your infant if you were required to think of them separately?

to the consternation of some music therapists who felt the term analytical should refer only to Freudian perspectives. The approach of Paul Nordoff and Clive Robbins became known as Creative Music Therapy, much to the consternation of music therapists who had not trained with Nordoff and Robbins but who were using music creatively. Alongside these, Helen Bonny's Guided Imagery and Music, known as GIM (and now BMGIM), was emerging gradually with its own separate levels of training in the US.

By the time Kenneth Bruscia's seminal work *Improvisational Models of Music Therapy* was published in 1987, the definition of distinct techniques had taken hold. And by the time Music Psychotherapy was emerging in the US in the late nineties as a separate model (Bruscia 1998), at least one training course in the UK had already defined itself, perhaps wisely, as Psychoanalytically Informed.

One of the more recent brands to have arrived on the shelf is Community Music Therapy, known as CoMT, championed by a group of therapists, including Brynjulf Stige and Trygve Aasgaard (2005). One of the many new models and approaches introduced at the 11th world Congress of Music Therapy in Brisbane, Australia, was Music Advanced Directives (Chadwick & Wacks, 2005). There were numerous others.

Once started, branding has quickly taken hold, allowing groups of practitioners with a marketable product access to the theoretical and therapeutic marketplace. All of this on the face of it looks rather impressive. Surely the identification of distinct approaches and core techniques promotes discussion and debate. Students can shop around for a brand they like before starting a training course. As consumers of higher education services this obviously makes sense in an education market place, indeed there are sometimes advantages in learning how to do one thing properly.

Yet inevitably, individual brands tend to hold exclusive symposia in order to engage in internal debates. This allows the brand protection against competition. Discussing findings and ideas within an inner circle avoids any serious conflict of interest. At best, this allows practitioners time and space to develop a theoretical stance potentially worthy of a separately named approach.

Defining separate music therapy approaches, sometimes miles apart, within a wider accredited arts therapy profession does, however, pose some problems and questions. For example, how can subdisciplines be of value to the music therapy profession as a whole, and how should they be appraised?

Relativism and Music Therapy Models

For such a tiny profession it seems we now have a disproportionately wide range of approaches. There are a number of reasons for this. We have learned through experience that the old adage, "united we stand, divided we fall" is useful in the age of competition. It is thought to be a sign of maturity that we are now able to tolerate differences between models. However, whether we are tolerating these differences because we have "grown up" as a profession or simply because we need to be part of a larger group in order to hold our own in competition with other therapies, such as psychotherapy, remains to be seen. In addition, the nature of our work is wide-ranging, music bearing relevance to most human functions, and thus to a wide range of human dysfunctions. With each new clinical population comes the need to define how best to use music therapeutically.

Once defined, there is a need to produce evidence of the value of a new model or approach. Evidence Based Practice (or EBP) would seem to encourage practitioners to test out predefined methods of treatment rather than attempt evaluations of uniquely muddled music therapy encounters.

In addition, there is the impact of relativism to consider: the relativist position that any theory can be thought of as true, depending upon a person's cultural and moral perspective. As long as one can define a theory and believe that it is true, then there is truth, relative to oneself. On the face of it this would seem a useful thing. However, this has led to a situation where some argue that creationism is as valid a truth as evolutionary theory, even though one is based on faith, the other on scientific observation.

For example, Analytically Informed Music Therapy (AIMT) exists alongside BMGIM, though these approaches are contradictory; BMGIM relies on musical techniques instigated by the therapist that specifically set out to move the patient from a state of consciousness to a state of altered consciousness, whilst AIMT avoids such techniques. In a relativist world anything goes—as long as it is true for someone.

Critics of relativism argue that it has become increasingly difficult to have a genuine disagreement in order to protect core truths. Knowledge that has taken hundreds and thousands of years to painstakingly acquire is now in a pick-and-mix situation, up against easier options.

Relativism met music therapy head-on at the World Congress of Music Therapy in Washington in 1999. At that auspicious meeting it was fascinating to walk between rooms and listen to inner circles discussing the intricacies of their models. Somewhat uncomfortable with having to align myself with a particular approach, I found myself on a panel of experts in the music psychotherapy hall—I had recently had a paper published that was concerned with psychoanalytic concepts, yet also with musical awareness (Streeter 1999). I wonder if I was alone in this discomfort. Many therapists may have felt resistant to being associated with separated theoretical frameworks, as if models were now beginning to dictate the debate and thus determine the future of how the profession would evolve.

On entering rooms in which a particular approach is being presented, it is certainly possible to enquire about what this or that means. But imagine standing up alone in a room full of club members and questioning the very brand itself—not an easy option.

At worst, relativism is capable of isolating the individual against the crowd and thus impeding critical debate. The fear of theoretical disagreement brings with it the splitting off of ideas. This may not mean that disagreements have disappeared, merely that they remain latent beneath the surface, unresolved. A situation in which people fear expressing their views counteracts the very notion of academic debate.

Perhaps we can look to feminism to help out here. Unlike relativism in which differences of opinion are apparently underplayed, feminism is a political theory that relies on critical debate to empower change. In the seventies, some women burned their bras, some women didn't; some women wanted wages for housework, some women thought this was missing the point; some women wanted bookshops that denied access to men, others protested fiercely against this. The feminist debate raged its way over the scrubbed-pine kitchen tables of the seventies and in and out of our relationships.

Yet in 1981, despite our differences, indeed because of them, thousands of women found the strength to engage in a 19-year-long, 24-hour open-air protest against the storing of nuclear missiles at Greenham Common, until they were eventually taken away.

Without those years of experimental personal politics and the fierce debates that powered them, would we ever have managed it?

And is it still possible to make mud pies?

The Nursing Couple

> *Psychotherapy takes place in the overlap of two areas of playing; that of the patient and that of the therapist.*
>
> —Winnicott 1971

One of Winnicott's central ideas was that "there is no infant, only a nursing couple" (Winnicott, 1965, p.39). This concept seems a helpful way forward in considering what might lie beyond the proliferation of separate music therapy approaches. Winnicott's thesis leads me back to the central core of my own work: the unknowable, unpredictable act of sharing the creation of musical form. Sharing the creation of music with a child with autism, for example, has the potential to reach beyond the disability.

In making mud pies, neither the mud nor the pie is usefully separated. Rather, they are constantly in relation to one another, as is the nursing couple, as is the musician-therapist and the musician-client. This is the central core of music therapy as I have practised it: an uncertain creative act between two people or a group of people, that when guided by the informed therapist, results in benefit to the client, or clients, and potentially the music therapist herself.

The process of allowing music to emerge from within a relationship is at heart a maternal activity that draws on the central human experience of interdependency, which both women and men have access to and can engage in. Vulnerable fragmented edges of musical contact, connections that cannot easily be mapped out or individually defined—this is the stuff of music therapy as I have experienced it and as I have attempted to teach it.

Whilst recognising the value of defined techniques and models, the infinite possibilities for finding shared expression in music require real flexibility on the part of the musician-therapist and a tolerance to bearing the unknown. So often a moment, potentially full of contact, disintegrates with the sheer force of a precomposed melody, an identifiable metre, a technique for slowing down or speeding up. The unique quality of music therapy is its capacity to provide opportunities for revisiting, or perhaps visiting for the first time, the unpredictable process of genuine, shared communication, and thus relationship.

It seems to me that the job of any therapist is to help the patient feel understood. Knowing another human being requires a genuine desire to encounter the unknown, a capacity to withstand uncertainty. It is not about creating a product or embarking on a sale.

As Bridget Jones said, "He loves me—just the way I am." The capacity to be in music with another person and to accept them—just the way they are—requires a journey without a map. A supervisee noted of work recently completed with a young woman that had lasted for three years, "On looking back I realise that the whole of the therapy was actually in four sections, although I did not know it at the time."

> *Children play more freely when the other person is able and free to be playful.*
>
> —Winnicott 1971

We need to value and protect the muddle capacity and ensure that it is not overshadowed by the aim capacity.

CONCLUSION

A male academic recently told me at a conference that out of nine music therapy researchers he knew of, five had dropped out. He was at pains to add that they were all women. I suggested we leave gender out of the discussion, but it seems important here that I mention it.

I am left with a question: Can fundamentalism arise from branding and if so, how do we avoid it? It is easier to buy into a brand than to embark on an unmapped journey. Thus music therapy students often start by wanting answers to specific questions and end by being able to tolerate unanswerable questions. Music therapy academics have a responsibility to inform and guide but not pre-determine, in my view, the map of any music therapy encounter. Our job is to help therapists acquire the necessary critical thinking skills to choose the right mix of music therapy techniques that relate to the problems of the individual patient.

Feminism teaches that some kinds of freedom have to be fought for, whether or not it is uncomfortable to fight for one's rights. Liberation was a word much used in the seventies. Let us find the strength to climb over the fences and under the wires, utilise any means of making music that can meet a patient's therapeutic need, whether or not it relates to a named model that has been described in a book. By placing clients and their needs at the centre of the therapeutic decision-making process, we honour the fact that music is a meeting place.

If the nursing couple can remain at the heart of our work, spontaneous and thus musically prepared to go anywhere, an inspiration rather than a model, then we will not go far wrong. And if we keep hold of the fact that music therapy, a predominantly female profession, first took flight in the era of feminism, then we need not be frightened to assert ourselves at the highest academic level within the profession. Let us not fall into the trap of "liking the condition and finding it natural" (Choderlos de Laclos, 1783). That there is a disparity between the balance of women to men in the clinical field and the balance of men to women in the academic literature need not be of concern, unless the literature itself starts to control the practice.

POSTSCRIPT

Although feminism is sometimes misleadingly thought of as a desire on the part of women to take control of men, my experience of the women's movement, a term I actually prefer to the term feminism, is that wherever there are pockets of discrimination against women, women can raise awareness by exploring their identity, and sharing this knowledge with others.

Sadly it is the case that sexism is still part of many women's experience of daily life. Until it is over, we all have a responsibility, in whatever field we are engaged in, to change this. Right now in some areas of the world girls are unable to go to school let alone train as music therapists. Whilst such intolerable prejudice is alive in the world there is a responsibility to address it in whatever corners of society it rears its ugly head.

The attempt to gain balance between our muddle and our aim capacities, and to recognise the wide range of potentials within each, is a task we can all, male and female, share. As such, and at this time in history, it has never been more necessary.

REFERENCES

Ball, Stephen J. and Vincent, Carol (2005) "Making up" the middle class child: Families, activities and class dispositions. Paper for BERA Conference, Cardiff, Wales: University of Glamorgan.

Ball, Stephen J. (2004) Education for sale: A commodification of everything. Kings Annual Education Lecture, Institute of Education, University of London, June 17, 2004.

Beck, Ulrich & Beck-Gernsheim, Elizabeth (1995) *The Normal Chaos Of Love*, Cambridge: Polity Press.

Bruscia, Kenneth E. (1987) *Improvisational Models of Music Therapy*. Springfield Illinois: Charles C Thomas.

Choderlos de Laclos, (1783) On the Education of Women. Cited in Germaine Greer (1970/1971). *The Female Eunuch*. London: MacGibbon & Kee.

Chadwick, Donna & Wacks, Karen (2005) *Music advance directives: Music choices for later life*. Paper given at the 11th World Congress of Music Therapy, Brisbane, Australia.

Ehrenreich, Barbara (1989) *Fear of Falling: The Inner Life of the Middle Class*, New York: Pantheon.

Greer, Germaine (1970/1971) *The Female Eunuch*. London: MacGibbon & Kee.

Hoskyns, Sarah & Bunt, Leslie (2002) *The Handbook of Music Therapy*. London: Routledge.

Nordoff, Paul & Robbins, Clive (1971) *Therapy in Music for Handicapped Children*. London: Victor Gollancz, Ltd.

Thatcher, Margaret (1987) There is no such thing as society. By Douglas Keay, for *Woman's Own Magazine* (September 23).

Stige, Brynjulf & Aasgaard, Trygve (2005) Researching community music therapy: Topics, objectives and methods. Paper given at the 11th World Congress of Music Therapy, Brisbane, Australia.

Streeter, Elaine (1999) Finding a balance between psychological thinking and musical awareness. *Journal of British Music Therapy 13*, 15–20.

Winnicott, Donald W. (1965) *Maturational Processes and the Facilitating Environment: Studies in the Theory of Emotional Development.* London: Karnac Books.

Winnicott, Donald W. (1974) *Playing and Reality.* Harmondsworth: Pelican Books. (First published in 1971 by London: Tavistock)

Chapter Sixteen

CONSIDERATION OF POTENTIAL INFORMANTS FROM FEMINIST THEORY FOR MUSIC THERAPY PRACTICE

Jane Edwards

INTRODUCTION

Elucidating aspects of feminist theory could be useful in developing some deeper theoretical constructs to support the practice of music therapy. Since many feminist theorists have contributed to debates about various forms of representation within society, I would suggest that discussions of clinical and community-based practices with music therapy clients benefit from reflection on these views. I hope that music therapy students and practitioners seeking a broader frame of reference by which to approach complex situations in their own lives or in therapy work with their clients can be stimulated and encouraged by reflection upon and reference to the ideas presented here.

I am a feminist. Since I am also an academic, I feel it necessary to ensure that it is clear to the reader that I do not present myself here as a feminist scholar. I have not undertaken any in-depth study of feminism in the way I have studied music therapy. I use the term feminism to refer to a tradition of theory and practice or even a way of perceiving the world that acknowledges that injustices occur against individuals and groups because of systemic problems that are broadly socially determined. My experience of contact with the varied theoretical discourse that constitutes contemporary feminism has led me to understand that feminists work to think about, deconstruct, disrupt, and interrogate existing values that operate in the construction of social values with the goal of emancipation and positive social change through encouraging and valuing the human agency of all citizens. These existing "relations of power" (Foucault, 1995) act to include and exclude, value and disenfranchise, privilege and disengage, and can prohibit agency and self-determination. Inherent in this view is the idea that all members of society participate in upholding or maintaining these values whether they are considered to be members of oppressing or oppressed groups.

These power values can operate consciously and unconsciously. Indeed, oppressive mechanisms are more powerful if they operate unconsciously under the guise of a neutral system, free of values or stratification. This determination can be read or experienced in various fora such as in ones interpersonal relationships, the media,[1] scholarly writing, the law, and so on. Oppression can occur against any group through preventing or limiting access to opportunities for choice and power or even through negotiation in professional work, personal life, division of labour in the home, in relation to identity, the body, and other constructs concerning the self. Feminist theory often concerns itself with these issues in relation to women, but it should be remembered that feminist theorising usually gives consideration to a range of human experiences, with critical appraisal of social norms that can be informed or even re-formed from feminist principles.

My motivation to write this chapter comes from the view I hold that most societies can and should "do better" in terms of their treatment of others. Frequently fielding the accusation (or perhaps I mistake people's admiration) that I am a Utopian, or even more recently a "Pollyanna," I find myself constantly asking "what's wrong with this picture?" and even "how did this picture come to be painted or photographed in this way?" How is it possible, for example, that at the time I am writing this, it is a fact that in the history of the albeit relatively new university where I currently work, not one woman has ever been promoted from my level to the next level? This cannot help but shape something of the energy I bring to the topic of feminism, and the ideas around power that inform this chapter.

The current circumstances for many of our clients, and those citizens we feel concern for but do not necessarily work with, are unacceptable to my value system. I consider that feminism offers one way to identify and question these discourses, and believe that these ideas can be used to collectively re-view our world of work, of power, of personal experience. Perhaps, like therapy, engagement with feminist theory offers a way to "catch sight of ourselves," since our perceptions are complexly influenced from preexisting values, terrains of knowledge, and ideas. We can hardly have a thought that should not be held up to some kind of scrutiny as problematic or "biased." Or to put it another way, "We always 'see' from points of view that are invested with our social, political,

[1] In *Bowling for Columbine* you might remember that Michael Moore asked the producer of *Cops* why he didn't show corporate thieves being arrested instead of poor non-white people. The answer was basically that when the police arrest a magnificently wealthy person they treat them with the greatest of courtesy and respect, and that would not be interesting television.

and personal interests, inescapably -centric in one way or another, even in the desire to do justice to heterogeneity" (Bordo, 2003, p.223).

As an example, I rarely have the experience of realising how many "givens" are in unconscious operation for me, but recently I watched the film *Buena Vista Social Club* (Wim Wenders, 1999). In the part of the film where the Cuban musicians come to New York City, I was struck by the way that US iconography was not etched on their mental landscapes. For example, they saw a line up of doll mannequins of US Presidents in a shop window and decided that the characters must all be famous people. Since the Clinton doll was holding a saxophone they concluded he might have been a visiting musician they performed with in Cuba. They pointed to Marilyn Monroe's image nearby and wondered aloud if she was famous but they had no name or context for her.

In reflecting upon and exploring existing and potential feminist informants for music therapy, it is important to suggest and claim that I, like most of you who will read this, have been brought up in an environment that has given heed to feminist issues and has incorporated, even unconsciously internalised, a value system that has an awareness of feminism in the same way that I, as an Australian citizen who lives and works in Ireland and has only visited the US five times can recognise images of Clinton, Nixon, Reagan, and Carter as well as Bush Sr., and Bush Jr., among others. I suggest that feminism is present in many points of view or debates for us even if it is not always called that; perhaps sometimes instead it is just referred to as "rights" or "women's issues." It is not possible then to reflect on the "inclusion" of feminist theory in this chapter as an addition to thinking about ways of working in music therapy, since for someone like myself feminism has been a surround or even a backdrop for all parts of my life—particularly those which are political or professional, as well as, of course, the personal. As I have suggested elsewhere:

> I would argue that music therapy is always a socio-political work—in simple terms, what we do with our clients and their families in turn effects our society simply by being part of the warp and weft of the fabric of our community behaviour . . . . Since the civil rights movement and the movements that followed, including the many strands of feminist theory and feminism, I think it is impossible to live without consciousness of the ways in which our society and community shape our perspective to "other" whether we understand that in Marxist terms or perhaps even with reference to Kristeva's useful notion of abjection.[2]

[2] Jane Edwards, *Voices*, August 6, 2002. See also, Julia Kristeva (1982) *Powers of Horror: An Essay on Abjection.* New York, Columbia University Press.

It seems to me that it has not been possible to be a citizen of the first world over the past forty years without being aware of terminology related to feminist thought such as "patriarchy," "subordination," "oppression," "minority," "identity" or "consciousness." These words have been actively discussed and used in writings about feminist theory; however, it is important to note their origins and use in the struggle and achievements of the Civil and Human Rights movements in the USA and beyond. I have elsewhere suggested that there is an emerging consciousness of these ideas in music therapy, even if they do not always take the shape and name of "feminism" and, as Susan Hadley and I have argued, a book like this one in which these ideas are developed and acknowledged is long overdue for our field (Hadley & Edwards, 2004).

In many of the feminist traditions which I find influential and interesting, the oppression of women by a social construct described as *patriarchy* is a primary arena for consideration of the revolutionary change needed in order for all citizens to have self-determining lives. The concept underpinning reference to patriarchal structures is that patriarchy is an inherited set of patterns that become internalised "frames" of reference, collectively and individually. Like any ideology,[3] patriarchy's mechanisms operate unconsciously and are difficult to extricate as "givens" since they are presented as normal and "correct."

A final introductory thought is that I understand, and use here, the term feminism to refer to many different traditions and theories, with a range of points of agreement and disagreement, solidarity and conflict. It is almost impossible for me to imagine a contemporary feminist perspective that is only prepared to accept one true way of knowing, living, and experiencing a feminist identity, or purports to hold one "correct" feminist theoretical stance. I agree with Susan Bordo's observation that "contemporary feminism remains a diverse and pluralist enterprise." (Bordo, 2003, p.216). It is important to me that every feminist can think about the potential as well as the limitations of a feminist perspective in any critical scrutiny of public or private life. It would be a misreading of this stance to consider that I find a personal and professional life informed from feminist ideals a hopeless enterprise. I suggest that the multifaceted nature of feminism is no more problematic than what we think we mean by terms such as democracy, psychoanalysis, or quantum physics. I especially reject the use of "feminist" as a monolithic term, or "feminism" used as a descriptor to identify a theory that is supposedly obvious, with the assumption

[3] I like the example Nicholas Cook gave about this in *Music: A very short introduction*, where he stated from a British perspective "During the Thatcher/Reagan years, it was received wisdom that ideology was what the other guy had. Capitalist democracy wasn't an ideology, it was just the way things were; it was the Russians who had ideology and look what happened to *them.*" (Cook, 1998, p.102)

that we all know what is meant by the employment of the term, and I dislike its frequent use as a synonym for misandry.

AN OVERVIEW OF SOME ARENAS OF FEMINIST THOUGHT

It is beyond the scope of this chapter, this book, our profession, and human capacity to ever be able to provide comprehensive representation of any one idea, approach, or experience. Rather, I wish to discuss and represent my own view about a panoply of feminist theoretical arenas with which I have come into contact and the way these are useful or at least interesting to the situation of the work of therapy, offering the possibility to view interaction with clients in a wider context than either a medical or wellness model. Many of these are contested sites of dialogue and exchange and it is important to point out that in a great number of cases theorists writing on the same topics do not agree with each other. In fact there are some theorists, such as psychoanalyst and philosopher Julia Kristeva (1984), often quoted in the feminist literature, who do not identify themselves as feminist and find the term feminist problematic and incongruent with their theoretical propositions.

Representation

The issue of representation has been a preoccupation of the various waves of feminism, especially when looking at arenas where achievements of men have been prized and acclaimed. In my daily life the question "Where are the women?" can be asked in almost every glance at the newspaper (especially the obituary section of the *Irish Times* newspaper where one is grateful for being female since so very few of them ever seem to die in this country), every board and committee meeting, and every government decision made on behalf of the electorate. One must be careful however not to only focus on gender balance and representation in engaging with feminist ideas. I am taken by Naomi Klein's observation that while her generation of student activists stood against the wall challenging their professors over the poor representation of minority groups in texts for course schedules they failed to notice that the wall was being sold off to corporate interests (Klein, 2000). Feminism offers more than a way to critique relations between men and women. It imagines and reinvents a world in which the forces oppressing any citizen can be challenged, dismantled, and discarded.

In this section, I will look at various ways in which some feminist theory has helped conceptualise issues around representation and discuss how, as music therapists, we can give consideration to these ideas within our work. Of course each of the topic headings intersects each of the others. The use of numbers and a list of terms are used to assist the flow of the chapter and to spotlight some particular theoretical domains of relevance to the discussion.

1. The Body

Kim Arnold and Kate Boulay presented a paper on the concept of beauty at a recent Utopian studies conference at the University of Limerick. Taking the television programme *The Swan*[4] as their topic, they questioned what has gone on in our society, not just that women will allow this to be done to them, nor that there are medical personnel prepared to carry out procedures on these healthy women, but that we, the viewers, are fascinated to watch this grotesque and deforming process.

> The problem with feminist critics and with us is that we wind up in an either/or situation. Either the women participating in The Swan have agency or they are misguided fools. Obviously it is preferable to think of them as women with wit and agency and women who . . . are making concerted efforts to improve their lives. Although, it is unfair to expect these particular women to act in a non-atomized way when almost all women do so all the time, we consider these women as a microcosm of abstract femaledom. It seems intolerable that cultural identity be so ruthlessly staged upon their bodies. (Arnold & Boulay, 2005)

It is not original to note that the capitalist consumer project requires that we continuously feel anxious. In this way we will pay money for things we don't need in order to alleviate our anxiety; so "the economy" turns. If idealised beauty is used as a means by which most women can think of themselves as "nothing" and inadequate, a vast amount of money can be spent on making adjustments that allay the anxiety, but cannot remove it, and encourage the

[4] I had never heard of this program so in case there is a reader who also never watches TV, women "win" the chance to have 16 plastic surgery procedures. The process is filmed and edited. Women semifinalists are selected for a final beauty competition and the winner takes home a large money prize.

buying into an ideal(ogy) which by its nature can never be achieved, therefore requiring ongoing spending and effort.[5]

The more that products can be manufactured and advertised with promises to the purchaser that beauty will be attained, and the more anxiety that can be generated about whether or not one has it, the more money can be made. However this awareness does not necessarily help women such as myself to feel less compelled by the insistence that they make at least some effort to attain ideal beauty; having perfect hair, working against wrinkles—I am sure these themes are familiar to many.

As a therapist then, I take my own body, including my conscious and unconscious conceptions of my body, its inadequacies, and my often-failed expectations of it, into work with others where their own body is a site of contested expectations and even failures. Working with children with severe burn injury with no hope of ever being free of scar tissue in their adult lives, I have become aware of norms about the intactness and smoothness of skin. Working with adults with enduring mental illness, I am aware that their bodies often are bloated and far too large from the effects of medications. These body changes seem to defy the "improvement" the medication is bringing, as constant media messages inform that the obese person is a liability to society, costing more in health care in the long term and ensuring that a person will have a shorter life expectancy. Every fashion magazine and television drama shows beautiful, thin people having exciting and fulfilled lives. At the same time we can find spaces to consider and be critical of our own preoccupation with what we look like and how this preoccupation and resultant unease potentially stops us from having time to be effective in wider domains of social and political activity, or to be truly engaged with and responsive to our clients' complaints of the inadequacies of their own bodies in the "marketplace" of status-conscious humans.

I suggest that our support of clients with injuries and disabilities through creative expression and development has potential to create new spaces to envision such domains as beauty, art, and personal representation, allowing different self-constructs to emerge. We can monitor and support our clients' expressions of difference, embracing their difference and their and our anger at the variously operating corporate interests that construct their identity as problematic and inferior.

[5] A young friend preparing for her wedding showed me a magazine that caters to "brides." She had memorised the section devoted to "figure flaws" with advice on how to buy a dress to overcome these for your special day. Virtually every female body shape in the article was represented as being problematic and needing some help or "disguise" as it was phrased.

2. Health

In writing about issues of representation and the body, some feminists have also provided critical perspectives elucidating discourses of health and illness and how these are formed and framed by patriarchy. Of course feminists are not the only theorists to consider issues of health and illness and the power operatives and assumptions playing out in personal and corporate arenas of health service receipt and delivery; but feminist writers have exposed power frames in relation to health and illness in uniquely interesting ways. As practitioners, students, and health service recipients ourselves, we can use some of these ideas to interrogate the structures of power that inform both the places of our work as well as impact the experiences of those with whom we work, whether coworkers or patients.

In some feminist theorising around health concepts, the issue of scientific perspectives to health and illness are challenged as leaving ordinary, non-expert, self-knowledge without a place in contemporary health care. Bordo (2003) has suggested that "Since the seventeenth century, science has 'owned' the study of the body and its disorders. This proprietorship has required that the body's meanings be utterly transparent and accessible to the qualified specialist . . . and utterly opaque to the client herself" (p.66). Health service provision seems to require that we accept that we do not know, and are therefore demystified by "expert" opinion. We must consider how it is that we as "patients" play along with this. As music therapists also, we can give consideration to how our own role as "expert" is constructed by ourselves and in conjunction with the client, perhaps in a mutual fantasy that our expertise will "cure" them. If we truly wish to engage with the life narratives of our clients, their own lived identities and the framing of their experiences in relation to these, we must be prepared to "learn" the patient by coming alongside them, rather than starting from a position of authority and "knowing." I have said before in relation to patients with head injury that we may well know in an "expert" way about brain functions and the deficits caused by lesions in certain areas, however in a therapeutic relationship with a client, we must learn what those deficits mean for that particular person's communication, interests and personhood (Edwards, 2005).

In a discussion of how it is that women's health advocacy and feminist theory have not had a stronger association, Ellen Kuhlmann and Birgit Babitsch (2002) proposed that while "Feminist theories and women's health research share the common intention of reflecting critically on biology as a stable and fixed framework for the categories 'bodies' and 'gender' . . . [the] mere transfer of feminist concepts to women's health research . . . can hardly be the goal of future work" (Kulmann & Babitsch, 1999, p.441). Some radical feminist approaches have put forward the idea that instead a revolution is needed, not just some kind of reframing or seeing of the social and individual needs to which health provision attends. For example, Carrie Klima (2001) writing about women's health stated that ". . . [in] a radical feminist approach . . . women would be approached to determine how their health care needs might be met based on their lives and their experiences, and the services would be designed to meet these needs" (p.288). Should we be ashamed that this is being proposed as a "radical" view?

It is possible however that some feminist discussion of the body leads so far away from a medical essentialism of the body as a "thing," or even a container for the category "health," that health service provision with its short-term pragmatic agenda, does not have the capacity to consider these arguments. As music therapists we might see how we can keep some of these ideas at play in the health and treatment contexts in which we work, and also consider how power in health care contexts is gendered, invested, and "played," and how this might influence which beans are counted into which pile or jar in allocation of service funds; we should continue to be critical, responsive, and alert to these phenomena.

I am not alone in suggesting that in the West we seem to have difficulty developing systems of health care based on need that deliver the best possible service to the widest number of people based on the best possible evidence of benefits for individuals and communities. As music therapists, we need to help our managers and administrators and project leaders to stand up for client needs, to advocate rather than "dispense," and we must resist the efforts of our systems to create burnt-out automatons who have lost the capacity for creativity in our own lives, and therefore might unconsciously resist the expression of creative need in our clients.

3. Gender

As a species we are relatively homogenous. It is rare for a fully-grown human to be twice as large as another for example whereas some breeds of dogs are three times the size of others. Nonetheless, it seems to be a human proclivity to obsessively define aspects of our difference from each other. Considering how these "differences" are constructed, the basis on which they operate, and who benefits from them has been a consistent theme in many areas of feminist scholarship.

> . . . men and women are caught up in a network of millennial cultural determinations of a complexity that is practically unanalyzable: we can no more talk about "woman" than about "man" without getting caught up in an ideological theatre where the multiplication of

> representations, images, reflections, myths, identifications constantly transforms, deforms, alters each persons imaginary order and in advance, renders all conceptualisation null and void. (Cixous, 1999, p.443)

Many feminist theorists such as Hélène Cixous quoted here have proposed that it is not just our internalisation of patriarchy that is problematic in trying to imagine a different world in which we can breathe, but rather that within a patriarchal system, the continuous use of binary oppositions as sense-making of self constantly disrupts what is possible for individual freedoms. The terms "woman" and "man" become instantly problematic when trying to use the imagination to conceptualise and then develop a different system of human experience than that which we have inherited. "'Masculinity' and 'Femininity,' at least since the nineteenth century and arguably before, have been constructed through a process of mutual exclusion" (Bordo, 2003, p.174). Constantly reinforcing the view that what women are and have cannot be anything like men and vice versa. This is summarized by Andrea Dworkin in her often-quoted statement "while the system of gender polarity is real, it is not true" (Dworkin, 1975).

We must increasingly realise that as we enter therapy relationships with our clients, these relationships come laden with power differentials that include those influenced by gender.[6] There is no *view from nowhere*, to adopt Thomas Nagel's postmodern catch cry (Nagel, 1989). Instead, all of our experiences and histories swim into therapy processes alongside us and there is always a power dynamic operating that the best use of our own countertransference must elucidate; not in order that one person has power and one person doesn't but rather that the ways the therapist has access to power are used to facilitate the client's recovery and the client's use of power should be able to be thought about by the therapist. It may otherwise be the case that a struggle ensues where the unconscious recreation of previous power relations can violate attempts to elucidate the current story. There is no Freudian blank screen upon which the patient or client casts their shadow from which we interpret and "solve" their misery and limitations—we inevitably become intertwined in a co-created history of gender, power, and subjective value relations that we must always give heed to in understanding what our clients are telling us as they story their lives, as well as considering what we might be unconsciously relating to them

[6] Of course these relationships are also impacted by the complexity of intersections between gender and other influential registers such as culture, economic class, level of education, access to education, and so on.

about the values that we perceive as important and necessary in generating action and change in the way we are listening to them.

Feminism as I understand it asks us to be aware of the danger of perceiving our middle class (mostly white) therapeutic training about health and illness, as neutral and "objective," and as a consequence unwittingly reducing or even obliterating the authority of the client's own experience. As an example, some women with whom we work perhaps will not experience their depression as something to do with being female despite evidence to show that many more women are diagnosed with depression than men. Our knowledge that there may be something about their femaleness or their experience of woman-ness in the world which impacts upon their current place of being, could be a starting place from which a mutual exploration can take place around how their circumstances are responded to and constructed. However we must be aware that a client may not experience her own individual circumstances as related to issues of gender or gender construction. We therefore need to give time to understanding the patient's life narrative rather than trying to tell their story for them.

4. Sexuality

Some feminist theorists have disrupted our self-evident preconditioned notions that our gender status informs our sexuality (e.g. Butler, 2004), helpfully dis-engaging our notions of gender category from ideas about sexuality. Whether able to be identified as gay, bi, hetero, trans, asexual, and other ways of viewing sexuality, our gender alone does not, cannot, be a sole determinant of our sexual experiences and preferences.

Similarly, some of our normative ideas about gender relations as derived from the nature of genitalia have negatively impacted gendered role expectations—that is, ideas such as the female is a "receptor" for the male.[7] I like the way the feminist ideas I was introduced to early in university life questioned this assumption and asked whether it was possible to have an equally valid view that the male was "enclosed" by the female in the sexual act; but of course I now acknowledge that both views are problematic and bizarre. Ultimately, the idea that the way sex is performed between men and women dictates relations in other domains between genders has, for me, become less and less relevant. I agree that existing ". . . discourses . . . construct female and male bodies in ways that constitute and validate the power relations between

[7] In writing this I have started to think about the inevitable redundancy of the metaphor of "plug" and "socket" for male and female parts with the introduction of wireless technology. Think how many generations we have laboured with the idea that plugs and sockets are part of a *natural* system of how devices are connected.

men and women" (Gatens, 1999, p.231) and I am hoping that a radical agenda for all citizens is to continue to interrogate and ultimately relinquish this peculiar view.

Power does not operate in terms of "who's on top" but who gains, who loses, who has autonomy, for whom is the right to say "yes" or "no" available in any given situation. To require women to abdicate power because of an anatomical legacy has seemed to me one of the more absurd notions of the 20th century. I wish we could use the genius of some psychoanalytic ideas in a more enlightened way than to continue to perceive "female bodies as lacking or castrated and male bodies as full or phallic" (Gatens, 1999, p.231).

As music therapists, we must be aware that we may have taken in and be adhering to some of these normative assumptions about sexuality that do not allow us to be open to client experiences outside those that are congruent with our own. In addition, we are often obliged to work within systems that are informed from frames holding pejorative views of the needs of people from queer communities (e.g. DSM-IV), that is, not open to the expression of "other," but rather using the health or welfare system to reinforce social norms and potentially as punishment for those who do not conform to agreed categories of gender and sexual orientation.

I think then that some of our work in teams can be to offer reframing of situations and events. We might question whether if most males in the world were cross-dressers, would it be the case that men who did not engage in cross-dressing were "abnormal"? We might question why we so readily accept that wearing dresses as a little boy is considered a normal part of development and even amusing, but continuing this behaviour past a certain age is completely unacceptable in many sectors of society. As creative arts therapists could we consider whether some actions considered pathological are inherently creative, and encourage the telling and expression of these in different terms than psychological pain where the person's story warrants or requests it? Or consider whether the psychological pain experienced is externally imposed as much as internally experienced as shame for some of our clients. We can take opportunities to question in every professional work place whether majority status always requires the imprimatur of "normality." For example, since there is so much violence in society (especially through war), should we consider violent behaviour normal, and pacifism and concern about violence as a neurotic trait indicative of weakness and even pathology?

5. *Music*

The question of representation within music has been challenged (see Citron, 1993; McClary, 1991). What Nicholas Cook describes as the "vicious circle" whereby the lack of compositions from women is not constructed as a social phenomenon related to opportunity or existing conventions, but rather is essentialised as a problem of the inadequacy of femininity in the face of the creative task; the best explanation for the absence of women from the canon must be that women are not capable of successful musical composition.[8]

One difficulty with pointing out issues of lack of representation is that it engages assumptions that where women want to be is where men are, instead of the idea that "a woman's place is where *she* wants it to be." The low or even non-representation of women in some sectors of music is easily problematised to be both about opportunities and about choices but it could be argued that historically it has also been about perceptions of women's ability in playing. Here I am thinking of perceptions of who can play drums, electric bass, trombone, or until relatively recently in the Berlin Philharmonic, who can play classical music at all! The problem of sexism per se is rarely voiced in these representations. It might not be that women are kept out because individual men do not want them to be there, rather that if musical structures, for example rock music, are created around aspects of male identity—that is, created by men to demonstrate and play out some aspects of masculine experience and agency—women will always be inadequately represented.

In terms of our own practice, we must become more aware of the ways music itself conveys or reinforces social identity constructs and in a sense offers ways to embed discrimination. Think of the many years of Western musicology when music of the so-called Western canon was consistently represented as superior to what was described as "ethnic" music; in simple terms the idea being that Western classical music was free of cultural reference, it was just "good" music.

We might consider whether clients and students we work with can think about or deconstruct aspects of their music preferences and examine the extent to which these preferences liberate or reinforce for them certain shackles of representation. We might try to engage music therapy students with ideas about representation in music, to ask them to read a couple of Susan McClary's essays, or require them to consider how they view human relations of power and how they might see these reflected musically, politically, personally.

[8] As recently as 10 years ago, a professor of music put this view to me as fact: "Since there are no compositions from women in the past, you have to come to the conclusion that women can't compose." In the same department another staff member confided his "worry" that so many women were being appointed. I pointed out that we were nowhere near 30% of the staff, and his response indicated that he thought 40% would be the tolerable maximum. Or the professor in one of the physical science departments who told me they had no gender issues in their department because they didn't have any women.

6. The Voice

Ultimately, as music therapists, I believe we are concerned with how the client's voicelessness becomes sounded and heard. Sometimes I regard gender as relatively neutral in the face of other barriers to access to power. I am therefore compelled by some of the arguments that critically engage the preoccupation with gender perspectives in feminist theory, for example Bordo's statement:

> If we wish to empower diverse voices, we would do better, I believe, to shift strategy from the methodological dictum that we foreswear talk of "male" and "female" realities . . . to the messier, more slippery, more practical, struggle to create institutions and communities that will not permit some groups of people to make determinations about reality for all. (Bordo, 2003, p.225)

Mary Daly and Chiara Saraceno (2002) in a discussion of the notion of *social exclusion* have suggested that adopting this frame of reference in examining imbalances in women's access to choice, and access to secure futures, allows for an approach that "emphasizes participation, involvement and customary way of life as against consumption, average income and well-being as primarily financial" (p.87). They also suggest that this term social exclusion, which has gradually replaced the term "poverty" in European Union (EU) legislation, has the benefit that it does not treat people as "passive objects of social and economic policies" but rather "social exclusion emerges as more dynamic, actor-oriented, multifaceted and methodologically plural than poverty" (Daly & Saraceno, 2002, p.87). It is possible to see in this example how feminist theory can move from the domain of the abstract radical to the pragmatic, responding to circumstances of all citizens, not just women.

Notions of inclusion and empowerment have appeared in some recent music therapy writings (e.g. Daveson, 2001; Proctor, 2001; Rolvsjord, 2004); it is wonderful to have the chance to read the study by Susan Baines (2003) incorporating feminist principles as a means of promoting agency and empowerment among participants in a community mental health programme, especially because of her commitment to including client's voices in the reporting of the project. If I had to imagine what music therapy would be more like if feminist voices and principles were stronger, Baines's work would be an exemplar. I like her conceptualisation of the music therapist as "paid professional facilitator" (Baines, 2003). The qualified therapist is not the "authority" on how this client or this group should *do* music therapy. At the same time, an online journal with which I am associated, *Voices* (www.voices.no), takes the theme of providing space for people in music therapy from around the world to be heard in a forum which has different expectations, but possibly a wider readership than a traditional academic journal format.

Therapists who use terms such as "action research" and "empowerment" are obliged to consider that theirs is not the only authorial voice that should be included in publications, nor theirs the only observations that are relevant to understanding client experiences. I am sure I am not the only person to feel that there are potential difficulties for inclusion of clients in the reporting of our music therapy work where their story has been central and where we have advocated for and facilitated their agency, however in reading some of the experiences of Alan Turry and his client Maria (Turry, 2005), I feel as if some steps might be taken towards negotiating this territory successfully in some cases.

In a parenting program for women abused in childhood who are either pregnant or have children, Toni Day and Helen Bruderer (2002) provided song writing as means to give voice to the experiences of this group of women. These amazing songs are now part of a training resource for workers. The songs of these women give voice to their pain, distrust, anxiety, and ultimately power and determination to live and have different lives. Toni, a music therapist and Helen, a social worker, ably employed feminist principles in providing a space for agency and determination in this group. It is not necessarily easy to embrace these principles as part of a therapeutic approach, especially when authority about musical decisions, or about text that can be used, or ideas about who decides what and how can and must get challenged constantly in a group process where adherence to a feminist frame is negotiated successfully.

Advocating Feminisms

The more difficult task for me in writing this chapter has been to consider the ways these theoretical discussions can become relevant in the practice of music therapy. When I have tried to answer the question, "then what does this mean for music therapy practice?" I have found myself expecting that I will know. I want to write inherently loose statements such as "what I will find myself doing with clients in response to this theorising will be different from you" however I think that leaves the reader, and myself, with the idea that these are just thoughts and writing, at risk of having nothing to do with practice. As I argued in the introduction, the task I set for myself in this chapter was partly to explicate how these ideas influence practice, rather than "introduce" them to the field.

It is important to me that we are not left with a hopeless and helpless attitude to the big ideas of sociopolitical theory but instead can see the benefits of opening up our work to the scrutiny of theoretical interrogation. At the same time, I think it is my feminist leanings that make me so frustrated sometimes at the insistent certainty of some writings in our field. We are potentially such an uncertain practice and I wonder if that uncertainty is responded to sometimes with an overstatement of authority in writing about topics in music therapy. I would like us to be better able to embrace the gift of uncertainty that comes with patients' stories and experiences. I have elsewhere presented on this topic in music therapy regarding my frustrations about researching in medical communities (and the two times I have presented the paper, I have read this section quickly):

> . . . as a music therapist in health care . . . we do not have uncertainty. We have proof, efficacy, knowing, evidence, statistical analysis, we have significance, authority and completeness of knowing . . . we do not have works in progress, we do not have creative not knowing . . . . (Edwards, 2004)

In my view this inability to be creative, present, and calm in the face of the uncertainty that music therapy interactions inevitably bring has limited what can be known in our profession and forced us to adopt or even appropriate forms of telling that do not allow for the range of complexities in our work to be embraced.

To expand upon this idea, in metaphysical terms, "forms are not fixed things, but temporary arrestations in continuous metastable flows, potentialities or evolutionary events" (Battersby, 1999, p.351). I like these thoughts of Christine Battersby around the way that body and self have been conceptualised. She has suggested that "we need to theorize agency in terms of patterns of potentiality and flow. Our body-boundaries do not contain the self; they *are* the embodied self" (Battersby, 1999, p.355). It is so important to be able to engage this potential and flow within our interactions with patients, but also in our engagement with emergent ideas in our field.

I therefore do not find feminism "impossible" because of its inability to offer a unilateral response to issues such as poverty, marginalisation, or disability. I am more compelled by theories such as feminism that can provide a way of seeing from different viewpoints, therefore creating dialectic instead of reinforcing dogma.

When advocating for a feminist approach to music therapy, perhaps it is most useful when we can try to keep in mind that power and its antecedents are experienced in different ways by different individuals and groups. Something that is evidence of an oppressive power operative in one context might be necessary for freedom and safety in another.[9] There can be no coherent "project" of "our position" or "our stance" as feminists. As music therapists, if we want to think about and even use feminist theory in our work, we must be able to consider alternate points of view, challenge ourselves and each other, especially when the thought-killer of hegemony makes an appearance, and we must try our best to be self-critical without being self-destructive.

For the past two decades, bell hooks has been one of the voices arguing this point that feminism can never be experienced or acted upon in the same way by everyone. She has been a strong advocate for re-theorising feminism, challenging white middle class women that our ideas about patriarchal power and its redistribution need critical reappraisal. In particular, the critique of the normative assumption of the objective mind being that of the white, educated male by some feminist theorising does not stand up to scrutiny from hooks who argues that in the new imaginary of self-within-society advocated by some feminists, the normative male is just being replaced by the normative female. One straightjacket replaced by another.

Voices of women such as hooks who are not white and/or middle class have been asking "who is this revolution for?" The "solidarity project" of second wave feminism—the view there is a sisterhood across the world and we unite hands to stand together against oppression—has received serious criticism on the basis that to be in solidarity one needs to have some experience that is like the sisters one proclaims to stand for and beside. For women who have more than one aspect of identity or personhood that jeopardizes their access to power, focussing on trying to make one part better might even make another worse.

While hooks offers a particularly difficult critique for the ears of white middle class women such as myself who call ourselves feminists, she also challenges the contribution of postmodernism which she points out is dominated by white male intellectuals. For hooks, postmodern writing and thinking is problematic as a means to pursuing a radical agenda, in spite of the alignment of the postmodern theorist with the idea of "other." In her view postmodernism is caught in a bind: on the one hand it has limitless potential for liberating the academy from its exclusivity and adherence to the idea of a superior master

[9] I volunteered to attend a series of focus groups in one workplace where a staff conduct manual was being developed. The members were absolutely convinced that raising your voice was always undesirable behaviour and constituted bullying. I tried to make a case that in a dangerous situation, shouting out a warning might save a person's life and that some people can be vicious and cruel with a low sounding voice and a smile on their face. I could not persuade them to change their mind.

narrative, but on the other postmodernism is interpreted and claimed by the expertise of the scholar. As she wrote about postmodernism (1990):

> As a discursive practice it is dominated primarily by the voices of white male intellectuals and/or academic elites who speak to and about one another with coded familiarity. Reading and studying their writing to understand post-modernism in its multiple manifestations, I appreciate it but feel little inclination to ally myself with the academic hierarchy and exclusivity pervasive in the movement today.

We might keep in mind however that hooks suggests that if we give up the modern conception of the self as embodying an essence, we can begin to more successfully emphasize the significance of the authority of experience, especially the experience of oppressed people. Ultimately, if feminist practices are to root their way more deeply into music therapy, this is possibly the best gift awaiting our renewal as a professional group. A harnessing of the capacity of music, whether precomposed, improvised, or composed in sessions to author and honour the experience of our clients, is part of the unique power available within music therapy processes. One of the greatest capacities of professional therapy facilitation through music is to come alongside clients into a new realm of self-determined agency, sometimes even from the source of our and their anger and rage about their circumstances.

SOME FINAL THOUGHTS

Most feminists recognise that power is not just something one has and another doesn't but is something constantly negotiated between actors in a range of sites. It is important that we can admit though that in many cases our clients have almost no access to power as regards their circumstances or conditions. Sometimes their very opportunities to have better circumstances might be sabotaged by ideas of inferiority and nothingness that we have worked hard alongside them to challenge and even re-form but nonetheless are perhaps etched onto the visual landscape of the housing estates in which they live, the newspaper headlines that reflect their identity as problematic, and the lack of expectation from others about their future. You might ask whether you live beside anyone who could be a potential client of yours?[10] Do you socialise with

[10] A New York colleague in feedback on this chapter wrote "in New York everyone is a client" in response to this. I am however living in a country where the privileged and the

people who have the same difficulties as your clients? Are you in a church group, social movement, local government committee with anyone from your client group? How represented is your client cohort in your acquaintanceship, in your life? I can ask myself exactly the same questions and squirm as I think through my answers.

On the one hand we can talk about the importance of boundaries all we like, but on the other we have to admit that they may have a self-serving function as a way to turn around our discomfort that not only is it the case that our clients do not have the same access to power that we have but, as well, they have almost no chance of ever achieving economic or social equality with us.

Sometimes at social functions in Ireland, the UK, or Australia when people mock or become angry about social inclusion measures, or measures to ensure representation of women or minority groups, I can scarcely contain my rage and anger and, ultimately, despair. It seems axiomatic that white middle class people will see their own effortless privilege as normal. They worked hard for what they have and if only others would work hard, they could have it too.

At the same time I can accept criticisms, such as those by Bordo (2003), of an emerging non-reflexive postmodern view that finds all situations have potential for resistance and subversion. This might seem perfectly reasonable for the person sitting behind their laptop in the developed world, but for the Thai prostitute indentured to a pimp from her early teens and beaten and demeaned regularly with no chance to pay off her debt, resistance and subversion should not be assumed as available options (see Bales, 2002).[11]

I also appreciate that many music therapists I come into contact with feel disillusioned at their own lack of power as evidenced by their poor pay and conditions, and poor access to arenas in which they can negotiate for change. Often a music therapist will leave a poorly paid, inadequately resourced post and another music therapist will apply for it. Thus, we seem to be reluctant to create conditions that challenge this consciousness. Perhaps we need permission to see the relationship between our own agency as professional and corporate citizens, and the agency of our clients. It is therefore exciting to hear of new initiatives for change such as that state-registered music therapists in the UK are now paid on the same level as clinical psychologists, and the recent recognition of music

disadvantaged live completely separate lives, and where the music therapy work I am helping to develop is concerned with professional service to a large degree within disadvantaged communities.

[11] Interestingly, in his chapter on child slavery and prostitution in Thailand, Bales describes how the economic boom that caused the increase in demand for prostitutes has also meant that Thai village girls, through watching the TVs bought with money made from the sale of their older sisters or cousins, are no longer so easily duped into accepting their family demands that they be sold to a dealer.

therapy as a professional organisation in the EU. I hope this recognition can help us to feel more valued and heard, and in turn be more effective advocates for our clients.

Naomi Wolf has proposed that women have inherited "power-shy reflexes" (Wolf, 1993). Wolf's thesis is that we/I retreat when we feel that our corporate or professional likeability might be compromised by the collective aversion to women being anything other than polite, demure, deferential, and constantly fascinated by male opinion and behaviour. She suggested this is especially true for middle class and wealthy women with our access to a voice in a range of fora such as the workplace, the community, and political life, that is, arenas where attitudes, opinions and even policy and legislation might be changed. I state this here as a challenge to us to stop being so "nice." If things are to change, sometimes the political will get personal. I keep a card on my bookshelf that states "well behaved women rarely make history," a catchphrase coined by Laurel Thatcher Ulrich. Perhaps we/I can take more opportunities to realise that people who don't like us probably dislike most other people who are considered intelligent, influential, and are forthright in their expression of views.

A feminist approach to music therapy will not always be gentle, calm, and/or polite. Perhaps this is why it has taken so long for many of us in music therapy to name and claim a feminist stance. Let's value what a feminist perspective can bring to our professional lives remembering that for change to happen, strong feelings might need to surface. We expect and support these changes in our patients; it's time to also expect them in our profession.

REFERENCES

Arnold, Kim & Boulay, Kate (2005) Utopian beauty: Goddess or guise? Paper presented at *Exploring the Utopian Impulse,* the First Ralahine Conference on Utopian Studies, University of Limerick, Ireland, March 11th and 12th.

Baines, Susan (2003) A consumer-directed and partnered community mental health music therapy program: Program development and evaluation. http://www.voices.no/mainissues/mi40003000132.html

Bales, Kevin (2002) Because she looks like a child. In Barbara Ehrenreich & Arlie Russell Hochschild (eds.) *Global Woman.* London: Granta.

Battersby, Christine (1999) Her body/Her boundaries. In Janet Price & Margrit Shildrick (eds.) *Feminist Theory and the Body.* Edinburgh: Edinburgh University Press.

Bordo, Susan (2003) *Unbearable Weight: Feminism, Western Culture, and the Body*. Tenth anniversary edition. Berkley: University of California Press

Butler, Judith (2004) *Undoing Gender*. London: Routledge

Citron, Marcia. J. (1993) *Gender and the Musical Canon*. Cambridge: Cambridge University Press.

Cixous, Hélène (1999) Sorties. In Janet Kourany, James Sterba, Rosemarie Tong (eds.), *Feminist Philosophies: Problems, Theories and Applications*. 2nd edition. New Jersey: Prentice Hall.

Cook, Nicholas (1998) *Music: A Very Short Introduction*. Oxford: Oxford University Press.

Daly, Mary & Saraceno, Chiara (2002) Social exclusion and gender relations. In Barbara Hobson, Jane Lewis & Birte Siim (eds.) *Contested Concepts in Gender and Social Relations*. UK: Edward Elgar Press

Daveson, Barbara (2001) Empowerment: An intrinsic process and consequence of music therapy practice. *Australian Journal of Music Therapy*, *12,* 29-38.

Day, Toni & Bruderer, Helen (2002) *A Journey of Healing and Hope through Song*. Brisbane: Queensland Government

Dworkin, Andrea (1975) The root cause. Paper delivered at the Massachusetts Institute of Technology, Cambridge, USA, September 26.

Edwards, Jane (2005) The musical mind. Paper presented in the Comhaimseartha series; Irish World Academy of Music and Dance, Limerick, Ireland, April 14.

Edwards, Jane (2004) What to make of these sounds—Balancing rigour and uncertainty in music therapy research. Colloquia series, Faculty of Music, University of Cambridge, England, May 12.

Foucault, Michel (1995) Truth and power. In Douglas Tallack (ed.) *Critical Theory: A Reader*. New York: Harvester Wheatsheaf.

Gatens, Moira (1999) Power, bodies and difference. In Janet Price & Margrit Shildrick (eds.) *Feminist Theory and the Body*. Edinburgh: Edinburgh University Press.

Hadley, Susan & Edwards, Jane. (2004) *Sorry for the silence: The contribution of feminist discourse(s) to music therapy theory* [Online] Voices: A World Forum for Music Therapy. http://www.voices.no/mainissues/mi40004000152.html

hooks, bell (1990) Postmodern Blackness. *Postmodern culture, 1* http://www.africa.upenn.edu/Articles_Gen/Postmodern_Blackness_18270.html

Klein, Naomi. (2000) *No Logo*. London: Flamingo.

Klima, Carrie (2001) Women's health care: A new paradigm for the 21st century. *Journal of Midwifery and Women's Health, 46*, 285–291.

Kristeva, Julia (1984) *Revolution in Poetic Language,* Trans. by Margaret Waller, New York: Columbia University Press.

Kuhlmann, Ellen & Babitsch, Birgit (2002) Bodies, health, gender—Bridging feminist theories and women's health. *Women's Studies International Forum, 25*, 433–442.

McClary, Susan (1991) *Feminine Endings: Music, Gender, and Sexuality.* Minnesota: Minnesota Press.

Moore, Michael (2002) *Bowling for Columbine* [motion picture]. Santa Monica, CA: Metro-Goldwyn-Mayer Studios.

Nagel, Thomas (1989) *The View from Nowhere*. Oxford: Oxford University Press.

Proctor, Simon (2001) Empowering and enabling: Improvisational music therapy in non-medical mental health provision. http://www.voices.no/mainissues/Voices1(2)Procter.html

Rolvsjord, Randi (2004) Therapy as empowerment: Clinical and political implications of empowerment philosophy in mental health practises of music therapy. *Nordic Journal of Music Therapy, 13,* 99–111.

Turry, Alan (2005) Music Psychotherapy and community music therapy: Questions and considerations. http://www.voices.no/mainissues/mi40005000171.html

Wenders, Wim (1999) *Buena Vista Social Club* [motion picture]. Santa Monica, CA: Artisan Entertainment.

Wolf, Naomi (1993) *Fire with Fire: The New Female Power and How it Will Change the 21st Century.* London: Chatto & Windus.

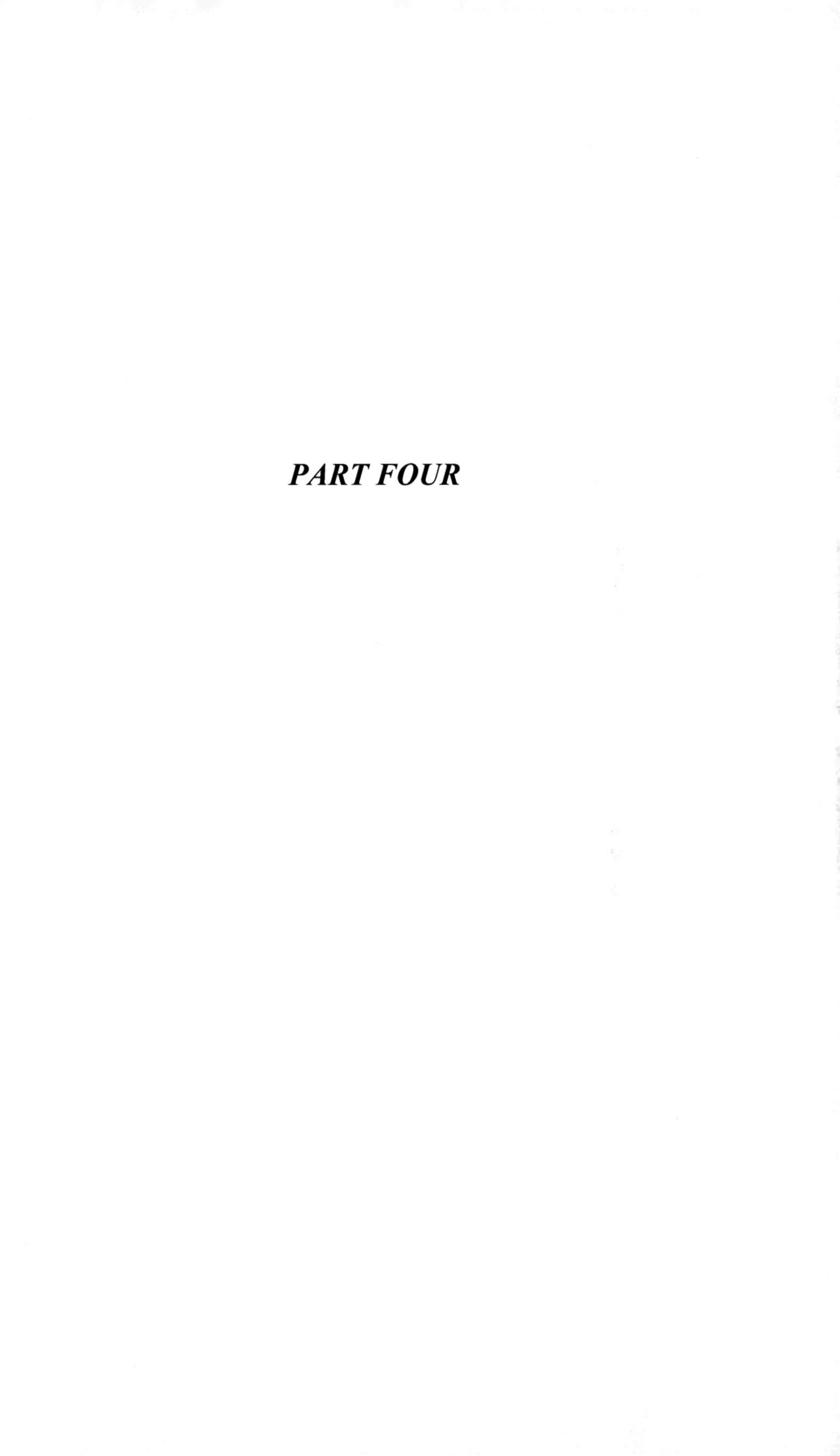

PART FOUR

PART FOUR

INTERLUDE IV

The final five chapters focus on specific areas of training in music therapy: pedagogy, supervision, assessment, research, and ethics. In chapter seventeen, Susan Hadley reflects on how both the content and the process of her teaching in music therapy have been influenced by her feminist worldview. She describes aspects of her evolving feminist teaching style and provides examples from her classroom experiences. She also shares the risks, challenges, and rewards that she has encountered while developing her approach to teaching.

In chapter eighteen, Michele Forinash addresses the topic of a feminist approach to music therapy supervision. She looks at philosophies of feminist supervision and research in feminist supervision. She then explores issues of openness, collaboration, biases, assumptions, reflexivity, multiples perspectives, authority, power, advocacy, activism, and cultures of music as they relate to the supervisory relationship in music therapy.

In chapter nineteen, Sue Shuttleworth provides a brief orientation to assessment and the assessment process in music therapy. She then describes feminist-diversity therapy principles and assumptions regarding assessment. She examines the philosophy, goals, design, and implementation of assessment strategies that are of concern to feminist therapists. Finally, she suggests ways for adapting and integrating feminist perspectives into music therapy assessment.

In chapter twenty, Barbara Wheeler presents information on feminist research and applies this to music therapy research. She describes existing music therapy research that is consistent with feminist research. She suggests a number of possible topics for music therapy research from a feminist perspective in the hopes that these may provide a beginning for music therapy researchers in this area.

In the final chapter, Cheryl Dileo provides a brief overview of both feminist ethics and feminist therapy ethics. She outlines several issues of relevance to feminist therapy: therapist self-disclosure, dual/overlapping relationships, and power. She then suggests that the field of music therapy would be enhanced significantly by an incorporation of feminist ethics within its approach to professional ethics, and recommends ways in which this can be accomplished within the various music therapy codes of ethics throughout the world.

Chapter Seventeen

DEVELOPING A FEMINIST PEDAGOGICAL APPROACH IN MUSIC THERAPY

Susan Hadley

The writing of this chapter is part of a larger process of developing a feminist approach to teaching music therapy. I have been teaching for almost a decade now and have been trying to craft a unique voice. I have been influenced throughout my life by various teachers and readings. These have all impacted my approach to teaching as have the various students who have accompanied me on this journey.

As a music therapy educator, my goal is not only to teach students about a variety of health conditions and music therapy approaches, but to help them to learn more about themselves in order to be more effective therapists. Simultaneously, in order to be an effective educator, I must also continually learn more about myself. Some of the ways I have been learning more about myself include reflecting critically on the ways in which my gender, race, culture, sexuality, religion, and ability impact my values, judgments, and actions. As I have become more aware of how these factors influence me, I have become more aware of the complex ways in which my students talk about issues related to gender, race, sexuality, religion, and ability. At times, when a student's view hits me with a great deal of dissonance, I began to think more about my role in their education. As I have struggled with this, I have come to believe that it is important for me to help students become more aware of the ways in which their perspectives and their opportunities in life, as well as those of others, are shaped by the social system of which they are a part (Cannon, 1990, p.127).

I have felt some tension about my teaching style from early on. I have a very relaxed style and have consciously tried to lessen the specific hierarchical role between teacher and student. As a teaching assistant during my graduate training, one of my professors compared me with a (white male) fellow student. The other student had a very formal approach to teaching. The professor commented that we were at two ends of a spectrum and that we would both benefit from moving in on the continuum. When I became a full-time faculty member, I continued with my relaxed style and even encouraged students to call me by my first name. I still feel that this approach is valid, but after a while—

because within the academy women are not accorded the same respect as their male counterparts and because the students sometimes felt confused about role expectations—I began to emphasize my credentials and reinforced the rigid hierarchical boundaries of academia. Now, perhaps because I have tenure and have been promoted or perhaps because I have matured, I feel that a modified version of my initial approach is worth revisiting for feminist reasons.

As I have been developing my approach, I have begun to reflect critically on both the content and the process of my teaching. In this chapter, I will explore how both of these areas have been influenced by my feminist world-view. I will also share the struggles I have encountered and explore possibilities for further development.

Critical and Feminist Pedagogies

Like many feminists, I have been influenced writings in liberatory pedagogy (Freire, 1970/2000; hooks, 1994) as well as by writings in feminist pedagogy (Bright, 1987; Fisher, 1987; Lorde, 1984; Schniedewind, 1985, 1993; Shrewsbury, 1993; Thompson, 1987; Warren, 1993; Weiler, 1991). Paulo Freire (1970/2000) critiques education, as it is widely practiced, as mirroring oppressive society. In what he calls the "banking" system of education, "students are the depositories and the teacher is the depositor" (p.72). Freire lists ten attitudes and practices to further illustrate this analogy:

(a) the teacher teaches and the students are taught
(b) the teacher knows everything and the students know nothing
(c) the teacher thinks and the students are thought about
(d) the teacher talks and the students listen—meekly
(e) the teacher disciplines and the students are disciplined
(f) the teacher chooses and enforces his choice, and the students comply;
(g) the teacher acts and the students have the illusion of acting through the action of the teacher
(h) the teacher chooses the program content, and the students (who were not consulted) adapt to it
(i) the teacher confuses the authority of knowledge with his or her own professional authority, which she and he sets in opposition to the freedom of the students
(j) the teacher is the Subject of the learning process, while the pupils are mere objects (Freire, 1970/2000, p.73)

Freire writes that "Banking education anesthetizes and inhibits creative power . . . [and] attempts to maintain the *submersion* of consciousness" (Freire, 1970/2000, p.81). In contrast to the "banking" system of education, Freire proposes a "problem-posing" education, a dialogical approach in which "people teach each other, mediated by the world," where the "students—no longer docile listeners—are now critical co-investigators in dialogue with the teacher" (pp.79–81). In this kind of education, "people develop their power to perceive critically *the way they exist* in the world *with which* and *in which* they find themselves; they come to see the world not as a static reality, but as a reality in process, in transformation" (p.83). Freire's pedagogical theory developed as a way of liberating poor people from the oppressive structures in Brazil in the 1960s and 1970s. By teaching those who were not literate to read, by engaging them in dialogue, and getting them to see themselves as agents, they gained critical consciousness. This consciousness allowed them to express critically their discontent with the current social structures and led to social transformation.

Because of the liberatory aspect of Friere's pedagogical approach, many feminist teachers have drawn from his approach and revised it, given the very different political/social context in which most feminist educators teach. Contrasting the concept of the teacher as banker, many feminist teachers aspire to be "midwife-teachers"[1] (Warren, 1993; Belenky, Clinchy, Goldberger, & Tarule, 1986). Karen Warren (1993) states that "when acting as a midwife, the teacher creates a safe learning atmosphere, both physically and psychologically, where learners are not afraid to take risks . . . . The teacher midwife steps aside when the student is engaged in the learning process, yet continues to guard the learning environment to allow a blossoming of the student's curiosity and quest for knowledge" (p.33–34). Some feminists believe that midwife-teachers are the opposite of banker-teachers. "They do not administer anesthesia. . . . While bankers deposit knowledge in the learner's head, the midwives draw it out. They assist the students in giving birth to their ideas, in making their own tacit knowledge explicit and elaborating on it" (Belenky et al, 1986, p.217). One of the first challenges for a midwife-teacher though is "to deprogram the students' dependence on spoon-fed learning and to inspire curiosity" (Warren, 1993, p.35).

[1] Some might argue that the notion of a feminist teacher as a midwife has essentialist overtones. However, I am thinking of the role of midwife as being carried out by males or females. The etymology of the word "midwife" is "with woman," meaning one who supports the woman in the process of birthing a child. Furthermore, this notion of midwifery as a process of giving birth to ideas has long historical roots, with Socrates being famous for practicing a form of midwifery through dialogical engagement.

Comparing Freirean pedagogy and feminist pedagogy, Kathleen Weiler (1991) states that both:

- rest upon visions of social transformation
- have common assumptions concerning oppression, consciousness, and historical change
- assert the existence of oppression in people's material conditions of existence and as a part of consciousness
- rest on a view of consciousness as more than a sum of dominating discourses, but as containing within it a critical capacity (Gramscian "good sense")
- see human beings as subjects and actors in history
- hold a strong commitment to justice and a vision of a better world and of the potential for liberation (Weiler, 1991, p.450).

Although these aims are great in theory, putting them into practice can be complicated. Weiler (1991) suggests that this is because these aims

> . . . do not address the specificity of people's lives [and] do not directly analyze the contradictions between conflicting oppressed groups or the ways in which a single individual can experience oppression in one sphere while being privileged or oppressive in another. (p.450)

She goes on to say that by challenging dominant values, accepted meanings, and relationships, Freirean and feminist teachers "raise conflicts for themselves and for their students, who also are historically situated and whose own subjectivities are often contradictory and in process" (p.451). As a feminist teacher, it is important to acknowledge the conflict within us—that is, to be aware of what Audre Lorde calls "the oppressor within us"—and also acknowledge the conflicts within the members of the classroom (Weiler, 1991, p.451). If these conflicts are not acknowledged, it can lead to a retreat to "safer" and more traditional approaches.

bell hooks (1994), whose pedagogical practice emerged from an interplay of anticolonial, critical, and feminist pedagogies, draws upon her experiences in her all-black grade schools, the work of Freire, and on feminist thinking about radical pedagogy when delineating ways of teaching to transgress. Her grade-school experiences taught her that for African-Americans, and for women, the life of the mind was a counter-hegemonic act. Her grade-school teachers made sure they really *knew* their students—where they lived, who they lived with, the conditions in which they lived, where they worshipped, shopped, etc. Educating black students was for them a political act connected to antiracist struggle. It was liberatory and exciting. Her experiences in desegregated schools were in stark contrast and showed her the difference between "education as the practice of freedom and education that merely strives to reinforce domination" (hooks, 1994, p.4). Freire's work reinforced for hooks that learning can be liberatory. And in college, she found that the feminist classroom was the one space in which students could raise critical questions not only about issues of gender inequality in various areas in their lives and the lives of others, but they could also raise critical questions about pedagogical processes. However, hooks (1994) felt that neither Freirean nor feminist pedagogy gave attention to the notion of pleasure in the classroom. She feels that learning should be exciting and fun. Although making learning fun had been discussed by educators in grade schools, she found that it had not been considered in higher education (p.7). She states that excitement is not just generated by ideas but "is deeply affected by our interest in one another, in hearing one another's voices, in recognizing one another's presence" (p.8). She describes teaching as "a performative act"[2] not in the sense that the teacher is the spectacle, but in the sense that the teaching "serves as a catalyst that calls everyone to become more and more engaged, to become active participants in learning" (p.11).

Developing a feminist music therapy pedagogy

My philosophy of education is that people learn by doing and that it has a longer-lasting impact if people enjoy it and it is meaningful. The music therapy classes that had the most lasting impact on me were those that were experiential in nature, those that integrated theory, practice, and personal experiences. In my teaching, I have adopted a similar approach. However, I began to realize that there were lacunae in what and how I had been taught specifically in the ways that gender, race, class, age, religion, sexuality, ability, culture, etc.—and the various intersections of these—impact our being-in-the-world. I was exposed to a liberal individualist understanding of what it means to be human and to be a therapist. As these understandings began to be challenged, I realized that I had to change the ways in which I had been communicating ideas within my classes. As I looked at the AMTA standards of clinical practice, one of them stood out as having profound implications for my approach to teaching and supervision. The standard I am referring to states:

[2] hooks's use of the term *performative act* differs from that of Judith Butler's, whose use of the term *performativity*, derived from the work of philosopher John L. Austin, refers to the way in which sex/gender identities are constituted.

> *To recognize the impact of one's own feelings, attitudes, and actions [and I would add—embodiedness] on the client and the therapy process.*

We are all embodied-in-the-world. This captures the sense in which our identities bear the marks of multiple signifiers: gender, race, class, age, physical ability, and other physical features. Therefore, when I think of my embodied self encountering another embodied person, I think of the myriad assumptions, biases, and stereotypes that we each immediately bring to that encounter. Many of these assumptions, biases, and stereotypes are oppressive and have been ingrained in us through our personal and societal histories. It takes a great deal of critical reflection to become aware of and disrupt those assumptions that inhibit more rich and productive ways of relating to each other. As a music therapy educator, it has become very important for me to help students become more aware of the impact that they have on the client and the therapy process in terms of how these assumptions, biases, and stereotypes can play out on both sides of the therapeutic relationship. I also want to help students to become more aware of the impact of their theoretical orientation, their understanding of the nature of therapy and the therapy process, their selection of music, their use of language, etc. on the client and the therapy process. Adopting a feminist pedagogical approach to my teaching provides me with a framework within which to explore these issues.

What I appreciate in feminist pedagogy is the commitment to "making visible the invisible" (Crumpacker & Vander Haegen, 1987, p.65). It pays attention to women's and men's roles and locations. Feminist pedagogy is based on certain assumptions about knowledge, power, and political action (Weiler, 1991, p.456). These assumptions include "the power of consciousness raising, the existence of oppression and the possibility of ending it, and the desire for social transformation" (Weiler, 1991, p.455).

In developing a feminist pedagogical approach for teaching music therapy, I have had to look at the process and the content of my teaching. I am just beginning this journey and realize that over time my understandings and process will evolve. However, my hope is that by sharing what I am trying to develop it will stimulate further discussion in the music therapy community and that the multiple perspectives that emerge in these discussions will lead to new insights.

In this section, I will describe aspects of my evolving feminist teaching style. I realize that by talking in terms of "teacher" and "student" I am already setting up the hierarchical relationship. I would say that as a "teacher" I see myself also as student within the dialectic of the learning process, that is, in the sense that I am continually learning through the engagement with the "students" who also teach through sharing their unique experiences and understandings. Also, I am in a continual process of gaining more knowledge of the subject matter that we are learning about, and learning ways of seeing previously learned information from ever-new perspectives. What I explain to the students is that what I bring is more experience with some of these concepts, but that there is much that they also bring which can enrich my understandings and the understandings of the entire group.

Remaining a Learner/Participant

As a feminist teacher, it is very important to acknowledge that I am also a learner and participant in the classroom. In fact, I have found that by teaching a class I learn a lot about the subject matter myself. When this new material is exciting to me and I share that excitement with the students, I feel that they also become excited. I also find that I learn a lot from listening to and observing the students. They bring creative ideas and fresh viewpoints and critiques that are valuable. One student particularly exemplified this philosophy in a supervision group. She had been placed with a woman living with Rhett's syndrome who many students found difficult to work with because she is non-verbal, non-ambulatory, and does not hold on to any instruments for long. This particular student commented: *I am excited to work with* [this woman] *because she has had music therapy for so long, she has had more experience in music therapy than I have, and therefore I can learn so much from her.*

I have found it important also to be a participant in the classroom. Therefore, I will lead experiences and be a participant in experiences. I require students to keep a journal and I have begun to keep a journal about the class experiences. I have shared some of my vulnerabilities as I also require them to be vulnerable.

Safeguarding the Initial Learning Environment

It is very important to create a supportive classroom environment in order for people to take risks and openly reflect on very difficult issues. Feminist educators have written about ways in which this can be achieved (e.g. Thompson, 1987; Cannon, 1990; Warren, 1993). One way of addressing this is to have *ground rules.* Lynn Weber Cannon (1990) presents her classes with a list of ground rules for class discussions. These include:

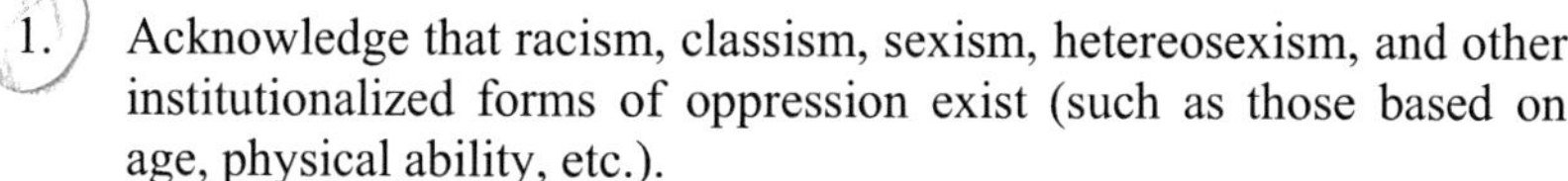

1. Acknowledge that racism, classism, sexism, hetereosexism, and other institutionalized forms of oppression exist (such as those based on age, physical ability, etc.).

2. Acknowledge that one mechanism of institutionalized racism, classism, sexism, hetereosexism, and the like is that we are all systematically *misinformed* about our own group and about members of other groups. This is true for members of privileged and oppressed groups. [italics mine]
3. Agree not to blame ourselves or others for the misinformation we have learned, but to accept responsibility for not repeating misinformation after we have learned otherwise.
4. Agree not to "blame victims" for the condition of their lives. . . .
5. Agree to combat actively the myths and stereotypes about our own group and other groups so that we can break down the walls that prohibit group cooperation and group gain.

(Cannon, 1990, pp.130–132)

Another way to create a supportive classroom environment is to have the class brainstorm together to come up with ground rules for the class and ways of insuring that these are upheld. This way the group members have control in terms of what would make it a safe environment in which they could take risks. In this process it is important that all voices are heard and respected. Confidentiality is a ground rule that is often stressed so that open communication can occur.

It is also important that students are able to name their *fears*. Warren (1993) describes a way of doing this anonymously by having students put their fears into a hat. Then a class member randomly picks one and reads it as if it were her or his own. The class members validate the fear and suggest ways to resolve it (p.35). Martha Thompson (1987) gets her students to write a response to a set of questions about their knowledge and attitudes towards the subject matter. By sharing these, the class members find commonalities and differences in each unique response and realize that they can each learn from the others (p.82). During this whole process, it is very important that the teacher model and foster openness. It may be important that teacher also engage as a participant in these experiences.

Awareness of Power

The analysis of power differentials is integral to feminist approaches, especially as it relates to gender but also as it relates to other oppressed groups. Creating a more egalitarian environment is essential.

Given the hierarchical and differential power levels embedded within the educational system, no matter how hard a teacher tries to minimize her power, she can not rid herself of it completely. The feminist educator is working within a larger academic system which imposes its authority on her/him. Therefore, it is very important to acknowledge the power differentials and to discuss the ways in which this can to some extent be minimized. The feminist educator has power and authority but must strive not to be authoritarian. The authority and power of the teacher is based on the teacher's subject position as someone of a particular gender, race, class, age, ability, etc. (Weiler, 1991, p.454). Weiler (1991) notes that the teacher is "seen and heard by the students not as an abstraction, but as a particular person with a certain defined history and relationship to the world" (p.454). By recognizing the implicit power and limitations perceived due to the teacher's gender, race, class, age, ability, etc., in relationship to those of the students, it opens up a space for liberating discourse which can demystify how power plays itself out (Bright, 1987, p.98).

In an educational setting, power is relevant both to process (how the class is conducted) and in terms of content (what is learned). Patricia Spencer Faunce (1985) calls for a pedagogical approach which reflects a "reciprocal model of influence," one that emphasizes "openness, freedom, consensus, cooperation, questioning, and personal commitment" (p.311). She believes that the classroom experiences should "integrate consciousness-raising techniques and values into a fluid assortment of other practices intended to encourage self-revelation, interpersonal sharing, equalitarianism, intellectual provocation, cooperation, and political awareness" (p.311).

Some ways in which a more egalitarian atmosphere can be created is to have a circular arrangement of chairs; the use of first names for everyone; group consensus on what is learned, how learning should take place, learning outcomes and grading methods; self and peer evaluations; and shared leading of activities. Some ways to encourage political and personal awareness is through open dialogue with others and through reflective papers and journals.

In terms of content, I think that it is important to explore the subject positions of teachers, therapists, supervisors, and clients in terms of their gender, race, class, sexuality, abilities, nationalities, and the various intersections of these. That is, we cannot talk about a generic therapist and a generic client without looking at all of these aspects and without understanding the complexity of socially constructed identities. In one of my senior classes, I provide readings on making systems of racial privilege visible (e.g. McIntosh, Kaufman, Wildman & Davis), feminist therapy (e.g. selections from this book), making systems of ability privilege visible (e.g. Asch, Linton, Wendell, Garland-Thompson, Cusack), and soon will also introduce work on positioning theory in terms of discourse (e.g. Drewery, Young). In addition, I have shown them the very powerful video *The Color of Fear* which involves a group of men from various different racial/cultural groups sharing their experiences of race, racism, prejudice, etc., at a weekend retreat. I also encourage the students to explore critically their privilege and oppression. However, discussions arising in these classes can bring up difficult emotions for students. As Weiler (1991) notes, "In settings in which students come from differing positions of privilege or oppression, the sharing of experiences raises conflicts rather than building solidarity. In these circumstances, the collective exploration of experience leads not to a common knowledge and solidarity based on sameness, but to the tensions of an articulation of difference" (p.469). Discussing the tensions that these discussions can bring to the surface, Patricia Romney, Beverly Tatum, and JoAnne Jones (1992) note that "some discomfort must be present to facilitate change because change cannot occur if individuals remain quiescent and unaffected" (p.98).

De-program students' dependence on banking system of education

In my classes, I describe the differences between a banking system of education and a feminist approach to education. In many classes, although I strive for a more feminist approach, I must say that much of it is still done in a banking system. It takes more work on the part of the students and the teacher to move away from that which is so familiar to us. However, I am continually striving to move away from an overdependence on a banking system. All of my classes are experiential and so there are many opportunities for students to learn from and provide feedback to the others and thus to mutually impact each other. I believe that the students have within them creative responses in terms of how to use music therapeutically with various populations. The role of the class is to broaden their understandings through sharing the multiple ways of using music therapeutically and discussing what each found valuable and innovative and what was less effective for them. Also the process of exploring the assumptions and biases each student brings to the experience can help each class member to think more critically about how they select music, use language, and interact with others.

In the seminar-type class I have with my senior students, I ask the students to read chapter two of Freire's *Pedagogy of the Oppressed.* We then discuss the two pedagogical approaches he describes and their experiences of each. Many comment that the classes they have had that were more dialogical and required greater critical and creative reflection on their part have had a greater impact on them. However, they all seemed to agree that they like classes with a banking approach because they don't have to think so much—it is more straightforward. Using a line from the movie *Good Will Hunting*, I suggest that they could spend less in late fees at the library in order to learn much of this material. Some students have then said that they feel that the role of the teacher is to explain what they don't understand in their readings. Although this is a legitimate role of a teacher, I have suggested that this implies that the instructor is the "all-knowing" one and that his/her interpretation is the only correct interpretation. One student said that he felt that Freire's approach was a utopian ideal—fine in theory but unrealistic in practice. However, Weiler (1991) states that "the struggle against oppression leading to humanization is thus utopian and visionary." She quotes Friere (1985) as follows: "To be utopian is not to be merely idealistic or impractical but rather to engage in denunciation [the naming[3] and analysis of existing structures of oppression] and annunciation [the creation of new forms of relationships and being in the world as a result of mutual struggle against oppression]" (p.57).

In my teaching practice, I have adopted an approach that has many aspects of a banking system of education while at the same time I have tried to move myself and the students from an overdependence on a banking system. This is a process that I hope will evolve further away from a banking system in time.

Emotions and Experience as Sources of Knowledge

Berenice Fisher (1987) discusses the role of emotions in feminist teaching and relates this to the role of emotions in consciousness raising (p.47). She states, "the power of consciousness-raising stems from the potential of shared experiences and feelings to shed light on the nature of women's [and other oppressed groups'] oppression" (p.47). As therapists, we know that by exploring emotions we can initiate change. An emotion has "a cognitive and evaluative aspect that is part of the way we understand and respond to the world" and thus is a potential source of strength (Fisher, 1987, p.48).

However, to talk about emotions as a source of knowledge, a source which is typically undervalued in academe, it is important to recognize that the dominant society shapes our sense of who we are and what we feel (Lorde, 1984). As Lorde points out, "Within living structures defined by profit, by linear power, by institutional dehumanization, our feelings were not meant to survive" (Lorde, 1984, p.34). However, by getting in touch with our deeper emotions we can begin to interrogate the dominant power structures and this can lead to action. As Lorde states:

> As we begin to recognize our deepest feelings, we begin to give up, of necessity, being satisfied with suffering and self-negation, and the

[3] Naming is an important process when talking about oppression because, as Romney, Tatum, & Jones (1992) state: "One of the characteristics of oppression is that dominant groups (those with the greatest social power) have assumed the right to name the oppressed, both literally and figuratively" (pp.99–100).

> numbness which so often seems like their only alternative in society. Our acts against oppression become integral with self, motivated and empowered from within. (Lorde, 1984, p.58)

The exploration of emotions goes hand in hand with examining one's personal history as a significant source of knowledge. And collective sharing of personal histories provides a richness and deepening of experience, bringing out commonalities and differences. When students have claimed that there is no need for feminism and that racism is no longer a real problem, it is through sharing of personal experiences in class and hearing about others' experiences through reading and watching videos, that we realize the erroneousness of such claims. This inevitably brings up many previously unexpressed or unrecognized feelings. It also often leads to other ways in which people have felt oppressed due to ageism, ableism, heterosexism, etc.

When examining our personal experiences and the experiences of others we become more aware of the social processes and ideology that shape us (Weiler, 1991, p.466). We begin to see that there are ways we respond as if reflexively, without even realizing the detrimental nature of these responses. Once this realization takes place, the next step is to find ways of reshaping our responses. As Lorde writes, "For we have, built into all of us, old blueprints of expectation and response, old structures of oppression, and these must be altered at the same time as we alter the living conditions which are the result of those structures" (1984, p.123).

One way to do this is to find alternative narratives by which to live. That is why I also share with students the rich concepts in narrative therapy[4] (Morgan, 2000). In this way, when the tape plays in our head that contains the old, ingrained, uninterrogated dominant story that shaped our previous ways of responding in oppressive ways, we can have available another tape that contains an alternative story. When we are responding in oppressive ways, we are seeing the other as less than we are. Our understandings have been constructed in a context in which there are differential power relations involving race, class, sexual preference, gender, and other forms of disadvantage. Although we may have grown up within the dominant story, there are always many stories which exist side by side. To develop an alternative story, one that is not oppressive, we must gain a richer picture of those who we have typified in a certain way, and also of ourselves. We need to trace the history of the oppressive narrative,

[4] Narrative therapy is a recent approach which is based on the premise that we are storied beings and that our growth is stifled when we live by debilitating narratives. The objective is to identify these debilitating narratives and to help the client to create a more productive narrative by which to live.

explore the effects of the oppressive narrative, situate the oppressive narrative in context, and in doing so discover new ways of understanding and being in relation with the other (Morgan, 2000).

Reflexivity

Self-reflexivity is described by Brynjulf Stige (2001) as the exploration of our role in the supervisory/therapeutic/educational/research process, and as the exploration of our role in the community and society we are living in (p.172). Even Ruud (1998) describes reflexivity as an awareness of "how our pre-understanding of a phenomenon informs our reading of the situation and our interpretations" (p.17). He suggests that our identity is not static, not ready-made, but a process, one that is characterized by our reflexivity (p.37). Thus, our values and interests are integral to how we perceive ourselves and how we perceive the world. Ruud (1998) further suggests that reflexivity is essential for lasting change to occur (p.136).

In my teaching, I emphasize the importance of reflecting on our various positions within the cultures to which we belong and the significant impact that this has on our work. We work together to gain greater awareness of our biases and I try to provide a space in which we can question long-held assumptions. In this process, it is very important to acknowledge commonalities and recognize and respect differences amongst the multiple perspectives of the class members. It is also very important to make connections between personal experiences and social realities. This process has frequently led to greater self-awareness and personal growth. When this change is substantial I would consider that transformation has taken place.

Community, Empowerment, and Leadership

Carolyn Shrewsbury (1993) considers community, empowerment, and leadership to be three central concepts in feminist pedagogy. In most educational settings, students participate as individuals, taking little responsibility for the class as a whole (Shrewsbury, 1993, p.12). In feminist classrooms, there is often an emphasis on cooperative learning, on mutuality in the learning process, and on community building. This can be done in a variety of ways, such as involving students in cooperative assignments.

Feminist teachers also desire to move learning beyond the walls of the classroom. Of course, in music therapy this works well due to our clinical training requirements. However, more work needs to be done in homeless shelters, women's shelters, with underprivileged youth, and with community groups, in addition to the work we do with the client populations we most often work with.

Shrewsbury (1993) states that "by focusing on empowerment, feminist pedagogy embodies the concept of power as energy, capacity, and potential rather than as domination" (p.10). In our classes, I feel that it is important that the students are empowered and that they understand the importance of empowerment in the clients' lives. Some people have suggested that empowering students is risky because the teacher has to abdicate power. If, as I have discussed, power is not domination, then this is not really a problem. I do not feel disempowered and I feel that my knowledge and experience is recognized and respected by the students. As such, I can put my energies into helping to empower the students. Some students have been in conflict about how empowerment can occur. In a lively discussion in one class it was suggested that if, as some class members were suggesting, we believe that individuals have the power inside them to overcome obstacles but are just not actualizing it, then we are not seeing the ways in which the social system contributes to the oppression of people. Others felt that if we see it as a systemic problem then what is the role of individual empowerment and hence what is the role of therapy? Later, in the same class period, when discussing ways to shift differential power relations, one student suggested the Robin Hood approach of taking power from those who have and giving it to those who do not. Not liking this notion, another student responded:

> *When a woman has one child she can't imagine loving a child as much as her first. However, when she has a second child more love comes. Can empowerment be similar? Do you need to take power from some in order for others to become empowered or can more power just come . . . from somewhere—who knows where?*

In addition to focusing on community and empowerment, the development of leadership is also an important aspect of feminist pedagogy. In music therapy, as in women's studies, the majority of students are women. Clare Bright (1987) notes that "as student and as female, the training to be passive, malleable, modest, inactive, and deferring is extremely potent. More than an act of will or mere understanding is required to begin the process of reclaiming the self as agent" (p.99). Many are not comfortable with being "authority" figures although they certainly have the capacity for leadership. Finding ways of developing into the role of leader is an empowering experience for students. As teachers, then, we act as important role models for our students. One of the ways I work on developing leadership is to have the senior students take turns in leading group supervision of the music therapy students who are involved in clinical work. The rotation of leadership allows time between leading to reflect on what they did in the leadership role while also learning from watching their peers. Each student leader completes a self-evaluation and peer evaluations each week. The groups are also attended by a music therapy faculty member who also provides feedback to the students. By doing this they are all involved in the teaching and the learning process.

Making Learning Fun

Like hooks (1994), I feel that learning should be fun and engaging. I think it is important to get to know the students as individuals and to show a genuine interest in them and their ideas. It is very important that their voices are heard. It is important to interact with students according to their needs. Of course, a healthy sense of humor doesn't go astray. By interacting authentically with the students and sharing my excitement and enthusiasm, we have had many fun moments in classes. I sometimes get the feeling that they do not feel as though they are learning as much if they are having fun. This needs to be addressed so as not to be misunderstood. Having fun here is not to be equated with a lack of seriousness and a lack of focus, but having fun helps to break down barriers and engages the whole person in interactive processes of mutual acceptance, mutual affirmation, and a celebration of the learning experience. I also feel that it is important to be flexible so that there can be spontaneous shifts in direction when necessary.

Advocacy

As a feminist music therapy professor, I understand advocacy in terms of advocating for students and clients and also encouraging students to become advocates for others. I used to have a sticker on my office door that indicated that my room was a safe space for individuals who are gay, lesbian, bisexual, or transgendered to come and talk. Although this sticker was removed at some point without my knowledge, many students come and talk to me about issues related to their sexuality and how it feels to live within a conservative rural community. Other issues that students come to seek guidance about and that are concerns for a feminist professor include date rape, pregnancy, decisions or feelings around having an abortion, and experiences of racism and pervasive homophobia. Many of these students have felt as though it is problematic for their voices to be heard. I feel that it is part of my role to provide a safe space for their voices to be heard and to advocate for these students. I also feel that it is part of my role to have my students reflect on the ways in which they inhibit the sounding of these students' voices. This can also be transferred to the clinical setting and being aware of the role we can play as advocates for clients.

Content

In our music therapy program we have begun to incorporate feminist therapy approaches into our curriculum. We include feminist therapy as one of the theoretical models that are studied in music therapy with adult populations. When learning about assessment, students are exposed to feminist assessment approaches amongst an array of others. When learning about supervision we talk about ways in which feminist ideas can influence the way we approach supervision. Students also read about feminist music therapy. However, much more can be done in each of these areas. In fact, I would love to see music therapy programs develop a graduate class dedicated exclusively to exploring feminist music therapy.

I also feel that music therapy educators should encourage students to analyze established treatment theories, research, songs, etc., in terms of the underlying assumptions vis-à-vis gender, race, class, ableness, sexuality, and so on.

Thompson (1987) provides students with reading materials that "describe the experiences of women and men who differ by age, class, ethnicity, race, religion, sexual preference, or who are differently abled" (p.84). We could do this with songs. She then asks the students to generate lists of key words that describe the experiences, emotions, or behaviors of each particular group. The students share their lists with each other. Under each list they group items into categories. They can then explore how a certain category or concept is applied differently to different groups and different life situations. This helps students to become aware that a certain concept can apply to a diversity of experiences.

Thompson (1987) writes that this kind of analysis leads to theory building which ultimately needs to lead to action. Action refers to translating abstract ideas into concrete realities. As mentioned previously, this could be done by having music therapy students work in women's shelters and homeless shelters. Another way which was suggested by Thompson (1987) could be to have students write a letter to a particular audience (the student paper, a local newspaper, a family member, a friend) about a social issue that has been explored in class. Alternatively, students could write a song about a social issue that has been explored in class.

Risks, Challenges and Rewards of a Feminist Approach

Ellen Kimmel and Judith Worell (1997) and their working group discuss the personal experience of being a feminist teacher in terms of risks, challenges, rewards, and needed supports (p.128–135). As I read through their list, several of them spoke to my experiences:

Risks

-Backlash from negative reactions to feminism
-Stigmatization and devaluing of feminist scholarship
-Professional liabilities in feminist publishing
-Marginalization of career and scholarship efforts

Challenges

-Struggling with appropriate use of power with peers and students
-Becoming a realistic and useful role model for students
-Attending to the impact of feminist teaching on students' academic and personal lives
-Assessing the effects of feminist pedagogy on the individual, the institution, and the larger social system
-Developing resources and methods to meet the goals of feminist pedagogy

Rewards

-Affirmations of self in the pursuit of important goals
-Congruence between personal values and professional life
-Visibility and voice within the institution and community
-A sense of meaning and purpose associated with membership in a revolutionary social movement
-Connection to the feminist community
-Being a midwife to the emergence of feminist consciousness in students
-Participating in students' personal growth and empowerment
-Learning from students
-Collaborating with students and colleagues

In addition to these rewards, the following comments from some of the journals of my senior undergraduate students reinforce for me the importance of further developing a feminist pedagogical approach. The members of this class were: Erica Arnold, Scott Dawson, Andrea McClellan, Ai Sato, Kate Zlokas, and Megan Zulauf.

A lot of students take human diversity and I did too. After I took that class I thought I had completed and accomplished "diversifying" myself. Then I took this class and I realize that I am not where I want to be yet as far as having a multicultural and feminist approach.

This past week I witnessed a male treat a female poorly in a social/public setting and I sat back and watched it happen. This male is a co-worker and I felt like it was such a difficult position for me to be in. [This student then reflected on how this situation could easily be played out in the therapy situation and how she needs to intervene more actively in this kind of situation]

I guess what I want to say is that everybody is different and the same at the same time. We should get to know the individual that we work with in depth without prejudice or stereotypes . . . we should respect anybody as a person because everybody is valuable and precious in the world. Then, I wonder why I am trying to be a music therapist. I wonder why I want to work with populations that we work with. I wonder why music therapy treats people we treat. . . . I would like to work with people who we treat, partly because they are the people who do not have as much power in the society. I respect them a lot. I would like to show them that they are very valuable in spite of how the society treats them. However, I feel like I am still grouping people even though I do not want to.

I have personally experienced a raised consciousness this semester and raising my consciousness has caused me to examine my beliefs and societal norms.
One student was working at a restaurant with some people who were not from this country. They asked her why people were treating the African-American customers in the negative way they were. In her journal reflection she wrote: *It was new for them to see this treatment [of African Americans] and I feel like even though I've seen it my whole life, it's becoming new to me as well because I am beginning to see it in a different way now.*

[At the end of a paper entitled "My Privilege and Oppression made Visible"] *Although my awareness has increased, I must say that I often still do not view myself as privileged. In the same way, I still do not view myself as racist although I am. I realize that as a white person I do not view myself as raced. I realize that I view myself as the norm and view others to be outside the norm. It is difficult to admit that I am racist. It is difficult to accept that I have earned things in my life through no merit of my own. It is difficult to accept stories of oppression from other races because of the implications to myself. If their experience of racism on a daily basis is true, what does that say about me? What does it say of my character as a good, responsible, respectable and deserving white person? It destroys it. It is so much easier to deny its existence and sweep it under the carpet. It is the denial surrounding these issues that empowers them. I believe that as we recognize and give voice to that which is silent and face our fears, we can begin to move forward.*

This class has been the most beneficial class to me as a human being . . . in helping me become a better person, a better thinker, and a better mediator.

REFERENCES

Asch, Adrienne (2004) Critical race theory, feminism, and disability: Reflections on social justice and personal identity. In Bonnie G. Smith & Beth Hutchison (eds.) *Gendering Disability*. New Brunswick, NJ: Rutgers University Press.

Belenky, Mary Field, Clinchy, Blythe McVicker, Goldberger, Nany Rule, & Tarule, Jill Mattuck (1986) *Women's Ways of Knowing: The Development of Self, Voice, and Mind*. New York: Basic Books.

Bright, Clare (1987) Teaching feminist pedagogy: An undergraduate course. *Women's Studies Quarterly*, *15*, 96–100.

Cannon, Lynn Weber (1990) Fostering positive race, class, and gender dynamics in the classroom. *Women's Studies Quarterly*, *18*, 126–134.

Crumpacker, Laurie & Vander Haegen Eleanor M. (1987) Pedagogy and prejudice: Strategies for confronting homophobia in the classroom. *Women's Studies Quarterly*, *15*, 65–73.

Cusack, Caroline (1993) Alienation. In Barbara Brandt, Caroline Cusack, & Simon Hall (eds.) *The Sea Isn't Always Blue*. Western Australia: Rocky Bay, Inc.

Drewery, Wendy (2005) Why we should watch what we say: Position calls, everyday speech and the production of relational subjectivity. *Theory and Psychology*, *15*, 305–324.

Faunce, Patricia Spencer (1985) Teaching feminist therapies: Integrating feminist therapy, pedagogy, and scholarship. In Lynne Bravo Rosewater & Lenore E.A. Walker (eds.) *Handbook of Feminist Therapy: Women's Issues in Psychotherapy*. New York: Springer Publishing Company.

Fisher, Berenice (1987) The heart has its reasons: Feeling, thinking, and community-building in feminist education. *Women's Studies Quarterly*, *15*, 47–58.

Freire, Paulo (1970/2000) *Pedagogy of the Oppressed* (30th anniversary edition). New York: The Continuum International Publishing Group, Inc.

Garland-Thomson, Rosemarie (1996) *Extraordinary Bodies.* New York: Columbia University Press.

hooks, bell (1994) *Teaching to Transgress: Education as the Practice of Freedom.* New York: Routledge.

Kaufman, Cynthia (2001) A user's guide to white privilege. *Radical Philosophy Review*, *4*, 30–38.

Kimmel, Ellen & Worell, Judith (with Judith Danulik, Mary Ann Gawalek, Kathy Lerner, Geraldine Stahley, & Susan Kahoe) (1997) Preaching what we practice: Principles and strategies of feminist pedagogy. In Judith Worell & Norine G. Johnson (eds.) *Shaping the Future of Feminist Psychology: Education, Research, and Practice.* Washington, DC: American Psychological Association.

Linton, Simi (2005) *My Body Politic: A Memoir.* Ann Arbor, MI: University of Michigan Press.

Lorde, Audre (1984) *Sister Outsider*. Trumansburg, NY: The Crossing Press.

McIntosh, Peggy (1997) White privilege and male privilege: A personal account of coming to see correspondences through work in women's studies. In Richard Delgado & Jean Stefancic (eds.) *Critical White Studies: Looking Behind the Mirror*. Philadelphia, PA: Temple University Press.

Morgan, Alice (2000) *What is Narrative Therapy? An Easy-to-Read Introduction.* Adelaide, South Australia: Dulwich Centre Publications.

Romney, Patricia, Tatum, Beverly, & Jones, JoAnne (1992) Feminist strategies for teaching about oppression: The importance of process. *Women's Studies Quarterly, 20*, 95–110.

Ruud, Even (1998) *Music Therapy: Improvisation, Communication, and Culture*. Gilsum, NH: Barcelona Publishers.

Schniedewind, Nancy (1993) Teaching feminist process in the 1990s. *Women's Studies Quarterly*, *21*, 17–30.

Schniedewind, Nancy (1985) Cooperatively structured learning: Implications for feminist pedagogy. *Journal of Thought*, *20*, 74–87.

Shrewsbury, Carolyn M. (1993) What is feminist pedagogy? *Women's Studies Quarterly*, *21*, 8–16.

Stige, Brynjulf (2001) The fostering of not-knowing barefoot supervisors. In Michele Forinash (ed.) *Music Therapy Supervision.* Gilsum, NH: Barcelona Publishers.

Thompson, Martha E. (1987) Diversity in the classroom: creating opportunities for learning feminist theory. *Women's Studies Quarterly*, *15*, 81–89.

Warren, Karen (1993) The midwife teacher: Engaging students in the experiential education process. *The Journal of Experiential Education*, *16*, 33–38.

Weiler, Kathleen (1991) Freire and a feminist pedagogy of difference. *Harvard Educational Review*, *61*, 449–474.

Wendell, Susan (1996) *The Rejected Body: Feminist Philosophical Reflections on Disability*. New York: Routledge.

Wildman, Stephanie M. & Davis, Adrienne D. (1997) Making systems of privilege visible. In Richard Delgado & Jean Stefancic (eds.) *Critical White Studies: Looking Behind the Mirror*. Philadelphia, PA: Temple University Press.

Worell, Judith & Remer, Pam (2003) *Feminist Perspectives in Therapy: Empowering Diverse Women*. Hoboken, NJ: John Wiley & Sons, Inc.

Young, Iris Marion (1990) *Justice and the Politics of Difference*. Princeton, NJ: Princeton University Press.

Chapter Eighteen

FEMINIST MUSIC THERAPY SUPERVISION

Michele Forinash

When presented with the opportunity to write this chapter and address the topic of a feminist approach to music therapy supervision, I had a number of responses. First, I wondered whether feminist perspectives were implicit in the music therapy literature, needing only to be named as feminist; then I contemplated whether we needed to create a feminist theory of music therapy and specifically a theory of feminist music therapy supervision.

As I began to write, I found it extremely challenging as I had to grapple with my very personal issues around feminism. The first issue had to do with my difficulty and reluctance in claiming competence—let alone expertise—in feminist theory. I also had to face my philosophical struggle with issues of authority and power in society, as well as in supervisory relationships which I will discuss more fully below. Finally, I had to face my difficulty in owning my own voice and ideas about feminist theory.

As I read, I realized that engaging in the process of writing this chapter has allowed me to go through some very typical stages found both in feminist supervision theory (Porter & Vasquez, 1997) as well as in theories of developing multicultural awareness in music therapy supervision (Preist, 1994 as adapted by Estrella, 2001). These stages range from denial and/or ignoring gender and cultural differences; to recognizing differences but not knowing what to do about them; to appreciating those differences; and finally to an integration in which the supervisor develops a solid understanding of how differences in culture and gender influence the supervision process.

Looking at these various stage models also caused me to wonder whether our profession was in fact also moving through similar developmental stages. It appears that our profession is in the early stages of appreciating those differences and this book in particular will likely move us ahead in the integration of feminist theory. Further questions arose for me as I contemplated the gender and ethnicity of music therapists in the US. In 2004, 88% of the membership of the American Music Therapy Association was female and 90% of the membership was Caucasian. What, if anything, does this mean in terms of feminist perspectives in music therapy?

In reading feminist theory, at times I have been surprised by the realization that, as Shona Russell and Maggie Carey (2003) state, "what [is] very clear is that feminism means very different things to different people." Like-wise, the various authors in this book also have defined their own unique understanding of feminism. That openness to the multiple perspectives is the guiding principle which has given me the courage to explore the topic of feminist music therapy supervision and my relationship to it.

Supervision

In a previous publication (Forinash, 2001) I described supervision as a process.

> Supervision is a relationship, one in which both supervisor and supervisee actively participate and interact. It is a process of unfolding—not simply following a recipe, but engaging in a rich and dynamic relationship. Supervision then is also a journey, or odyssey of sorts, in which supervisor and supervisee learn and grow and from which both will very likely leave transformed in some way. (p.1)

While that isn't a necessarily anti-feminist description of supervision, it also isn't an explicitly feminist description of supervision. How can we articulate a feminist perspective of music therapy supervision? After reviewing the literature we will come back to that description and find ways to make it more explicitly feminist.

Philosophies of Feminist Supervision

Judith Worell and Pamela Remer (1992) building on the work of Natalie Porter (1985) discuss what they consider unique aspects of feminist supervision. "In particular, feminist supervision is sensitive to power differentials between trainee and supervisor, as well as to broadly valued philosophical goals" (p.333). They go on to list nine essential components of feminist supervision including 1) a focus on process, 2) awareness and analysis of gender and sex-role, 3) relationship between one's theoretical orientation and feminist principles, 4) analysis of goals of therapy, 5) openness to a redefinition of health and pathology, 6) awareness of both external and internal issues in therapy, 7) supervision process providing ongoing feedback for client, 8) focus on creating women's groups, and 9) respect for the supervisee's experience and strengths (pp.333–334).

Porter (1995) offers a four-stage developmental model of feminist supervision. In stage one there is a focus on developing a perspective that is anti-racist, feminist, and multicultural. In this stage supervisees are exposed to "alternative explanations to traditional formulations" (p.167) of their clients' presenting issues. Supervisors not only teach about cultural differences but challenge basic assumptions made on the part of the supervisee. While stage one is concrete and directive, stage two is a more philosophical perspective of "exploring the roots of racism, sexism and ethnocentrism in society" (p.168). The third stage focuses on the supervisee's own internalized feelings and attitudes especially those of a racist and sexist nature. Stage four focuses on "adopting a social action, collective perspective" (p.170) where the emphasis is on systems and collective action (pp.167–171).

In a later publication, Natalie Porter and Norine Vasquez (1997) coined the term "covision" to describe feminist supervision that focuses on process and collaboration. They offer nine principles of feminist supervision which include: 1) the need to analyze power differentials and use power only in the "service of the supervisee" (p.162); 2) the need for a mutually respectful and collaborative relationship; 3) a focus on self-reflection and self-examination; 4) respect for diversity of women's lives; 5) awareness of "social construction of gender and the role of language" (p.165); 6) a call for activism; 7) maintaining ethical standards; 8) awareness and respect for the growth and development of the supervisee and how that changes the supervisory relationship; and 9) a need for supervisors to advocate for supervisees and clients (pp.162–167).

They go on to offer a definition of feminist supervision as

> . . . a collaborative, respectful process, personal but unintrusive, balanced between supervisory responsibility and supervisee autonomy. Feminist supervision emphasizes an open discussion and analysis of power dynamics, and targets the best interests of the supervisee. It is a process that remains focused on the social context of the lives of the client, supervisee, and supervisor. (p.169)

Daphne Hewson (1999) focuses on the issues of power in the supervisory relationship. She writes about differences between having "power over" someone versus having the "power to." She argues that some feminists see power as something "bad and destructive" (p.407) and attempt to have total equality in the supervisory relationship. This equality is essentially false as there is a power differential in the supervisory relationship. She seeks to make power structures explicit, for only when they are explicit can they be negotiated.

Research in Feminist Supervision

Anne Prouty, Volker Thomas, Scott Johnson, and Janie Long (2001) engaged in grounded study research analyzing the methods that feminist supervisors used in supervision. They reported three types of methods: contracting methods, collaborative methods, and hierarchical methods. They also provide an analysis of when these different methods are used and what the supervisor's process was in determining which method to use. They found that supervisors used "contracts to minimize hierarchy and to promote clarity" (p.93). Supervisors used "collaborative techniques not only to teach but to create a collaborative learning environment" (p.94) and they only used "hierarchical methods when they felt that collaborative methods would not be sufficient" (p.94).

Dawn Szymanski (2003) developed the Feminist Supervision Scale (FSS) which can be used to "assess feminist supervision practices in clinical supervision" (p.222). This scale has four subscales: collaborative relationships, power analysis, diversity and social context, and feminist advocacy and activism. While the results of the study may be limited in terms of generalizability, the FSS can be used to evaluate current supervision practice as well as in training as a way to "encourage discussion and exploration of the four dimensions" (p.229). It was also particularly interesting to note that "the FSS was related but conceptually distinct from both multicultural competence and perceived supervisory working alliance" (p.221).

The Culture of Music in Supervision

Karen Estrella (2001), writing specifically about multicultural issues in music therapy supervision, stresses the need to examine the culture of music in addition to many of the topics discussed above. In particular, she writes of the need to understand the role of music in the different cultures of clients, therapists, and supervisors.

> To fully understand the meaning of music in different cultures, we must become sensitive to our own cultural encapsulation. We must recognize the ways in which we take music making and music listening for granted as normal and universal. While music certainly exists as a universal phenomenon, it is by no means a singular universal construct. The meaning and function of church music for a working-class African American woman, and of pop rock-and-roll for an upper-class white adolescent [girl] are different. How culture defines, contextualizes, and prioritizes the experience of music is essential knowledge for music therapists. (p.54)

From these rich resources how might we begin to articulate a feminist perspective of music therapy supervision? What then are the cornerstones of feminist music therapy supervision?

Cornerstones of Feminist Music Therapy Supervision

Openness

As supervisors we first must model openness. For me this encompasses many things. We must recognize that we live in a racist and sexist world and thus we, as supervisors, must strive to create change, both within ourselves as well as in society at large. This can only happen when we acknowledge where we are. A colleague of mine, Carylbeth Thomas, frequently tells students in her supervision class to "Start where you are." This holds true for a beginning dialogue on feminism in supervision.

Supervision as a Collaborative Process: Honoring the Individual

Music therapy supervisors have articulated this idea that supervision is not a "top down" event, where the supervisor knows the answers and tries to teach or give this information to the supervisee. Lisa Summer (2001) states:

> The beginning music therapy student should not be treated as a tabula rasa upon which the supervisor impresses her techniques, theory, skills and style. Music therapy students should not be imitations of their teachers and supervisors, nor should they be trained uniformly as if they emerge from some prototypical music therapy student template. (p.69)

In a previous publication (2001) I supported this idea:

> Supervisors are not expert, all-knowing omnipotent beings, and likewise supervisees are not simply blank slates upon which to download the correct manner of working as music therapists. Both are complex individuals who bring their unique perspectives and multiple levels of experience to the relationship and to the understanding of music therapy. (p.1)

Dorit Amir (2001) writes about the need to create a secure place for the supervisee, to encourage the supervisee to trust her inner knowledge, to offer her own understanding as well as to help the supervisee locate personal blind spots. Thomas (2001) writes of the need for the supervisor to stay open to the uniqueness of each student and support each student according to his/her needs.

Cleary these ideas of focusing on supervision as a relationship, honoring the individual growth and development of the supervisor and supervisee, showing respect for each other, are at the heart of feminist theory.

Understanding our Biases, Questioning our Assumptions

Before we can really honor the unique individuals involved in the supervision experience, we have to gain an awareness of each person's unique perspective and question the assumptions that underlie that perspective. The feminist principles of making explicit the sociocultural, gender, and historical issues we bring to the supervisory relationship has been well documented in feminist theory. As a qualitative researcher, I liken this to the epoché found in phenomenological inquiry. This serves two purposes:

> Stating one's approach and involvement in the research topic allows the reader to understand the preconceptions and influences that the researcher brings to the event. It also allows the researcher to be conscious of potential biases, and therefore less influenced by them. (Forinash, 1995, p.372)

Relating this to supervision, rather than trying to erase, hide, or "get over" our biases, by making them explicit, both supervisor and supervisee can gain understanding of these biases. According to feminist thought we need to go beyond simply recognizing the biases and actually challenge them. Ongoing dialogue and discussion can provide an avenue for challenging our assumptions and opportunities for growth.

A Call for Reflexivity

Staying open to the supervisee's experience requires reflexivity. We must demonstrate a willingness to challenge our assumptions as well as the assumptions of our supervisees. We must be open to an alternative—perhaps even paradoxical—understanding of a situation, whether it is in supervision or in society at large. For me reflexivity is a thread which is woven throughout our feminist supervisory experiences. This is not a reflexivity that derails us into a constant questioning and paralyzes our ability to make decisions. It is a reflexivity that calls us to be responsible for the choices we make and to analyze what we are doing and why.

This is not a one-time event, but an ongoing process of being willing to examine one's own process. As Brynjulf Stige (2001) states:

> *Reflexivity* also needs to be part of the [supervision] process . . . . (Self)-reflexivity then could be understood both as the supervisor's and supervisee's exploration of their own roles in the supervision process, and as their exploration of their own role in the community and society they are living in. (p.172)

This requires that both supervisor and supervisee "take responsibility for their actions, feelings, and beliefs" (Porter and Vasquez, 1997, p.164).

As stated throughout the feminist literature, supervisors have a very important opportunity to model reflexivity for their supervisees. As Stige indicates above, this reflexivity includes not only the supervisory relationship, but also one's role in both community and society. One must be vigilant and always question assumptions as bias. Discrimination based on gender is often both subtle and pervasive. It is also important to keep in mind that our assumptions become more complicated when gender biases intersect with biases based on race, class, ability, etc.

Reflexivity also calls us to acknowledge the biases that we bring to the supervisory experience. It is only by recognizing and naming these that we are able to create change.

Multiple Perspectives

Reflexivity also then embraces the idea that there can be and usually are multiple valid perspectives of experiences. We seek and embrace alternative meanings which take into account issues of culture and power. Let's go back for a moment to my initial query about whether feminist perspectives are inherent in music therapy supervision literature and just need to be named. In terms of this tenet of multiple perspectives, music therapy literature comes up short. Feminist theory has a focus on understanding women's experience in society. This is often overlooked in the music therapy literature. As we supervise, do we honor that women's experience of society is often different than perceived in traditional patriarchal models? Given that our field is made up largely of women, do we just assume an understanding of women's experience? A feminist perspective would challenge us to take what may be a quiet assumption and make it a much more articulate and vocal point of view. How do our women supervisees experience the society of the clinical world? How can we help our

men supervisees develop an appreciation and awareness of women's experience, whether they be fellow colleagues, bosses, subordinates, or clients?

As we supervise someone how can we embrace the multiple perspectives that our supervisees and their clients bring to supervision?

This calls us to use another phenomenological idea—that of "free phantasie variation" (Kenny, 1996, p.61). Free phantasie variation refers to the idea of uncovering essences of an event or experience through reflective thinking during which one imagines the experience being studied in different forms (Forinash & Grocke, 2005). In feminist supervision we would not necessarily be looking for essential structures of the experience. We would use this concept to allow us to imagine a variety of meanings of the event.

Likewise, in transcendental phenomenology multiple perspectives are embraced. "Experiences are viewed from two perspectives: what was experienced (the textural description, or noema) and how it was experienced (the structural description, or noesis)" (Forinash & Grocke, p.323).

To embrace multiple perspectives we must ask questions such as: How might this supervision process be understood differently? How might we find an alternative way of looking and understanding the client's issue or the supervisee's conceptualization of it?

Awareness of Power

Issues of power and equality must be discussed. Prouty, Thomas, Johnson, and Long (2001) wrote about feminist family-therapy supervision. In their article they discuss various methods of supervision. They highlight three basic methods of feminist supervision which, to me, reflect a balanced use of power in supervision. One method is that of "contracting." In this method a verbal understanding of what is to be accomplished in supervision is created. This includes the supervisee sharing her goals for supervision and having the option to change or discard them as supervision progresses.

Power is also equalized in the contracting process through "mutual evaluation" (p.89) in which both supervisee and supervisor evaluate each other. Supervisees have the power to challenge evaluations and "make additions to their evaluations before they became part of their record" (p.89).

They go on to discuss collaborative methods in feminist supervision which include fostering competence, offering multiple perspectives, providing various options for the supervisee to choose from, and providing ongoing mutual feedback (p.90–91).

Finally, they discuss hierarchical methods which were used much less frequently and usually only when the client was not safe, or the clinical "situation was beyond the therapist's current therapeutic abilities" (p.91). These methods include behavioral directives where the supervisee is told how to act or what to say in the session, and reading directives, where the supervisor suggests certain readings for the supervisee.

Modeling is also discussed as a hierarchical method and is described as role play or when the supervisor takes part in the therapy session and models a way of interacting.

In all of these methods it is clear that the supervisee has the ability to influence the direction of supervision; there is respect for a variety of ways of looking at the issues in supervision; and she is given options to choose from whenever possible. The supervisor only assumes the traditional, more powerful role when there are issues of safety.

Porter and Vasquez (1997) call supervision "covision" (p.155) as a way of equalizing issues of power. Sue Hadley (personal communication, July 14, 2005) sees covision as not meaning equal vision but rather as a way for supervisor and supervisee to gain understanding together. She goes on to say that:

> Although we view it together it doesn't mean that we don't have specific roles or differential levels of experience or even power. It does seem to suggest that we each may have "expertise" that the other does not, whether in music therapy, life, music, etc. It also seems to support the notion that because we are sharing our views together it can lead to greater understanding—for all of us, supervisor and supervisee. What I like about it is that this viewing together or understanding together allows for dissensus, which when worked through can lead to expanded vision for all involved. (July 14, 2005)

I would argue that, as supervisors, we do have tremendous power over supervisees in terms of grading, how we focus supervision, how we make sense of what issues come up in supervision. While our supervisees may indeed have more expertise in certain areas such as foreign language, musical styles, etc., in terms of the clinical awareness, the supervisor is likely to have the expertise. Of course we should always question our use of power and strive to use power in service of the supervisee and her clients. As we have seen in previous discussions, pretending not to have power and expertise as a supervisor can be seen as condescending. Finding a way to use our power in an appropriate balance of support and challenge is essential.

Advocacy and Activism

One of the more difficult struggles I have in identifying as a feminist supervisor has been centered on the concept of advocacy and activism. At the heart of feminist ideals is the concept that helping an individual adjust to her environment is not the focus of therapy and thus not the focus of supervision. We should not encourage our supervisees to adjust to the absurd sexist and racist encounters but rather question each instance of sexism and racism that we encounter. This applies not only to supervision and the supervisory relationship, but also to our encounters in the world. The personal is indeed political.

Of course once one takes such a position of activism it opens us to further criticism and marginalization. By confronting sexism and racism we risk being excluded by those who are reluctant to take such an activist stance. In working with a supervisee it is important to identify the sexist and racist ideas that exist in the world, while remaining open to all voices, and allowing supervisees to develop their own feminist consciousness.

My favorite bumper sticker says, “If you aren’t outraged, then you aren’t paying attention.” While I believe this was meant as a statement about the current political situation, it certainly applies to owning a feminist perspective. Essentially, as we acknowledge sexism and racism in supervision and in society, we experience a sense of outrage.

As feminist supervisors then, we need to take an activist stance and confront these sexist and racist situations. For me this activism takes the form of consciousness-raising. Through questioning, challenging and confronting inequalities we can begin to effect change, which is important not only for our supervisees and their clients, but for all those who are impacted by implicit sexism and racism.

The Cultures of Music

A final cornerstone of feminist music therapy supervision is an examination of the cultures of music. Our tool as music therapists is quite complex. Music has a multitude of forms and uses and defies generalization. Yet, much of music therapy is founded in western music. As music therapy begins to find a more truly international voice (see, for example, www.voices.no) we must continue to examine not only different forms of music, but also how music is used and understood by different cultures. How do women in various cultures experience music? As Sue Hadley also emphasizes:

> . . . [W]hat is being communicated in the music that we use? Are we upholding patriarchal values by using certain types of music? Are we

> supporting gender and cultural stereotypes? We and our supervisees need to analyze song choices based on the patriarchal, white, middle-class, heterosexual values they are supporting. (personal communication, July 14, 2005)

In Summary

As we provide a description of feminist supervision first and foremost, a feminist supervisor must help articulate and examine the many concepts shared above, for if these concepts are left unspoken, then it is not feminist supervision. These concepts do not exist in isolation. One can't just pick one or two of these concepts to embrace. They exist in relationship and build on each other. They are entwined and intermingled.

Feminist supervision is a way of thinking and of seeing the world. While how one uses the elements of feminist supervision may be quite individual, the ideas discussed above are basic and essential elements of feminist supervision.

Earlier in the chapter I offered a definition of supervision which is not expressly feminist. Having reviewed the cornerstones of feminist supervision I would now describe feminist supervision as a rich and dynamic relationship which is a collaborative process, in which both supervisor and supervisee are open to self-examination and reflection. Assumptions about our world view are challenged and multiple perspectives on a situation are actively sought and embraced. Power differentials are discussed and power is always used in service of the supervisee and his/her client(s). Supervision is always pursued with the idea of challenging sexism, racism, ableism, and other forms of oppression.

IN CLOSING

Yes, the music therapy literature does have ideas that are essential to feminist theory. Ideas such as multiple perspectives, respect, embracing a not-knowing approach, all support feminist theory. What is missing, however, is the articulation of these ideas as essentially feminist. To just "assume" them only further denies a true feminist perspective. We must embrace these ideas and articulate them as essentially feminist rather that putting them under the umbrella of traditional patriarchal thought.

REFERENCES

Amir, Dorit (2001) The journey of two: Supervision for the new music therapist working in an educational setting. In Michele Forinash (ed.) *Music Therapy Supervision.* Gilsum, NH: Barcelona Publishers.

Estrella, Karen (2001) Multicultural approaches to music therapy supervision. In Michele Forinash (ed.) *Music Therapy Supervision.* Gilsum, NH: Barcelona Publishers.

Forinash, Michele (2001) *Music Therapy Supervision.* Gilsum, NH: Barcelona Publishers.

Forinash, Michele (1995) Phenomenological research. In Barbara Wheeler (ed.) *Music Therapy Research: Quantitative and Qualitative Perspectives.* Gilsum, NH: Barcelona Publishers.

Forinash, Michele & Grocke, Denise (2005) Phenomenological inquiry. In Barbara Wheeler (ed.) *Music Therapy Research. 2nd Ed.* Gilsum, NH: Barcelona Publishers.

Hewson, Daphne (1999) Empowerment in supervision. *Feminism & Psychology 9*, 406–409. London: Thousand Oaks

Porter, Natalie (1985) New perspectives on therapy supervision. In Lynn Bravo Rosewater and Lenore E. Walker (eds.) *Handbook of Feminist Therapy: Women's Issues in Psychotherapy.* New York: Springer.

Kenny, Carolyn B. (1996) The story of the field of play. In Mechtild Langenberg, Kenneth Aigen, & Jorge Frommer (eds.) *Qualitative Music Therapy Research: Beginning Dialogues.* Gilsum, NH: Barcelona Publishers.

Porter, Natalie (1995) Supervision of psychotherapists: Integrating anti-racist, feminist, and multicultural perspectives. In Hope Landrine (ed.) *Bringing Cultural Diversity to Feminist Psychology: Theory, Research, and Practice.* Washington, DC: American Psychological Association.

Porter, Natalie & Vasquez, Norine (1997) Covision: Feminist supervision, process and collaboration. In Judith Worell and Norine G. Johnson (eds.) *Shaping the Future of Feminist Psychology: Education, Research, and Practice.* Washington, DC: American Psychological Association.

Priest, Ronnie (1994) Minority supervisor and majority supervisee: Another perspective of clinical reality. *Counselor Education and Supervision, 34*, 152–158.

Prouty, Anne, Thomas, Volker, Johnson, Scott & Long, Janie (2001) Methods of feminist family therapy supervision. *Journal of Marital and Family Therapy 27*, 85–97.

Russell, Shona & Carey, Maggie (2003) Feminism, therapy and narrative ideas: Exploring some not so commonly asked questions. *International Journal of Narrative Therapy and Community Work, vol. 2* http://www.dulwichcentre.com.au/feminism.htm

Stige, Brynjulf (2001) The fostering of not-knowing barefoot supervisors. In Michele Forinash (ed.) *Music Therapy Supervision.* Gilsum, NH: Barcelona Publishers.

Summer, Lisa (2001) Group supervision in first time music therapy practicum. In Michele Forinash (ed.) *Music Therapy Supervision.* Gilsum, NH: Barcelona Publishers.

Szymanski, Dawn, M. (2003) The feminist supervision scale: A rational/ theoretical approach. *Psychology of Women Quarterly, 27*, 221–232.

Thomas, Carylbeth (2001) Student centered internship supervision. In Michele Forinash (ed.) *Music Therapy Supervision.* Gilsum, NH: Barcelona Publishers.

Worell, Judith & Remer, Pamela (1992) *Feminist Perspectives in Therapy: An Empowerment Model for Women.* England: John Wiley and Sons.

Chapter Nineteen

VIEWING MUSIC THERAPY ASSESSMENT THROUGH A FEMINIST THERAPY LENS

Sue A. Shuttleworth

> *A crucial challenge for feminist assessment is to incorporate contextual variables beyond that of gender that define women's lives (e.g., race, culture, sexual orientation, age, immigration status) in a manner that reflects the meaning of that context for the particular woman for whom an assessment is being conducted.*
>
> —Santos de Barona and Dutton, 1997, p.53

On a personal note, I entered into this project as a novice in the field of feminism and feminist therapy, with minimal readings on the subject. With extensive experience as a music therapy educator, and prior to that, as a music therapy clinician, I have been interested in both clinical and educational assessment for a number of years. I saw this project as a wonderful means of expanding my knowledge and providing creative stimulation.

During my doctoral study, I had the opportunity to investigate women as leaders. This area was interesting to me as I have experienced a variety of leadership styles through different university department chairpersons, including two female leaders. One of my research projects was a case study, analyzing the leadership around a significant event within the department. I chose an event occurring under the leadership of the first female chairperson, and highlighted differences in her leadership style, as compared to her male predecessors. Leadership characteristics included a focus on collaboration, an optimistic outlook, and an involvement-focused initiative to empower the departmental faculty members. At the time, these leadership characteristics were unfamiliar within the context of the department and some resistance was encountered. Because she actively demonstrated trust and respect for her co-workers, had a clear vision, and communicated with positive energy and enthusiasm; her innovative project was accepted and a transformation in the faculty members' perceptions of themselves and the department occurred. Analyzing her leadership style from a feminist perspective highlighted some of the assets of women leaders. Some of these same characteristics can be found within the feminist-diversity approach to therapy.

Following a brief orientation to assessment and the assessment process in music therapy, this chapter will describe feminist-diversity therapy principles and assumptions regarding assessment. To understand the feminist therapy approach more fully, specific areas that may concern the feminist therapist regarding the philosophy, goals, design and implementation of assessment strategies will be presented. I know of no writings that are specific to music therapy assessment from a feminist perspective. However, there is much in the music therapy literature that supports the basic assumptions of a feminist-diversity approach and allows for adaptation and integration of the feminist perspective into music therapy assessment.

OVERVIEW OF ASSESSMENT

General Definitions and Functions

Varied definitions and interpretations of the term *assessment* exist dependent upon the perspectives of the user. From the creative arts therapist's perspective, assessment can refer to either the process of discovering an individual's strengths, need areas, and background, as well as monitoring progress; or only considered to be the initial step of information gathering (Feder & Feder, 1998). Functions of assessment in psychotherapy and counseling may vary from identifying the goals of therapy and the client's problems, to increasing understanding of the client and facilitating the client's self-understanding, to identifying appropriate therapeutic interventions.

Oftentimes, *assessment* and *evaluation* are used interchangeably (Meyer et al., 2001; Worell & Remer, 2003). Although actions involved with both terms form the basis for decision making, the term *evaluation* is most frequently applied to the process of monitoring client progress, and in turn, making judgments about the efficacy of treatment (Feder & Feder, 1998).

Assessment within a Music Therapy Context

Assessment in the music therapy literature has been described as the process of appraising the client's needs, strengths, background, present functioning level, concerns, and resources in preparation for treatment (AMTA, 2003b; Hanser, 1999; Bruscia, 1998; Davis, Gfeller, & Thaut, 1999). The American Music

Therapy Association (AMTA) delineates music therapy assessment as identification of the client's current functioning level to be completed prior to music therapy service (*Standards of Clinical Practice*, 2003b). Kristin Cole (2002) labeled assessment as a general term that designates varied methods for gathering information in regard to a client or student. She further delineated three types of music therapy assessment: informal, formal, and standardized. The music therapy assessment may be designed for a variety of therapist objectives; such as descriptive, evaluative, diagnostic, interpretative, or prescriptive (Bruscia, 1998, pp.27–28), and be reflective of the therapist's purpose and philosophical orientation (Isenberg-Grzeda, 1988). Tony Wigram (2002) made a distinction between three different forms of music therapy assessment (p.247). The function of the "music therapy assessment" is to gather evidence that demonstrates the need of music therapy as an intervention. The "initial period of clinical assessment in music therapy" occurs over the initial two or three sessions and evaluates the most appropriate therapeutic approach for work with the client. The "long-term music therapy assessment" is then distinguished by its use of evaluation of music therapy effectiveness over time.

Richard Scalenghe and Kathleen Murphy (2000) described music therapy assessment in the context of the managed care setting. They reported that managed care organizations, accrediting bodies, and regulatory bodies look at assessment as an ongoing process, occurring across time. From referral to initial client contact, through each session, and at periodic intervals, assessment is implemented to identify problems, strengths, and needs, and to report progress and outcomes.

Feminist Definition of Assessment

Maryann Santos de Barona and Mary Ann Dutton (1997), discussing psychological assessment from a feminist perspective, provide a very broad working definition of assessment: "*Assessment* is the act of identifying and naming human experience relevant to the questions asked, and to that end it integrates the theory, science, and practice of psychology" (p.38). Although there are divergent approaches to assessment, Judith Worell and Pamela Remer (2003) identified common goals in feminist approaches to assessment and diagnosis. These are to develop and use assessment and diagnostic procedures:

- that highlight the impact of sexism and oppression in women's lives
- that reveal women's strengths and personal resources
- that make our reality visible to ourselves and others, and
- that validate our experiences (p.13)

In order to more fully understand Worell and Remer's stated goals, a discussion of factors affecting the assessment process follows.

Assessment Concerns from the Feminist Perspective

A problematic area for the feminist therapist is the use of diagnostic labels and category descriptions as found in the *Diagnostic and Statistical Manual of Mental Disorders* (*DSM*). Feminist practitioners criticize the *DSM* for minimizing the effects of oppressive circumstances and culture and applying a classification system that reinforces societal stereotypes and is sexist (Worell & Remer, 2003). However, the feminist therapist in the United States, where a *DSM* diagnosis is expected, finds herself in a bind when needing to obtain third-party reimbursement for services. For most clients, failure to use a *DSM* diagnosis results in no services, unless the therapist provides free services. Beyond this difficult issue, when the therapist is involved in assessment, at the very least there are specific considerations that must be observed. A multitude of psychological and social variables can be overlooked or unwittingly mishandled when making decisions stemming from assessment methods. Assessment approaches from both a multicultural and a feminist perspective view some of these variables in a similar way.

Sources of Bias

Bias in testing

One such variable is bias. One source of biased assumptions and values may be a formal or informal test. First, tests may have biased items if the language is culture-bound, including terms of sexism, ethnocentrism, ageism, ableism, racism, classism, and heterosexism (SEARCH variables). An example of sexist terminology is *policeman* instead of *police officer* when administering a career interest inventory.

Second, bias may occur if the test items are based on experiences specific to some groups in a culture more than to other groups, resulting in a group-based experience advantage. An example might be assessing skills and characteristics of a woman from a male perspective, such as looking at early life responsibility with regard to having a paper route, typically a male experience. Third, biased items may assume the perspective of a particular group. For example, life history questions may assume a heterosexual orientation. Charles Ridley, Lisa Li, and Carrie Hill (1998) confirm that testing instruments are almost always culture-bound.

A third way that biased assumptions are incorporated into tests is through inappropriate norm groups for comparison of scores. Many formal tests are normed on Caucasians, and the scores of diverse ethnic group members are interpreted on these norms. For a less biased approach, test scores can be normed on diverse groups and even provide separate norms when possible (Ridley, Li, & Hill, 1998; Santos de Barona & Dutton, 1997; Worell & Remer, 2003). However, Worell and Remer indicated that there is general agreement that using cross-sexed norms on career interest inventories restricts women's exploration of nontraditional careers.

Therapist's beliefs

The belief system of the therapist can provide another source of bias. Stereotypical beliefs may include preconceived ideas of symptoms of a certain group of individuals. For example, a therapist may "see" dependency more often in females, believing that females are economically dependent on males, as well as fitting the traditional female-gender stereotype. Whereas dependency may be more likely ignored in males, not considering that the male may be dependent on the female for maintaining the household. Oftentimes, these preconceived beliefs are so ingrained in society and accepted as the norm that the biased nature is out of the awareness of the therapist. The result may be a misjudgment about the client.

In addition, the theoretical orientation of the therapist may present a source of bias, especially in regard to determining what symptoms are pathological and in whom the symptoms are pathological (Worell & Remer, 2003, p.124). In turn, the assessment methods for gathering information about the symptoms may be biased. The therapist may want to analyze aspects of a theoretical orientation to determine possible bias points. Worell and Remer proposed looking at areas of a theory using four criteria:

1) Is the theory gender-balanced or gender-free? If so, the theory will view women and men as similar in psychological makeup with any differences attributed to socialization, the development of cognitive and affective processing, and the strategies that a person uses to present him or herself.
2) Is the theory flexible and multicultural? The theory allows for a broad range of healthy lifestyles and requires that constructs and interventions are selected based on sensitivity to the ethnic and cultural values of the client.
3) Is the theory interactionist? If so, it is considered that there is a reciprocal interaction between individual variables (i.e. behavioral, cognitive, affective) and environmental variables,

such as institutional and cultural. Multiple variables must be considered in order to understand the individual.

4) Does the theory look at development as a lifelong process? If so, this life span view allows for changes in behavior at any time and at all ages. (p.95)

In addition to considering sources of bias, another area of concern for the assessment process from a feminist perspective is that of environmental and contextual factors.

Contextual Factors

Sometimes sex bias may occur within the assessment process when the individual's environmental context is not considered in the analysis of individual behavior. The environmental context (e.g. poverty, patriarchy), how the individual interacts with the environment, and the effects of the environment on the individual are often minimized. For example, if a therapist does not believe that women live in an environment that may discriminate against them, then the woman's response to her situation may be judged as overreacting or even abnormal. As in Gestalt psychology, one must look beyond a narrow area of functioning to a broader view of the individual's life in order to have a more holistic picture of the person. A multidimensional approach to the assessment process would allow for a more thorough analysis of the effects of the environment on the client's behavior. Also necessary would be the consideration that environmental stressors could be sources of pathology. A multifaceted approach to assessment is also important to accommodate the variety of socio-cultural factors that affect testing.

Socio-cultural Factors

Ridley, Li, and Hill (1998) supported a definition of culture that attempts to separate itself from the concepts of race and ethnicity. They agree that culture includes both external referents, such as institutions, roles, and artifacts, and internal referents, including attitudes, values, beliefs, and consciousness. This interpretation indicates that almost every aspect of a person's experience is affected by culture. Therefore, accurate assessments would include a broad range of data. Also important is to validate the client's cultural belief systems, which may differ from that of the therapist's, with regard to the assessment process. This validation may facilitate client-therapist rapport and encourage the client to expand on the problem from a cultural perspective.

From this perspective of culture, the assessor must take both referents into consideration, with some aspects of the client's psychological state being evident (external) and other aspects less obvious (internal). For example, a single working mother of three children presents with depression which began about the time she was laid off from work. The layoff was a direct result of downsizing and not work performance. She has been unsuccessful in finding new work. One of her external cultural referents might have included the expectations of her family to be a good mother and to meet the needs of her children. The external referent may then become internalized into the woman's perception of herself—I am a bad mother because I can't provide for my children.

Additional sociocultural factors that can impact assessment methods include differences in communication styles, health beliefs, variations in learning styles, and an individual versus a collective orientation. Santos de Barona and Dutton (1997) emphasized the importance for the psychological assessor to be familiar with the sociocultural context of the client in order to avoid a misdiagnosis or misinterpretation of assessment results.

Styles of communication

The assessor's awareness about styles of communication among diverse cultures can also prevent inaccurate interpretation of assessment results. Nonverbal communication methods, such as the use of silence, facial expressions, and gestures may be interpreted in a variety of ways dependent upon the particular cultural meaning. For example, a woman whose ethnicity differs from that of the therapist may appear reticent and verbally unresponsive during the initial music therapy assessment. The music therapist, a Caucasian American, may negatively interpret the woman's nonverbal cues, unaware that in the woman's culture it is appropriate and expected to not seek attention and say little with persons other than family members.

Health beliefs

Like cultural sensitivity and awareness of differences in communication styles, the assessor should also understand that different cultures have quite different beliefs about illness, disability, and treatment. Certain illnesses may be seen as a stigma and the therapist may need to be sensitive in interactions with family members, as well as the client.

Variations in learning style

In some cultures, persons are taught to listen to and obey an authority figure rather than challenge. Information may be sought in a more indirect and quiet manner. Other cultures may encourage learning through observation and imitation rather than discovery learning. These examples of passive learning are quite common in Asian and Hispanic cultures. Awareness of these diverse learning styles would be extremely helpful for the therapist during the assessment process.

Individual versus collective orientation

The values of a culture may focus on the importance of serving the group and the group's needs and goals rather than focusing on individual achievement. Traditional Asian, Native American, and Hispanic families may be more concerned with social norms and group cooperation than traditional Anglo-American families where the emphasis is on individual pleasure and success.

All of the above areas are important for the therapist-assessor to become familiar with in order to avoid inaccurate findings and recommendations. Just as important, the therapist-assessor may more easily facilitate the understanding of the client if a multicultural perspective is in practice.

Epistemology

Epistemology or methods of knowledge generation become critically important during the assessment process when diverse populations are considered. A broad-based strategy has been recommended where multiple data-gathering methods are utilized (Ridley, Li, & Hill, 1998). Both a multi-method and a multi-level assessment may decrease the chances that language or reading barriers may underestimate the capabilities of the client or create misunderstandings of personality. Mary Ballou (1990) suggested that a feminist approach to clinical practice "…incorporates diverse methods that derive knowledge from multiple sources through varying methods of inquiry" (p.41).

ASSESSMENT IN FEMINIST THERAPY

Principles of Empowerment Feminist Therapy

From a feminist perspective, the areas of concern in clinical assessment that were described above can be ameliorated, in part, by following eight assumptions about assessment and diagnosis. These assumptions form the foundation for the Empowerment Feminist Therapy (EFT) developed by Worell and Remer (2003). Let me first describe the four guiding principles of EFT:

1. *Personal and social identities are interdependent.* This principle implies that clients are understood in the context of their sociocultural environment. Every social location (or identity) of

the client is considered; including age, gender, ethnicity, social class, sexual orientation, physical abilities, and characteristics. Once the social locations are identified, the relevance or importance of each to the client is assessed. The identities are then looked at in reference to their dominant and subordinate cultural expectations (e.g. privilege, injustice, oppression).

2. *The personal is political.* This principle holds that a good deal of the client's pathology is due to social and political influences, with the external environment being a main source of problems. Pathology, then, is reframed and symptoms are viewed as coping strategies for an unhealthy environment. Another aspect of this principle is to initiate social change so that society is free of sexism and oppression of minority groups.
3. *Relationships are egalitarian.* Referring to client-therapist relationships, the egalitarian therapeutic relationship minimizes the power base of the therapist, thus making it more difficult to impose one's values on the client. Through this balanced and collaborative client-therapist relationship, clients are considered experts on themselves and become empowered. Worell and Remer (2003) do note that achieving an egalitarian relationship is very difficult and often is the ideal, not the reality. (p.73)
4. *Women's perspectives are valued.* This principle states that women should acknowledge and own their personal characteristics, define themselves, and validate their woman-centered views of the world (Worell & Remer, 2003, p.74). Characteristics such as empathy, nurturance, intuition, and relationship-focus become valued and respected.

EFT Assumptions about Assessment and Diagnosis

When conducting assessments, the following assumptions can be made when following the Empowerment Feminist Therapy approach (Santos de Barona & Dutton, 1997; Worell & Remer, 2003).

1. In order to have accurate assessment and diagnosis, information about the client's personal and social identities and cultural contexts should be collected, and then utilized to guide the therapy process (Worell & Remer, 2003). As in multicultural assessment (Ridley, Li, & Hill, 1998), the first step is to begin with a clear understanding of the client's cultural influences and experiences. As suggested by Worell and Remer (2003), EFT

clinicians assess for (a) acculturation; (b) identity development level for each relevant social location; (c) client cultural values; (d) client experiences with oppression, discrimination, and being stereotyped; (e) experiences with gender-role socialization; (f) access to societal resources (e.g. health care, good nutrition, educational opportunities, social support); and (g) power arrangements in the home (Phinney, 1996; Ridley, Li, & Hill, 1998; Santos de Barona & Dutton, 1997). (p.131)

2. Assess women's lives in reference to their cultural contexts and apply this information in interpreting other assessment and diagnostic information (Worell & Remer, 2003). As stated earlier in the chapter, EFT therapists look at the environment for causes of pathology, with most cases having a combination of individual and environmental factors contributing to the client's problems. There are many everyday stressors (poverty, living and/or working in a sexist, racist, or otherwise oppressive society) for women, as well as being the victims of rape, domestic and intimate partner violence, and sexual abuse, that could lead to problem behaviors. When the client and therapist view her behaviors in the context of her real life, the behaviors begin to make sense as reasonable responses or coping strategies to her chaotic and often traumatic environment.
3. Create assessment strategies to be used to promote social change (Worell & Remer, 2003). Social change may be addressed in both subtle and overt manners. For example, subtle ways within assessment strategies may include assumptions made and not made about client's lives or the nature of the client's close relationships (e.g. how the client defines her "family," etc.)
4. Create environmental context assessment strategies. A variety of methods to assess environmental contexts include gender-role analysis (gender socialization experiences)—a process to identify the gender-role messages one has received throughout life (either directly or indirectly), identify them as negative or positive, determine how they have been internalized, and then develop a plan for any desired change. Power analysis, another contextual assessment strategy, facilitates awareness of power differentials in society and the ability to access resources for personal and external change. Other environmental contextual assessments include personal and social identity analysis and the Power and Control Wheel (Domestic Abuse Intervention Project). The Power and Control Wheel was created by battered

women from their personal experiences. Further descriptions of these assessment strategies can be found in Worell and Remer's book, *Feminist Perspectives in Therapy: Empowering Diverse Women* (2003).

5. Utilize a collaborative approach with clients for assessment, diagnosis, and interpretation. Found in both multicultural and feminist therapy, the strategy of clarifying the assessment process and its purpose to the client is of paramount importance. Results of assessment procedures and tests are shared with the client who is encouraged to contribute her interpretations (as the expert on herself). In addition, if a diagnostic label is selected, then it and its potential consequences are examined in dialogue with the client.
6. "Reframe symptoms as ways of coping with oppressive environments" (Worell & Remer, 2003, p.130). Women's "symptoms" are reinterpreted into behaviors, reactions, coping strategies, signs, or indicators that are exhibited for good reasons and as a reflection of a pathological environment.
7. "Assess for client strengths and resiliencies" (Worell & Remer, 2003, p.130). Through implementation of this strategy, a balance can be achieved with the deficit/symptom approach to assessment. By identifying client survival strengths through initial assessment, the goal of EFT—"to help clients access internal and external resources to accomplish both internal/ personal and external/societal change" (Worell & Remer, 2003, p.137)—is addressed.
8. "Value and use multiple ways of knowing" (Worell & Remer, 2003, p.130). Throughout the assessment process and the subsequent analysis of assessment data, utilization of objective, subjective, rational, and intuitive means of knowing are encouraged.

ANALYSIS OF MUSIC THERAPY ASSESSMENT

A review of the music therapy literature through the lens of feminist therapy highlights some commonalities with the basic principles. Cultural diversity, awareness of one's biases, a collaborative attitude, valuing women's ways of knowing, and feminist transformation of music therapy are areas that have been indirectly or directly addressed in the music therapy literature.

Cultural Diversity and Sensitivity

The utilization of culturally sensitive assessment methods and content has been addressed over the last few years. The AMTA's *Standards of Clinical Practice* (2003b) include culturally appropriate methods of assessment as the standard for quality services. Additionally, content of the assessment may include cultural and spiritual background. Cultural background, along with spirituality, is defined as "[a]n interrelationship among a client's musical experiences, personal belief system, and cultural background, which may be influenced by the client's geographical origin, language, religion, family experiences, and other environmental factors" (AMTA, 2003b, p.22). This definition supports the feminist therapy principle of viewing the individual within the context of his or her sociocultural environment, developing an understanding of the client's cultural influences, and acceptance and understanding of cultural diversity.

This culturally sensitive perspective has been supported in writings on multicultural training for music therapists (Troppozada, 1995; Darrow & Molloy, 1998), music therapy assessment (Chase, 2003a; Chase, 2003b; Adler, 2001; Cole, 2002), music therapy implementation (Chase, 2003b; Bright, 1993), music therapy ethics (Dileo, 2000), and feminist music therapy (Curtis, 2000). Manal Troppozada (1995) upheld the interdependence of personal and social identities in a discussion of the definition of culture, indicating that membership in a variety of cultures (e.g. socioeconomic, religious, racioethnic, etc.) creates changing interactions throughout one's lifetime. In reference to oppressions experienced by women, Sandra Curtis (2000) reported that a combination of oppressions interact, depending on each woman's unique experience (e.g. racial oppression, ethnic oppression, gender oppression, etc.). Cheryl Dileo (2000) stated in her chapter on multicultural and gender perspectives in reference to ethical thinking in music therapy, "…the client's unique blend of cultural issues influences all aspects of music therapy treatment" (p.149).

Primary to the music therapist is the impact that gender and culture has on music behavior, whether it be a macro-culture of ethnicity or a micro-culture of family or peer group (Bright, 1993). Ruth Bright (1993) advises the music therapist to view and understand "culture" from a multilayered perspective when considering music preference and music behavior.

One method of gathering cultural background information is through a pre-assessment format (either written or verbal) that may include cultural history and determination of how cultural membership impacts the client's life (Cole, 2002; Chase, 2003b). This preliminary assessment procedure—generally including medical history, general behavioral characteristics, medications, other therapies, and music preferences—then assists the therapist in determining areas to address in the assessment. Kristen Chase (2003b) provided excellent suggestions for adapting such a tool to meet the needs of diverse clientele, including the use of inclusive language.

Chase (2003b) also suggested an alternate format, integrating cultural considerations within the music therapy assessment rather than a separate pre-assessment format. Communication patterns, family and gender roles and organization, high-risk behaviors, health care practices, death rituals, and religious practices are all important considerations for inclusion in either a pre-assessment tool or during the assessment itself.

Self-awareness of Bias

Although one can never be completely bias-free, we are often unaware of biases that we hold. An awareness of our biases that may impact the assessment process is an important goal for our development as culturally sensitive feminist music therapists. Bias may enter into the music therapy assessment process via two of the factors identified by Connie Isenberg-Grzeda (1988)—therapist's beliefs and the client population—that influence the music therapy assessment design. The first factor, the therapist's beliefs, worldview, and theoretical orientation, may limit interpretation of data and lead to misjudgments or analysis errors. For example, if interpreting a client's musical improvisation is based solely on the therapist's gender and cultural norms rather than inclusion of the client's, an error in interpretation may occur when those norms are different, the therapist views his or her beliefs as the correct ones, or there is a lack of understanding of the client's cultural perspective. How one views health and illness, and normality and pathology also impact the assessment protocol (Isenberg-Grzeda, 1988). As discussed earlier, are certain client behaviors symptoms of pathology or ways of coping with the environment? Dileo (2000, p.151) described the traditional Western/American standards and values found in therapy, identified as predominantly male-oriented, that are present in client assessment and diagnosis. As such, they have an impact on our views of pathology and may raise questions in regard to gender issues.

The second factor, the client population, may be perceived by the therapist from a biased viewpoint. The therapist's perceptions of the client in reference to a specific client group (e.g. persons with HIV-AIDS, gay and lesbian clients, women) may impact how the assessment is conducted. For example, assumptions and prejudgments regarding a client's music preferences based on the individual's gender, ethnicity, religion, sexuality, etc., may be detrimental to establishing a trusting relationship and providing a successful music experience. Linda Gantt (2000) encouraged creative arts therapists to enter the assessment process with an open mind and without preconceived notions as to what will be found. Specific suggestions for an unbiased psychosocial assessment in therapy with gay and lesbian clients include using appropriate terminology, more broadly defining "family" to "family of origin" and "family of choice," and discussing client's living arrangements (Chase, 2003b; Chase, 2004). When biases are eliminated or at least in the therapist's awareness, and each person is treated as an individual, new information will be found and a trusting therapist-client relationship can develop.

Self-awareness of potential biases (such as religious bias, heterosexual bias, and ethnic bias) is a component of a competent music therapist (Dileo, 2000), especially in working with persons from diverse cultures. Toward this end, Dileo (2000, p.169) offered a variety of thought-provoking exercises and a self-assessment to facilitate increased awareness of these potential biases. Chase (2003b) also encouraged self-awareness activities to expand one's cultural awareness. She presented a *Cultural Self-Assessment for Music Therapists,* including questions to facilitate an analysis of one's cultural perspectives in regard to personal and musical history (2003b, p.62).

A Collaborative Attitude

Several music therapists write about the importance of developing a trusting relationship during the assessment process (Wigram, 2000; Hintz, 2000; Chase, 2003b). To this end, it is often necessary and/or desirable to conduct the assessment over several sessions if the therapist is not constricted by institutional time parameters. A collaborative approach to the assessment can assist in building trust with the client.

Some components of what we typically do in music therapy assessment consist of collaborative efforts. Successfully determining music preferences, regardless of the method, cannot be done without the collaboration of the client or family members. Varied music therapy methodology used during the assessment process may incorporate collaborative efforts, such as musical improvisation or songwriting. The feminist therapy view of collaboration extends beyond these examples of protocol collaboration. A collaborative stance is crucial to the quality of the assessment, validating the client's self-knowledge and facilitating empowerment. Collaborative efforts should encompass the total assessment process, from determining what to assess and what methods to use, to interpretation of the results.

Communicating the results of the assessment to the client, when appropriate, is one of AMTA's clinical practice standards (AMTA, 2003b). This is a beginning toward demystifying the therapy process, one of the techniques utilized in feminist therapy to develop an egalitarian client-therapist relationship and empower the client (Curtis, 2000; Worell & Remer, 2003). The collaborative approach can also provide some balance to the power inherent in the therapist's role. Curtis (2000) and Dileo (2000) both addressed the issue of power, Curtis from a feminist music therapist perspective and Dileo from a multicultural and gender perspective. Feminist therapists accept that the elimination of all power differentials is impossible but the therapist should work toward a therapeutic relationship that is equal in respect and value (Curtis, 2000). From the multicultural and gender perspective, power becomes an issue when the client has experienced some form of oppression or discrimination from others in power, brings these issues to therapy, and the therapist reinforces them (Dileo, 2000). The therapist becomes "one of them" and a trusting relationship is derailed.

Multiple Sources and Valuing Women's Ways of Knowing

The use of observation, interview, nonverbal and verbal interaction, testing, and collection of information from other disciplines or sources are all recognized music therapy assessment methods acknowledged by AMTA (2003b). Multiple means of collecting and interpreting music therapy assessment data for one client have been advocated, including the integration of quantitative and qualitative methods (Wigram, 2000). The simultaneous implementation of formats such as a checklist, rating scale, and narrative were suggested for use with "culturally" diverse clients (Chase, 2003b). With a multilayered approach to assessment, a more complete and accurate picture is possible. In addition, varied methods may allow the client to participate more actively in the assessment process, thereby empowering the client and indicating respect for the client's self-knowledge.

Another assessment area that relates to valuing women's knowledge is the gathering of information regarding strengths, assets, and resources. Within the AMTA *Professional Competencies* (2003a), assessing the client's assets is identified as part of the music therapy assessment process. Standard assessment practice includes the identification of family and other support systems (AMTA, 2003b). Chase (2003b), in presenting cultural considerations for music therapy assessment, includes identification of family roles, gender-related roles of men and women in the family, views of sexual orientation and nontraditional families, and client's sources of strength.

Feminist Transformation of Music Therapy

Curtis (2000) investigated the possibility of transforming music therapy theory into a feminist model of therapy. A model for feminist theory transformation (Worell & Remer, 1992) was applied to Michael Thaut's (2002) theoretical model of music therapy, focusing on the human response to music (i.e. neuropsychological processes in music perception) and how those responses can be used in therapy. Curtis analyzed the music therapy theory against five criteria for transformation: the theory must be ". . . gender free, flexible, interactionist, life-span oriented, and such that it does not violate the three major principles of feminist therapy (e.g. the personal is political, the client-therapist relationship should be egalitarian, and the female perspective is to be valued)" (p.176). She found that music therapy theory meets or could be easily adapted to meet Worell and Remer's five criteria. Due to the flexibility inherent in music therapy theory (i.e. a focus on human response to music), a modification of music therapy theory to include a specific focus on women—women of diverse cultures, races, classes, abilities, sexual orientation—and on women's issues could easily be integrated. Curtis also suggested that the music therapy theory could be modified to be interactionist and life-span oriented. Although music therapy is not based on feminist principles, Curtis concluded that it does not contradict or violate them and that it is compatible with feminist therapy (Curtis, 2000, p.180).

INTEGRATION OF THE FEMINIST PERSPECTIVE INTO MUSIC THERAPY ASSESSMENT

A Process-oriented Model

The feminist perspective is a sensibility, a center that, if adopted, pervasively informs the complete therapeutic process (Hill & Ballou, 1998). This look at assessment through the lens of feminist therapy has been an attempt to demonstrate this perspective from an initial step of the therapeutic process. Although there are specific feminist therapy techniques, the suggestions for integration of the feminist perspective into music therapy assessment are primarily attitudinal and philosophical, based on feminist and culturally sensitive therapy principles.

Santos de Barona and Dutton (1997) formed an assessment working group to identify principles that should inform a feminist analysis of psychological assessment. The group identified five areas of importance:

1) In order to capture an adequate understanding of the client, the day-to-day factors within his or her life should be integrated into each component of the assessment process. Factors to be considered include developmental issues; life history, including experiences with oppression and privilege; socioeconomic status; physical condition; ethnic and cultural factors including acculturation, sexual orientation, geographical influences, spiritual or religious influences, physical strengths and challenges, age, social support (and barriers to support); kinship grouping; and household arrangements (Santos de Barona & Dutton, 1997, p.48).
2) Collaboration is fundamental, accomplished by combining the client's knowledge with the therapist's, and acceptance of joint responsibility for the assessment process so that the client is actively involved in a forthcoming manner or in data collection to document well-defined behavior.
3) Diverse means to gather knowledge (e.g. testing, personal knowledge, intuition) are deemed valuable. The basis on which various assessment decisions are made is acknowledged.
4) When assessment procedures are misused, social, political, professional, or personal action is taken.
5) Assessment conclusions and the formulations about them must be considered as a snapshot of the client at the time of the assessment, not necessarily long-lasting realities.

Based on the above ideas, Santos de Barona and Dutton (1997) presented a process for feminist assessment, identifying five stages where application of the principles would be warranted. They encourage continuous and active involvement of the client. 1) Initially, the therapist collaborates with the client to reach an understanding about the assessment's purpose and agree on the referral question. 2) Then, the therapist and client jointly determine multiple methods and multiple sources for collecting assessment information. 3) Involve the client as much as possible in collecting data, such as through sharing anecdotal information regarding specific life events or being taught to record the frequency or duration of a specific behavior. 4) Analyze the data within the context of the client's life (based on sociocultural factors) and the referral question, integrating knowledge of the client with the collected data. 5) Determine a conclusion in regard to the referral question, communicating with the client to ensure understanding of recommendations.

Suggestions for Music Therapists

The review of literature has indicated that there are commonalities between a culturally sensitive, feminist-oriented assessment approach and current and/or proposed music therapy assessment practice. In synthesizing the material on music therapy assessment, transformation of feminism into music therapy, multicultural assessment, and assessment in feminist therapy, several suggestions are proposed for the music therapist considering adopting a feminist approach to music therapy assessment.

A good starting point is to engage in self-reflection on your personal biases, gender norms, cultural identities, cultural values and attitudes, and theoretical orientation (Chase, 2003a; Dileo, 2000; Ridley, Li, & Hill, 1998; Worell & Remer, 2003). Since the music therapy assessment is when the therapeutic relationship begins to develop, an awareness of what you are bringing to the process is invaluable. Utilization of cultural self-assessments (Chase 2003b; Dileo, 2000), a gender-role analysis, and a power analysis (Worell & Remer, 2003) can facilitate this self-exploration. You may also wish to analyze your theoretical orientation for personal bias by applying the Worell and Remer (2003) model described earlier.

Become familiar with assumptions, principles, and goals for assessment in feminist therapy and determine your stance toward them. This chapter has attempted to provide current information and additional sources in these areas.

In designing therapist-constructed assessment tools or utilizing formal or standardized instruments, be watchful for bias in language and assessment content. If a formal instrument is used, document any alterations of standard administration procedures along with the rationale for the modifications (Santos de Barona & Dutton, 1997).

Approach each client as a unique individual with a multifaceted history and current life situation. In collaboration with the client, consider the internal and external sociocultural factors impacting the client's life (including gender-role socialization, cultural identities and experiences with oppression), the environmental stressors and their effects on the individual, and the interaction of these factors. Assess from the cultural context of the woman's real life and reframe, where appropriate, her symptoms as coping strategies for an unhealthy environment. Additionally, integrate assessment procedures that reveal the personal and social resources available to the client. This aspect of the assessment may be implemented through a pre-assessment protocol or within the actual music therapy assessment, perhaps utilizing multiple assessment methods. Power and gender-role analysis, a focus in feminist therapy, can also be part of the assessment. How in-depth the assessor goes in these areas at this initial stage may be determined by the circumstances of the client. For example, a more thorough assessment would be warranted for an abused client where it is important to determine how the client sees herself in regard to the presence or lack of power and her gender-role in relationship to events in her life. The power and gender-role analysis may additionally be integrated with music therapy treatment approaches and/or as pre-post tests.

Involve the client actively and in collaborative efforts during the assessment to validate his/her own knowledge, to strive for a more egalitarian relationship, and to empower the client. Informing the client of the purpose of the assessment and procedures, as well as assessment decisions, can assist in establishing the collaborative stance.

In work with clients from diverse ethnic and sociocultural groups, become culturally literate by expanding your knowledge of the client's cultural norms, beliefs, values, healing practices, view of music, and music preferences (Chase, 2003b; Chase, 2004; Curtis, 2000; Dileo, 2000). This lengthy process may occur through reading, listening to music, meeting with people from other cultures, and consultation with resource agencies (Chase, 2004; Curtis, 2000).

The final suggestion for the music therapist considering a feminist approach to music therapy assessment is to create assessment strategies with social and political change in mind. One subtle way this could be accomplished is to follow many of the feminist therapy principles previously discussed, especially striving toward an egalitarian relationship and a collaborative stance.

PERSONAL REFLECTIONS

Through the process of looking at music therapy assessment from the perspective of a feminist-diversity approach, I was surprised to find so many areas of commonality with my philosophies of music therapy and music therapy education. Although this chapter did not address assessment for the music therapy university student, aspects of Worell and Remer's approach to assessment from the feminist-diversity perspective could easily be applied. Utilizing a collaborative attitude and viewing the student as a unique individual with a multitude of internal and external sociocultural factors that impact their daily lives may be approaches that already exist in current practice among some educators and clinical training supervisors. The music therapy educator might also find several of the other suggestions for the music therapy clinician presented in this chapter to be helpful when considering the assessment process.

As Marcia Hill and Mary Ballou (1998) suggested, the feminist perspective is a sensibility that pervades all that a feminist therapist does, informing each step of the therapeutic process.

By looking at one aspect of music therapy, clinical assessment, support has been found for Curtis's (2000) analysis that music therapy is compatible with feminist therapy and can be adapted for integration.

REFERENCES

Adler, Roberta (2001) *Musical Assessment of Gerontologic Needs and Treatment*: *The MAGNET survey.* St. Louis, MO: MMB Music, Inc.

American Music Therapy Association (2003a) *AMTA Professional Competencies*. In *AMTA Member Sourcebook.* Silver Spring, MD: Author.

American Music Therapy Association (2003b) *Standards of Clinical Practice.* In *AMTA Member Sourcebook*. Silver Spring, MD: Author.

Bright, Ruth (1993) Cultural aspects of music in therapy. In Margaret Heal & Tony Wigram (eds.) *Music Therapy in Health and Education*. London: Jessica Kingsley Publishers, Ltd.

Bruscia, Kenneth (1998) *Defining Music Therapy* (2nd ed.). Gilsum, NH: Barcelona Publishers.

Chase, Kristen (2003a) Multicultural music therapy: A review of literature. *Music Therapy Perspectives, 21,* 84–88.

Chase, Kristen (2003b) *The Multicultural Music Therapy Handbook*. Columbus, MS: SouthernPen Publishing.

Chase, Kristen (2004) Therapy with gay and lesbian clients: Implications for music therapists. *Music Therapy Perspectives, 22,* 34–38.

Cole, Kristen (2002) *The Music Therapy Assessment Handbook*. Columbia, MS: SouthernPen Publishing.

Curtis, Sandra (2000) Singing subversion, singing soul: Women's voices in feminist music therapy. *Dissertation Abstracts International, 60* (12). 4240. (UMI No. AATNQ44871)

Darrow, Alice-Ann & Molloy, Della (1998) Multicultural perspectives in music therapy: An examination of the literature, educational curricula, and clinical practices in culturally diverse cities of the United States. *Music Therapy Perspectives, 16,* 27–32.

Davis, William, Gfeller, Kate, & Thaut, Michael (1999) *An Introduction to Music Therapy: Theory and Practice* (2nd ed.). Dubuque, IA: McGraw-Hill College.

Dileo, Cheryl (2000) *Ethical Thinking in Music Therapy.* St. Louis, MO: MMB Music, Inc.

Feder, Benjamin & Feder, Elaine (1998) *The Art and Science of Evaluation in the Arts Therapies: How Do You Know what's Working?* Springfield, IL: Charles C. Thomas.

Gantt, Linda (2000) Assessments in the creative arts therapies: Learning from each other. *Music Therapy Perspectives, 18,* 41–46.

Hanser, Suzanne (1999) *The New Music Therapist's Handbook* (2nd ed.). Boston, MA: Berklee Press.

Hill, Marcia & Ballou, Mary (1998) Making therapy feminist: A practice survey. *Women & Therapy, 21,* 1–16.

Hintz, Michelle (2000) Geriatric music therapy clinical assessment: Assessment of music skills. *Music Therapy Perspectives, 18,* 31–40.

Isenberg-Grzeda, Connie (1988) Music therapy assessment: A reflection of professional identity. *Journal of Music Therapy, 25,* 156–169.

Meyer, Gregory, Finn, Stephen, Eyde, Lorraine, Kay, Gary, Moreland, Kevin, Dies, Robert, Eisman, Elena, et al. (2001) Psychological testing and psychological assessment: A Review of evidence and issues. *American Psychologist, 56,* 128–165.

Phinney, Jean (1996) When we think about American ethnic groups, what do we mean? *American Psychologist, 51,* 918–927.

Ridley, Charles, Li, Lisa, & Hill, Carrie (1998) Multicultural assessment: Reexamination, reconceptualization, and practical application. *Counseling Psychologist, 26,* 827–911.

Santos de Barona, Maryann & Dutton, Mary Ann (1997) Feminist perspectives on assessment. In Judith Worell & Norene G. Johnson (eds.) *Shaping the Future of Feminist Psychology: Education, Research, and Practice.* Washington, DC: American Psychological Association.

Scalenghe, Richard & Murphy, Kathleen (2000) Music therapy assessment in the managed care environment. *Music Therapy Perspectives, 18,* 23–30.

Shuttleworth, Sue A. (2001) Exploratory case study: Leadership. Unpublished manuscript, Nova Southeastern University, North Miami Beach, Florida.

Shuttleworth, Sue A. (2003) *Development and pilot testing of an experiential learning formative assessment instrument for undergraduate music therapy clinical students.* Unpublished doctoral dissertation, Nova Southeastern University, North Miami Beach, Florida.

Thaut, Michael (2002) Neuropsychological processes in music perception and their relevance in music therapy. In Robert Unkefer & Michael Thaut (Eds.) *Music Therapy in the Treatment of Adults with Mental Disorders: Theoretical Bases and Clinical Intervention* (2nd ed.). St. Louis, MO: MMB Music, Inc.

Troppozada, Manal (1995) Multicultural training for music therapists: An examination of current issues based on a national survey of professional music therapists. *Journal of Music Therapy, 32,* 65–90.

Wigram, Tony (2000) A method of music therapy assessment for the diagnosis of autism and communication disorders in children. *Music Therapy Perspectives, 18,* 13–22.

Wigram, Tony, Nygaard Pederson, Inge & Ole Bonde, Lars (2002) *A Comprehensive Guide to Music Therapy: Theory, Clinical Practice, Research and Training.* Philadelphia, PA: Jessica Kingsley Publishers.

Worell, Judith & Remer, Pamela (2003) *Feminist Perspectives in Therapy: Empowering Diverse Women* (2nd ed.). Hoboken, NJ: John Wiley & Sons, Inc.

Chapter Twenty

FEMINIST PERSPECTIVES IN MUSIC THERAPY RESEARCH

Barbara L. Wheeler

I begin this chapter on feminist perspectives in music therapy research with some questions. What areas of music therapy might be examined from a feminist perspective—and why haven't music therapists looked at these areas? For a discipline in which approximately 88% of the practitioners are women[1] and with as strong a research base as music therapy has, not to have considered any of these questions raises questions in and of itself. Beyond that, the practice of music therapy is based largely on relationships—how fully can we have investigated relationships in music therapy if we have not looked closely at how relationships are mediated through gender and if the influence of gender power differentials has not been an important part of our investigations?

I would also like to state who I am in relation to this material. I am a woman. I suppose that I am a feminist in many ways—certainly I have lived my life with many of the benefits that feminism has provided and have always agreed with its basic principles, although I have never been involved in a formal way in the feminist movement. I have learned more about feminism in writing this chapter and certainly find my beliefs and values to be congruent with feminism. I know more about research, having studied and done various types of research throughout my career and edited two music therapy research books, *Music Therapy Research: Quantitative and Qualitative Perspectives* (Wheeler, 1995) and *Music Therapy Research,* 2nd Edition (Wheeler, 2005). This chapter has provided me with an opportunity to apply feminist principles to what I know about music therapy research.

[1] This number is taken from the 2004 *AMTA Sourcebook* (American Music Therapy Association, 2005) and reflects the percentage of music therapists in the United States who are members of the organization. It is thought that women constitute a smaller percentage, although still a large majority, in some countries. In the UK, for instance, women constituted 82% and men 18% of music therapists in 2004 (Denize Christophers, personal communication, Aug. 8, 2005), while a rough estimate of the number of German music therapists is that 72% are women and 28% are men (Thomas Wosch, personal communication, Oct. 1, 2005).

BACKGROUND OF FEMINIST RESEARCH

Feminism has had broad implications for many aspects of how people in the United States think[2] and the way that things are viewed. Women of my generation, the baby boomers,[3] have lived most of our adult lives in a world that was drastically changed by feminism and feminist thought. Some women of my generation have played a role in these changes. Women younger than I am—many music therapists—have lived their entire lives in a world that was changed by the gains of feminism. I speak here of the influences on women, but of course men have also been strongly affected by feminism. Feminist research is an important component and outgrowth of feminism as a social and political movement.

Feminist research is defined by Yoland Wadsworth and Kaye Hargreaves (1991) as:

> Research which is carried out by women who identify as feminists, and which has a particular purpose for knowing (a "why"), particular kinds of questions, topics and issues to be known about (a "what"), and an identifiable method of knowing (a "how"), which distinctly draw on women's experience of living in a world in which women are subordinate to men.

Feminist research "aims to transform existing views or ways of being in the world" (Grenz & Willey, 2002, p.2). It is "based in the lives of women and seeks, in one way or another, to improve the conditions of those lives" (Anderson & Damarin, 1996, p.270). Sandra Harding (1987) makes the point that feminism is a perspective rather than a method, and Virginia Olesen (2000) emphasizes that it is "highly diverse" (p.216). Mary Crawford and Ellen Kimmel (1999) find three common themes that stem from the feminist orientation of the authors of feminist psychological research: (a) reflexivity, (b) methods that serve rather than drive the inquiry, and (c) a social change orientation.

Shulamit Reinharz (1992) suggests that feminist methodological literature centers on "four central questions: (1) is there a feminist research method; (2) if

[2] I am writing this from my perspective as a US citizen. I believe that similar views prevail in other western countries, but I am presenting this from my own perspective and experience.

[3] "Baby boomer" refers to the generation born following World War II (generally considered the years 1946–1964), in which many more babies than would have been expected were born.

so, what does it actually consist of; (3) should there be a feminist research method; and (4) what is the relation between feminist research methods and other methods?" (p.4).

Researchers from many disciplines are concerned with the areas on which feminist research may focus and, thus, may conduct feminist research. Sociologists have been active in feminist research (see DeVault, 1999; Fonow & Cook, 1991; Naples, 2003; Nielsen, 1990; Stanley, 1990, for examples), and psychologists are also concerned with feminist research (see Fine, 1992; Kimmel & Crawford, 1999). Other disciplines are, of course, also concerned with feminist issues and involved in feminist research.

Many music disciplines are also involved with feminist perspectives and feminist research. These include musicology (see McClary, 1991; see also Ruud, 2000, for an example of some of the connections), including various aspects of popular music and music performance (see Burns & Lafrance, 2001; Cook & Tsou, 1994), and music education (see Lamb, Dolloff, & Howe, 2002). These areas may support feminist music therapy research and provide models but are not covered in detail in this chapter.

Epistemological Questions

Feminist researchers take various epistemological positions. Epistemology is concerned with questions regarding what are legitimate objects of study, the relationship between the knower and the known, the nature of causality, and what is meant by truth in research. Epistemology of science thus influences the decisions that are made about what can be researched.

In terms of feminist epistemology, Elizabeth Anderson (2004) suggests:

> Feminist epistemology and philosophy of science studies the ways in which gender does and ought to influence our conceptions of knowledge, the knowing subject, and practices of inquiry and justification. It identifies ways in which dominant conceptions and practices of knowledge attribution, acquisition, and justification systematically disadvantage women and other subordinated groups, and strives to reform these conceptions and practices so that they serve the interests of these groups.

Harding (1987) says:

> Once we undertake to use women's experience as a resource to generate scientific problems, hypotheses, and evidence, to design

> research for women, and to place the researcher in the same critical plane as the research subject, traditional epistemological assumptions can no longer be made. These agendas have led feminist social scientists to ask questions about who can be a knower (only men?); what tests beliefs must pass in order to be legitimated as knowledge (only tests against men's experiences and observations?); what kinds of things can be known (can "subjective truths," ones that only women—or only some women—tend to arrive at, count as knowledge?); the nature of objectivity (does it require "point-of-viewlessness"?); the appropriate relationship between the researcher and her/his research subjects (must the researcher be disinterested, dispassionate, and socially invisible to the subject?); what should be the purposes of the pursuit of knowledge (to produce information *for* men?). (p.181)

Harding (1986) distinguishes three separate epistemological forms of feminist theory and practice: (a) positivist, (b) feminist standpoint, and (c) postmodern. These are presented here, largely as they apply to psychological research.

Positivist feminist researchers, also called *feminist empiricists,* identify with the positivist research paradigm that is predominant. They aim to correct biases against women in areas such as the research topics that are selected, how participants are chosen, and how results are interpreted. Positivist feminists also work to challenge discrimination against women within the professions in which their research is based.

Feminist standpoint research, intended to link progressive politics with research and scholarly practices, is widely used in the social sciences and biology. Feminist standpoint researchers suggest that women, by virtue of their life experiences, have a different perspective on the nature of reality than do men, and that a subjective position is needed to create meaning. Those who practice feminist standpoint research have tended to celebrate femaleness and female differences.

Postmodern feminist researchers take advantage of the blurring of academic disciplines and analyze problems of identity, gender, and social relations without regard to traditional barriers among disciplines. These researchers draw from deconstructionist ideas in emphasizing that the meaning of terms and concepts that are expressed through a particular language are not fixed, that these meanings are not ahistorically defined but reflect hierarchical binary relationships (for example, reason/emotion: male/female) that are governed by larger systems of differences that presuppose deeper power relationships (personal communication, Susan Hadley, Sept. 3, 2005). These researchers also analyze variables from a power perspective. *Getting Smart* by Patti Lather (1991) is an important book about postmodern feminist research (see also Alvesson, 2002, for a comprehensible discussion of postmodernism in general).

These three viewpoints on feminist research have been developed and refined as well as debated (see Haraway, 1991; Harding, 1993, 1998, 2004). Each has implications for feminist research.

Although few music therapy researchers have explicitly discussed any of these epistemological viewpoints, they may prove useful as music therapists develop a tradition of feminist music therapy research. Positivist feminist research in music therapy would follow the dominant, positivist paradigm. Since much music therapy research is conducted within a positivist paradigm, this would seem to be a natural area for feminist music therapy research. In the areas suggested in the earlier paragraph, these researchers would work to influence the research topics that are selected, how participants are selected, and how results are interpreted in order to help to correct biases against women. Feminist standpoint researchers in music therapy would emphasize their positionality or that of the research participants in their research. Postmodern feminist music therapy researchers might cross disciplinary lines, would consider the multiple meanings that language has, and might analyze variables from a power perspective.

EXISTING FEMINIST MUSIC THERAPY RESEARCH

Feminist Research

There are a few examples of feminist music therapy research. An early example is a thesis by Michelle Heineman (1982), *A Study of Career Aspirations and Perceived Career Success in Female and Male Registered Music Therapists.* Heineman began with a "concern . . . that women are underrepresented in managerial and administrative positions" (p.20). Her study was "an attempt to find some causes for the underrepresentation of women in supervisory and administrative positions in the field of music therapy" (p.20). Heineman was interested in whether there were differences in the career aspirations and the perceived career success of female and male music therapists. To seek answers, she sent surveys to 500 active Registered Music Therapists; usable surveys were returned by 195 therapists. Each questionnaire consisted of 30 statements that were intended to reflect career aspirations and perceived career success, and respondents were asked to rate their responses on a scale of 1 to 5. Heineman did not find statistically significant differences between men and women on the main questions, but 4 out of 15 statements measuring career aspirations showed significant differences between men and women in directions consistent with societal stereotypes.

> Significantly more women than men agreed that the career of their spouse took precedence over their own career, that they would stop working or work part time when they had children, that they could not see themselves working until retirement age and most importantly, that they could not see themselves supervising other music therapists. (Heineman, pp.30–31)

Of the statements measuring perceived career success, there were statistically significant differences between the groups on 2 of the 15 statements. Significantly more women than men said that they were working fewer hours per week than they desired. Women also felt more than men that significant others in their lives considered them successful; the researcher felt that this indicated that society viewed women as more successful in the helping profession of music therapy than it did men, because men, in pursuing the helping profession of music therapy, were working in a profession that did not fit the gender stereotypes for men. Heineman concluded her discussion by suggesting:

> There are forces operating in our society which define rigid roles for both women and men. The same barriers which exist to prevent women from holding supervisory positions also exist to prevent men from being successful in a helping profession. It would seem that there is a need in our educational process to encourage individual achievement rather than sex-stereotyped roles. (p.32)

Another example of feminist music therapy research is a survey by Sandra Curtis (1990), published as "Women's Issues and Music Therapists." Curtis sent the survey to 1,870 women music therapists who lived in the United States and Canada and received 836 or 45% of the surveys back. The survey included structured and open-ended questions about considerations in career choice and also a ranking of items in three areas of women's lives. The open-ended questions looked at role models, awareness of bias (in general and in their own work situations), the effects of sex-role stereotyping, and general satisfaction with the profession of music therapy. Curtis presented the results in the following areas: (a) the women and their situations; (b) career considerations; and (c) women's personal, work, and family lives. She found that the women had a variety of perceptions and she reported them numerically and also with quotations from the women's responses. In her conclusion, Curtis suggested that the survey had opened a dialogue for which many had felt a need and that:

> Perhaps through the establishment of regular dialogues women could explore together the experience of being female in a patriarchal society (Bell, 1981); discover differences and learn to value those differences; and move away from a dichotomous either/or approach to one in which a number of solutions are allowed. (Curtis, p.65)

As a feminist researcher, Curtis intended for the information that she gathered to make a difference in women's lives through opening this dialogue.

Curtis (2000) also conducted an experimental study on the effectiveness of feminist music therapy in her dissertation, *Singing Subversion, Singing Soul: Women's Voices in Feminist Music Therapy.* After laying the foundation for and describing a model of feminist music therapy, she studied six women who underwent feminist music therapy sessions (another 29 women enrolled in the study but were unable to complete 8 of the 16 feminist music therapy sessions required for participation). She measured the women's self-esteem using the Tennessee Self Concept Scale (TSCS) and did content analyses of their songs and interviews. Curtis describes the sessions as:

> The first 30 minutes were spent in feminist analysis of power and gender-role socialization by means of lyric analysis; the next 30 minutes were spent in further feminist analysis and in finding their own voices through the feminist music therapy technique of song-writing; the final 30-minute segment was dedicated to exploring self-nurturance through relaxation and music techniques. (p.308)

Curtis presented the results individually for each participant, including examples of their song and interview content and TSCS scores, in addition to analysis and comments on what occurred for each woman. The women reported many positive changes in all areas.

Randi Rolvsjord has published several pieces of research that incorporate feminist perspectives. She used Julia Kristeva's concepts, viewed by some as feminist and certainly congruent with feminist thought, to explore the status that music therapists give to music as a language and how this can contribute to the potential of music therapy (Rolvsjord, 2004a). Rolvsjord's work may be classified as theoretical inquiry and is thus included as a type of research. She has also advocated the use of resource-oriented music therapy (Rolvsjord, 2004b) and incorporated this into a research agenda (Rolvsjord, Gold, & Stige, 2005). Resource-oriented music therapy, described later in this chapter, gives power to the person who is the focus of the therapy and is thus congruent with feminist values and perspectives.

Elizabeth York did a study that is clearly feminist. She and her research assistant, Maureen Hearns, worked with 40 women who had been abused and who were being served by a local agency. In "Finding Voice: A Music Therapy Clinical and Research Protocol with Women Survivors of Intimate Partner Violence" (York, 2006; see also York & Hearns, 2005), York presents the results of a qualitative research study that utilized a grounded theory approach to data collection and qualitative data representation labeled "ethnographic drama." Thirty sessions were conducted over an 8-month period, resulting in the development of an ethnographic performance piece that was later performed around the state by the women themselves and recorded onto a CD. This study is an example of feminist research that incorporates feminist perspectives in both its purpose and outcomes.

Related Research

Some music therapy research contains elements of feminist research, although it is not done from a feminist perspective. Examining some of that research may provide insights into how music therapy could develop more of a feminist research tradition. Other research could be more useful if it included references to areas that might be of interest to feminists. This section will examine this already-existing music therapy research from these perspectives.

A search of the CD-Rom published by the American Music Therapy Association (2004) of the terms "feminist," "feminine," and "feminism" brought up 19 references in the three journals included on this disc: *Journal of Music Therapy; Music Therapy: Journal of the American Association for Music Therapy;* and *Music Therapy Perspectives.* These included a number of contributions that considered feminism from an analytic point of view, such as feminine archetypes or feminine symbolism, and references to instruments as feminine, none of which are related to the current topic of interest. There were also references to feminine roles that do not seem related to the current topic as they are presented there. A search of the CD-Rom for "gender" brought up 80 references, a few of which are discussed below. A search of the website for the *Nordic Journal of Music Therapy* with keywords "feminist" and "feminism" brought up seven references to these words, two of which are included in this chapter as examples of research incorporating a feminist perspective.

There are a few references that, while not explicitly feminist, do seem relevant. The content of two studies is clearly related to feminism, although they do not take this perspective. One is "Domestic Violence: Assessments and Treatments Employed by Music Therapists" by Michael Cassity and Kimberly Theobold (1990), in which they surveyed music therapists about these areas. Another is "Music for The Soul: A Music Therapy Program for Battered Women" by Jennifer Whipple and Rebecca Lindsey (1999). Their description of work with women in a shelter for battered women includes data on the women's responses taken on a weekly basis; as such, it could be classified as descriptive research, although its primary purpose appears to be to describe a program rather than to present research. Although the authors do not tie their research to feminism, using music therapy to assist this population could clearly be linked to feminist thought and research. Indeed, the later study by York (2006) that was described above adopts a feminist perspective in using music therapy with this same population.

Additional studies that are not explicitly feminist include several historical articles on women who have contributed to music therapy. One of these is Marian Erdman, born in 1923, who created a music therapy position in the American Red Cross and whose work was chronicled by Sheri Robb (1999). The contributions of three early pioneers who were women, Eva Agusta Vescelius, Isa Maud Ilsen, and Harriet Ayer Seymour, are described by William Davis (1993). A recent collection of the work of Florence Tyson (Tyson, 2004), gathers together important information on the historical contribution as well as the writings of this music therapy pioneer. Susan Hadley (2001) presents Mary Priestley's contributions in

> a multi-modal qualitative research design, with one of the modes of inquiry being oral history . . . . The idea was to combine the oral history with (1) my lived experience as a client in the method (which I called loosely phenomenological, but which is more participatory research . . .) and (2) my philosophical inquiry into the underlying assumptions of the method. Each mode of inquiry was necessary for a greater understanding of both the person and the method and that is how I think that it deviates from the "purely" historical. In some ways it was "hermeneutical" in that each of the areas could be likened to texts that I interpreted and reinterpreted and which deepened my understanding of each. (Hadley, personal communication, July 7, 2005)

This acknowledgment of the contributions of women to music therapy and the description of their work are important for presenting a balanced view of the history of music therapy. Although this is far from an exhaustive list of women who have been important in developing music therapy, it provides a good beginning. (It should be noted that all of these articles about women in music therapy have appeared since 1993, and most of them since 1999.) The question that should be raised as far as women's contribution to music therapy is probably not: How many of those who have contributed have been written about? A more relevant question would be: Why have more of the leaders in music therapy not been women, given the overwhelming percentage of women who practice music therapy?

Some quantitative studies provide information on gender differences, but these are relatively few and far between. Of course, many studies look at differences between female and male participants on variables of interest, but a few were found in which the researcher does more than that. These include a survey of job satisfaction of music therapists (Braswell, Decuir, & Jacobs, 1989) that included analyses of gender differences in several areas. Of 1,344 surveys that were returned, 1,167 (87%) were from women and 166 (12%) were from men. One area that they analyzed was salary differences between men and women while statistically controlling for the influence of age, length of music therapy service, and degree. They found, after removing the influence of these other variables, that gender differences remained at a highly statistically significant level. They present other variables that were also important in predicting salary and discuss these various influences. In doing so, they share some of the complexity of these influences, making it clearer how gender fits with other influences. In other analyses, they did not find gender to be a significant predictor of job satisfaction, nor did they find job satisfaction scores to be significantly different between males and females. In analyzing and presenting gender as a variable, these authors contribute to an understanding of the role of gender in the job satisfaction of music therapists.

Another study in which differences in the responses of females versus males (in this case, girls versus boys) were found, and in which the reasons for the differences were discussed, was of junior and senior high school music students' attitudes towards individuals with a disability (Darrow & Johnson, 1994). The researchers found differences between girls' and boys' responses and related them to previous literature in which the same differences were found. They say:

> This result presents an important question. If one believes that sensitivity is not innate but a learned attribute, why is it not taught as effectively to male students? As teachers and therapists, perhaps there is cause to examine our own gender attitudes with regard to our students and clients. (p.276)

The authors' suggestion to look at these attitudes that go with gender differences is quite consistent with what might be suggested as an outcome of a feminist research study.

A study that is related to feminist perspectives on music therapy research investigated the effects of rap music on sexual aggression against women. Negative effects of rap music were supported in an earlier study, reported in "The Influence of Misogynous Rap Music on Sexual Aggression Against Women" (Barongan & Hall, 1995). This study found that men who were exposed to misogynous rap music were "more likely to show a woman a misogynous vignette that involves either physical aggression or rape than men who are exposed to neutral rap music" (p.198). Showing such a misogynous vignette was considered to be an act of sexual imposition. In a later study of influences on male misogynous behavior (Barongan, 1999), however, similar effects of rap music were not found. Although these studies and the related research that the authors describe were not conducted by music therapists, they clearly raise significant themes that could be analyzed by music therapists from a feminist perspective.

POSSIBILITIES FOR FEMINIST MUSIC THERAPY RESEARCH

There is a place for the use of many types of research methods in feminist music therapy research. It is often felt that qualitative methods are more congruent with feminist views than quantitative research, as the underlying tenets of qualitative research may be quite consistent with some of the underpinnings of feminism. This includes a valuing of collaboration, treating people as equals, understanding that things can only be understood in context, and acknowledging the complexity of situations so that they must be described in detail in order to do them justice. While these similarities do point to possibilities for feminist qualitative research, qualitative research is by no means the only possible venue for feminist research in music therapy. Indeed, four of the five studies cited above as examples of feminist perspectives in music therapy research—the Curtis survey of the attitudes of women music therapists, the Curtis dissertation on the viability of feminist music therapy, the Heineman study of career aspirations and perceived success of women music therapists, and the Barongan study (which is not actually music therapy research but studies a related area) that pointed to influences of rap music on sexually impositional male behavior—are quantitative research, while only one—the York study using music to work with women who were in abusive relationships—is qualitative research.

We can take what has been said about feminism and the concerns of feminists, along with the music therapy research that has been done, to consider what music therapy research with a feminist perspective might look like. What topics might be addressed? How might this affect what is known about music therapy and music therapists? And how might we investigate the topics that we select?

An overall question that might be investigated in numerous ways comes from questions asked by Shona Russell and Maggie Carey (2003) and adapted to music therapy: What is the impact of the social marker of gender on our work in music therapy? That is, how do women's experiences change our understandings of relationships, and how do women differ from each other in these experiences?

I will also look at some areas that might be investigated through feminist music therapy research. There are many topics that might be covered from this perspective, but I will focus on just a few, along with ideas of methods of research that might be used to investigate the topics. The topics suggested are only some of those that could be investigated using these methods, and the methods described are only some of those that might be used to study the topics.

Relationships in Music Therapy

One topic that we might investigate using feminist research methods is relationships in music therapy. We could focus on these relationships in any of a number of ways.

Since music therapy involves various types of relationships—among and between the therapist, the client or clients, and the music—many aspects of relationships might be investigated from a feminist perspective. The way that these relationships are formed and how they are mediated through gender are potential topics for investigation. We might also look at gender power differentials that exist in a relationship, how they are determined, how they change, what factors influence this change, and how changes in power are exhibited.

Several approaches to music therapy research lend themselves naturally to examining relationships. One of these is participatory action research, also known as action research, as described by Brynjulf Stige (2002, 2005). Stige (2005) defines this type of research:

> The term *participatory action research* has come into use to denote situated research advocating the primacy of the voices and goals of the participants themselves. A broad range of labels is commonly used to denote some related practices of research, including *action research, participatory research, thematic research, collaborative research, mutual inquiry, community-driven research,* and *emancipatory research.* (p.404)

We can see from this statement that many of the same principles held by feminists are also held in participatory action research. Indeed, this research approach has much in common with feminism and may be seen as having feminist roots (Hunt, 2005). In participatory action research, the participants play an important role in generating the data for the research and also in other aspects, including formulating the research questions and designing the method. "Outcomes are defined by the characteristics of the process: empowerment of participants, collaboration and participation, social change, and acquisition of knowledge" (Stige, 2005, p.411). Stige suggests:

> Participatory action research may turn out to be a constructive and context-sensitive alternative for music therapists who want to explore and document the value of their work and to combine this with a self-critical awareness about how value is linked to perspective. Contemporary social and intellectual developments such as postcolonialism and feminism will probably become more influential in music therapy in the future, and this will certainly increase the relevance of participatory action research. (p.413)

We could picture music therapists working with female clients designing research to address questions of power in music therapy sessions and using these steps to follow what might become a feminist approach to research using participatory action research methods. As an example, there might be a desire to understand more about how power relationships develop in the therapy and affect the process and outcome of therapy. The intent with participatory action research would be to incorporate group members' perceptions of these relationships into the study. Group members and therapist might be involved in developing the question and deciding how to go about researching it (in other words, designing the study) and then, of course, conducting the research.

A resource-oriented approach to music therapy includes discussion of relationships. Randi Rolvsjold (2004b) works within a resource-oriented approach to music therapy that emphasizes the resources that a client has rather than his or her deficits. She places this in a societal context and speaks of power relationships as important from this perspective. Power relationships are central to feminist theory, and music therapy research using a resource-oriented approach and including feminist theory could be a logical way to investigate these relationships. The investigation by Rolvsjold and her colleagues (Rolvsjold, Gold, & Stige, 2005) that was mentioned above is an example of an approach to this.

Another approach to research that holds promise for investigating relationships from a feminist perspective is arts-based research. Arts-based research is defined by Diane Austin and Michele Forinash (2005) as:

> . . . a research method in which the arts play a primary role in any or all of the steps of the research method. Art forms such as poetry, music, visual art, drama, and dance are essential to the research process itself and central in formulating the research question, generating data, analyzing data, and presenting the research results. (pp.458–459)

Drama has been used in some feminist research that would be considered to be arts-based research. Reinharz (1992, pp.224–225) points to several researchers who use drama in feminist research, including: (a) Vivienne Griffiths, who suggests that drama is useful because it requires collaboration, enables people to find their voice, is concrete, and is context-dependent; (b) Honor Ford Smith, who helped black women to share information about their lives through drama; and (c) Marianne (Tracy) Paget, who wrote an article about a physician who did not relate to a woman's cancer, but Paget then decided that the article would be more effective if viewed as theatre, so arranged to have it performed and found that this clarified the roles.

Just as drama has been used to express these feminist perspectives, some of which concern relationships, we could picture using various forms of music. York's research with women who were abused, which culminated in an ethnographic performance piece, is an example of arts-based feminist research in music therapy that combines music with drama. (See her chapter in this book.)

Equality in research is a principle in other types of qualitative research in addition to participatory action research. This suggests that other qualitative research approaches may also be appropriate for investigating relationships from a feminist perspective.

Improvisation Content and Related Material

Music therapy improvisations may also be examined from a feminist perspective. This may, of course, include information about relationships that occur through improvisation, as considered in the previous section.

There are also areas of interest that might be examined from a feminist perspective. For example, we might analyze improvisations from a power perspective: Do women and men exhibit different musical or interpersonal patterns when they improvise? If so, how are these influenced by societal gender role-related expectations or gender power differentials? Do they achieve a balance in the improvisation and, if so, how? How can these be described? Are there patterns to them? What language is used to describe the improvisations?

The Improvisation Assessment Profiles (IAPs) developed by Kenneth Bruscia (1987) are designed to analyze improvisations. They include the following scales:

- *Salience* (with five scales forming a spectrum: compliant, conforming, attending, controlling, dominating),
- *Integration* (with the spectrum: undifferentiated, synchronized, integrated, differentiated, overdifferentiated),
- *Variability* (rigid, stable, variable, contrasting, random),
- *Tension* (hypo-tense, calm, cyclic, tense, hyper-tense),
- *Congruence* (unengaged, congruent, centered, incongruent, polarized),
- *Autonomy* (dependent, following, partner, leader, competitor/resister) (Bonde, 2005, p.501)

The IAPs can be used to analyze improvisations and provide information on numerous aspects of them, including those in which we are interested.

Phenomenological inquiry has been used to study improvisations. Lawrence Ferrara (1984), a musicologist, developed a phenomenological method for analyzing music. Ferrara's method was later adapted by Michele Forinash and David Gonzalez (1990) to analyze improvisations in music therapy. Ferrara's method has been used by numerous music therapy researchers (see, for example, Amir, 1990; Arnason, 2002; Trondalen, 2003) to analyze improvisations, often in the form adapted by Forinash and Gonzalez. These methods could be used to analyze improvisations from a feminist perspective, looking at how improvisers interact and relate to one another (musically and interpersonally), who leads and who follows, the patterns that are followed, and so forth.

We might use related methods to examine musical experiences (other than improvisation) that are used in music therapy for the same types of information. How do clients' compositions reflect areas of interest to feminists? What songs are chosen for lyric analysis and what do these choices say about music therapy from a feminist perspective?

Feminist Music Therapy

A feminist approach to music therapy was developed and described by Curtis (2000; 2006) and later researched with positive results. As this type of therapy is developed further, additional research should be done on it. This might include experimental studies in which feminist music therapy is compared with other types of music therapy and non-music therapy or in which various aspects of feminist music therapy are evaluated and compared. It might also include qualitative studies that include, for instance, women's perceptions of their experiences in feminist music therapy, perhaps including how it differs from their experiences in non-feminist music therapy. This could be done through phenomenological inquiry or narrative inquiry. Or it could use a grounded theory method that leads to information about categories that make this therapy effective or that distinguish it as feminist music therapy. Adapting from questions asked by Russell and Carey (2003), we might ask: Where is feminist-informed music therapy going, and what strategies best advance thinking in relation to feminist practice with individuals, families, groups, and communities?

We could study various aspects of feminist music therapy through case studies. These could be either qualitative or quantitative and would allow us to focus on an individual (or an individual unit, which might be a group of women) and her experience of feminist music therapy. The study could be of the client who is experiencing the therapy or the therapist who is involved with it.

Responses of Women

The results of much of the experimental research that is done in music therapy raise questions as to how and why females and males respond differently to situations. The first step in examining these responses is to *ask* the questions. Much of the research that has been done simply does not do this, so this first step is crucial. If differences are found between females and males, music therapists must explore possible reasons why these differences exist.

And what might we learn about the effects of gender role socialization and gender power differentials in music therapy sessions? Or how does gender (of the client or the therapist) influence who comes to music therapy? Are there influences of gender role socialization and gender power differentials on what occurs in music therapy—what happens in the sessions themselves or the outcomes? These are only a few of the many questions that we could ask. We could picture quantitative experimental studies looking at some of these questions.

An example of research that asked questions about women's experiences and that resulted in an artistic product with a feminist perspective —in this case a play—is "The Vagina Monologues" by Eve Ensler (2001), in which the author formed the stories told by women into a play. This is an example of using mixed genre methods in a form of narrative inquiry, a combination of performance ethnography, critical ethnography, and autoethnography (Carolyn Kenny, personal communication, July 28, 2005).

One technique that might be fruitful for studying responses is George Kelly's Personal Construct Psychology and the repertory grid technique (Abrams & Meadows, 2005; Aldridge, 1996). The repertory grid technique intends to elicit the inner experiences and perceptions of a participant using an interactive computer technique. It could be useful in helping to understand many aspects of women's (and men's) experiences in music therapy, with a focus on those issues that are of interest in feminist research.

Characteristics and Perceptions of Music Therapists

One way to study perceptions is through surveys. Quantitative surveys are good ways to get information on people's perceptions. Curtis used a survey to gather information in her 1990 study of women's issues in music therapy. We might pursue a number of questions using quantitative surveys: What do we know about the large proportion of white women music therapists and why white women so dominate this profession?[4] What are the effects of this disparity on salary? On longevity in the field? On satisfaction with the work? Currently, people have many opinions regarding these questions, but there has been no actual study of them.

As we structure surveys to reflect a feminist perspective, we should keep in mind Lips's point (1985, cited in Curtis, 1990) that although structured

[4] In addition to the variable of gender, there are other axes such as class, sexual orientation, ability, religion, culture, etc., that could be examined. The question can thus be expanded to: "Why do white, Anglo-Saxon, protestant, middle class, heterosexual, able-bodied women so dominate this profession?"

questions provide more manageable data, they elicit responses based on generalities and can encourage the dichotomization between men and women. Curtis also refers to Schaef (1981) when she says, "'Soft' data garnered from open-ended questions focuses on synthesis rather than analysis. It is this synthesis which provides the opportunity to describe, to understand, to explore together, and possibly to grow" (Curtis, p.62). The surveys that we structure should thus include open-ended questions as much as possible in order to gather these perspectives and to develop the ability to synthesize.

There are numerous qualitative methods through which to gather information on the perceptions of music therapists. We could picture using narrative inquiry. Carolyn Kenny (2005) says about narrative inquiry:

> *Story* is the simplest and most direct way to define a narrative. Narrative inquiry creates an intersubjective space that reflects a dynamic relation-ship between researcher, the context of research, and the reader. Narrative mediates between an inner world of thought-feeling and an outer world of observable actions and states of affairs. . . . Narrative inquiry attempts to formalize the nature and character of narratives to communicate dynamic elements of our worlds and our experiences that would be lost without a story. (p.416)

The researcher might gather information on a number of the areas suggested as of possible interest in feminist research through narratives written by women. These narratives might be of women's experiences or feelings or of events in their lives—all have potential for shedding light on issues of importance to women. These narratives could serve as both the data and the method of presentation of the results. Narrative would be a particularly useful way to express what the research participants have to say.

Another way would be through various first-person research methods, defined by Bruscia (2005) as "any method in which researchers or participants gather data from themselves, using processes such as introspection, retro-spection, self-perception, self-observation, self-reflection, self-inquiry, and so forth" (p.379). Bruscia (2005) describes a number of possible methods of first-person research that may be adapted to feminist research topics. For example, heuristic research procedures might be used for self-examination by a music therapist of ways in which her gender influences her day-to-day work. This could include description of what occurs and what she feels and might also involve analysis that could result in categories into which these influences fall.

Adapting from questions asked by Russell and Carey (2003), we might ask: What do feminist therapists and community workers want? That is, how do feminist interpretations of inequality in families and relationships lead to new ways of thinking about and practicing therapy and community work?

Historical Questions

Russell and Carey (2003) ask: Why did the feminist challenge to therapy emerge historically, and how have these challenges changed over time and place? There is a need for historical research on the history of women in music therapy. This research might study the role of women in the history of music therapy (as has been done and was reported earlier in this chapter) and might focus on how their gender influenced this work. It might lead to an understanding of why men have so dominated a profession that is comprised of an overwhelming majority of women. Eventually, this research might be of the history of feminism in music therapy.

SUMMARY

This chapter has presented information on feminist research and applied this to music therapy research. It has described the inroads that have been made to music therapy research with a feminist perspective. Several researchers have contributed to this and have made a good beginning on research from a feminist perspective.

A number of possibilities of topics for music therapy research from a feminist perspective have been presented. These may provide a beginning for music therapy researchers in this area. There are many additional possibilities for music therapy research from a feminist perspective.

REFERENCES

Abrams, Brian & Meadows, Anthony (2005) Personal construct theory and the repertory grid technique. In Barbara L. Wheeler (ed.) *Music Therapy Research,* 2nd Ed. Gilsum, NH: Barcelona Publishers.

Aldridge, David (1996) *Music Therapy Research and Practice in Medicine: From Out of the Silence.* London: Jessica Kingsley Publishers.

Alvesson, Mats (2002) *Postmodernism and Social Research.* Buckingham, UK: Open University Press.

American Music Therapy Association (2004) *Music Therapy Research CD-ROM* (2nd ed.). Silver Spring, MD: Author.

American Music Therapy Association (2005) *AMTA Member Sourcebook 2004.* Silver Spring, MD: Author.

Amir, Dorit (1990) A song is born: Discovering meaning in improvised songs through phenomenological analysis of two music therapy sessions with a traumatic spinal-cord injured young adult. *Music Therapy, 9,* 62–81.

Anderson, Elizabeth (2004) Feminist epistemology and philosophy of science. In Edward N. Zalta (ed.) *The Stanford Encyclopedia of Philosophy* (Summer 2004 Edition). http://plato.stanford.edu/archives/sum2004/entries/feminism-epistemology/

Anderson, Jane H. & Damarin, Suzanne K. (1996) Poststructural feminism and research in educational communications and technology. In David H. Jonassen (ed.) *Handbook of Research for Educational Communications and Technology*. New York: Macmillan Library Reference.

Arnason, Carolyn L. R. (2002) An eclectic approach to the analysis of improvisations in music therapy sessions. *Music Therapy Perspectives, 20,* 4–12.

Austin, Diane & Forinash, Michele (2005) Arts-based research. In Barbara L. Wheeler (ed.), *Music Therapy Research,* 2nd Ed. Gilsum, NH: Barcelona Publishers.

Barongan, Christy & Hall, Gordon C. Nagayama (1995) The influence of misogynous rap music on sexual aggression against women. *Psychology of Women Quarterly, 19,* 195–207.

Barongan, Maria C. (1999) Sexual aggression from a feminist perspective: An examination of motivational factors and situational cues. *Dissertation Abstracts International, 59*(8), 4454B.

Bonde, Lars Ole (2005) Approaches to researching music. In Barbara L. Wheeler (ed.) *Music Therapy Research,* 2nd Ed. Gilsum, NH: Barcelona Publishers.

Braswell, Charles, Decuir, Anthony, & Jacobs, Keith (1989) Job satisfaction among music therapists. *Journal of Music Therapy, 26,* 2–18.

Bruscia, Kenneth E. (1987) *Improvisational Models of Music Therapy.* Springfield, IL: Charles C. Thomas.

Bruscia, Kenneth E. (2005) First-person research. In Barbara L. Wheeler (ed.) *Music Therapy Research,* 2nd Ed. Gilsum, NH: Barcelona Publishers.

Burns, Lori & Lafrance, Melisse (2001) *Disruptive Divas: Feminism, Identity, and Popular Music.* New York: Routledge.

Cassity, Michael David & Theobold, Kimberly A. Kaczor (1990) Domestic violence: Assessments and treatments employed by music therapists. *Journal of Music Therapy, 27,* 179–194.

Cook, Susan C. & Tsou, Judy S. (1994) *Cecilia Reclaimed.* Champaign, IL: University of Illinois Press.

Crawford, Mary & Kimmel, Ellen (1999) Promoting methodological diversity in feminist research. In Ellen B. Kimmel & Mary Crawford (eds.) *Innovations in Feminist Psychological Research.* Cambridge, UK: Cambridge University Press.

Curtis, Sandra L. (1990) Women's issues in music therapy. *Music Therapy Perspectives, 8,* 61–66.

Curtis, Sandra L. (2006) Feminist music therapy: Transforming theory, transforming lives. In Susan Hadley (ed.) *Feminist Perspectives in Music Therapy.* Gilsum, NH: Barcelona Publishers.

Curtis, Sandra L. (2000) Singing subversion, singing soul: Women's voices in feminist music therapy. (Doctoral dissertation, Concordia University, 1997). *Dissertation Abstracts International, 60* (12-A), 4240.

Darrow, Alice-Ann & Johnson, Christopher M. (1994) Junior and senior high school music students' attitudes toward individuals with a disability. *Journal of Music Therapy, 31,* 266–279.

Davis, William B. (1993) Keeping the dream alive: Profiles of three early twentieth-century music therapists. *Journal of Music Therapy, 30,* 34–45.

DeVault, Marjorie L. (1999) *Liberating Method: Feminism and Social Research.* Philadelphia: Temple University Press.

Ensler, Eve (2001) *The Vagina Monologues.* New York: Villard.

Ferrara, Lawrence (1984) Phenomenology as a tool for musical analysis. *The Musical Quarterly 70,* 355–373.

Fine, Michelle (1992) *Disruptive Voices: The Possibilities of Feminist Research.* Ann Arbor, MI: University of Michigan Press.

Fonow, Mary M. & Cook, Judith A. (1991) *Beyond Methodology: Feminist Scholarship as Lived Research.* Indianapolis, IN: Indiana University Press.

Forinash, Michele & Gonzalez, David (1989) A phenomenological perspective of music therapy. *Music Therapy, 8,* 35–46.

Grenz, Sabine & Willey, Angela (2002) Marginal research: Reflections on location and representation. In Gail Wilson (ed.) Mar*ginal Research: Reflections on Location and Representation.* London: Gender Institute, London School of Economics.

Hadley, Susan (2001) Exploring relationships between Mary Priestley's life and work. *Nordic Journal of Music Therapy, 10,* 116–131.

Haraway, Donna (1991) Situated knowledges: The science question in feminism and the privilege of partial perspective. In Donna Haraway, *Simians, Cyborgs, and Women: The Reinvention of Nature.* New York: Routledge.

Harding, Sandra (1986) *The Science Question in Feminism.* Ithaca, NY: Cornell University Press.

Harding, Sandra (1987) *Feminism and Methodology.* Bloomington, IN: Indiana University Press.

Harding, Sandra (1993) Rethinking standpoint epistemology: What is strong objectivity? In Linda Alcoff & Elizabeth Potter (eds.) *Feminist Epistemologies.* New York: Routledge.

Harding, Sandra (1998) After the neutrality ideal: Science, politics and "strong objectivity." In E. Carol Polifroni & Marylouise Welch (eds.) *Perspectives on Philosophy of Science in Nursing: An Historical and Contemporary Anthology.* Philadelphia: Lippincott-Raven.

Harding, Sandra (2004) *Feminist Standpoint Theory Reader: Intellectual & Political Controversies.* New York: Routledge.

Heineman, Michelle (1982) *A study of career aspirations and perceived career success in female and male registered music therapists.* Unpublished master's thesis, Florida State University, Tallahassee, FL.

Hunt, Meagan (2005) Action research and music therapy: Group music therapy with young refugees in a school community. *Voices: A World Forum for Music Therapy.* http://www.voices.no/mainissues/mi40005000184.html

Kenny, Carolyn (2005) Narrative inquiry. In Barbara L. Wheeler (ed.) *Music Therapy Research,* 2nd Ed. Gilsum, NH: Barcelona Publishers.

Kimmel, Ellen B. & Crawford, Mary (1999) *Innovations in Feminist Psychological Research.* Cambridge, UK: Cambridge University Press.

Lamb, Roberta, Dolloff, Lori-Anne, & Howe, Sondra Wieland (2002) Feminism, feminist research, and gender research in music education: A selective review. In Richard Colwell & Carol Richardson (eds.) *The New Handbook of Research on Music Teaching and Learning.* New York: Oxford University Press.

Lather, Patti (1991) *Getting Smart.* New York: Routledge.

McClary, Susan (1991) *Feminine Endings: Music, Gender and Sexuality.* Minneapolis, MN: University of Minnesota Press.

Naples, Nancy A. (2003) *Feminism and Method: Ethnography, Discourse Analysis, and Activist Research.* New York: Routledge.

Nielsen, Joyce McCarl (1990) *Feminist Research Methods: Exemplary Readings in the Social Sciences.* Boulder, CO: Westview Press.

Olesen, Virginia L. (2000) Feminisms and qualitative research at and into the millennium. In Norman K. Denzin & Yvonna S. Lincoln (eds.) *Handbook of Qualitative Research,* 2nd Ed. Thousand Oaks, CA: Sage Publications.

Reinharz, Shulamit (1992) *Feminist Methods in Social Research.* New York: Oxford University Press.

Robb, Sheri L. (1999) Marian Erdman: Contributions of an American Red Cross hospital recreation worker. *Journal of Music Therapy, 36,* 314–329.

Rolvsjord, Randi (2004a) Music as a poetic language. *Voices: A World Forum for Music Therapy,* http://www.voices.no/mainissues/mi40004000138.html

Rolvsjord, Randi (2004b) Therapy as empowerment. Clinical and political implications of empowerment philosophy in mental health practices of music therapy. *Nordic Journal of Music Therapy, 13,* 99–111.

Rolvsjord, Randi, Gold, Christian, & Stige, Brynjulf (2005) Research rigour and therapeutic flexibility: Rationale for a therapy manual developed for a randomized controlled trial. *Nordic Journal of Music Therapy, 14,* 15–32.

Russell, Shona & Carey, Maggie (2003) Feminism, therapy and narrative ideas: Exploring some not so commonly asked questions. http://www.dulwichcentre.com.au/feminism.html (Originally published in *International Journal of Narrative Therapy and Community Work,* No. 2)

Ruud, Even (2000) "New musicology", Music education and music therapy. *Nordic Journal of Music Therapy* [online papers], http://www.njmt.no/artikkelruudnewmusic.html#top

Stanley, Liz (1990) *Feminist Praxis.* New York: Routledge.

Stige, Brynjulf (2002) *Culture-centered Music Therapy.* Gilsum, NH: Barcelona Publishers.

Stige, Brynjulf (2005) Participatory action research. In Barbara L. Wheeler (ed.) *Music Therapy Research,* 2nd Ed. Gilsum, NH: Barcelona Publishers.

Trondalen, Gro (2003) "Self-listening" in music therapy with a young woman suffering from anorexia nervosa. *Nordic Journal of Music Therapy, 12,* 3–17.

Tyson, Florence (2004) *Psychiatric Music Therapy in the Community: The Legacy of Florence Tyson* (Michael G. McGuire, ed.). Gilsum, NH: Barcelona Publishers.

Wadsworth, Yoland & Hargreaves, Kaye (1991) What is feminist research? Melbourne, AU: Action Research Issues Association. Available at http://www.wnmu.org/gap/wadsworth.htm

Wheeler, Barbara L. (1995) *Music Therapy Research: Quantitative and Qualitative Perspectives.* Gilsum, NH: Barcelona Publishers.

Wheeler, Barbara L. (2005) *Music Therapy Research,* 2nd Ed. Gilsum, NH: Barcelona Publishers.

Whipple, Jennifer & Lindsey, Rebecca (1999) Music for the soul: A music therapy program for battered women. *Music Therapy Perspectives, 17,* 61–68.

York, Elizabeth (2006) Finding voice: A music therapy clinical and research protocol with women survivors of intimate partner violence. In Susan Hadley (ed.) *Feminist Perspectives in Music Therapy.* Gilsum, NH: Barcelona Publishers.

York, Elizabeth & Hearns, Maureen (2005, July 20) *A music therapy research protocol with women victims of intimate partner violence.* Presentation at the 11th World Congress of Music Therapy, Brisbane, Australia.

Chapter Twenty-One

FEMINIST THERAPY ETHICS: IMPLICATIONS FOR MUSIC THERAPY

Cheryl Dileo

I write this chapter not as a "Feminist" or "Feminist Therapist" per se but as a music therapy professional committed to the advancement of ethics in her field of endeavor. Although I am very concerned with women's issues, more than a feminist, I consider myself one who is concerned with all types of culture (besides that of gender) within a biopsychosocial model. I find that identifying with feminism or feminist therapy for me is limiting, as the lens I would use as a feminist therapist is not completely consistent with a multicultural lens. My intent is to illuminate cultural/gender differences through research and practice. I am very concerned about women's health issues, and my goal is to gain a greater understanding and to promote research regarding gender/cultural differences in health needs and conditions, rather than to implement a feminist model with certain fixed assumptions about these needs.

With more than 30 years of interest, research, and writing on the topic of professional ethics in music therapy, I am aware that my concept of ethics continues to grow and change, especially in the light of the growing implications for multicultural practice and feminist thought in the field of music therapy. I embrace the continuing challenge of how to educate music therapy professionals and students on professional ethics in the best way possible. For me, the acquisition of astute ethical thinking is the hallmark of what it means to be a professional (Dileo, 2000). Thus, it is important to examine the implications of both feminist and feminist therapy perspectives on current music therapy ethics, and this will be the focus of the present chapter.

It is clear in the literature that there is no *one* version of feminist therapy, however, there are certain tenets to which most, if not all, feminist approaches to psychological practice may adhere: 1) feminist therapy is political with the goal of social transformation; 2) feminist practice attempts to instill a feminist consciousness, thus providing a new lens for women's reality; 3) the creation of theory emerges from personal experience and relationships; the personal inevitably becomes political; 4) gender is one source of oppression that intersects with other sources (race, socioeconomic status, sexual orientation, etc.); 5) human diversity is embraced as fundamental to theory and practice;

6) the experiences of the oppressed are heard and validated, with an acknowledgement of the role of the therapist as potentially oppressive. It is an imperative for therapists both to self-reflect on their own experiences of oppression as well as on the potential for furthering oppression in their role as therapists; 7) the concept of human identity is ever expanding to include multiple subjectivities; 8) context, especially the sociopolitical, is a critical determinant of one's distress. Patriarchal assumptions are challenged, and the person is seen as powerful and capable of effecting change; and 9) feminist therapy is evolving and growing (Brabeck & Ting, 1997). Thus, "feminist ethics of psychological practice present a mandate for moral action that empowers individuals, creates social structures and ensures that all people are attentively cared for so as to nurture and develop each person's potential within the contexts in which each lives" (Brabeck & Ting, 2000a, p.5).

In a similar manner, Jeanne Maracek and Rachel Hare-Mustin (1987) describe three principles of feminist therapy as: 1) an approach aimed at raising clients' consciousness so that they may distinguish between the problems caused by the external sexist society and the intrapsychic reasons for problems, over which they may exert control; 2) the establishment of an egalitarian power relationship between the client and therapist wherein the client determines personal therapeutic goals and grows to rely on self; and 3) a process that validates female identity in all its forms.

OVERVIEW OF FEMINIST ETHICS

It is important to make the distinction between feminist ethics as a subfield of ethics philosophy, and feminist therapy ethics, which is relevant to professional therapists. The former, feminist ethics, is still in its beginning stages. Although there is not yet a consensus among feminists regarding its principles, Brabeck (2000) enumerates five general assumptions that are underlie this approach:

1. assumptions that women and their experiences have moral significance
2. the assertion that attentiveness, affective response, and subjective knowledge can illuminate moral issues
3. the admonition that feminist ethics engage in analysis of the context and of the power dynamics inherent in that context
4. the claim that feminist critiques of male oppression must be accompanied by a critique of racist, classist, homophobic distortions, and

5. the injunction that feminist ethics require action directed at achieving systemic social justice (Brabeck, 2000, pp.5–6)

Feminist ethics is not dissimilar to traditional ethics (that examines the nature and consequences of and motives behind actions) (Tong, 1993). However, feminist ethics provides different lenses for viewing these issues. Although a thorough description of the various "lenses" utilized in feminist ethical thought is not possible in this limited chapter, I will mention several of the ones I feel are salient to this discussion.

Carol Gilligan's (1989) ethics of care emphasizes women's ethical responsibility to and for others in their lives. This morality stems from subordination and oppression, with the self being identified with close relationships. Similarly, relational feminists, in refuting the ethics of individual moral decision making, emphasize a relationship-based morality, specifically the "values of empathy, nurturance and caring over or in addition to justice, rights, and moral rules" (Brabeck & Ting, 2000b, p.21) as well as human interdependence. As one's location within various power hierarchies influences one's perceptions and actions, an individual's time and place context is of critical importance, and it is an ethical imperative to lovingly understand the individual in these sociocultural contexts (Brabeck & Ting, 2000b).

Feminist virtue ethicists (Kitchener, 1999) stress the need for moral character in making ethical decisions and taking ethical action. Virtue ethics is aspirational, relying on ideals rather than on principles (as is the case with traditional ethics), and focuses on what behaviors therapists need to aspire to in becoming ethical. Thus, when virtues of caring, compassion, nonmaleficence, beneficence, etc. are used in making decisions, a greater ethical sensitivity is achieved.

FEMINIST THERAPY ETHICS

Feminist ethical thought forms the basis of the more specific ethical guidelines for professional feminist therapists. According to Laura Brown (1991):

> A focus on ethics is a focus on power and how it is used and shared in the process and practices of therapy; it is about the meaning of ethical practice in the relationship of the therapist to her interpersonal world and her intrapsychic reality. (p.1)

Most feminist therapy codes of ethics depart from the traditional rule/principle-based codes (from the Hippocratic model) common among helping professions. There are a number of issues that render rule-based codes of ethics inconsistent with feminist ethics. Hannah Lerman and Natalie Porter (1990b) present a comprehensive description of the problems with existing rule-based codes. They state that these codes are reactive, not proactive, and detail the minimum acceptable behaviors rather than strive toward the optimum. These codes establish extreme right-wrong dichotomies (in which there is no middle ground) that are irrelevant to the complex nature of human behavior, as well as the contexts that contribute to unethical actions. There is little mention of how to prevent unethical behavior. Furthermore, rule-based codes are guilty of ignoring the unique contexts of women and minority groups. Procedures for filing grievances are often paternalistic and condescending to the groups they seek to protect, and at the same time more focused on the prevention of legal action towards the professionals involved than on clients. Lastly, provisions are added to codes regularly, and become increasingly more detailed without a full consideration of the initial values involved in their construction.

Another major argument against rule-based codes is that they describe the practitioner's responsibility to not harm, exploit, or damage clients, but de-emphasize that which can be done to help the client. For example, all codes outlaw sexual relationships with clients. However, few if any emphasize the need for the therapist to self-evaluate attitudes or biases towards clients. Taken further, the ethics codes will most certainly prohibit therapists from making overt racist or sexist remarks in public. However, there are no stated sanctions for therapists who harbor internal biases towards these groups that may manifest only subtly in clinical work (Lerman & Porter, 1990b).

Lastly, although codes may stress the need for professionals to acquire continuing education, specifics for doing this are lacking. For example, whereas professionals may be admonished not to work outside of their area of specialization or competence, no guidelines are provided for achieving this competence, e.g., with gender issues, child abuse, or clients from cultural minority groups. There is no mention of the negative effects or harm that might befall a client, for example, if the therapist does not understand his or her culture. There are no admonitions against subtle violations, such as facilitating overdependency (Lerman & Porter, 1990b). Rule-based codes "do not provide an atmosphere that facilitates emotional growth and attitudinal changes" (Lerman & Porter, 1990b, p.9).

Brown (1990) has recommended that ethical behavior should be viewed on a continuum rather than in dichotomous right-wrong or good-bad terms. As mentioned above, either extreme may be harmful to clients. For example, on one "wrong" end of the spectrum one may view sexual involvement between a client and a therapist. However, on the other, "right" end, one may find a therapist who is distant, aloof, and removed from the client. The latter is not addressed in any code.

With the weaknesses of rule-based ethics apparent, feminist therapists have developed codes of ethics that are more consistent with feminist thinking. These codes share some distinctive features: 1) non-sexist language regarding competence, confidentiality, client welfare and therapist responsibility; 2) an emphasis on the need for specialized knowledge and skills in working with women clients; 3) an emphasis on the need for therapists to be self-aware and actively working on their own issues; and 4) the imperative that therapists become aware of and open about their values (Worell & Remer, 1992).

The Feminist Therapy Institute has developed a code of ethics for its practitioners (Feminist Therapy Institute, 1999). This code is noteworthy in its provision of guidelines rather than admonitions, and enforcement of the code is done through education rather than through sanctions. The code strongly emphasizes the need for an awareness of power differentials in the therapeutic relationship, as well as an understanding of context as it influences behavior. Therapists' ongoing self-examination is an imperative. In summary, it provides an acknowledgement of the need for therapists to balance heart and head in their work (Worell & Remer, 1992).

Several issues of relevance to feminist therapy are given particular attention in this code: therapist self-disclosure, dual/overlapping relationships, and power. Each of these will be discussed in subsequent sections of this chapter.

Therapist Self-Disclosure

The use of the therapist's intentional self-disclosure in feminist therapy is considered one of its distinguishing features (in contrast to other forms of psychotherapy) and important to achieving its therapeutic goals (Brown & Walker, 1990; Enns, 1993; Lerman & Porter, 1990; Mahalik, Van Ormer, & Simi, 2000). These goals may include: the nurturance of feminist consciousness in the client (Brabeck & Brown, 1997; Mahalik, Van Ormer, & Simi, 2000); a reduction in the power difference in the relationship (Brown, 1991; Brown & Walker, 1990; Enns, 1993; Greenspan, 1986; Mahalik, Van Ormer, & Simi, 2000); the enhancement of therapeutic growth (Brown & Walker, 1990; Lerman & Porter, 1990; Mahalik, Van Ormer, & Simi, 2000; Russell, 1986); a facilitation of therapist's solidarity with the client (Brown, 1990; Brown & Walker, 1990; Greenspan, 1986; Mahalik, Van Ormer, & Simi, 2000; Russell, 1986); and a diminishing of the client's sense of shame (Greenspan, 1986). Self-disclosure also enhances the client's ability to make an informed choice about his or her therapist and allows the therapist to establish a "real" relationship with the client (Mahalik, Van Ormer, & Simi, 2000).

Feminist therapists vary as to the appropriateness of various types of self-disclosure used, as the content of what they reveal may vary widely and include one or more of the following: theoretical orientation, personal values, political beliefs, lifestyle, religion, socioeconomic background, and reactions to clients, among others. However, there is a divergence of opinion in the literature regarding what types of self-disclosure are appropriate (see Brown & Walker, 1990; Greenspan, 1986; Hare-Mustin, et al., 1979; Rochlin, 1982).

James Mahalik, E. Alice Van Ormer and Nicole Simi (2000) discuss the need to reframe the issue of therapist self-disclosure from a dichotomous "do-don't" position to a continuum. In this manner, one can be more cognizant of the various types of information about the therapist that are continually being made available to the client, e.g., gender, race, age, ethnicity, disabilities, dress, setting for therapy, public activities, and so forth. In acknowledging this continuum, one may also recognize the potential harm inherent in the therapist's not disclosing enough information, as well as disclosing too much to the client.

An assessment of the context is crucial for determining the potential impact of self-disclosure and its ethical use. Obviously the content of self-disclosure will affect clients differentially. The revelation of the therapist's sexual orientation, for example, may make some clients bond more readily and make others feel uncomfortable (Mahalik, Van Ormer, & Simi, 2000).

Power issues within the client-therapist relationship are also influenced by self-disclosure, as a therapist's self-disclosure may tip the scales of balance, change the essence of the relationship, create an overlapping relationship, and confuse boundaries. The therapist's own issues may inadvertently assume center stage in the therapy process (Mahalik, Van Ormer, & Simi, 2000).

When the therapist's self-disclosure is used to reinforce his or her function as a role model for the client, serious problems may also arise. Clients may indeed perceive that the therapist's way of solving his or her own problems is the ideal or only way, privilege his or her experiences, and create a sense of disempowerment in the client.

When therapists share their political views, for example, concerning women's social justice, they may well be imposing their own values on the client. Jeanne Maracek and Diane Kravetz (1996) speak to this contradiction and note: "although feminist therapists value free choice and self-determination for women and view the therapist's role as validating and honoring the client's values, feminist therapists also ascribe and promote values specific to a feminine vision that are not value neutral" (p.196). These authors recommend that the therapist's feminist approach should be disclosed as early as possible in the therapy process, so that the client can make an informed choice about his or her selection of therapists.

Brown (1994) suggests that when therapist disclosure is used, it should be based on a conscious, calculated, and thoughtful decision of the therapist and with a specific clinical intent based on the needs of the client. Any disclosures that are impulsive run the risk of creating problems in the relationship. In more fully understanding their use of self-disclosure, therapists should thus ask themselves: "how would self-disclosure help form or maintain my therapeutic alliance with this client? What unique experiences has this client had that are different from others and mine that I need to respect when using self-disclosure? How does where the client and I are in the therapeutic work affect the client's experience of my self-disclosure?" (Mahalik, Van Ormer, & Simi, 2000, p.197). When this type of careful assessment precedes the therapist's use of disclosure, this practice may be more optimally used for the client's benefit.

Dual or Overlapping Relationships

Dual or overlapping relationships (Berman, 1985) are of special concern for all professionals, and represent a complicated area of ethical problem solving, as sometimes they are unavoidable (Dileo, 2000). Dual relationships involve the therapist establishing a second role (besides the therapist role) with a client simultaneous with or following therapy. These second roles can be professional (teacher, supervisor, business partner, employer, mentor) or nonprofessional (friend, family member, lover, social partner).

Dual relationships can involve misuse of the therapist's power and can have damaging effects on the therapy process and client. From a feminist therapy perspective, this is especially true for women clients, who may hold a lower power status by virtue of their gender. Furthermore, dual relationships often result from unclear boundary issues of the therapist (Dileo, 2000), and thus, a discussion of these issues is also included in this section of the chapter.

Dual relationship concerns apply not only to clinical therapists, but also to therapists functioning in other professional roles, i.e., educators and supervisors, as creating multiple roles with students and supervisees is equally problematic and potentially damaging to these parties (although this section will focus primarily on dual relationships with clients, the implications are the same for students and supervisees). As stated above, dual relationships must be considered prior to the onset of therapy (preexisting relationships with potential clients), during therapy (creation of additional relationships with current clients), and post-therapy (establishing a different relationship with a former client).

The potential for establishing dual relationships is ever present, especially for therapists who live in small communities and for feminist therapists who embrace social activism as part of their value system. The likelihood that clients will be encountered in non-therapy situations is great. Furthermore, some dual relationships cannot be eliminated.

Jeanne Adleman and Susan Barrett (1990) discuss two important components of the traditional therapeutic alliance in feminist therapy, particularly as these relate to the issue of dual relationships: the *symbolic* relationship and the *real* relationship (Brown, 1983). The symbolic relationship comprises the expectations of the client for the therapist, i.e., what the client needs the therapist to represent in her life, the fact that she can rely on the therapist and that the therapist will focus on the client's needs. Thus, the client is able to draw from the therapist in a symbolic manner, and the therapist acknowledges and honors this relationship.

Concurrently, the therapist conveys to the client that he or she is also a human person with needs, issues, limits and vulnerabilities, as well as competence, i.e., aspects of the "real" relationship. An optimal therapeutic alliance is able to integrate both types of relationships, and the therapist is ethically competent in being there for the client as well as taking care of him/herself (Adleman & Barrett, 1990).

Boundary problems ensue when the therapist distorts either the real or the symbolic relationship. For example, when the symbolic relationship is distorted, the therapist attempts to be "perfect," always available and always completely "on," neglecting care for herself and her own emotional needs. She risks using the clients to meet her needs. When the real relationship is distorted, the therapist puts her own needs first and uses the therapy setting to work through her own issues.

If a therapist is not aware of power dynamics present in the therapeutic relationship, attempts at forming friendships with clients may result in unintentional emotional abuse toward the client especially when the therapist treats this friendship like other friendships and when there is denial of the client's need to please the therapist. The therapist may deny also that he or she is still an authority figure to the client, that his or her knowledge of the client was gained within a different context; and that the relationship is not influenced by expectations that existed in the previous relationship (Lerman & Rigby, 1990).

> Viewed in this light, we can see that true informed consent, whether for friendship, a business partnership, love relationship, or any other relationship, by a client or former client, cannot generally be expected to exist, regardless of the client's expressed wish or the verbal

> expression of intent and understanding at its start. (Lerman & Rigby, 1990, p.56)

In confronting and dealing with the ethical issues involved in dual relationships, therapists need to acknowledge the existence and full implications of such a relationship, assess its risks and benefits for all parties concerned, and engage in effective self-care practices so that their needs are not brought into the therapy situation (Brown, 1991).

Furthermore, Judith Worell and Pamela Remer (1992) present a series of questions for therapists to consider in making ethical decisions about dual relationships. These questions examine the *nature of the therapy-client relationship* (goals of therapy, emotional status of client, current and anticipated type and length of relationship; and power differential); *the nature of the dual relationship* (power differential, potential negative effects to parties involved); *the health of the therapist* (emotional health of therapist and effectiveness of self-care procedures); *context issues* (nature, size, and norms of the shared community), and *theoretical underpinnings of therapy* (aspects of this orientation that are compromised or violated by the dual relationship). As a general rule, dual relationships are more dangerous when: the client is especially vulnerable, when the power differential is large, when the therapist is impaired emotionally and not involved in self-care, when communities are small and values are shared, and when the theoretical constructs of therapy are violated. Thus, therapists should be aware of client-therapist differences in vulnerability, influence, and power when deciding whether to interact with clients outside of therapy, and when these relationships cannot be avoided, to make them "growth-producing whenever possible and at the very least, non-damaging" (Adleman & Barrett, 1990, p.88).

Lerman and Rigby (1990) make further recommendations for dealing with dual relationships. The therapist should develop a network of colleagues with whom he or she can discuss issues of dual relationships, so that prevention may be optimized. Issues of dual relationships should be discussed with clients at the beginning of the therapy process, so that the rights of both parties may be defined and future behaviors may be determined. The therapist should also be vigilant in his or her self-examination, including an awareness of the therapist's needs for power, as small ethical violations usually precede larger ones, and awareness of the smaller issues will serve to prevent the larger ones (Brown, 1987).

> Therapist or not, we are all human beings. In most cases, it is only after our formal training that we fully come to know that the therapist role cannot merely be assumed and then removed at will. The burdens

> of the therapeutic role can be heavy. Emotional self-care and prevention can help with blind spots. (Lerman & Rigby, 1990, p.57)

Power Issues in Therapy

Feminist therapists, along with their clients, experience issues of disempowerment in their lives, and may also share the human need for both direct and covert power (Lerman & Rigby, 1990; Miller, 1986; Smith & Siegel, 1985). Therefore, client empowerment may be seen as a primary focus and ethical issue in feminist therapy (Smith & Douglas, 2000). Two types of power are identified by Brown (1990): *power within*, that strength maintained internally that facilitates active decisions and choices about one's life; and *power over*, the control exerted by one or more persons over the individual, thereby influencing his or her choices. The latter may be considered the primary type of power in culture and to some extent, the type of power existing in the therapeutic relationship. Feminist therapists acknowledge the societal context that has disempowered women, whereas other approaches to therapy may blame the woman and deem this an individual "failure."

Adrienne Smith and Mary Ann Douglas (2000) describe the three ethical imperatives of the therapist for empowering clients. 1) *Value the client's perception of therapy*. This does not require that therapists agree with the client, but does mandate that differences are discussed authentically, openly, and respectfully. This also implies avoiding power struggles in therapy (even the term, "client resistance," implies an untoward assumption of power by the therapist). 2) *Value the client's decisions for his or her life*, even when these are inconsistent with the views of the therapist. Empowerment thus implies the client's right, for example, to stay in an abusive relationship, and the therapist who might interfere with the client's decision (except in cases of potential homicide or suicide) or to persuade the client to do otherwise, acts in an unethical and disempowering way. However, it *is* an obligation of the therapist to express her opinion about the client's decision. The therapist also refrains from attributing the client's actions to denial (when the client chooses not to confront certain issues), and to honor the client's own internal needs for this. 3) *Acknowledge the power differentials in the relationship*. The ethical therapist uses his or her power cautiously and seeks to minimize it. Feminist therapists share the view that power is a dynamic in all relationships, and acknowledge that therapists indeed have power, and that clients are far from powerless.

Ethical therapists must constantly self-evaluate to assure that they are not disavowing their own power and/or are not misusing that power with clients. For feminist therapists in particular, care for the client is required to uncover the hierarchies of power in every circumstance. Further, "feminist ethics require practitioners to critique the ways in which one's own positions in the hierarchy of power within any context affects one's perceptions and moral sensibilities" (Brabeck & Ting, 2000b, p.28). To this end, therapists are called upon to acknowledge and understand their own histories and present situations of disempowerment as well as their own attempts to self-empower. An awareness is needed of how they have either internalized, deflected, and/or worked to counter oppression personally and through social action. This awareness leads to a greater empathic identification with clients, and prevents a view of themselves as separate from those they attempt to help. Therapists must also embrace their successes and forgive themselves for their failures. "Only through a thorough self-awareness can we be open to our clients' issues around empowerment and only by understanding our own difficulties can we sustain our clients while they struggle" (Smith & Douglas, 2000. p.45).

In addition, feminist therapists are called to come to terms with their own actions to perpetuate oppression directly or indirectly, as this awareness leads to an understanding of the potential for all people to be oppressors. A therapist's accountability for personal or social actions or lack thereof enables a greater ability to empower clients. In a similar manner, therapists' clear understanding of their own personal power minimizes the potential for gaining power in therapeutic relationships and helps them serve as effective and responsible role models for their clients (Smith & Douglas, 2000). Furthermore, the therapist's power in the relationship should be understood as only temporary; this diminishes as the client him- or herself assumes greater personal power (Lerman & Rigby, 1990; Miller, 1976).

> Implicit in all of the above is the assumption that we share the ongoing process with our clients. . . . In addition, we continually explain the process of therapy itself and acknowledge our part and the client's part in the changes happening. Affirming the client's reality, validating her perceptions and providing adequate information for informed decision making is the basic structure for empowerment. (Smith & Douglas, 2000, p.47)

Brabeck and Ting (2000b) emphasize the need for therapists to self-evaluate power hierarchies not only in their relationships with clients, but also in all other professional practices.

> For example, in conducting ethical research, an ethical feminist would raise questions regarding power relationships that might

> influence the research process. Does the researcher or participant determine what questions to ask and what questions to answer? Should the author of the research be the university-based person or are others who are participants the major contributors? Whose needs are served by the research? Is tenure, money, reputation, or prestige the motivation behind the work? Ethical feminist researchers engage in such an analysis of the power relationships in their work to develop new knowledge. (p.28)

Power issues must also be considered when feminist therapists set fees for their services, and how these structures relate to power hierarchies. For example, if fees are set lower than the therapist would like, because of clients' limited resources, the therapist may harbor resentment, and therapy may be negatively influenced. The therapist must also consider what the meaning of reduced fees communicates to clients, e.g., pity? Whereas, the use of a sliding scale for every client as a deliberate choice of the client may better communicate the therapist's commitment to his or her own values (Brown, 1990).

As another example, clients who receive free services because of financial indigence may feel unable to confront the therapist on issues and out of gratitude for the services become disempowered. The therapist then should communicate to these clients that it is the therapist's decision to do this in an attempt to act according to his or her own beliefs (Brown, 1990).

> For clients who run into financial difficulties, we can share power and decision making with the client in these circumstances by raising the question to her and asking that we share the decision with her. The therapist's willingness to risk income in exchange for respect of the client's integrity can be a powerful statement of feminist values in action. Only when we are clear about our right to a livable income can we assure the rights of clients to good quality therapy regardless of income. (Brown, 1990, p.66)

Bartering with clients for services is ethically unsound as an alternative to direct fees for services, as it may exacerbate power hierarchies, and result in abuse of both client and therapist (Dileo, 2000).

IMPLICATIONS FOR MUSIC THERAPY

The process of evaluating feminist therapy ethics from the current author's objective, more traditional-ethics vantage point has indeed been enlightening. In doing this, I have been convinced of the need to reevaluate my personal as well as the profession's current approach to music therapy ethics, and in the end, I feel that the field of music therapy would be enhanced significantly by an incorporation of feminist ethical ideals within its approach to professional ethics for its practitioners. In the following paragraphs, I am making recommendations for how this can be accomplished (not only for the code of ethics in the United States, but various music therapy codes throughout the world).

1. *Re-evaluate the rule-based formula for music therapy codes of ethics.* Whereas, I believe that all codes of ethics are inherently complex and difficult for a profession to articulate in an adequate fashion for use in ethical problem solving, I do contend that the profession should consider the possibility of shifting some of the focus of its codes from rule-based to aspirational, emphasizing the role of the therapist's own virtues in becoming an ethical professional. Along with this, there is a pressing need for professional guidelines in all ethical areas, e.g., competence, confidentiality, etc.
2. *Emphasize preventive ethics (assume proactive rather than reactive stances).* An inherent issue in music therapy codes of ethics is that they do not adequately detail how a therapist may prevent ethical problems before they occur. With a greater emphasis on providing structures for thinking ethically, therapists may assume a preventive position and deliberately work to both think and subsequently behave ethically.
3. *View ethics on a continuum.* When ethics are seen on a continuum, rather than as right-wrong rules, therapists can more readily ascertain the range of behaviors possible and how their own behavior is situated on this continuum. Furthermore, therapists may also be able to assess what ideal behavior may be along this continuum, rather than simply reacting to a negative imperative.
4. *Stress the context of ethical behavior.* Whether from a multicultural context or feminist context, most codes have severe limitations resulting from their failure to embrace how working in various contexts may influence ethical decision making. With the realization that codes of ethics, (as well as

corresponding approaches to clinical practice in music therapy) stem from a northern-European, white, male-dominated perspective (Dileo, 2000), comes the imperative to consider carefully and critically how these approaches are and are not relevant to the clinical diversity that music therapists encounter in everyday clinical situations. This is one of the issues of greatest urgency to be considered for adjusting codes of ethics to the realities of current music therapy practice.

5. *Emphasize and embrace the need for self-awareness.* Perhaps one of the greatest contributions that feminist therapy ethics brings to light is its emphasis on the need for the therapist to be self-aware and for constant self-monitoring and scrutiny. As this is considered to be at the heart of ethical practice (Dileo, 2000), it needs to be afforded a place of prominence in the current codes of ethics.
6. *Address issues of power.* The issues concerning the power of the therapist's role and the potential for misuse of this power need to receive a great deal of emphasis in the current codes, not only for female clients, but for all clients. Again, guidelines for minimizing this power and for empowering clients as a primary goal of therapy require a salient place in the codes.

As I make these recommendations for revisions of music therapy approaches to professional ethics, I also remain skeptical of some practices in feminist therapy, i.e., the use of self-disclosure and the mandate for therapists to become social activists. I have not been convinced that self-disclosure is as useful in the therapy process as it is regarded by feminist therapists. I retain a conservative position on its use, and believe that it should only be used in the most extreme circumstances (if ever) and only then with the most careful of deliberations by the therapist. I also do not feel that music therapists need to feel compelled to rectify social injustices as part of their work, although some may choose to do this. The ethical and boundary issues that ensue from activism, from my perspective, are indeed controversial, and have the potential to diminish what happens in the therapy relationship itself. However, being informed about options helps therapists to make better choices for how they choose to practice and live their lives.

In spite of these reservations, I feel it is essential for music therapists to be knowledgeable about feminist therapy and feminist therapy ethics. In doing so, whether or not they choose to embrace these approaches, their views of their own work as well as of themselves will inevitably be changed for the better.

REFERENCES

Adleman, Jeanne & Barrett, Susan E. (1990) Overlapping relationships: Importance of the feminist ethical perspective. In Hannah Lerman & Natalie Porter (eds.) *Feminist Ethics in Psychotherapy*. New York: Springer.

American Psychological Association (1992) Ethical principles of psychologists and code of conduct. *American Psychologist, 47*, 1597–1611.

Baier, Annette (1994) *Moral Practices: Essays on Ethics*. Cambridge, MA: Harvard University Press.

Bell, Linda (1993) *Rethinking Ethics in the Midst of Violence: A Feminist Approach to Freedom*. Lanham, MD: Rowman & Littlefield.

Berman, Joan R.S. (1985) Ethical feminist perspectives on dual relationships with clients. In Lynne Bravo Rosewater & Lenore E.A. Walker (eds.) *Handbook of Feminist Therapy*. New York: Springer.

Brabeck, Mary M. (2000) *Practicing Feminist Ethics in Psychology*. Washington, DC: American Psychological Association.

Brabeck, Mary M. & Brown, Laura (1997) Feminist theory and psychological practice. In Judith Worell & Noreen G. Johnson (eds.) *Shaping the Future of Feminist Psychology*. Washington, DC: American Psychological Association.

Brabeck, Mary M. & Ting, Kathleen (2000a) Introduction. In Mary M. Brabeck (ed.) *Practicing Feminist Ethics in Psychology*. Washington, DC: American Psychological Association.

Brabeck, Mary M. & Ting, Kathleen (2000b) Feminist ethics: Lenses for examining ethical psychological practice. In Mary M. Brabeck (ed.) *Practicing Feminist Ethics in Psychology*. Washington, DC: American Psychological Association.

Brown, Laura S. (1983) Finding new language: Getting beyond analytic verbal shorthand in feminist therapy. *Women and Therapy, 3,* 73–80.

Brown, Laura S. (1990) A feminist framework for ethical theory. In Hannah Lerman & Natalie Porter (eds.) *Feminist Ethics in Psychotherapy*. New York: Springer.

Brown, Laura S. (1990) Ethical issues and the business of therapy. In Hannah Lerman & Natalie Porter (eds.) *Feminist Ethics in Psychotherapy*. New York: Springer.

Brown, Laura S. (1991) Ethical issues in feminist therapy: Selected topics. *Psychology of Women Quarterly, 15*, 323–336.

Brown, Laura S. (1994) Boundaries in feminist therapy: A conceptual formulation. *Women and Therapy, 15* (1), 29–38.

Brown, Laura S. & Walker, Lenore E.A. (1990) Feminist therapy perspectives on self-disclosure. In George Stricker & Martin Fisher (eds.) *Self-disclosure in the Therapeutic Relationship*. New York: Plenum Press.

Cole, Eve B. & Coultrap-Quin, Susan (1992) *Explorations in Feminist Ethics: Theory and Practice*. Bloomington, IN: Indiana University Press.

Dileo, Cheryl (2000) *Ethical Thinking in Music Therapy*. Cherry Hill, NJ: Jeffrey Books.

Douglas, Mary Ann (1985) The role of power in feminist therapy: A reformulation. In Lynn B. Rosewater & Lenore E.A. Walker (eds.) *Handbook of Feminist Therapy*. New York: Springer.

Elshtain, Jean B. (1991) Ethics in the women's movement. *Annals of the American Academy, 515*, 126–139.

Enns, Carolyn Z. (1993) Twenty years of feminist counseling: From Naming Biases to Implementing Multifaceted Practice. *The Counseling Psychologist, 21*, 3–87.

Feminist Therapy Institute. (1999). Feminist therapy code of ethics. http://www.feministtherapyinstitute.org/ethics.htm

Fitzgerald, Louise F. & Nutt, Roberta (1986) The division 17 principles concerning the counseling/psychotherapy of women: Rationale and implementation. *The Counseling Psychologist, 14*, 180–216.

Gilbert, Lucia A. (1980) Feminist therapy. In Annette E. Brodsky & Rachel T. Hare-Mustin (eds.) *Women and Psychotherapy: An Assessment of Research and Practice*. New York: Guilford Press.

Gilligan, Carol (1982) *In a Different Voice: Psychological Theory and Women's Development.* Cambridge, MA: Harvard University Press.

Greenspan, Miriam (1986) Should therapists be personal? Self-disclosure and therapeutic distance in feminist therapy. *Women and Therapy, 5,* 5–17.

Hare-Mustin, Rachel T., Maracek, Jeanne, Kaplan, Alexandra G., & Liss-Levinson, Nechama (1979) Rights of clients: Responsibilities of therapists. *American Psychologist, 34*, 3–16.

Hume, David (1817) *A Treatise of Human Nature.* London: Thomas and Joseph Allman.

Kitchener, Karen S. (1999) *The Foundation of Ethical Practice, Research and Teaching in Psychology*. Mahwah, NJ: Erlbaum.

Lerman, Hannah & Porter, Natalie (1990a) *Feminist Ethics in Psychotherapy.* New York: Springer.

Lerman, Hannah & Porter, Natalie (1990b) The contribution of feminism to ethics in psychotherapy. In Hannah Lerman & Natalie Porter (eds.) *Feminist Ethics in Psychotherapy*. New York: Springer.

Lerman, Hannah & Rigby, Dorothy N. (1990) Boundary violations: Misuses of the power of the therapist. In Hannah Lerman & Natalie Porter (eds.) *Feminist Ethics in Psychotherapy*. New York: Springer.

Mahalik, James R., Van Ormer, E. Alice, & Simi, Nicole L. (2000) Ethical issues in using self-disclosure in feminist therapy. In Mary M. Brabeck (ed.) *Practicing Feminist Ethics in Psychology*. Washington, DC: American Psychological Association.

Maracek, Jeanne & Hare-Mustin, Rachel T. (1987) Feminism and therapy: Can this relationship be saved? Unpublished manuscript.

Maracek, Jeanne & Kravetz, Diane (1996, August) *A room of one's own: Power and agency in feminist therapy*. Paper presented at the 104th Annual Convention of the American Psychological Association, Toronto, Ontario, Canada.

Meara, Naomi, M., Schmidt, L.D., & Day, Jeanne D. (1996) Principles and virtues: A foundation for ethical decisions, policies and character. *The Counseling Psychologist, 24*, 4–77.

Miller, Alice (1981) *The Drama of the Gifted Child*. New York: Basic Books

Miller, Jean B. (1986) *Toward a New Psychology of Women*. (2nd Ed.) Boston: Beacon Press.

Noddings, Nel (1984) *Caring: A Feminine Approach to Ethics and Moral Education*. Berkeley: University of California Press.

Rochlin, Martin (1982) Sexual orientation of the therapist and therapeutic effectiveness with gay clients. *Journal of Homosexuality, 7*, 19–35.

Russell, Mary (1986) Teaching feminist counseling skills: An evaluation. *Counselor Education and Supervision, 25*, 320–331.

Shogan, Debra (1988) *Care and Moral Motivation*. Toronto, Ontario, Canada: OISE Press.

Smith, Adrienne J. & Douglas, Mary Ann (1990) Empowerment as ethical imperative. In Hannah Lerman & Natalie Porter (eds.) *Feminist Ethics in Psychotherapy*. New York: Springer.

Smith, Adrienne J. & Siegel, Rachel F. (1985) Feminist therapy: Redefining power for the powerless. In Lynn B. Rosewater & Lenore A. Walker (eds.) *Handbook of Feminist Therapy*. New York: Springer.

Tong, Rosemarie (1993) *Feminine and Feminist Ethics*. Belmont, CA: Wadsworth.

Worell, Judith & Remer, Pamela (1992) *Feminist Perspectives in Therapy: An Empowerment Model for Women*. Chichester: John Wiley & Sons.

INDEX

C

D

E

F

G

R